ALS
Advances in Life Sciences

Frontiers in Crustacean Neurobiology

Edited by
K. Wiese
W.-D. Krenz
J. Tautz
H. Reichert
B. Mulloney

1990

Birkhäuser Verlag
Basel · Boston · Berlin

Editors' addresses:

Dr. K. Wiese
Zoologisches Institut
Universität Hamburg
Martin-Luther-King Platz 3
D-2000 Hamburg 13/FRG

Dr. W.-D. Krenz
Zoologisches Institut
der Universität Basel
Rheinsprung 9
CH-4051 Basel/Switzerland

Dr. J. Tautz
Fakultät für Biologie
Universität Konstanz
Postfach 5560
D-7750 Konstanz/FRG

Dr. H. Reichert
Laboratoire de Neurobiologie
Département de Biologie Animale
Université de Genève
20, rue Ecole de Médecine
CH-1211 Genève 4/Switzerland

Dr. B. Mulloney
University of California at Davis
Zoology Department
Davis, CA 95616/USA

Cover illustration: F. Meinhardt, Universität Konstanz.

Deutsche Bibliothek Cataloguing-in-Publication Data
Frontiers in crustacean neurobiology / ed. by K. Wiese ... – Basel; Boston; Berlin:
Birkhäuser, 1990
(Advances in life sciences)
ISBN 3-7643-2355-8 (Basel...)
ISBN 0-8176-2355-8 (Boston)
NE: Wiese, Konrad [Hrsg.]

Printed in Germany on acid-free paper
ISBN 3-7643-2355-8
ISBN 0-8176-2355-8

ACKNOWLEDGEMENT

The editors are much obliged to :
Dr. Brian J. Corrette,
who contributed all knowledge and organized all equipment required for computer aided text processing and printout used in this volume
and to
Torsten Rüting,
Petra Skiebe and Bernd Lühr, all students of neurobiology at the University of Hamburg, who set aside their own projects for quite some time to prepare this book

ABOUT THIS BOOK

In a situation where neuroscience diversifies into numerous directions it is a challenge to show recent developments in the field whithin one book. This volume uses as a bracket the object of study, the crustacean CNS. This choice is justified by the many physiological details of nerve function and the wealth of information about neuronal circuitry underlying behavior which have been collected from work in crustaceans. The number of investigators using crustacean preparations is on the one hand small enough to assemble their contributions in one book; on the other hand the diversification of research interests within the number of contributors remains large enough to provide a fairly good coverage of the many directions of research in neuroscience. Besides presenting a full set of outstanding achievements as a means to serve in general orientation, our book aims also at an inventory of smaller, individual, research activities to enable the reader to search for promising hook-up points which might turn out prolific sources of relevant information in the future.

The editors

CONTENTS

6. PATTERN GENERATORS AND THEIR MODULATION

7. NEUROANATOMY AND IMMUNOCYTOCHEMICAL MAPPING

8. DEVELOPMENTAL NEUROBIOLOGY

Foreword

Donald Kennedy
President, Stanford University

Almost exactly a dozen years elapsed between the time I set aside (I thought temporarily!) my own interest in crustacean nervous systems and the arrival of an invitation from Konrad Wiese to participate in this symposium. The intervening years have plainly been productive ones for the field; indeed, I can only hope that there is no causal connection between its properity and my absence.

Discontinuous contact with an intellectual venture, whatever disappointments it may present, does offer one virtue; it provides a more dramatic, almost stroboscopic view of progress. To the lapsed practitioner, the rate of advance in crustacean neurobiology over the decade seems remarkable; equally remarkable is the number of able young researchers, many of them the scientific progeny of my colleagues from the "sixties" and "seventies".

How to summarize the changes they have wrought? Those of us who began working with crustacean nervous systems thirty years ago or so were attracted by several features. First of all, there was a limited motor system with readily identifiable neurons. It was difficult to look at those old methylene blue stains of Retzius and not want to do an experiment immediately! Kees Wiersma often did, and it was he who most persuasively called our attention to the advantages offered by neuronal parsimony in combination with stereotyped motor output patterning. Ted Bullock exploited these features in his elegant early experiments on cardiac ganglia, and that has attracted later investigators to pursue other simplified systems like the stomatogastric. (Among the reasons for liking crustacea is that they put skeletal muscle and skelemotor innervation on the inside as well as the outside!) And in the periphery the differentiation of motor systems into slow and fast types, along with the presence of peripheral inhibition, has made them attractive for studies on developmental as well as neural control mechanisms.

As Wiersma also first showed, interneurons are just as specific and identifiable as motoneurons -- not only in terms of their sensory fields, but in their output connections as well and in their capacity to generate unique and behaviorally meaningful motor "commands". The movements themselves are stereotyped and easily measured: not only is the behavioral repertoire limited, the presence of a rigid exoskeleton makes the movements themselves more reproducible and more easily measured. These properties, of course, also apply to insects; if the truth be known most of us, in my generation at least, liked crustaceans better because they were bigger.

Last not least, of course, there are accessible and well-understood sense organs, particularly those that provide proprioceptive or reafferent signals associated with movement and its control. The muscle receptor organs of Alexandrowicz, later analyzed physiologically by Wiersma and Florey and by Eyzaguirre and Kuffler; the leg proprioceptors studied by Bush and others; the movement-sensitive hair cells and statocysts; all have provided good material for studying primary processes in sensory transduction and control, and the content of this symposium shows that they are still doing so. Perhaps even more important, they have supplied controllable inputs for analyzing such fundamental problems in the control of movement as load compensation and the role of motion-generated reafference.

All these properties link up to provide a very special opportunity, that of joining, in a rigorous way, observations at the cellular or even the molecular level with the behavior of the whole organism. And there is even reason to suppose that from the neurorganization underlining such behaviors, we will be able to make rewarding -- if not entirely -- extensions to the behavior of vertebrates. There was a time, not so very long ago, when those of us who chose to work on anthropoid material were regularly confronted with the suggestion that they were not working on "real" animals. On one of these occasions I suggested that crustacea might accordingly be called "virtual" animals. Rhyapologia no longer seem quite so necessary, now that vertebrate work has revealed so many more parallelism.

The contents of this volume reveal much that emerges in quite a straightforward way from these opportunities, and it is good to see the predictable extensions of research that were well under way in the 1970's. Work on the stomatogastric ganglion is richly represented; it has taught us even more than we expected about the role of specific connections in pattern generation. Stereotyped peripheral motor systems, notably the swimmeret rhythm, are still under active investigation. It is evident that we are gaining a much deeper understanding of sensory organization in complex systems like the statocyst and the eye.

But much other work represents new directions, ones that delight and surprise me after this Rip van Winkle decade. The much expanded role of neurotransmitters, and especially the neuropeptide explosion, has provided mechanisms we never foresaw. The richness of central synaptic mechanisms and what they have taught us about interneuronal complexity is a little unexpected. Perhaps most impressive of all is the growing understanding of connectivity during development, and of the influence one cell population may have on another in determining its properties in ways that are not dependent upon traditional neuronal interaction.

It is an extraordinary record of progress -- some predictable from where we thought we were in the mid-1970's, some of it not. I think we were right to believe that crustacea provided unusually good material for the examination of fundamental processes in the nervous system, and I think the contributions represented here are the best possible evidence that will still look right in another fifteen years. It is good that those with this special interest have been able to join and examine their accomplishments together, under circumstances that promise both intimacy and good fellowship. I look forward to the installment that will follow after another decade!

Frontiers in Crustacean Neurobiology
Advances in Life Sciences

CRUSTACEAN NEUROBIOLOGY: HISTORY AND PERSPECTIVES

Ernst Florey

Fakultät für Biologie, Universität Konstanz, D-775 Konstanz, FRG

UNCERTAIN BEGINNINGS

It is difficult to assign a definitive date to the beginning of what today we call "crustacean neurobiology". The term 'neurobiology' is of rather recent origin. Even the word 'biology' did not come into use before 1800. The term 'neurobiology' implies acceptance of the "neuron doctrine" or 'neuron theory' first formulated by the German anatomist Wilhelm von Waldeyer (1836-1921) in 1891: "the nervous system consists of numerous units (neurones) which are neither genetically nor anatomically connected. Each neuron consists of three major parts, the cell body proper, the nerve fiber, and the nerve terminals". The term 'neuron' is an invention of Waldeyer.

Structure and function of the nervous system of crustaceans became of interest even before the general acceptance of the neuron theory. It is no exaggeration to state that the elucidation of the histology of crustacean nervous systems, especially that of the crayfish, *Astacus*, has contributed decisively to the acceptance of this concept. Some of the best neurohistologists of the time have described details of the structure of the cells in the central nervous system of crayfish. I mention only Gustav Retzius' famous monograph of the central nervous system of the crayfish (Retzius, 1890), Wilhelm Biedermann's paper on the origin and the endings of nerves in the ganglia of invertebrate animals (Biedermann, 1891), and a third publication by a man you may not have expected to find among crustacean neurobiologists: Sigmund Freud.

SIGMUND FREUD (1856-1939)

In 1882, Freud published a 37 page paper on the results of his investigation of the structure of the nerve fibers and nerve cells of the crayfish (Freud, 1882). This paper is very important: it demonstrates that the nerve fiber (the structure we now call the 'axon') is an outgrowth of the cell body. Figure 1, taken from this publication illustrates the point. Freud (Figure 2) thus became a pioneer of neurobiology, and of crustacean neurobiology in particular. For several years, Sigmund Freud had been working in the physiology department headed by Ernst von Brücke (Figure 3). For crustacean neurobiologists such biographical data are revealing: Ernst Wilhelm von Brücke (1819-1892) was one of the famous pupils of Johannes

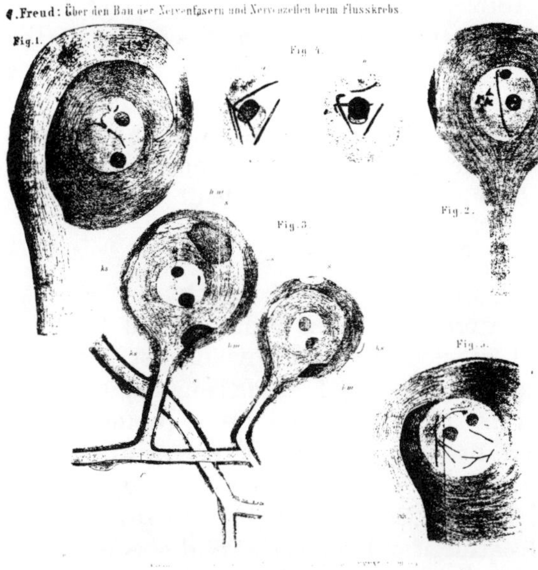

Fig. 1. Nerve cells in the abdominal (Fig. 1, 2, 5) and stomatogastric ganglia of *Astacus*. From Freud (1882)

Fig. 2. Sigmund Freud in 1884 (from Freud, 1968)

Fig. 3. Ernst Wilhelm von Brücke at the time when Freud worked in his Laboratory (from Freud, 1968)

Müller (1801-1858), and a friend of Hermann von Helmholtz (1821-1894). Von Helmholtz was very familiar with the nervous system of the crayfish as well as that of other invertebrate species: his doctoral thesis (De Fabrica Systematis Nervosi Evertebratorum, Berlin, 1842) was concerned with the structure of the nervous tissue of invertebrate animals! For all we know, Helmholtz was the first to recognize that the ganglion cells, discovered by Ehrenberg only nine years earlier, and the nerve fibers were connected. Christian Gottfried Ehrenberg (1795-1876), professor extraordinary and member of the Berlin Academy of Sciences, was a famous microscopist. He later concerned himself with detailed investigations of protozoans and microfossils. Earlier, however, he gave detailed descriptions of the nervous system, especially that of crustaceans.

In the years between 1877 and 1882 Freud published several papers on neurohistology, two of them concerned with the nervous system of the lamprey, *Petromyzon* (Freud, 1877, 1878). In the same year in which his crayfish study appeared, he joined Joseph Breuer (1842-1925) who also had been a member of von Brücke's department and meanwhile had started a private practice specializing in psychotherapy. Who knows how crustacean neurobiology would have developed had Freud not left the field!

CHARLES RICHET (1850-1935)

An interest in crustaceans and in problems of psychiatry is also characteristic of another famous researcher : Charles Richet (1850-1935), a pupil of Claude Bernard (1813-1878), started out as a physiologist and later published two papers on nerve-muscle physiology of crayfish in 1879. Richet was fascinated by psychiatry, and in 1875 reported on experiments in hypnosis, a phenomenon also used by Breuer when Freud joined him. Richet's experiments become widely known. Hypnosis was later extensively used in the psychiatric ward of the famous Salpetrière in Paris under Jean Martin Charcot (1825-1893) in the treatment of hysteria. Freud was to spend a year of study in Charcot's clinic 1885-1886. Richet discovered that the leg muscles of crayfish responded only to repetitive stimulation and that with continued stimulation the extent of contraction increased, a phenomen he called "addition latente", a term much discussed by later students of crustacean nerve-muscle physiology (see Wiersma, 1983). In 1913 Richet received the Nobel prize for his discovery of anaphylaxis.

WILHELM BIEDERMANN (1852-1929)

The nervous control of crayfish skeletal muscle has been the object of study of the physiologist Wilhelm Biedermann (Figure 4) working at the University of Prag in the laboratory of Ewald Hering (1834-1914) who is, perhaps, best known for his theory of color vision, but also for the respiratory reflex known as the "Hering-Breuer reflex". Breuer had spent some time in Hering's laboratory.

Fig. 4. Wilhelm Biedermann (from Schulz, 1930)

Biedermann was the first to recognize that crustacean skeletal muscle receives not only an excitatory, motor innervation that results in contraction, but another innervation by inhibitory nerve fibers which inhibit contraction (Biedermann, 1887, 1888). In his paper of 1887, Biedermann showed that in crayfish the leg muscle we now call the opener muscle is innervated by two axons which lie side by side and branch in the same pattern. He assumed that one of them is the excitatory and the other the inhibitory axon. Controversy about the nature of this inhibition raged until, 45 years later, a Dutch physiologist by the name of C.A.G. Wiersma succeeded in separately stimulating the excitatory and the inhibitory nerve fibers: - but we are getting ahead of our story. There is still much to be said about crustacean neurobiology of the last century.

ALBRECHT BETHE (1872-1954)

When it had become clear to some of the neurohistologists that nerve cells with their axon are the functional units of the nervous system, a very courageous young zoologist, Albrecht Bethe, then a pupil of Richard Hertwig (1850 - 1937) in Munich, embarked on an investigation of the central nervous system of the shore crab, *Carcinus maenas*. The title of his doctoral thesis (it was published in 1895) was "Studien über das Zentralnervensystem von *Carcinus maenas* nebst Angaben über ein neues Verfahren der Methylenblaufixation". After he received his Ph.D., Bethe went to the already famous Stazione Zoologica at Naples where he continued his studies of structure and function of the central nervous system of *Carcinus*. He systematically observed and analyzed the behavior and the reflexes of this animal, he examined the central nervous system histologically (Figure 5), and he became skillful in carrying out minute surgical operations on parts of the central nervous system, using localized electrical stimulation to assess the functions of numerous nervous pathways. It was an ambitious undertaking with the goal of mapping all the neurones that constitute this "simple nervous system" and to discover the function of each of them. Bethe was well aware of the concept of neuronal circuits that had been elaborated by the Viennese physiologist Sigmund Exner (1846-1926) - assistant and later successor of Ernst v. Brücke. What he now had in mind was, indeed, a complete description and analysis of a nervous system. Bethe's program

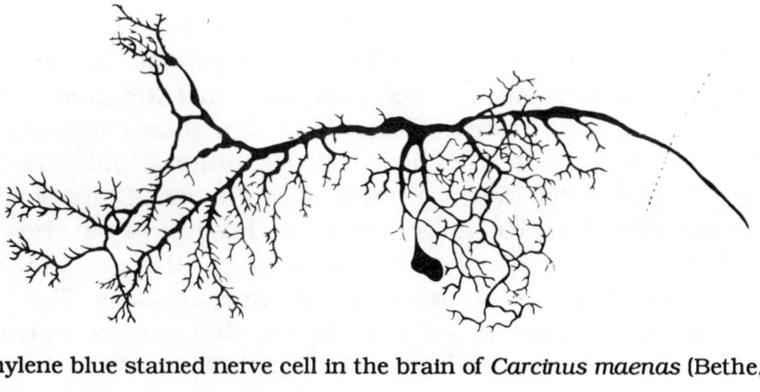

Fig. 5. Methylene blue stained nerve cell in the brain of *Carcinus maenas* (Bethe, 1887)

anticipated the research effort of neurophysiologists of the second half of our century: to establish the neural basis of behavior.

In the course of his Naples studies, Bethe became increasingly doubtful of the neuron doctrine. In 1898 he published his third "Mitteilung" of his studies which he entitled "The central nervous system of *Carcinus maenas*. An anatomical-physiological exploration" (Das Centralnervensystem von *Carcinus maenas*. Ein anatomisch-physiologischer Versuch). He described an experiment which, in his opinion, refuted the neuron doctrine which regarded the neuron as a functional unit and ascribed to the cell body the 'true nervous function'. The result of this experiment was greeted by the opponents of the neuron doctrine with joy and henceforth was referred to in the research literature and in physiology textbooks as "the Bethe experiment" (Figure 6): Bethe had stripped the cell bodies from the neuropil responsible for reflex movement of one of the second antennae and found that the antenna still responded to touch. Bethe concluded that thecell bodies are unnecessary for the functioning of reflex arcs. "We must stop calling the neuron a physiological unit" exclaimed Bethe. Indeed, the neuron doctrine was interpreted by many to imply that the cell body, the "ganglion cell", was endowed with those special qualities which were regarded as essential for any motor action initiated in the brain, and these ganglion cells were regarded as the seat of the mental abilities of the central nervous system. It was a "hot topic" indeed!

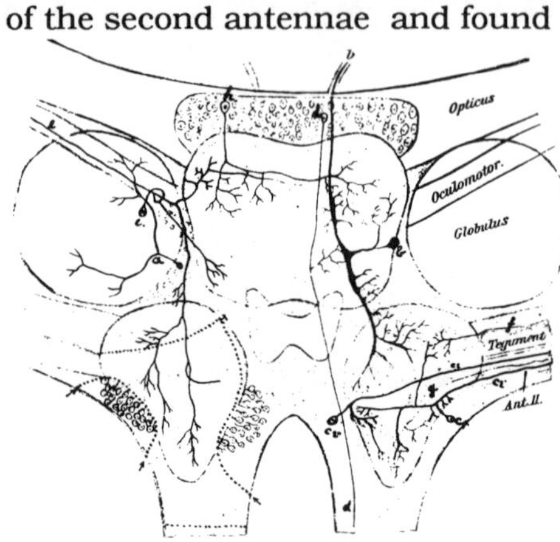

Fig. 6. Bethe's diagram of his "Carcinus Experiment" showing the neuronal circuit involved and (dotted lines) the cell groups he removed. (from Bethe 1888)

In its day, the Bethe experiment was a veritable bombshell. Bethe discussed the consequences of his findings extensively in his book "Allgemeine Anatomie und Physiologie des Nervensystems" (General Anatomy and Physiology of the Nervous System) published in 1903, and in two major reviews, "Die historische Entwicklung der Ganglienzellhypothese" (The Historical Development of the Ganglion Cell Hypothesis) published in 1904, and "Der heutige Stand der Neurontheorie" (The Present State of the Neuron Theory) also published in 1904. The first of these reviews ends with the words: "the doctrine of the specific central nature of the ganglion cells...has never been more than a morphological speculation. The *Carcinus*-Experiment...speaks against it with a clarity that leaves nothing to be desired". And in the other paper he concludes: "in view of the overwhelming evidence it must be incomprehensible to an outsider that there are still renowned men trying to uphold the neuron theory."

But Bethe also attempted a reconciliation: the term 'neuron' may still be used to describe the complete nerve cell with all its processes, but one should not regard these complexes as the units of nervous function. The "Bethe experiment" has been used by the opponents of the neuron theory as a decisive argument against its validity. It must be recognized, however, that these opponents, by and large, were histologists who doubted that the nerve fiber is an outgrowth of a ganglion cell: they regarded the nerve fiber as a product of the fusion of several cells whose nuclei were seen to line the course of the fiber: the nerve fiber, or axis cylinder, was thought of as being the product of the Schwann- or sheath cells. Bethe never followed this line of argument. He knew from his own histological studies that the nerve fiber was an outgrowth of the neuronal cell body. It is worth quoting from his paper: "After removal of the cell body, neurons for a time can carry out their function undiminished, indeed their reflex excitability is even increased. For the continued function of neurons their connection with the ganglion cell is necessary, however, so that I feel justified in assuming that the ganglion cell is a nutritive center for the entire neuron."

Persuaded by the brilliant histological preparations shown him by a young Hungarian neurohistologist, Stephan von Apathy (for details, see Florey, 1985), Bethe convinced himself that it is not the axons but the neurofibrils that are the true functional units of the nervous system. He argued that the neurofibrils are the conducting elements of the nervous system. The suggestion was not a new one: Ernst Haeckel (1834-1919), then one of the most influential zoologists, had already proposed it in his thesis of 1857 which was concerned with "the tissues of *Astacus fluviatilis*". Bethe concluded that "we must stop considering the neuron as a physiological unit and must admit that one and the same neuron is capable of many diverse actions, depending on which fibrillar tract is in operation." Bethe realized that it would be a hopeless undertaking to map all the fibrillar connections and he gave up. The last passage of the third *Carcinus* paper reads "As we now overlook my whole work, I reach the sad conclusion that nothing has been gained from it for our factal knowledge. Were there not satisfaction in the search for knowledge, one would have to say in resignation: it is too difficult for us humans." It took decades for physiologists to regain the courage required to start again the attempt of a complete morphological and functional analysis of a crustacean nervous system.

When Bethe returned from Naples, he accepted a post as assistant to the physiologist Richard Ewald (1855-1921) in the physiology department of Strassburg University headed by Friedrich Leopold Goltz (1834-1902). Here he took his doctoral degree in medicine. In 1911 Bethe became chairman of the department of animal physiology at Frankfurt University.

Fig. 7. Albrecht Bethe
(from Thauer, 1955)

Bethe has influenced neurobiology to an extent that is hardly appreciated today. One of his best known pupils and an ardent admirer was Erich von Holst (1908-1962). Bethe (Figure 7) was a true comparative physiologist. He is well known for his studies of insect walking, and of the reorganization of central motor programs after removal of legs. Studies of a similar nature on dogs, in which he crossed sensory nerves and noted the reestablishment of proper reflex connections, led him to the concept of the "plasticity of the nervous system". In fact, he coined the term (Bethe, 1926; Bethe and Fischer, 1931). He became an opponent of the concept of nerve centers with fixed action patterns based on immutable neuronal circuits. In 1899, together with Theodor Beer and Jakob von Uexküll he proposed that sensory physiologists use an 'objectivating nomenclature' to replace the 'subjective' terms of 'senses' (sense of smell or taste, light sense, etc.). Today this terminology is in general use: we speak of 'receptors' (e.g. chemo-receptors, photoreceptors). Bethe later referred to this joint publication (Beer, Bethe, and von Uexküll, 1899) as the "Drei-Männer-Manifest" (Bethe, 1940).

HERMANN JACQUES JORDAN (1877-1943)

Although Bethe's *Carcinus* studies were the most extensive, other authors also carried out important experiments on the functions of the nervous system of various crustaceans. An excellent account of these early researches can be found in volume four of the famous Handbuch der Vergleichenden Physiologie, edited by Hans Winterstein (1913) in which Silvestro Baglioni (1876 - 1937) covers the comparative physiology of the nervous system in a 428 page chapter, of which 45 pages are devoted to the crustaceans. For our story, however, it is of special interest to refer to a paper by Hermann Jordan, published in 1910.

In experiments on crayfish (*Astacus*) and crabs (*Carcinus*, *Cancer*), H.J. Jordan (1910) carried out local brain stimulation, did ablations of various brain areas, sectioned connectives, and studied the influence of the brain on the control of movement. He was able to elicit specific behavior, and by appropriate stimulation of the distal part of a sectioned circumoesophageal connective he was able to initiate or inhibit walking. Many years later,

Jordan became the teacher of C.A.G. Wiersma, and it is not difficult to discern in Wiersma's now classical studies on the crayfish central nervous system, the heritage of Jordan's early work.

Hermann Jacques Jordan had studied briefly under Theodor Boveri (1862-1915) at Würzburg. Before he became chairman of the Zoology Department at Würzburg, Boveri had been an assistant of Richard Hertwig in the Zoology Department at Munich when Albrecht Bethe was a student there. In 1897, Jordan went to Bonn to become a pupil of the physiologist Eduard (Friedrich Wilhelm) Pflüger (1829-1910). A year later, Anton Dohrn (1840-1909) took him on as assistant at his Zoological Station in Naples where Jordan worked for two years on the physiology of locomotion in *Aplysia*. It was at the Naples Zoological Station that Jordan became acquainted with Albrecht Bethe and his *Carcinus* work. He returned to Bonn to take his Ph.D. degree. His thesis, "Die Physiologie der Locomotion bei *Aplysia limacina*", was the result of the research he had done at Naples. After a five year interlude in Zürich, where he made a living reviewing current research literature for an abstracting journal, Jordan, who had become a Privatdozent, moved to the University of Tübingen where, in 1911, he became associate professor of zoology. His work there was mainly concerned with vegetative physiology, especially digestion and nutrition. He wrote a textbook of comparative physiology (published in 1913) that became very popular and influential. It was exclusively concerned with feeding, digestion and nutrition. Jordan then accepted a post at the University of Utrecht in Holland where, in 1919, he became professor of comparative physiology. In 1926 he took on a new Ph.D. student by the name of Cornelis Adrianus Gerrit Wiersma whom, in 1929, he made his assistant.

One may well ask what prompted Jordan to suggest to his doctoral student an investigation of the nervous control of crustacean leg muscles. Jordan, after all, is now known mainly for his work on the comparative physiology of digestion and nutrition. In 1929, it is true, he published a new textbook "Allgemeine vergleichende Physiologie der Tiere" (General Comparative Animal Physiology) with a wider scope. But to understand Jordan's interest in the nervous control of crustacean muscle it is necessary to go back to the time when Jordan was a Privatdozent at Tübingen. Jordan then had spent several months in the physiology department of the University of Jena where Wilhelm Biedermann, who meanwhile had become chairman of that department, introduced him to crustacean nerve-muscle physiology. Biedermann was an authority in the field of electrophysiology; his famous textbook "Elektrophysiologie" had appeared in 1895. But he still maintained his interest in comparative physiology, publishing on such diverse subjects as the digestive enzymes of *Helix*, and on iridescent colors in insects and birds. He also encouraged work on crustacean muscle innervation. In 1905, one of his assistants, Ernst Mangold, published a description of the innervation of the opener muscle of the crayfish claw, based on methylene blue staining (Figure 8). Crustacean neurobiology was still very much alive in Jena.

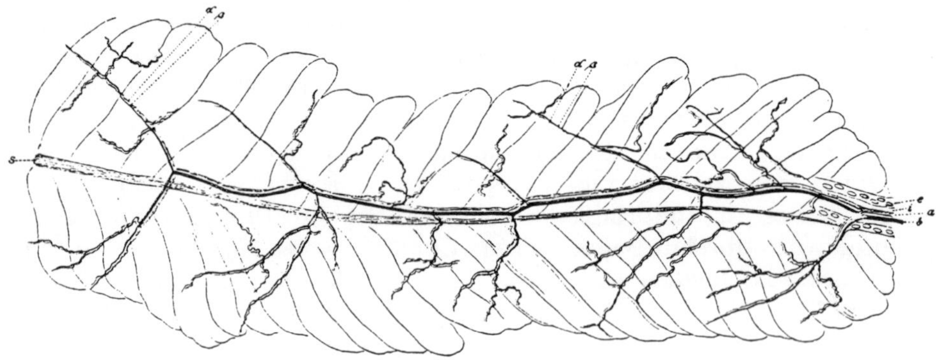

Fig. 8. Innervation of the opener muscle of the crayfish claw (*Astacus*). Two axons (a, b; α, ß) with parallel, diplotomic branching pattern. s = the tendon. (from Mangold, 1910)

Biedermann showed Jordan how to implant minute platinum electrodes into the chelipeds of crayfish in such a way as to permit stimulation of the leg nerve in the freely moving animal or in the isolated leg. Biedermann could also teach him how to cut the tendons of the closer or the opener muscle and how to record the muscle contractions without interference from the contractions of the antagonistic muscle. Jordan then spent some time at the Dutch marine laboratory at Den Helder that had been established by the Netherlands Zoological Society. There he extended his investigation from crayfish to crabs (*Carcinus, Cancer*). As already mentioned, the results of these studies were published in 1910, the year before Jordan was appointed associate professor at Tübingen. Later, when he had moved to Utrecht, movement control in invertebrates still held his interest. Jordan taught very successful courses in comparative physiology at Den Helder, and it would be very surprising if he had not included experiments on crustaceans in the laboratory exercises. He must have felt pleased to find in Wiersma a promising Ph.D. student who would resume the investigation of crustacean locomotor control he himself had begun eighteen years before and had left in 1910 with many questions still unanswered, - among them the nature of peripheral inhibition discovered by Richet (1879) and by Biedermann (1887, 1888). Several physiologists had suggested that this peripheral inhibition might be the result of conduction block in the nerve or to a special kind of action of the same nerve fibers which, under other conditions, would give rise to contraction. Clearly, there was room for a more detailed investigation of the nature of the peripheral innervation of crustacean muscle.

CORNELIS ADRIANUS GERRIT WIERSMA (1905-1979)

Wiersma took up the challenge, and as we know, he was very successful. His doctoral thesis was published in volume 19 of the Zeitschrift für vergleichende Physiologie in 1933 under the title "comparative investigations on the peripheral nerve-muscle system of crustaceans". In this publication we find the first records of extracellular excitatory junction potentials recorded with an Einthoven string galvanometer. Wiersma correctly called them 'muscle action currents'. The terms 'excitatory junction potential' or 'excitatory postsynaptic potential' came much later. Wiersma demonstrated once and for all that the leg muscles are innervated both by motor and by inhibitory neurons, and that stimulation of the one always caused excitation, and that of the other produced inhibition and only inhibition. Wiersma also showed that on stimulation of the motor axons two types of contraction could be elicited: a fast one, in which a twitch-like contraction followed a single muscle action potential, and a slow contraction which was accompanied by a series of muscle action potentials. In the closer muscle, the two types of contraction could be elicited by stimulation of different strength and duration, suggesting the existence of a dual motor innervation. The slow contraction required long lasting d.c. currents. Wiersma clearly showed that this slow contraction is due to repetitive firing of the motor axon and resembles a tetanus (Figure 9). It is interesting that the method of nerve stimulation used by Wiersma was exactly the same as that used by Biedermann, except that Wiersma used silver-silver chloride electrodes. These electrodes were implanted into the meropodite through small holes drilled into the exoskeleton. For the recording of muscle action currents, Wiersma followed a technique he learned in the laboratory of E.D. Adrian in Cambridge where he had spent a year (1930/31) as a Dondersfonds fellow.

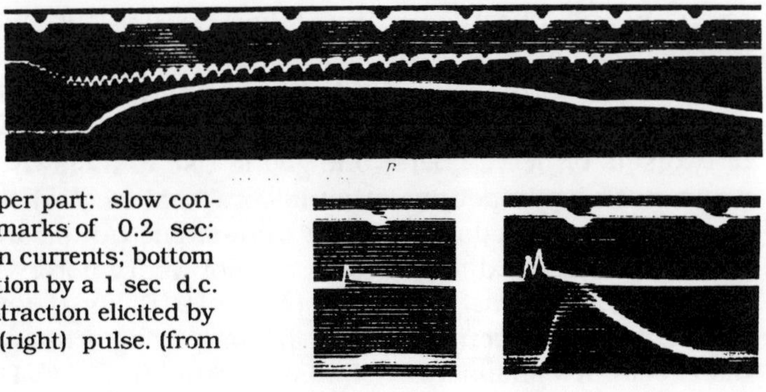

Fig. 9. Mechanical and electrical recording from the closer muscle of the crayfish (*Astacus*) claw. Upper part: slow contraction (top line: time marks of 0.2 sec; middle line: repetitive action currents; bottom line: contraction). Stimulation by a 1 sec d.c. pulse. Lower part: fast contraction elicited by a single (left) and double (right) pulse. (from Wiersma, 1933)

THE CAMBRIDGE TRADITION AND THE PLYMOUTH MARINE LABORATORY

GUSTAVUS PIOTROWSKI, KEITH LUCAS, EDGAR DOUGLAS ADRIAN

Cambridge already had a tradition in the field of crustacean nerve-muscle physiology: in 1893, Gustavus Piotrowski, a Polish physiologist spent some time in the physiology department at Cambridge, where he tried to extend Biedermann's experiments on crayfish muscle. Although he did not get much further, he concluded that his results were best explained by accepting Biedermann's view that contraction and inhibition were the result of the action of two different sets of nerve fibers (Piotrowski, 1893). In 1907, Keith Lucas, Fellow of Trinity College of Cambridge, and one of England's most ingenious physiologists held the Cambridge Research Table at the Plymouth Marine Laboratory where he tried out his new method of electrical stimulation with condensor discharges on isolated claws of the lobster, *Homarus* (Lucas, 1907). He discovered that the closer muscle responded to single stimuli with two types of contraction, fast and slow, depending on the

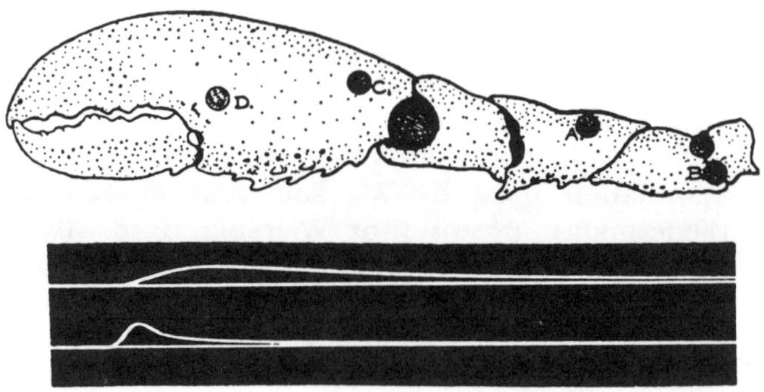

Fig. 10. Diagram of a lobster claw with holes (A - D) drilled for placement of stimulating electrodes. The mechanograms below show a slow and a fast contraction as elicited b a weak but long, and a strong but brief current pulse. (from Lucas, 1917)

strength and duration of the stimulus (Fig. 5). In 1917 the Journal of Physiology posthumously published Keith Lucas' last paper. It was concerned with the effects of indirect stimulation on the closer muscle of the claw of the crayfish, *Astacus*. Lucas provided good evidence for the existence of two sets of nerve fibers, one giving rise to a slowly developing contraction when weak but repetitive stimuli were applied, and the other one causing a fast twitch contraction resulting from single but stronger stimuli. At the end of the paper, the Editor placed a brief obituary note.

"Dr. Keith Lucas died on Oct. 5, 1916, as the result of an aeroplane accident, which occurred whilst he was flying. This paper was found among his effects. It was inscribed 'Finished. Aug. 3, 1914'. Dr. Keith Lucas was but 37 years of age. It is a lasting loss to Science that he has not been left to complete the study of the process of excitation along the lines in which he had been so successful, and by the methods over which he had unequalled mastery."

These simple words hide the tragedy of World War I which was raging when Lucas' paper was published. Lucas had enlisted in 1914 and was assigned to the Royal Aircraft Factory where he designed instrumentation and developed a new magnetic compass. In 1916 he became a pilot. While flying solo, he was killed in a midair collision. Lucas was a true comparative physiologist. He lectured in the zoology department at Cambridge on the comparative physiology of muscle, but, more important, he published two papers on the evolution of animal function (Lucas, 1911a,b) in which he advocated the union of physiology with the concepts of evolution.

Edgar Douglas (Lord) Adrian (1889 - 1977), incidently, was a pupil of Keith Lucas at Trinity College. By the time Wiersma went to his laboratory, Adrian was already an authority in the field of neurophysiology; in 1932 he received the Nobel prize.

Wiersma could build on Lucas' experiments; in fact, he worked on lobster claws at the Plymouth Laboratory, just as Lucas had done many years before him.

C.A.G. WIERSMA AND ANTHONIE VAN HARREVELD (1904-1987) THOMAS HUNT MORGAN

Even before he received his doctoral degree, Wiersma became assistant professor of medical physiology at Utrecht. In that same department another man was similarly appointed: it was Anthonie van Harreveld (Figure 11). Although van Harreveld was an M.D., he became engrossed by Wiersma's project of analyzing the nervous control of crustacean muscle. The two young scientists became close friends and spent their vacations together at the Marine Station at Den Helder experimenting on crabs.

Wiersma (Figure 12) graduated in 1933 after he had defended the doctoral thesis referred to earlier. His "promotor" was Hermann J. Jordan. In that same year there was another momentous event in the history of science: Thomas Hunt Morgan (1866-1945) received the Nobel prize for his studies in human genetics. In 1928, already famous for his work in *Drosophila* genetics, he had joined the California Institute of Technology at Pasadena where he was given the task of organizing a department of biology. Morgan was well aware of the opportunities offered to comparative physiologists by marine biological laboratories. He knew the Zoological Station at Naples where he had worked with Hans Driesch (1867-1941) and Curt Alfred Herbst (1866-1946) in 1895; he had also visited the Marine Laboratory on the island of Helgoland in 1894, and he was well acquainted with the Marine Biological Laboratory at Woods Hole, where he had worked in the years 1889 and 1890. In 1933 he founded the Marine Biological Laboratory at Corona del Mar near Los Angeles - and he consulted Hermann Jordan, whom he regarded as the most knowledgeable comparative physiologist, about possible candidates for the positions in comparative physiology he wanted to fill. Jordan recommended two young scientists whom he considered particularly promising, not only because they were passionate scientists, but also because he felt they might feel adventurous enough to leave their own country for the New World to pursue and advance comparative physiology. The two men were none other than C.A.G. Wiersma and Anthonie van Harreveld. Morgan offered each of them a post as assistant professor, and they did not hesitate to accept. It was clear to Morgan that both men would pursue their interests in crustacean nerve-muscle physiology, a field he himself was familiar with: if you look at back issues of the American Journal of Physiology, you will find in volume 6, published in 1902 a paper by Thomas Hunt Morgan entitled: the reflexes connected with autotomy in the hermit crab!

Fig. 11. Anthonie van Harreveld
(from Ochs, 1988)

Fig. 12. Cornelis Adrianus Gerrit Wiersma holding a specimen of *Podophthalmus*, a crab with extraordinarily long eyestalks containing long axons of higher order visual neurons which fire only in response to specific movement or orientation of optical stimuli presented to the eye. (from Hoyle, 1982)

Wiersma and van Harreveld arrived in Pasadena in 1934, and for many years there issued from their laboratory a series of important joint papers on various aspects of crustacean nerve-muscle physiology. To those of us who became more closely associated with them, Wiersma became affectionately known as 'Kees'; van Harreveld, however, was reverently called 'Van'. Curiously, to many crustacean neurobiologists, van Harreveld is mainly known as the originator of the "van Harreveld solution", the saline so well suited to keep crayfish neuromuscular preparations alive (van Harreveld, 1936). Van Harreveld later moved on to mammalian neurophysiology, although once in a while he returned to the crayfish, as in 1959 when he discovered - with Mendelson - that L-glutamate was a promising candidate for the transmitter substance of crayfish motoneurones. But I am getting ahead of my story!

The merits of van Harreveld in the field of crustacean neurobiology have been much underrated. In retrospect, it becomes evident that the "van Harreveld solution" was indeed responsible for the rapid development of crustacean neurobiology. All earlier experimenters had struggled with the difficulty of keeping their preparations alive and functioning. Exposure of the nerves and muscle of crayfish to air had to be avoided as much as possible, the life-time of physiological preparations was counted in minutes. Now, after 1936, it became possible to extend experiments to hours. A soon as the new saline was introduced, van Harreveld and Wiersma suceeded in working with single axons (van Harreveld and Wiersma, 1936, 1937). From then on, progress was rapid and went as far as it could with the techniques used: extracellular electrical recording of the summed "muscle action potentials" and mechanical recording of the contraction of the whole muscle led to more and more complications. I will mention only one of them, the so-called "paradox" which puzzled Wiersma for years. In a crab, *Blepharipoda*, stimulation of one of the two motor axons resulted in large "action potentials" but a small contraction, while stimulation of the other motor axon gave rise to a strong contraction but the "action potentials" were small. The topic has been reviewed so often that it is not necessary to go into details. With the methods they had available, van Harreveld and Wiersma, together with various postdoctoral fellows had discovered heterosynaptic facilitation and two modes of inhibition resulting from stimulation of the two efferent inhibitory neurons that supply each leg. They called these neurons the 'common inhibitor' and the 'true inhibitor', and the inhibitory effects were referred to as "simple" and "supplemented" inhibition respectively (Marmont and Wiersma, 1938).

When I arrived in his laboratory in 1951, Wiersma was already disenchanted with nerve-muscle physiology. He had become interested in the physiology of the central nervous system. He already had published most interesting data on the interactions of the four giant fibers in the ventral nerve cord, but now he began to think of an approach similar to that envisioned by Albrecht Bethe more than fifty years earlier.

MY OWN HISTORY

Before I went to Pasadena, my knowledge of crustacean neurobiology was very limited. Yet what little I knew turned out to be quite useful. In 1950, I had received my Ph.D. degree at the University of Graz. My research work was done partly in Graz, partly at the Stazione Zoologica at Naples. My teachers in Graz had been Karl von Frisch (1886-1985) and Karl Umrath (1899-1985). Von Frisch had studied in Vienna; among others he was a pupil of Sigmund Exner (his uncle). Karl Umrath had studied at the University of Prag where Biedermann had done his studies of crayfish nerve-muscle physiology and at the University of Jena under Ernst Haeckel and Wilhelm Biedermann. Between 1924 and 1927, Umrath spent some time in the laboratory of E.D. Adrian in Cambridge. Umrath had been an assistant of Otto Loewi (1873-1961) in the pharmacology department of the University of Graz but his heart was in biophysics and in comparative physiology.

Umrath took me on as a Ph.D. student and suggested that I work out the mechanism of action of convulsant drugs, such as strychnine and picrotoxin. Umrath thought that these compounds might inhibit the enzyme that inactivates the transmitter substance of sensory neurons of vertebrates. What was needed was a test system for the still unknown sensory transmitter, and a better knowledge of the effectiveness and the effects of these convulsants in different animal groups. A welcome reason to go to Naples and to study as many different species as possible! Of my "Naples experience" I have reported elsewhere (Florey, 1983). One of the results of my investigations was that crustaceans were insensitive to strychnine but responded with convulsions when injected with minute doses of picrotoxin. It became obvious that progress could be made only with the use of electrophysiological techniques. Arrangements were made for me to go to the laboratory of Hansjochen Autrum in Göttingen, then <u>the</u> authority in the field of electrophysiology. Autrum had designed the first d.c. amplifier sensitive enough for physiological work and had already published interesting findings concerning the electrical events in the eyes of insects. I stayed only a few months with Autrum because I received notification that I had been granted a Fullbright fellowship, and had been offered fellowships both from Harvard University, where John Welsh offered me a postdoctoral position, and from CalTech, where Wiersma had arranged for me to become a Hixon-Fellow.

THE BIOLOGY DEPARTMENT AT HARVARD AND JOHN HENRY WELSH

L.H. KLEINHOLZ, D.E. BLISS, W.G. VAN DER KLOOT, D.M. MAYNARD

I had accepted the CalTech fellowship, but felt I had to see Harvard first and to pay a visit to Professor Welsh (Figure 13) who had so kindly invited me to work in his biology department. The Fullbright commission was generous to permit the detour and John Welsh extended his cordial hospitality to the foreigner inviting me to stay in his family home, and introduced me to his staff and graduate students. There was Bill Van der Kloot (Figure 14), working on his Ph.D. thesis on spiders, and Dorothy Bliss, doing her thesis work on diurnal rhythms of *Gecarcinus*. I met Carrol Williams, was introduced to Kenneth Roeder, and met Lou Kleinholz (Figure 13) whose elegant demeanor impressed me. I was also given the opportunity of attending one of George Wald's biochemistry lectures.

Fig. 13. John H. Welsh (left) and L.H. Kleinholz in front of the Biology Building of Harvard University in the summer of 1951

John Welsh showed me his data on crustacean heart pharmacology and told me of his idea that acetylcholine excites the heart ganglion cells and that this explains why hearts with neurogenic heartbeat are excited by acetylcholine while those with myogenic heartbeat are inhibited. For the first time, I heard of the work of Alexandrowicz on the structure of the heart ganglion of various crustaceans. Welsh also introduced me to the theories concerning the structure-activity relationship of cholinergic drugs. A few years later, Donald Maynard (Figure 15) became a student of Welsh, who assigned to him the task of working out the interaction of the cells of the heart ganglion. At Welsh's suggestion, Maynard then went to Los Angeles to work with Theodore Bullock (Figure 14). This was the beginning of a new area of crustacean neurobiology: the work on "model systems". The heart ganglion was considered a model of a central nervous system. The idea was that one must first understand the interaction of small group of neurons of well defined function, before one can progress to more complex neuronal interactions in a central nervous system.

Fig. 15. Stephen Kuffler (left), Melvin Cohen and Donald Maynard (right) in serious discussion at the Symposium on Nervous Inhibition (Friday Harbor) in 1960

Fig. 14. William G. van der Kloot (left) and Theodore H. Bullock at the GABA symposium (City of Hope) of 1959

Kleinholz was among the pioneers in the field of crustacean neuro-endocrinology. He and his co-workers had discovered that the eyestalk of crabs, especially the sinus gland, released a hyperglycemic hormone under conditions of stress, causing an increase of blood sugar (Kleinholz and Little, 1949; Kleinholz, Havel, and Reichart, 1950). Bliss, working with Welsh, had found that an eyestalk hormone caused increased oxygen comsumption. These were the days when it became evident that the sinus gland is but a bunch of secretory nerve terminals and that the cell bodies of the secretory neurons were quite a distance away (see Bliss, Durand, and Welsh, 1954). This was the time when it was at long last recognized that neurosecretory cells were neurons capable of carrying nerve impulses, and that they secreted important hormones.

AT THE CALIFORNIA INSTITUTE OF TECHNOLOGY

E.J. FURSHPAN, S.H. RIPLEY

Pasadena forty years ago was an idyllic place. The campus of the California Institute of Technology (CalTech) was much smaller - and more pleasant - than it is today. Within a few minutes driving time one was out in the open country. When I arrived in the Biology building one day in the sfummer of 1951, Wiersma was out fishing for crayfish in a nearby river. Later on, I often went with him to catch more of the animals whenever our stocks got low. There was a dirt road leading through jungle-like vegetation where today there are only freeways and huge housing developments, and the river is now cemented in - I doubt that crayfish can live in it. Many a pleasant evening was spent at the Wiersma's comfortable home (Figure 16).Once a week, Kees Wiersma had to give a physiology lecture to some graduate students. To my amazement, he based his lectures on Jordan's old textbook of 1929 - except for those few hours he devoted to crustacean nerve-muscle physiology. Wiersma then had two doctoral students: E.J. Furshpan and Sherman Ripley.

Fig. 16. The Wiersmas: Jane, Whiskers, and Kees at their home in Pasadena in 1952

Ripley was given the task of working out the pattern of efferent innervation of the limb muscles in different groups of decapod crustaceans. Ed Furshpan and I were assigned to something new: Kees Wiersma had just received a reprint of a paper by J.S. Alexandrowicz (Figure 17) from the Plymouth Marine Laboratory. He called us to his office and explained to us Alexandrowicz' discovery of large sensory cells associated with certain muscle fibers of the abdominal extensor muscles of *Homarus* (Figure 18). Alexandrowicz referred to them as 'muscle receptor organs'. Wiersma immediately recognized the importance of these 'stretch receptor organs' as they were henceforth called. In fact, he foresaw that if it were possible to record action potentials from these large sensory cells, this would be the first case of working with isolated identified neurons with the immense advantage that these neurons evidently received synaptic contacts and thus would have properties otherwise expected only of central neurons. Wiersma then and there decided that we must drop any other work we were doing, or were planning to do, in order to make these stretch receptors available for physiological analysis. Dissection of these structures proved difficult, electrical recording revealed only silence. Ed Furshpan then found a way of preparing the receptor organs from a ventral approach - and although this made dissection easy, there still was no response from the neurons, no matter how much we stretched the muscle fibers. Finally, I remembered my experiences with picrotoxin and applied this substance to a fresh preparation. To our surprise the nerve cells began to fire. This was a day of joy. From then on we began each experiment with a dose of picrotoxin, but later, for reasons unknown, we could make the preparations perform even without the pharmacological prompting. We did a little pharmacology after all (Wiersma, Furshpan and Florey (1952). But then news reached the laboratory that Stephen Kuffler (Figure 15), then in Baltimore, was on the same track. Ed Furshpan felt that he could not possibly hope to compete with this accomplished and famous physiologist. He had to work for his Ph.D. and did not want to risk being scooped. He decided to change horses in mid-stream and from then on worked out the innervation pattern of single muscle fibers, discovering that there were fibers innervated by only one motor axon, others in the same muscle, by two. He did a vast amount of work, of statistical analysis - and except for writing it up in his thesis, never published his findings.

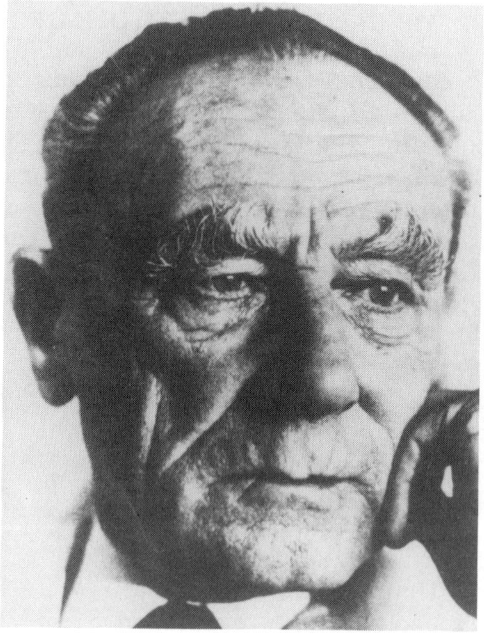

Fig. 17. Jerzy Stanislaw Alexandrowicz (from Bone, 1971)

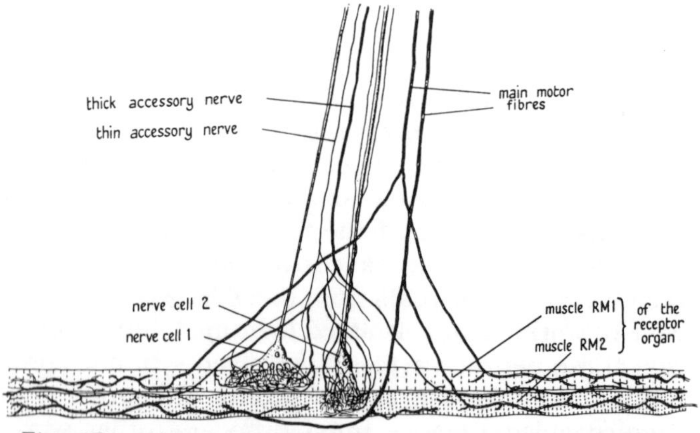

Fig. 18A. Alexandrowicz's often reproduced schematic drawing of a muscle receptor organ of *Homarus*. (from Alexandrowicz, 1952

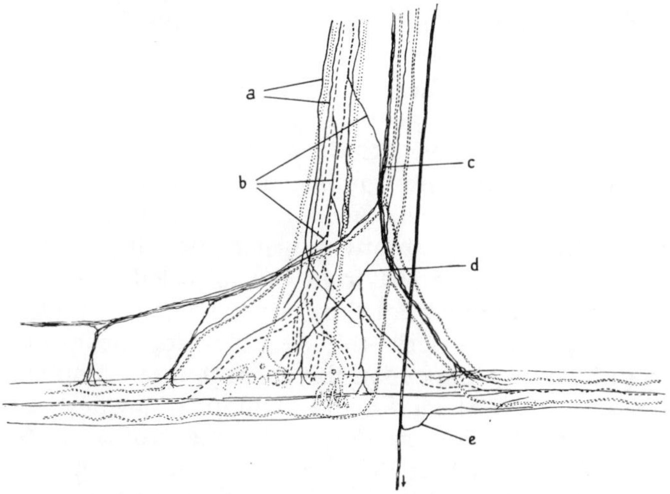

Fig. 18B. The other part of Alexandrowicz's figure which is never quoted: it shows additional axons (a,c,d) innervating the receptor neurons. (from Alexandrowicz, 1952)

Only years later did Harold Atwood take up the subject and now, especially through the work of Werner Rathmayer and his coworkers, we have identified muscle fibers just as years before identified neurons had been discovered. - But again, I am getting ahead of my story.

THE PLYMOUTH CONNECTION

E.J. ALLEN, J.S. ALEXANDROWICZ, C.F.A. PANTIN, B. KATZ, S.W. KUFFLER

How did Kuffler acquire the courage to work on crustaceans? How did Alexandrowicz get introduced to crustacean neurobiology? Jerzy Stanislaw Alexandrowicz (1886-1970) had studied medicine and natural science in Warsaw, Zürich, Munich, Heidelberg, Paris and Jena. He received his Ph.D. in Zürich, and his M.D. degree in Jena under Wilhelm Biedermann. And it was Biedermann who introduced Alexandrowicz to the crustaceans. If you read the acknowledgement at the end of Alexandrowicz' first paper (1934) on the innervation of the heart of decapod crustaceans, you find this confirmed. Alexandrowicz learned his methylene blue technique in Jena, but the fixation method was that invented by Albrecht Bethe. In the years of the first and the second world wars, and even during the first years after the war, Alexandrowicz lived through extraordinary hardships and deprivations. The events have been sketched out in two publications (Bone, 1971; Florey, 1983). Suffice it here to say that from 1950 on, Alexandrowicz held a position, first as technician, from 1951 to the end of his life as a research professor, supported by grants from the Royal Society of London. His detailed descriptions and functional analyses of crustacean muscle receptor organs and other receptor organs have become the firm basis on which much of current crustacean neurobiology is built. - Talking of Plymouth brings back memories of another important figure: E.J. Allen, who from 1895 through 1936 held the post of director of the Plymouth Marine Laboratory. Edgar Johnson Allen (1866-1942) has done important work on structure and function of marine animals and plants. He was the first to describe in lobster embryos the cells Alexandrowicz later identified as stretch receptor neurons. Allen helped many physiologists interested in working with crustaceans. Lucas benefitted from his knowledge as well as C.F.A. Pantin, who went to Plymouth from Cambridge where he had learned what was known about crustacean nerve-muscle physiology from Lucas. Indeed, in 1934, Pantin published a paper "on the excitation of crustacean muscle" - he had held a post as physiologist at the Plymouth Marine Laboratory from 1922 - 1929 before he became reader, and later professor in the zoology department at Cambridge. When Bernard Katz went to Plymouth in 1935 after he had received his doctorate from Leipzig University, it was Pantin who introduced him to crustacean nerve-muscle physiology. In 1936 Katz published his first paper on this subject, to be followed by several others years later, some with S.W. Kuffler (1913-1980) who had been his close associate during their years of exile in Australia.

Wiersma did not think very highly of these publications, much as he appreciated the other accomplishments of these already famous physiologists. We were all surprised when he consented to let Ed Furshpan go to London to work in Sir Bernard's laboratory. Together with Potter, Furshpan there produced his famous work on the electrical synapse between giant axon and giant motoneuron of the crayfish central nerve cord (Furshpan and Potter, 1954).

FROM FACTOR I TO GAMMA-AMINO-BUTYRIC-ACID

When I expressed to Kees Wiersma an interest in working on the problem of chemical synaptic transmission, he looked at me in dismay and said "you are just as bad as Feldberg and Katz and those boys". I had to wait until Kees had departed to Holland on a sabbatical leave of absence, before I could seriously embark on my cherished project of discovering the transmitter substance of sensory neurons. I travelled in my newly acquired automobile to a horse butcher in Los Angeles to obtain, twice a week, dorsal and ventral roots as well as parts of the spinal cord from freshly slaughtered horses. I prepared extracts to be applied to stretch receptor neurons - only to find that extracts of spinal cord always stopped the impulse generation while extracts from the spinal roots were essentially ineffective. It slowly dawned on me that this might mean that spinal cord tissue contains an inhibitory substance. It was not a farfetched hypothesis that this might eventually

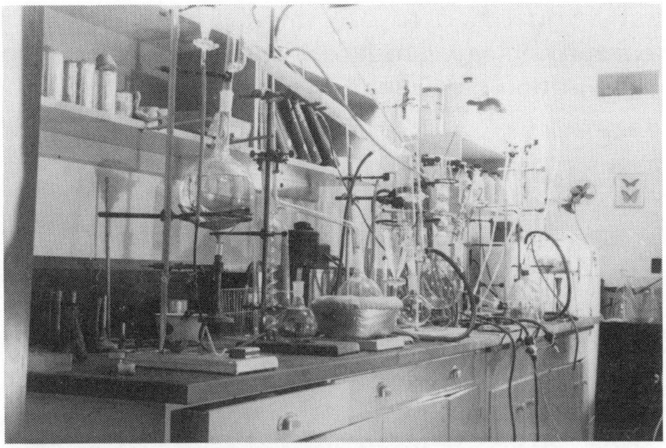

Fig. 19. My improvised neuro-chemistry laboratory at CalTech where I isolated "Factor I" in the spring of 1952

prove to be the transmitter substance of inhibitory neurons. If so, extracts of crayfish peripheral nerve which contains inhibitory axons ought to cause inhibition of the stretch receptor discharge. This was indeed the case. And at long last, a rationale for the action of picrotoxin came in sight: perhaps the convulsions caused by this alkaloid are not the result of enhanced action of sensory transmitter, but of a blocking of the action of an inhibitory transmitter. And it came about that I found that picrotoxin blocked the effect of the inhibitory substance in the extracts from nerve tissue that was known to contain inhibitory neurons or axons. I called this substance "factor I" (Florey, 1953). I sent the manuscript of the intended publication to Wiersma and van Harreveld for critical reading. Wiersma wrote back (I had returned to Germany to resume my fellowship with Autrum) I was welcome to publish it but he would not want to have his name on it. He found it too risky to enter the arena of chemical synaptic transmission. A few years later, in the laboratory of K.A.C. Elliott, at the Montral Neurological Institute, in collaboration with Alva Bazemore, we were able to identify the inhibitory substance with gamma-aminobutyric acid, GABA (Bazemore, Elliott, and Florey, 1956).

GRAHAM HOYLE (1923-1986) AND C.A.G. WIERSMA

T.H. WATERMAN, B.M.H. BUSH

Wiersma did not pursue the stretch receptor work. He knew this was now in capable hands: Kuffler and Eyzaguirre had done a magnificent job using microelectrodes - a method which Wiersma was reluctant to employ. He could not resist for long, however, because he accepted a postdoctoral fellow from England by the name of Graham Hoyle, - and Graham persuaded Kees that he just had to use microelectrodes if he wanted to get anywhere in neurophysiology. Indeed, three important papers resulted from the collaboration of these rather unlike scientists.

Fig. 20. Graham Hoyle in 1979 at the Friday Harbor Laboratories, looking in from outside one of the lab buildings

After Graham Hoyle left for Eugene, Oregon, where he had been offered a position as research professor, Kees happily went on with extracellular recordings, not of muscle activities but of central neurons. He already had begun this work while I was in his lab in 1951 and 1952. He patiently subdivided the cerebral commissures and studied the activities he could record with fine metal electrodes. He sat there for hours in front of the oscilloscope watching the various tracings, taking occasional pictures with his 35mm camera. With uncanny prescience he developed new concepts that have become houshold words only decades later: "command neuron", "parallel processing", - and years before Maturana, Lettvin, McCullock, Pitts, Hubel and Wiesel came up with their concept of movement and orientation specific higher-order visual neurons, Wiersma, in collaboration with Brian Bush and Talbot Waterman had found such 'units' in the optic ganglia of various decapod crustaceans. Publication, unfortunately, was delayed several years and when the papers finally appeared their impact was dulled by the clamour raised by the discoveries reported by the vertebrate physiologists.

Graham Hoyle was introduced to crustacean neurobiology by Kees Wiersma. And Hoyle has passed on his love of these animals to his many students who have advanced crustacean neurobiology beyond Wiersma's, and in many cases even Hoyle's, wildest dreams.

RAMIFICATIONS AND INTERCONNECTIONS

Kees Wiersma not only guided me into crustacean nerve-muscle physiology, he also taught me how to stimulate the cardio-regulator neurons of the crayfish. He opened for me the way to the stretch receptor neurons and thus made possible the later discovery that GABA might be the transmitter substance of inhibitory neurons. Pantin showed Bernard Katz how to make crustacean nerve-muscle preparations, and Katz introduced Kuffler to the game who, in turn instructed a German post-doctoral fellow by the name of Joseph Dudel in the use of the crayfish opener muscle: their collaboration resulted in the first definite demonstration of the phenomenon of presynaptic inhibition (Dudel and Kuffler, 1961). When I had become established in the zoology department of the University of Washington, I accepted a post-doctoral fellow from Germany by the name of Werner Rathmayer to whom I could pass on what I had learned from Wiersma. By now, Rathmayer has trained several accomplished researchers who have advanced crustacean nerve-muscle physiology. Together with Ted Wiens, a former student of Harold Atwood, who, in turn, was a student of Graham Hoyle, Werner Rathmayer revised the schema of muscle innervation originally proposed by Wiersma and Ripley. - Werner Rathmayer and I became colleagues at the University of Konstanz. One of our first advanced students was Hans Hatt, who then became a research associate of Joseph Dudel, thus closing a circle of traditions in crustacean neurobiology in more than one way: in the sixties I had begun to doubt that GABA is the transmitter substance of crustacean inhibitory neurons since I found that GABA-free nerve extracts could cause an inhibition which was antagonized by picrotoxin, and even when GABA was present in the extract, the effectiveness of the extracts could not be accounted for by their GABA content. With Bernd Koidl, one of the last pupils of Karl Umrath, I could later show that the inhibitory effect could be quantitatively accounted for by the L-glutamate and glycine present in the extracts. With his new method of ultrafast drug application, Hatt has now shown that there are, on crustacean muscle, Cl-channels coupled to receptors that can be activated by L-glutamate as well as by GABA. - Talking of GABA inevitably leads to E.A. Kravitz, who, together with D.D. Potter and W.N. van Gelder had joined Stephen Kuffler to prove that the transmitter substance of crustacean inhibitory neurons is indeed GABA. Van Gelder had come from the neurochemistry Laboratory of K.A.C. Elliott, where Bazemore and I had identified Factor I and GABA. Potter, it will be remembered, had worked with Furshpan in the laboratory of Bernard Katz on central synaptic transmission in the crayfish. - It is not the purpose of this outline to enumerate all the ramifications and roots of current research in crustacean neurobiology; those actively working in this field, undoubtedly will know their own place in this history which somehow joins all those present at this symposium - and so many others - through genealogic lines leading back to the early pioneers of crustacean neurobiology.

We all are indebted to our great teachers. Looking back at the historical development of crustacean neurobiology, it becomes obvious that our own immediate teachers have acquired their interest in crustacean neurobiology from their teachers. There is a web of knowledge that can be traced back and forth through space and time. In this essay I have illuminated only a few of the connecting lines and traditions.

CONCLUSION

The story presented here is quite incomplete. I have traced only a few of the traditions which have determined my own scientific development. My story leaves out important other schools, such as those of Leon Fredericq, of Angelique Arvanitaki, of Theodore Bullock, of Harry Grundfest, or that of Donald Kennedy. It omits the work of the Japanese, of the Italians, Mexicans, Belgians, Russians... What it does tell us, however, would be valid for all of them: that science is a very human enterprise which depends on human interaction, and that scientists follow traditions, - often without being aware of their origins.

REFERENCES

Alexandrowicz, J.S. (1951) Muscle receptor organs in the abdomen of *Homarus vulgaris* and *Palinurus vulgaris*. Quart.J.micr.Sci. **92**:163-199.

Allen, E.J. (1894) Studies on the nervous system of crustacea. I. Some nerve elements of the embryonic lobster. Quart.J.micr.Sci. **36**:461-482.

Baglioni, S. (1913) Physiologie des Nervensystems. In: H.Winterstein, ed., Handbuch der Vergleichenden Physiologie, vol.**4**:23-450.

Bazemore, A., Elliott, K.A.C. & Florey, E (1956) Factor I and γ-aminobutyric Acid. Nature 178:1052-1053.

Beer, Th., Bethe, A. & Uexküll, J.von (1899) Vorschläge zu einer objektivierenden Nomenklature in der Physiologie des Nervensystems. Biol.Zbl. **19**:517-521.

Bethe, A. (1896) Ein Beitrag zur Kenntnis des peripheren Nervensystems von *Astacus fluviatilis*. Anat.Anz. **12**:31-34.

Bethe, A. (1896) Eine neue Methode der Metylenblaufixation. Anat.Anz. **12**:438-4...

Bethe, A. (1897) Vergleichende Untersuchungen über die Funktion des Zentralnervensystems der Arthropoden. Pflüger Arch.ges.Physiol. **68**:449-545.

Bethe, A. (1897) Das Nervensystem von *Carcinus maenas*. Ein anatomisch-physiologischer Versuch. I. Theil. I.Mittheilung. Arch.f.mikr.Anat. **50**:460-546.

Bethe, A. (1897) Das Nervensystem von *Carcinus maenas*. Ein anatomisch-physiologischer Versuch. I. Theil. II.Mittheilung. Arch.f.mikr.Anat. **50**:589-639.

Bethe, A. (1898) Das Nervensystem von *Carcinus maenas*. Ein anatomisch-physiologischer Versuch. I. Theil. III.Mittheilung. Arch.f.mikr.Anat. **51**:382-452.

Bethe, A. (1903) Allgemeine Anatomie und Physiologie des Nervensystems. Leipzig.
Bethe, A. (1904) Der heutige Stand der Neurontheorie. Dtsch.Med. Wochenschr. **33**:1-11.
Bethe, A. (1904) Die historische Entwicklung der Ganglienzellhypothese. Erg.Physiol. **3**:2.Abt. 194-213.
Bethe, A (1926) Altes und Neues über die Plastizität des Nervensystems. Arch.f.Psychiatrie **76**:81-83.
Bethe, A. & Fischer, E. (1931) Die Anpassungsfähigkeit (Plastizität) des Nervensystems. Einführung und experimentelles Material. In: Handbuch der normalen und pathologischen Physiologie. Eds. A. Bethe, G. v. Bergmann, G. Embden und A. Ellinger, Berlin, J. Springer, Bd. 15,2 pp1045-1130.
Biedermann, W. (1887) Beiträge zur allgemeinen Nerven- und Muskelphysiologie. Zwanzigste Mittheilung. Über die Innervation der Krebsschere. Sitz.Ber.d.Akad.Wiss. Wien, Math. Naturwiss.Kl. Abt. III, **95**:7-40.
Biedermann, W. (1887) Zur Kenntnis der Nerven und Nervenendigungen in den quergestreiften Muskeln der Wirbellosen. Sitz.Ber.d.Akad.Wiss. Wien, Math.Naturwiss.Kl. Abt. III **96**:1-32.
Biedermann, W. (1888) Beiträge zur allgemeinen Nerven- und Muskelphysiologie. Einundzwanzigste Mittheilung. Über die Innervation der Krebsschere. Sitz.Ber.d.Akad.Wiss. Wien, Math. Naturwiss.Kl. Abt. III, **97**:44-82.
Biedermann, W. (1891) Ueber den Ursprung und die Endigungsweise der Nerven in den Ganglien wirbelloser Thiere. Jenaische Ztschr.f.Naturw. **25**:429-464.
Ehrenberg, C.G. (1833) Nothwendigkeit einer feineren mechanischen Zerlegung der Gehirns und der Nerven von der chemischen, dargestellt aus Beobachtungen von C.G. Ehrenberg. (Poggendorf's) Annalen der Physik **28**:449-473.
Ehrenberg, C.G. (1836) Beobachtungen einer bisher unerkannten Structur des Seelenorgans. Dümmler, Berlin, 57pp.
Exner, S. (1894) Entwurf zu einer physiologischen Erklärung der psychischen Erscheinungen. I.Theil. Franz Deuticke, Leipzig und Wien.
Florey, E. (1951) Vorkommen und Funktion sensibler Erregungssubstanzen und sie abbauender Fermente im Tierreich. Z.vergl.Physiol. **33**:327-377.
Florey, E. (1954) An inhibitory and an excitatory factor of mammalian central nervous system and their action on a single sensory neuron. Arch.intern.Physiol. **62**:33-53.
Freud, S. (1877) Über den Ursprung der hinteren Nervenwurzeln im Rückenmark von *Ammocoetes* (*Petromyzon Planeri*). Sitz.Ber.d.Akad.Wiss. Wien, Math.Naturwiss.Cl. III. Abth. **75**:1-13.
Freud, S. (1878) Über Spinalganglien und Rückenmark des *Petromyzon*. Sitz.Ber.d.Akad.Wiss. Wien, Math.Naturwiss.Cl. III. Abt. **78**:81-167.
Freud, S. (1882) Über den Bau der Nervenfasern und Nervenzellen beim Flußkrebs. Sitz.Ber.d.Akad.Wiss. Wien, Math.Naturwiss.Cl. III. Abt. **85**:9-46.
Furshpan, E.J. & Potter, D.D. (1959) Transmission at the giant motor synapses of the crayfish. J.Physiol. (Lond.) 145:289-325.
Haeckel, E. (1857)De telis quibusdam Astaci fluviatilis. Dissertatio inaug. histologica. T.G.Schade, Berolini.

Haeckel, E. (1857) Ueber die Gewebe des Flußkrebses. Müllers Arch. **14**:469-540.
Harreveld, A.van (1936) A physiological solution for freshwater crustaceans. Proc.Soc.exp.Biol. N.Y. **34**:428-432.
Harreveld, A.van & Wiersma, C.A.G. (1936) The double motor innervation of the abductor muscle in the claw of the crayfish. J.Physiol. (Lond.) **88**:78-99.
Harreveld, A.van & Wiersma, C.A.G. (1937) The triple innervation of crayfish muscle and its function in contraction and inhibition. J.exp.Biol. **34**:448-461.
Helmholtz, H. (1842) De fabrica systematis nervosi evertebratorum. Diss.Inaug. Berolini.
Hoyle, G. (1957) Comparative Physiology of the Nervous Control of Muscular Contraction. Cambridge University Press, Cambridge.
Hoyle, G. (1982) Muscles and their Neural Control. Wiley-Interscience, New York, 689pp.
Hoyle, G. & Wiersma, C.A.G. (1958) Excitation at neuromuscular junctions in crustacea. J.Physiol. (Lond.) **143**:403-425.
Hoyle, G. & Wiersma, C.A.G. (1958) Inhibition at neuromuscular junctions in crustacea. J.Physiol. (Lond.) **143**:426-440.
Hoyle, G. & Wiersma, C.A.G. (1958) Coupling of membrane potential to contraction in crustacean muscles. J.Physiol. (Lond.) **143**:441-453.
Jordan, H. (1910) Die Leistungen des Gehirnganglions bei den krebsartigen Tieren. Pflügers Arch.ges.Physiol **131**:317-386.
Jordan, H. (1913) Vergleichende Physiologie Wirbelloser Tiere. Erster Band, Die Ernährung, Nahrung, Nahrungserwerb, Nahrungsaufnahme, Verdauung und Assimilation. Gustav Fischer Verlag, Jena, 738pp.
Jordan, H.J. (1929) Allgemeine und vergleichende Physiologie der Tiere. W. de Gruyter & Co., Berlin, 761pp.
Katz, B. (1948) Neuromuscular transmission in crabs. J.Physiol. **87**:188-221.
Katz, B. & Kuffler, S.W. (1946) Excitation of the nerve-muscle system in crustacea. Proc.Roy.Soc.London, Ser.B **133**:374-389.
Kleinholz, L.H., Havel, V.J. & Reichart, R. (1950) Studies in the regulation of blood sugar concentration in crustaceans. II. Experimental hyperglycemia and the regulatory mechanisms. Biol.Bull. **99**:454-468.
Kleinholz, L.H. & Little B.A. (1949) Studies in the regulation of blood sugar concentration in crustaceans. I. Normal values and experimental hyperglycemia in *Libinia emarginata*. Biol.Bull. **96**:218-227.
Kuffler, S.W. & Katz, B. (1946) Inhibition at the nerve-muscle junction in crustacea. J.Neurophysiol. **9**:337-346.
Lucas, K. (1907) The analysis of complex excitable tissues by their response to electric currents of short duration. J.Physiol. (Lond.) **35**:310-331.
Lucas, K. (1917) On summation of propagated disturbances in the claw of *Astacus*, and on the double neuro-muscular system of the adductor. J.Physiol. (Lond.) **51**:1-35.
Mangold, E. (1905) Untersuchungen über die Endigung der Nerven in den quergestreiften Muskeln der Arthropoden. Z.allg.Physiol. **5**:135-205.
Maynard, D.M. (1953) Activity in a crustacean ganglion. I. Cardio-inhibition and acceleration in *Panulirus argus*. Biol.Bull. **104**:156-170.
Morgan, T.H. (1902) The reflex connected with autotomy in the hermit crab. Amer.J.Physiol. **6**:278-282.

Pantin, C.F.A. (1934) On the excitation of crustacean muscle. I. J.exp.Biol. **11**:11-27.

Piotrowski, G. (1893) On the muscle-nerve physiology of the crayfish especially with regard to inhibition. J.Physiol. (Lond.) **14**:163-197.

Retzius, G. (1890) Zur Kenntnis des Nervensystems der Crustaceen. Biologische Untersuchungen. Neue Folge, Bd. **1**:1-50, Central Druck, Stockholm.

Richet, Ch. (1879) Contributions à la physiologie des centres nerveux et des muscles de l'écrevisse. Arch.physiol. Norm.et Path. **6**:262-294, 522-276.

Waldeyer, W. (1891) Ueber einige neurere Forschungen im Gebiete der Anatomie des Centralnervensystems. Dtsch.Med.Wochenschr. **44**:1-64.

Waterman, T.H., Wiersma, C.A.G. & Bush, B.M.H. (1961) Impulse traffic in the optic nerve of decapod crustacea. Science **134**:1435.

Waterman, T.H., Wiersma, C.A.G. & Bush, B.M.H. (1964) Afferent visual response in the optic nerve of the crab, *Podophtalmus*. C.cell.comp.Physiol. **63**:135-155.

Welsh, J.H. (1939) Chemical mediation in crustaceans. II. The action of acetylcholine and adrenalin on the isolated heart of *Panulirus argus*. Physiol.Zool. **12**:231-237.

Welsh, J.H. (1942) Chemical mediation in crustaceans. IV. The action of acetylcholine on isolated hearts of *Homarus* and *Carcinides*. J.cell.comp.Physiol. **19**:271-279.

Welsh, J.H. & Maynard, D.M. (1951) Electrical activity of a simple ganglion. Fed. Proc. **10**:145.

Wiersma, C.A.G. (1933) Vergleichende Untersuchungen über das periphere Nerven-Muskel-System von Crustaceen. Z.vergl.Physiol. **19**:349-385.

Wiersma, C.A.G. (1947) Giant nerve fiber system of the crayfish: A contribution to comparative physiology of synapse. J.Neurophysiol. **10**:23-38.

Wiersma, C.A.G. (1962) The organization of arthropod central nervous system. Am.Zoologist **2**:67-78.

Wiersma, C.A.G. & Ripley, S.H. (1952) Innervation patterns of crustacean limbs. Physiol.Comp.Oecol. 2:391-405.

BIOGRAPHICAL LITERATURE

Bethe, A. (1940) Erinnerungen an die Zoologische Station in Neapel. Naturwissenschaften **28**:820-822.

Bone, Q. (1971) Obituary Professor J.S. Alexandrowicz. J.mar.biol.Ass.U.K. **52**:1007-1011.

Florey, E. (1985) The Zoological Station at Naples and the neuron: personalities and encounters in a unique institution. Biol.Bull. **168**:137-152.

Freud, E.L. ed. (1968) Sigmund Freud, Brautbriefe. Fischer Taschenbuch-verlag, Frankfurt a.M.

Hassenstein, B. (1970) Nachruf auf Erich von Holst. In: Erich von Holst, Zur Verhaltensphysiologie bei Tieren und Menschen. Gesammelte Abhandlungen, Bd. II, R. Piper & Co. Verlag München, pp.263-271.

Holst, E.von (1955) Albrecht Bethe. Naturwissenschaften **42**:165-167.

Hoyle, G. ed. (1977) Career Resume Wiersma, Cornelis Adrianus Gerrit (Kees-affectionately). In: Identified Neurons and Behavior of Arthropods. Plenum Press, New York and London, p.5.

Jahn, I., Löther, R. & Senglaub, K. (1982) Geschichte der Biologie. Theorien, Methoden, Institutionen, Kurzbiographien. VEB Gustav Fischer Verlag, Jena, 859pp.
Kühn, A. (1950) Anton Dohrn und die Zoologie seiner Zeit. Pubbl.Staz.Zool.Napoli, Suppl. 1950, 205pp.
Ochs, S. (1988) Anthonie van Harreveld (1904-1987) The Physiologist **31**:11-12.
Partsch, K.J. (1980) Die Zoologische Station in Neapel. Vandenhoeck & Ruprecht, Göttingen, 369pp.
Rothschuh, K.E. (1953) Geschichte der Physiologie. Springer Verlag, Berlin, Göttingen, Heidelberg, 249pp.
Schulz, Fr.N. (1930) Wilhelm Biedermann. Erg. Physiol. **30**:XII-XXVIII.
Smit, P. (1985) Jordan, Hermann Jacques. In: Biografisch Woordenboek van Nederland. Elsevier, Amsterdam, **2**:267-268.
Thauer, R. (1955) Albrecht Bethe. Pflüger's Arch.ges.Physiol. 261:I-IX.
Wiersma, C.A.G. (1975) Tribute to A. van Harreveld. J.Neurobiol. **6**:1-2.

Frontiers in Crustacean Neurobiology
Advances in Life Sciences

THE LOBSTER OLFACTORY RECEPTOR CELL AS A NEUROBIOLOGICAL MODEL: THE ACTION OF HISTAMINE

Barry W. Ache and Timothy S. McClintock*

Whitney Laboratory and Depts. Zoology and Neuroscience, Univ. Florida, St. Augustine, FL 32086
*present address: Sect. Molecular Neurobiology, Yale Univ. Sch. Med., New Haven, CT 06510

SUMMARY:

The suppressive action of the biogenic amine, histamine, on the output of lobster olfactory receptor cells provides new insight into peripheral organization in olfaction and reveals a new mechanism of action of biogenic amines. These findings are reviewed as one example of the pioneering role of crustacean chemoreceptors as model systems in neurobiology.

INTRODUCTION:

Crustacean models have played an increasing role in the chemical senses over the last 20 years. The utility of crustaceans for chemical senses research was established by James Case and Michael Laverack. These investigators first showed (e.g., Case and Gwilliam, 1961; Laverack, 1963) that single-fiber recording from the primary chemosensory neurons of crustaceans was trivial, at a time when our understanding of the chemosensory periphery was constrained by the need to do summated afferent fiber recordings in most other systems. Later, when the advent of patch electrodes made recording from small neurons routine (Hamill et al, 1981), crustacean olfactory receptor cells reliably provided information about odor-activated conductances (e.g., Anderson and Ache, 1985), when investigators were still constrained to study voltage- activated conductances in other olfactory receptor cells. The utility of crustaceans for chemical senses research also reflects the fact that biologically relevant "odors" for aquatic animals are mixtures of simple organic compounds such as amino acids, amines and nucleotides (review: Carr, 1988). Not only do these compounds allow for a degree of stimulus control not attainable with volatile odors, but some of them also function as intercellular signals in diverse biological systems. Much is already known about the cellular and molecular action of these molecules and, conversely, actions of these compounds defined in crustacean chemoreceptors may generalize to other systems.

METHODS:

Patch electrodes applied to the soma of the antennular (aesthetasc) chemoreceptors of decapod crustaceans such as lobsters can be used to record extracellular, intracellular, or single- channel neural activity from these cells (Figure 1). Anderson and Ache (1985) detail the method of tissue preparation and recording.

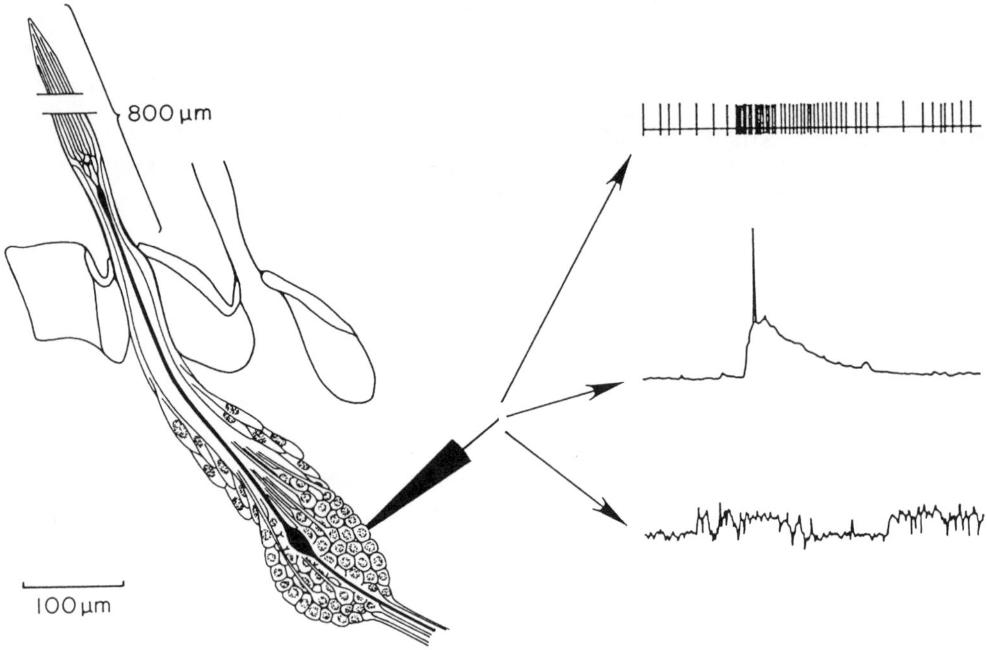

Fig. 1. Diagram of an aesthetasc (olfactory) sensillum of the Caribbean spiny lobster, *Panulirus argus*. Each of the approximately 350 bipolar receptor cells (only one shown) associated with each sensillum supports a highly branched outer dendritic segment connected to the soma by a thin inner segment. The axon projects, without synapsing, to the CNS. Patch electrodes applied to the soma allow extracellular, intracellular or single channel recording from the cell. (modified from Grünert and Ache, 1988)

Here we summarize a series of experiments on the potential effects of known neuroactive compounds on the soma of lobster antennular chemoreceptors. We focus specifically on the effect of the biogenic amine, histamine (HA), as one example of the pioneering role of crustacean chemoreceptor cells as models in neurobiology.

RESULTS:

Histamine applied to the soma of the olfactory receptor cells of the Caribbean lobster (*Panulirus argus*) and the American lobster (*Homarus americanus*) suppresses both the spontaneous activity and activity evoked by applying odorants to the outer dendritic segments of the cells (Figure 2) (Bayer et al., in press). This effect characterizes over 90% of the cells and has an apparent threshold between 0.1 and 1μM.

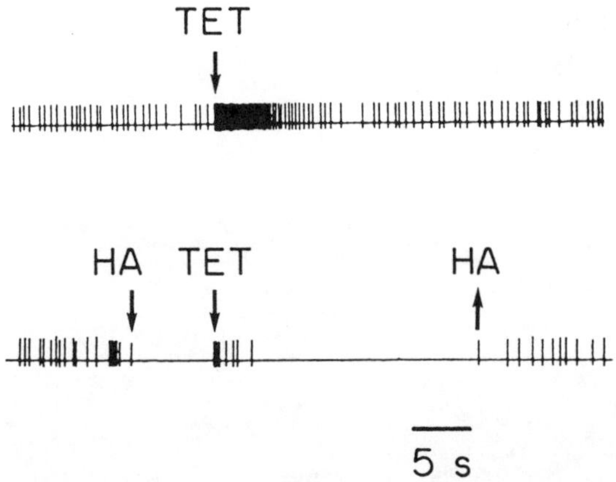

Fig. 2. Extracellular records from a *P. argus* olfactory receptor cell. Upper trace: excitatory discharge to dendritic application of a complex odorant, an extract of fish food (TetraMarin - TET). Lower trace: somatic application of 100μM histamine (HA, down arrow) suppresses both the spontaneous and the odor-evoked activity of the cell. Block relieved by saline rinse (up arrow).

The suppressive effect is specific to HA and cannot be mimicked by other biogenic amines, nor by compounds known to be neuroactive in other systems.The HA- induced suppression can be blocked by the vertebrate HA antagonist, cimetidine, or the nicotinic antagonist, tubocurarine, both at 1mM concentration. Increasing the dose of HA overcomes the cimetidine block. Other vertebrate HA antagonists, such as pyrilamine and burimamide, have no effect. The ability to reversibly antagonize the effect, together with the apparent specificity for the ligand, implies, although does not prove, that HA is acting via a receptor.

By voltage-clamping the isolated somata of the cells and pressure-ejecting HA on the soma membrane, it is possible to study the action of HA directly (Bayer, et al., in press; McClintock and Ache, in press a). Ejecting HA onto the isolated soma induces a macroscopic outward current associated with an increase in membrane conductance. The reversal potential of the HA-induced current follows, although stays slightly positive to, the imposed equilibrium potential of Cl^-. This finding implies that HA activates predominately a Cl^-conductance.

In outside-out patches taken from the soma, it is possible to isolate a Cl^- channel with a mean slope conductance of 44pS (*H. americanus*; 66pS in *P. argus*) that can be activated by external HA concentrations of 1μM or greater (Figure 3) (McClintock and Ache, in press a)

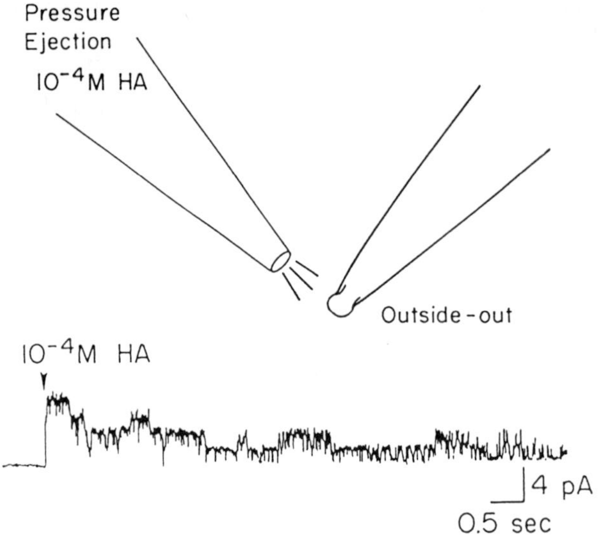

Fig.3. Unitary currents activated by application of 100μM HA to the outside face of an outside-out patch from the soma of an *H. americanus* olfactory receptor cell. The patch contains at least four active channels. Patch held at 0mV. Low pass filtered at a corner frequency of 2kHz.

Like the extracellular effect, the channel is blocked by cimetidine, but not pyrilamine. The channel is also permeable to Na with a Na:Cl permeability ratio of about 0.1, thereby presumably explaining the slight positive shift in the macroscopic reversal potential.

Several lines of evidence suggest that HA directly gates the channel (McClintock and Ache, in press a). Neither intracellular perfusion of 1mM GTP-gamma-S, a GTP-binding protein activator, nor 1 mM GDB-beta-S, a GTP-binding protein inhibitor, affects the ability of HA to activate the macroscopic current in voltage clamped somata. The calcium channel blockers, cobalt (5mM) and cadmium (5mM) do not affect the HA induced current, suggesting that Ca++ influx is not required. Recording in the cell-attached mode and applying HA to the cell fails to activate channels, suggesting that a soluble second messenger is not required. Adding 1mM GTP- gamma-S to the patch solution does not affect the ability of HA to activate the channel, thereby eliminating the possibility of direct action of a membrane diffusible G-protein. Finally, channel activity persists for at least 30 minutes in the absence of nucleotide triphosphates, eliminating a requirement for an external energy source.

Activation of a Cl^-conductance is able to account for the effect of HA on the output of the cells. Action potentials are thought to originate at or near the axon-soma juncture in these cells (Schmiedel-Jakob, et al., 1989). Recordings of a steady-state Cl^-channel (McClintock and Ache, in press b), demonstrate that ECl falls close to the resting membrane potential. By activating what is primarily a Cl^-conductance, HA would effectively clamp the soma at or near rest and thereby reduce the probability that an invading receptor potential brings the spike generator to threshold.

While it is possible to explain the observed suppression of spiking, the functional significance of somatic sensitivity to HA is as yet unclear. The high threshold, rapid onset and rapid decay of the effect are more consistent with synaptic action than blood- borne modulation (e.g., Kravitz, 1988). As yet, however, there is no evidence for efferent innervation or peripheral synapses in the lobster olfactory organ (Grünert and Ache, 1988), nor does biochemical or immunocytochemical evidence indicate that HA is present in the antennule (Orona, et al., unpublished data). Both immunocytochemical and biochemical evidence, however, indicate that HA occurs in the olfactory lobe, in particular in the cap region of the olfactory glomeruli (Orona, et al., submitted), where the afferent fibers are thought to terminate (Sandeman and Luff, 1973). It may be that the HA receptors are functional in the afferent terminals where they are postsynaptic to HA-ergic interneurons and that HA receptors on the soma are strays from these distant sites, a phenomenon not unknown in other invertebrate neurons (e.g., Seigelbaum, et al., 1986). Work towards resolving this question is in progress.

DISCUSSION:

The expression of a HA-gated Cl^- channel in lobster olfactory receptor cells has several implications. First, the presence of the receptor suggests that the cells are targets of some modulatory or regulatory process. This provides some of the first evidence that receptor cell sensitivity in olfaction, as is well known to occur in other sensory modalities, is subject to modulation.It remains to be determined, however, just how this modulation is effected.

The second implication is that lobster olfactory receptor cells express at least two different types of HA receptor proteins. This idea follows from the observation that HA also activates some lobster olfactory receptor cells as an odorant, i.e., when applied to the outer dendritic segments (Bayer, et al, in press). As an odorant, however, HA is usually excitatory. Activation of the somatic HA-gated channel would reduce, not increase, the probability of the cell responding because ECl is near rest. This finding has the practical implication of requiring caution when extrapolating "odor"-activated conductances found on the experimentally more accessible soma to other parts of receptor cells.

Thirdly, the finding that HA directly gates a Cl^- channel in lobster olfactory receptor neurons was the first direct demonstration that a biogenic amine could act by directly gating ion channels (McClintock, 1988; McClintock and Ache, in press a). HA was formerly shown to work via a second messenger (e.g., Sasaki and Sato, 1987). Given the broad biological significance of HA (review: Prell and Green, 1986), finding a new mechanism for the action of HA clearly has implications beyond the chemical senses. Indeed, HA as well as serotonin recently have been shown to act by directly gating ion channels in two other systems (Hardie, 1989; Derkach, et al., 1989).

Crustacean olfactory receptor cells can be expected to continue to contribute to our understanding of the chemical senses. Towards this end, recent work provides direct evidence that odors inhibit, as well as excite, lobster olfactory receptor cells (McClintock and Ache, in press c). Like HA-modulated sensitivity, this finding is potentially of fundamental importance to our understanding of how information is processed in olfaction.

ACKNOWLEDGEMENTS:

Work presented in this article owes much to Mr. Thomas Bayer and Dr. Ulrike Grünert, who discovered and initially characterized the effect, and to Drs. Edward Orona and Barbara-Anne Battelle, who helped pursue the still elusive source of endogenous HA. Ms. M. Milstead and Mr. J. Netherton prepared the illustrations. Financial support for preparing this review was provided by NSF 88-10261.

REFERENCES:

Anderson, P.A.V. & Ache, B.W. (1985) Voltage- and current-clamp recordings of the receptor potential in olfactory receptor cells in situ. Brain Res. **338:**273-280.

Bayer, T.A., McClintock, T.S., Grünert, U. & Ache, B.W. Histamine- induced modulation of olfactory receptor neurones in two species of lobster, *Panulirus argus* and *Homarus americanus*. J. Exp. Biol. (in press).

Carr, W.E.S. (1988) The molecular nature of chemical stimuli in the aquatic environment. In Sensory Biology of Aquatic Animals (ed. J. Atema, R. Fay, A. Popper & W. Tavolga) pp. 3-27. New York: Springer-Verlag.

Case, J. & Gwilliam, G.F. (1961) Amino acid sensitivity of the dactyl chemoreceptors of Carcinides maenas. Biol. Bull. **121:** 449- 455.

Derkach,V., Surprenant, A. & North, R.A. (1989) 5-HT3 receptors are membrane ion channels. Nature *339*: 706-708.

Grünert, U. & Ache, B.W. (1988) Ultrastructure of the aesthetasc (olfactory) sensilla of the spiny lobster, *Panulirus argus*. Cell Tiss. Res. **251**: 95-103.

Hamill, O.P., Marty, A., Neher, E., Sakmann, B. & Sigworth, F.J. (1981) Improved patch clamp techniques for high-resolution current recording from cells and cell-free membrane patches. Pfügers Arch. ges. Physiol. **391**: 85-100.

Hardie, R.C. (1989) A histamine-activated chloride channel involved in neurotransmission at a photoreceptor synapse. Nature **339:** 704- 706.

Kravitz, E.A. (1988) Hormonal control of behavior: Amines and the biasing of behavioral output in lobsters. Science ***241:***1775-1781.

Laverack, M.S. (1963) Aspects of chemoreception in crustacea. Comp. Biochem. Physiol. **8:** 141-151.

McClintock, T.S. (1988) A histamine-gated anion channel suppresses lobster olfactory receptor cell activity. Biol.Bull. 175: 307.

McClintock, T.S. & Ache, B.W. Histamine directly gates a chloride channel in lobster olfactory receptor neurons. Proc. Nat. Acad. Sci., U.S. (in press a).

McClintock. T.S. & Ache, B.W. K^+, Cl^-, and nonselective cation channels of lobster olfactory receptor neurons. J. Gen. Physiol. (in press b).

McClintock, T.S. & Ache, B.W. Hyperpolarizing receptor potentials in lobster olfactory receptor cells: implications for transduction and mixture suppression. Chem. Senses (in press c).

Orona, E., Battelle, B-A. & Ache, B.W. Immunohistochemical and biochemical evidence for the putative inhibitory neurotransmitters, histamine and GABA, in lobster olfactory lobes. (Submitted).

Prell, G.D. & Green, J.P. (1986) Histamine as a neuroregulator. Ann. Rev. Neurosci. **9:** 209-254.

Sandeman, D.C. & Luff, S.E. (1973) The structural organization of glomerular neuropile in the olfactory and accessory lobes of an Australian freshwater crayfish, *Cherax destructor*. Z. Zellforsch. **142:** 37-61.

Sasaki, K. & Sato, M. (1987) A single GTP-binding protein regulates K^+ channels coupled with dopamine, histamine and acetylcholine receptors. Nature **325**: 259-262.

Schmiedel-Jakob, I., Anderson, P.A.V. & Ache, B.W. (1989) Whole cell recording from lobster olfactory receptor cells: Responses to current and odor stimulation. J. Neurophysiol. **61**: 994-1000.

Siegelbaum, S.A., Belardetti, F., Camardo, J.S. & Shuster, M.J. (1986) Modulation of the serotonin-sensitive potassium channel in Aplysia sensory neurone cell body and growth cone. J. Exp. Biol. **124:** 287-306.

Frontiers in Crustacean Neurobiology
Advances in Life Sciences

ELECTROPHYSIOLOGICAL STUDIES ON CHEMORECEPTIVE NEURONS IN CRUSTACEA

H. Hatt

Physiologisches Institut der Technischen Universität München, Biedersteiner Straße 29, 8000 München 40, F.R.G.

SUMMARY

Single channel currents were recorded from the soma membrane of chemoreceptive neurons my means of GΩ seal patch clamp technique (cell attached and outside-out configuration). So far three types of ion channels could be identified in different neurons activated by either nicotinamide purine nucleotides or amino acids (and analogous substances).

Open times, reversal potential and the single channel conductance were determined. A new method for the controlled application and wash out of activator at excised membrane patches within less than 0.5 ms was used. The purine nucleotide channels were activated within about 1 ms and after an initial peak of opening desensitized completely with a time constant of 150 ms. The amino acid activated channels showed a fast rise time (≈1 ms) and desensitized within 200 ms to a low level of steady state activity.

INTRODUCTION

Electrophysiological studies of chemosensory cells on the walking leg in crustaceans have indicated the presence of four types of specialized receptor cells each sensitive to a certain class of compounds. From single unit analysis we proved the excistence of units, which were sensitive to amino acids, amines, pyridines or nucleotides (7,8,9,10,11,16). Receptor cell specificity and sensitivity and structure-activity relationships of stimulants of the different type of cells were described in detail.

Little is known about the first step of the chemo-electrical transduction. The stimulus molecules are thought to interact with highly specific receptor molecules in the membrane of the chemosensory cell and will result directly or indirectly in the activation of ion chanels, evoking the receptor potential, which then produces the action potential frequency. The patch clamp technique has opened the first direct electrophysiological access to the reaction of single receptor molecules. But in contrast to vision (4,12) and hearing (3,6), the basic mechanism by which a stimulus molecule binding activates channels in smell and taste is still unknown.

Here we present recordings from cell bodies of chemoreceptive neurons on the walking leg obtained with the 'patch clamp' method. The channels were measured on cells in situ and on freshly dissociated cells in culture medium. For the study of chemically activated channels, exised patches in the outside-out configuration were used, since the receptor molecules can be exposed to different stimulatory molecules in different concentrations. Such recordings can be done under steady state conditions, the reaction of channels being in the equilibrium. Measurements during rapid concentration changes of the chemical stimulus can provide additional informations. We developed a method to produce a ultrafast exchange (< 0.3 ms) of a solution passing the receptors in an excised outside-out patch membrane (5).

MATERIAL AND METHODS

An isolated preparation of the walking leg of the crayfish *Austropotamobius torrentium* was used, as described in detail by Hatt and Bauer (1980). The inner edge of the propodites bears a row of sensilla, which are innervated by eight bipolar sensory cells. Each of these cells has specific receptors in its dendrites of 700 μm length and 0.2 diameter. The perikarya (about 10 μm diameter) of the eight sensory cells of a sensillum form clusters only 5-50 μm beneath the cuticula. The distance between the base of the sensillum and the perikarya is about 500 μm.

Patch-clamp electrodes (fire-polished tips of 1 μm diameter and coated with Sylgard) were used to form GΩ-seals on the collagenase (2 h) treated perikarya of the sensory neurons. The patch pipettes were filled with physiological saline (in mM: Na^+ 205, CL^- 232, K^+ 5.4, Ca^{2+} 13.5, Mg^{2+} 2.6, Tris-maleate buffer 10; pH 7.6), in which agonist was dissolved.

In addition outside-out excised patches (11) could be established. The pipette was filled with an intracellular solution (in mM: 150 KCl, 5 NaCl, 2 $MgCl_2$, 1 $CaCl_2$, 11 EGTA, brought to pH 7.2 with 30 KOH). The patch was polarized through the voltage clamp and then moved to a special recording chamber. The measured currents were recorded on FM-analog tape and evaluated at an HP-computer.

RESULTS

From three of the four identified types of chemosensory neurons single channel activity could be studied so far.

1. Nicotinamide activated channels. In cell attached and in outside-out patches, concentrations of nicotinamide from 10^{-6} to 10^{-4} M activated openings of single channels located in the cell body of sense cells. The characteristic of these channels was similar to those of neurotransmitter activated channels: the I-V curve was approximately linear, showing a reversal potential of about $^+15$ mV and a conductance of about 33 pS. The mean open time was 1-2 ms dependent on the membrane potential (details see 11). On outside-out patches the same population of receptors were sequentially activated by nicotinamide at three different concentrations (Fig.1). As stimulant concentration increases the rate of channel openings

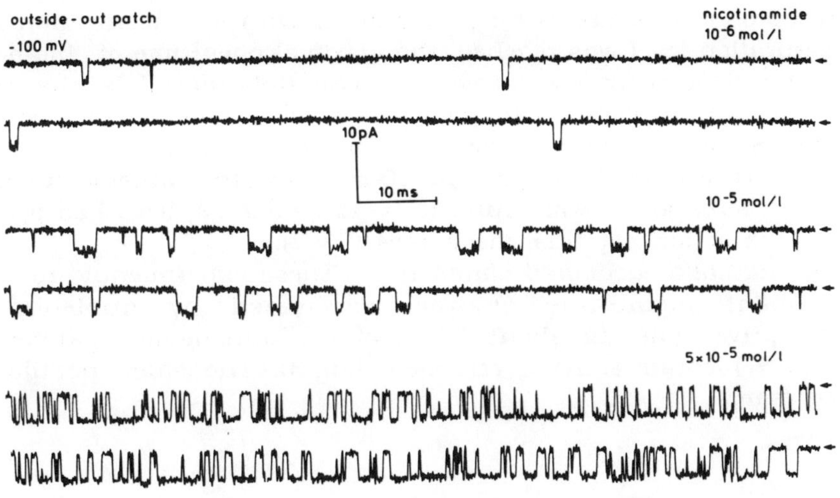

Fig.1. Original recordings from an outside-out patch of a pyridine sensitive cell stimulated with different concentrations of agonist (from 11).

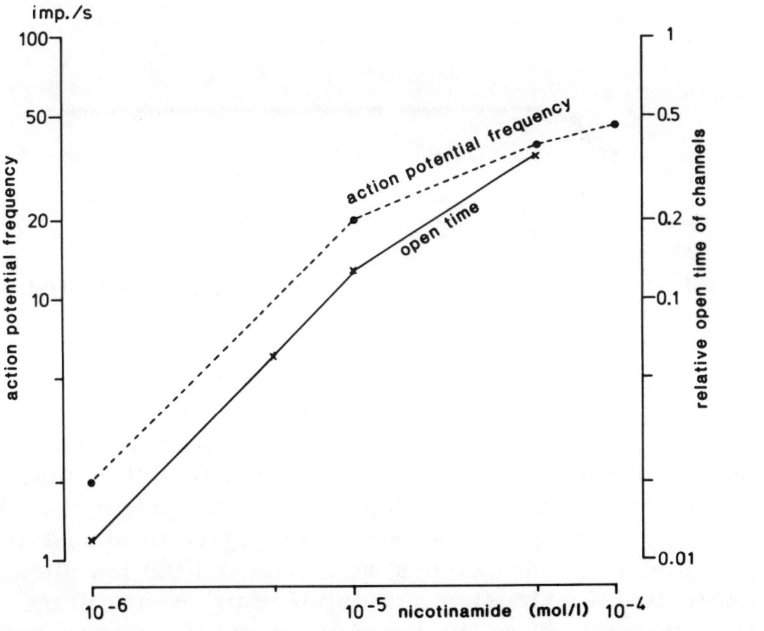

Fig.2. Comparison of the curves relating nicotinamide concentration to the action potential frequency and to the relative open time of channels in a patch as in fig.1.

rises (receptor number remaining constant!). With a concentration of 10^{-4} M the saturation level was reached, the maximal open time of channels was 50 %. The dose-response curve approximately parallels the relation between the action potential frequency of a nicotinamide-sensitive neuron and stimulus concentration, measured in previous studies.

The half sturation values are near 10-5 M. In other outside-out patches the effective substances was found to be the same as described previously recording the action potential discharges (Fig.2).

2. *Purine nucleotide-activated channels* . These experiments are the first to document membrane channels activated by nucleotides on chemoreceptive cells. In about 10 % of the outside out patches, liver extract (1 %) could activate channels (Fig.3). The same population of channels (same

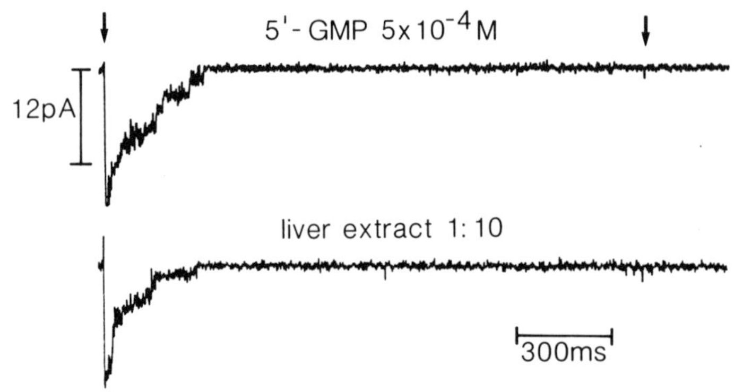

Fig.3. Outside-out patch of a nucleotide sensitive cell activated by 5-GMP as well as liver extract.

amplitude, burst length, and desensitization behaviour) was activated, when 5-GMP 5x10-4 M was used instead. A chemical analysis of the liver extract showed, that 5-GMP is present in that concentration range (Prof. Schildknecht, personal communication). When 5-GMP 1 mM was applied with the fast activation system (liquid filament system) for about 1.5 s, superposition of openings of channels was triggered in almost all activations (Fig.4). The first channel openings were seen 0,3-0.8 ms after the artefact of the piezocrystal extension on application of a voltage pulse. The extension is transmitted to the liquid filament that contains the stimulus solution, which then crosses the electrode tip. Seven channels open within about 0.2 ms and then one channel after the other closes, although 5-GMP is still present. The decay constant of desensitization was about 150 ms.

After 1.5 s drug application the patch membrane was exposed to normal physiological solution for 1 s. This time was long enough for resensitization of the channels. The next stimulus application activated the same number of channels as the first one (see Fig.4, left column, second trace). The rise time of activation of the average was 0.5 ms. The channels desensitized to zero within less than 600 ms with two time constants of about 26 and 150 ms. During long application of 5-GMP (>1 min), reopenings of channels could never be observed.

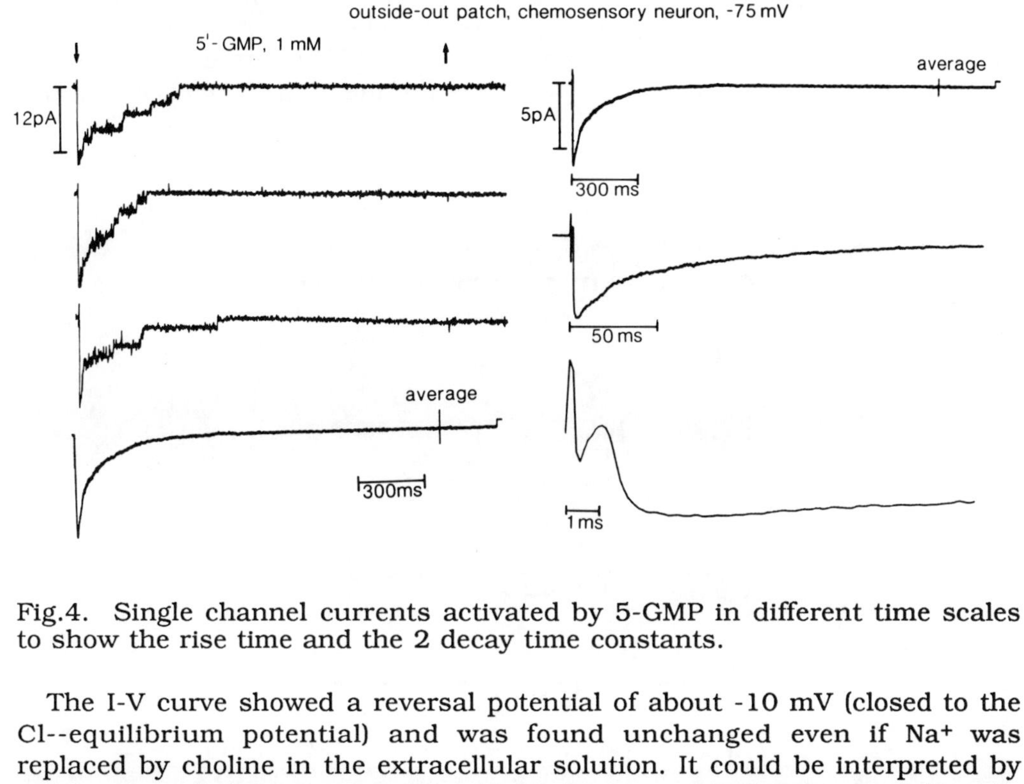

Fig.4. Single channel currents activated by 5-GMP in different time scales to show the rise time and the 2 decay time constants.

The I-V curve showed a reversal potential of about -10 mV (closed to the Cl--equilibrium potential) and was found unchanged even if Na^+ was replaced by choline in the extracellular solution. It could be interpreted by a net outward current carried by Cl^- leading to a depolarization of the cell. These assumption are supported by the high degree of dependence of the action potential frequency elicited by liver extract on the Cl^--concentration in the environment. Decreasing Cl^- outside from 100 mM to 1 mM we found an increase of 10 times in the action potential response to a certain stimulus concentration. 5-GMP was the most effective stimulus (threshold 5×10^{-6}M), followed by 5-IMP and 5-AMP. All other tested nucleotides were ineffective also in concentrations of 10^{-2} M: ADP, ATP, c-AMP, adenosine and adenine.

3. Amino acid activated channels. Only few experiments were done on patch membrane of amino acid sensitive cells. The preliminary results show, that serine5x10-4 M can activate single channels on the membrane (Fig.5). The first channel openings began 2 ms after the artefact in the respective trace. These delays contain time of flow in the tube and filament and diffusion across the unstirred layer at the patch. The rise time for activation (10-90 % of current) of the average was about 1 ms. The channels desensitized incompletely within less than 200 ms to a low level of steady state activity. This equilibrium activation stayed constant also during few min. of drug application. An evaluation of the single channel amplitude showed an unimodal distribution with a prominent peak of -4 pA at resting potential. The distribution of open times could be fitted by a single exponential, the decay constant of which is the mean open time. It is 3 ms at resting potential.

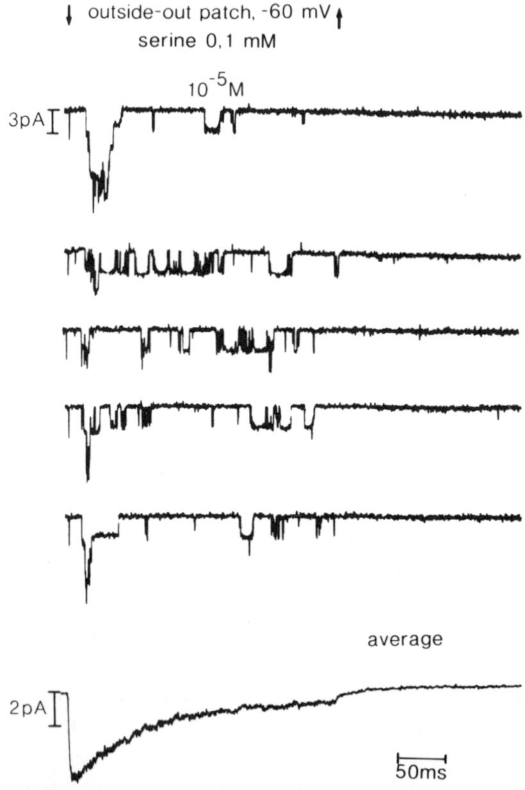

Fig.5. Single channel currents of amino acid sensitive cell activated by serine 0.1 M. Note: the fast rise time and the incomplete desensitization.

DISCUSSION

These results present single channel currents activated by natural stimuli on the soma of chemoreceptive cells of the crayfish. The receptors show the same characteristics as those on the dendrites. The channels activated by chemoattractants corresponds closely to transmitter-activated channels in crayfish and locust. The ultrafast activation system allowed to record the fast desensitizing nucleotid-activated and amino acid channels. The I-V curve, ion substitution experiments and data from action potential recordings might be indications for a Cl^--channel.

An interesting point was the result that the desensitization characteristic of the single channel activity correspond most closely to the time course of the action potential responses. The phasic or tonic response patter of the neurones seem determined by the kinetic characteristic of the desensitization behaviour of the single channels.

We might also consider whether the channels on external chemoreceptors are activated directly or via second messenger (2,11,13,14,15). The present data give no indication that a second messenger system is involved in the primary process of transduction of these stimuli since 1. the rise time of openings of up to 7 channels is shorter than 0.5 ms (activation of a second messenger cascade in this time seems improbable) and 2. in some outside-out patches the channels could be activated for more than 30 min without any loss of activity, although no second messenger was applied to thc intracellular solution in the pipette. A modulatory effect of second messenger molecules, however, seems probable.

REFERENCES

1) Anderson, P.A.V. & Ache, B.W. (1985) Voltage- and current- clamp recordings of the receptor potential in olfactory receptor cells in situ. Brain Res. **338:** 273-280.

2) Anholt, R.R.H. (1987) Primary events in olfactory reception. TIBS 12: 58-62.

3) Ashmore, J.F. & R.W. Meech (1986) Ionic basis of membrane potential in outer hair cells of guinea pig cochlea. Nature **322**: 368-371.

4) Fesenko, E.E., S.S. Kolesnikov & A.L. Lyubarsky (1985) Induction by cyclic GMP of cationic conductance in plasma membrane of retinal rod outer segment. Nature **313**: 310-313.

5) Franke, Ch., Hatt, H. & Dudel, J. (1987) Liquid filament switch for ultrafast exchanges of solutions at excised patches of synaptic membrane of crayfish muscle. Neurosci. Lett. **77:** 199-204.

6) Gitter, A.H., Zrenner, H.P. & Frömter, E. (1986) Membrane potential and ion channels in isolated outer hair cells of guinea pig cochlea. ORL **48**: 68-75.

7) Hatt, H. & Bauer, U. (1980) Single unit analysis of mechano- and chemosensitive neurons in the crayfish claw. Neurosci. Lett. **17:** 203-207.
8) Hatt, H. (1984) Structural requirements for stimulatory amino acids and related compounds in crayfish walking leg. J. Comp. Physiol. **155**: 219-231.
9) Hatt H (1989) Stimulus-driven chemosensory membrane channels on crayfish sensory cells. In Receptor and Transduction Mechanisms in Taste and Olfaction, (eds. J.G. Brand, J.W. Teeter, M.R. Kare & R.H. Cagan) Acad. Press, New York.
10) Hatt, H. & Schmiedel-Jakob, I. (1984) Electrophysiological studies of pyridine-sensitive units on the crayfish walking leg. I. Characteristics of stimulatory molecules. J. Comp. Physiol. **54:** 855-863.
11) Hatt, H. & Franke, Ch. (1987) Taste receptors in crayfish: Recording of single nicotinamide-activated channels. Neurosci. Lett. **73**: 137-142.
12) Haynes, L.W., Kay, A.R. & Yau, K.-W. (1986) Single cyclic GMP-activated channel activity in excised patches of rod outer segment membrane. Nature **321:** 66-70.
13) Labarca, P. & Bacigalupo, J. (1988) Ion channels from chemosensory olfactory neurons. J. Bioenergetics and Biomembranes 20: 551-569.
14) Labarca, P. & Simon, S.A. & Anholt R.R.H. (1988) Activation by odorants of a multistate cation channel from olfactory cilia. Proc. Natl. Acad. Sci. USA **85**: 944-947.
15) Lancet, D. & Pace, U. (1987) The molecular basis of odor recognition. TIBS **12**: 63-66.
16) Schmiedel-Jakob, I., Breuninger, V. & Hatt, H. (1988) Electrophysiological studies of chemoreceptors sensitive to pyridine on the crayfish walking leg. II. Charac- teristics of antagonistic molecules. Chem. Senses **13:** 619-632.

Frontiers in Crustacean Neurobiology
Advances in Life Sciences

EVIDENCE FOR NON-TOPOGRAPHIC AFFERENT PROJECTION AND GROWTH-RELATED CENTRAL REORGANIZATION IN THE CRAYFISH OLFACTORY SYSTEM.

DeForest Mellon, Jr.

Department of Biology, Gilmer Hall, University of Virginia Charlottesville, Virginia 22903 USA

SUMMARY

Projection of primary olfactory neurons within the ipsilateral olfactory lobes in the crayfish brain was determined by axoplasmic transport of tritiated leucine, following restricted exposure of small numbers of aesthetascs to the radioligand.

Label was found in all psilateral glomeruli in dose-dependent amounts, depending upon the number of aesthetascs exposed.

Maximum labeling of all ipsilateral glomeruli was observed following exposure of all available aesthetascs on an antennular filament. Restricting the label to a minimum of two aesthetascs resulted in very weak labeling of all ipsilateral glomeruli; regional labeling of selected glomeruli following restricted exposure was never seen.

We conclude that the projection of olfactory neurons from each sensory ganglion within an antennule is maximally divergent, involving all glomeruli in the ipsilateral olfactory lobe.

Growth of the olfactory system is marked by increases both in numbers of sensory ganglia and in numbers of olfactory lobe glomeruli.

INTRODUCTION

Despite existence of an impressive number of anatomical and electrophysiological studies, fundamental questions regarding the functional organization of the olfactory system remain unanswered.

The extent of our ignorance is apparent by comparison with other sensory modalities, such as vision or audition, where sensory cell capabilities, receptive field strucuture, and functional mechanisms involved with primary sensory processing in the central nervous system are well in hand.

With olfaction, however, basic questions remain, from peripheral sensory mechanisms to central processing.

Modality sensitivities of primary olfactory cells in vertebrates and invertebrates alike generally reveal broad capacities, confounding detailed description of the membrane receptors: their numbers, types, groupings and ultimate "spectral" capabilities. Studies in the insect deutocerebrum have begun to elucidate the neurophysiological substrates for species-specific pheromone coding, but our understanding of the immense odor-discrimination capabilities possessed by these animals is rudimentary at best. In vertebrates, afferent projection to the olfactory bulb is zonally spatiotoptic, but non-isomorphic, leading to uncertainty about the presence of central olfactory maps. Functional studies with tritiated 2-deoxyglucose hint at localized functional capacities within the bulbar glomeruli, but the resolution of that technique is, so far, unsatisfying. While electrophysiological investigations have revealed important details regarding the local circuitry of the olfactory bulb, the basic organizational principles that underlie the perception of odorant quality remain, nontheless, elusive.

During the last two decades, the work of Ache, Atema, and their colleagues has demonstrated elegantly the value of crustacean preparations in disclosing primary olfactory mechanisms. The expanding success of these studies with *Panulirus* and *Homarus* has provided impetus for broader examinations of the olfactory system in crustaceans.

It would be useful to know details of the projection pattern made by afferent fibers within the olfactory lobe, as a primary step in generating hypotheses about central olfactory processing. Accordingly we have investigated primary olfactory projection in the crayfish, *Procambarus*, using axoplasmic transport of tritiated leucine to trace the terminals of afferent fibers within the brain.

METHODS

Adult crayfishes were secured dorsal side down in a lucite chamber filled with pond water. The external filaments of their antennules were isolated from the bathing solution by means of barriers of periphery wax and petroleum jelly. Selected regions - including single segments - of aesthetasc-bearing portions of the antennules were exposed to tritiated leucine stock, dissolved in 2% ethanol, and having a specific activity of 130 Ci/mMol. Aesthetascs were exposed to the labeled amino acid for two hours. After a survival time of twenty-four hours, the animals were decapitated and their brains were fixed in Bouin's solution for one day. Fixed tissue was dehydrated, imbedded in paraffin, and sectioned at 10 micrometers. Serial sections were coated with Kodak NTB3 immulsion and incubated in the dark for one month at 4 degrees Celsius. Developed autoradiographs were stained with Luxol fast blue. Silver grain densities were analyzed visually from the stained material and quantitatively by computer, using the Bioquant routine. Counts of olfactory lobe glomeruli in adults and young animals were made by visual analysis of serially sectioned material stained with luxol fast blue. Sensory ganglion neuron counts were taken from elctronmicrographs of transversely sectioned bundles of distal dendritic segments within the antennule.

RESULTS

In decapod crustaceans, such as *Procambarus*, the major olfactory organs are blunt sensilla - termed aesthetascs - which are distributed ventrally in pairs along the distal half of the external antennular filament. Each aesthetasc houses the dendritic segments of about 200 bipolar sensory neurons, having their grouped cell bodies within a parochial sensory ganglion in the shaft of the antennular filament.

The basic neuroanatomical plan of the antennule is apparent from Figure 1,A. Axons from each sensory ganglion join the antennular nerve and reach the brain at the ventral aspect of the deutocerebrum. From there they run directly to the ipsilateral olfactory lobe, a kidney-shaped structure characterized by radially oriented, sub-conical glomeruli - regions of highly condensed neuropile. The afferent axons within the antennular nerve diverge to envelop the olfactory lobe as a fibrous cortex, ultimately turning inward where they make synaptic contact with second order neurons, depicted in Fig. 1,B.

The interneuronal targets of the sensory neurons are not known; probably they include some of the globuli cells, whose somata are found in great abundance lateral and medial to the olfactory and accessory lobes, and whose profuse fibers are observed in histological sections to enter both of these structures. But whaterever the target identities, the sensory axons terminate within the olfactory lobe glomeruli (Hanstrom, 1925; Bethe, 1898; Sandeman & Luff, 1973). This fact is well documented by studies using tritiated leucine (Sandeman & Denburg, 1976; Mellon et al, (1989) which is actively taken up and transported by the sensory neurons simply in response to bathing the lateral antennular filament in the stock tracer (Figure 2).There are about 175 to 200 glomeruli in each adult olfactory lobe, roughly the same number of aesthetascs as on each antennule. If a topographic relationship exists between the sensory neurons associated with an aesthetasc and a corresponding glomerulus within the olfactory lobe, restricting the access of tritiated label to small numbers of aesthetascs should result in restricted, regional labeling within the ipsilateral olfactory lobe. This pattern of labeling, however, was never observed. Instead, we found that the extent of glomerular labeling within the ipsilateral olfactory lobe exhibited a dosage effect: the more aesthetascs exposed to the leucine, the more intense the tritium label in the CNS. When single pairs of aesthetascs - out of a total number of about 170 - were exposed to leucine, very weak labeling of the olfactory lobe glomeruli was seen (Figure 3); nontheless, the label was generally and completely distributed to all of the available glomeruli.

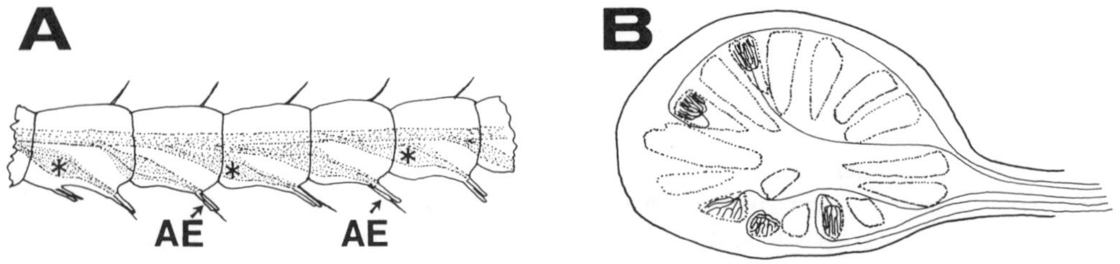

Fig. 1

A, Diagram of a portion of an external antennular filament from *Procambarus*. Pairs of aesthetascs (AE) arise ventrally from each segment at this level of the filament. Sensory ganglia, indicated by asterisks, house the sensory neuron cell bodies.

B, diagram of a highly simplified section through a *Procambarus* olfactory lobe. Five afferent fibers are illustrated entering the olfactory lobe, each terminating within a single glomerulus, as interpreted by Hanstrom (1925).

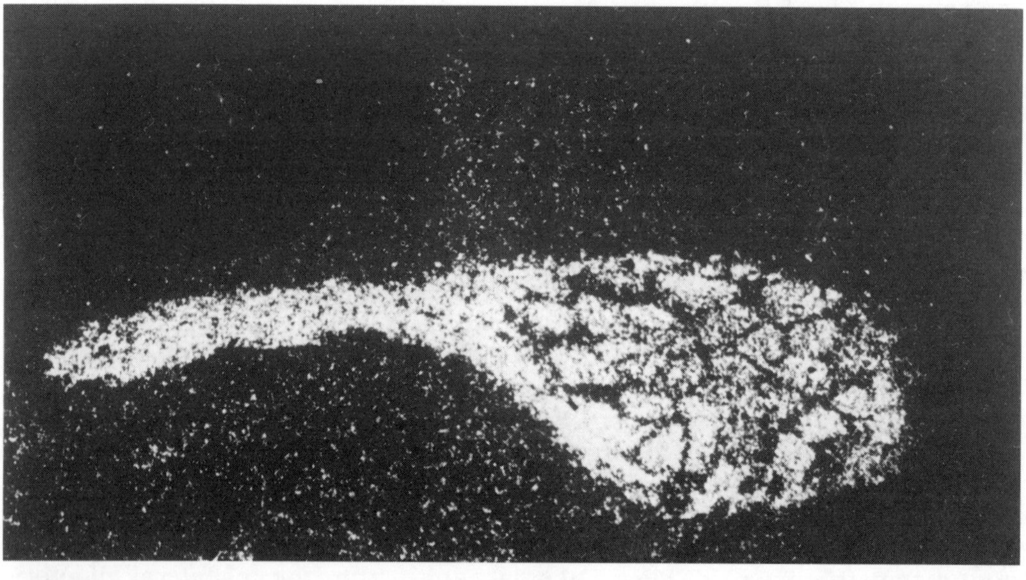

Fig. 2.

Autoradiograph of a section through the ventral end of an olfactory lobe from *Procambarus*, at the point of entrance by the antennular nerve.

The ipsilateral lateral antennular filament had been exposed to tritiated leucine.This darkfield micrograph shows both transected glomeruli and the longitudinally sectioned antennular nerve as it enters from the left and branches to envelop the olfactory lobe.

Magnification: 250X

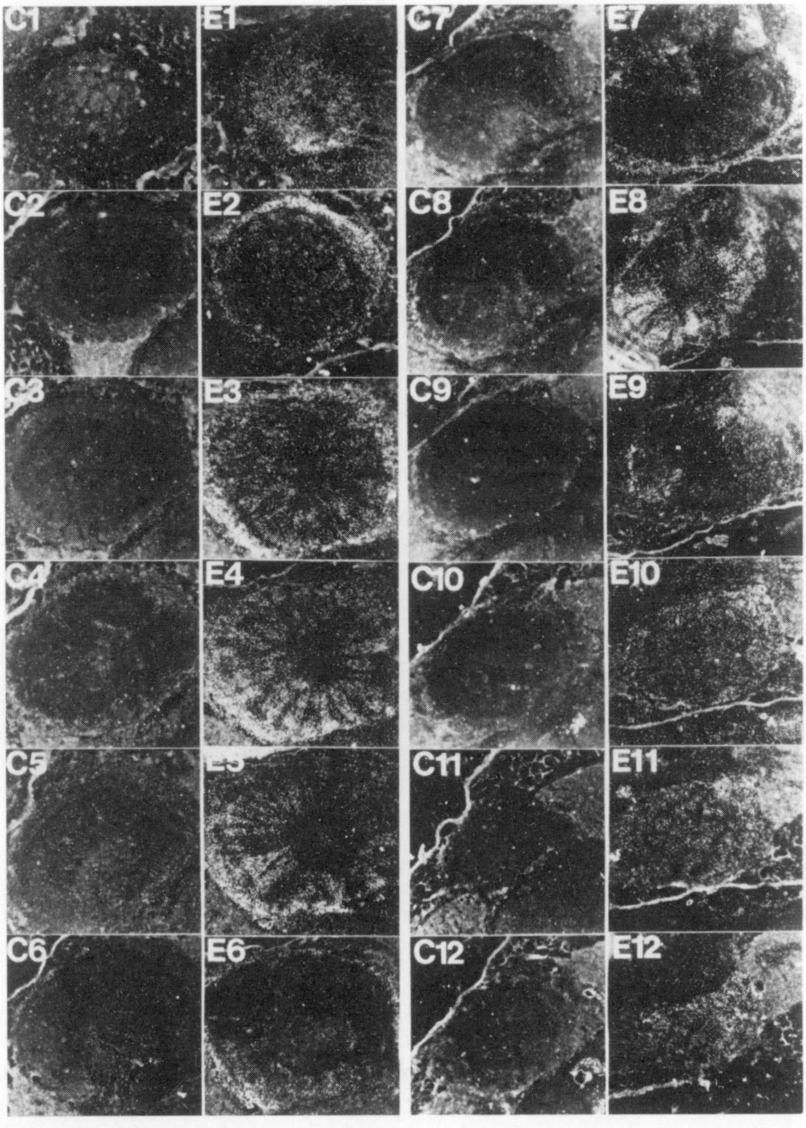

Fig. 3. Serial autoradiographs (darkfield illumination) comparing silver grain deposition in the olfactory lobes ipsilateral to antennules exposed to pondwater (C1-C12) and to the opposite antennule (E1-E12), on which only three aesthetascs (ca. 2% of the total number) had been exposed to tritiated leucine. Labeling of the olfactory lobe on the experimental side is diffuse and extensive, in virtually every glomerulus.Approximately every fourth section through the olfactory lobes is shown.

By extrapolation, each olfactory lobe glomerulus may receive the axon terminals of at least one of the neurons in each sensory ganglion. Olfactory projection in the crayfish, therefore, is non- topographic; it is also divergent in the sense that at least some (one?) of the sensory elements associated with each aesthetasc terminate in each glomerulus of the ipsilateral olfactory lobe. As with many other sensory systems, crayfish olfactory projection is profoundly dynamic.

Clearly, more aesthetascs are added on with each molt as the number of antennular segments increases, since, at hatching, baby crayfishes have only two or three. Moreover, linear dimensions of the brain increase by an order of magnitude following hatching. We were interested in whether existing sensory ganglia increase their compliment of individual sensory neurons, and whether new glomeruli arise within the growing brain. Our preliminary results suggest that the number of sensory neurons per aesthetasc remains constant as the animal grows, but that more glomeruli appear within the growing olfactory bulb. Young animals of 3 mm carapace length have about 18 olfactory lobe glomeruli on each side, while at 6 mm this number has more than tripled. The average of counts from two animals of 60 mm carapace length was 185 glomeruli. Interestingly, glomerular increment may take place by the process of splitting. Individual glomeruli grow in size as the brain (and the olfactory lobes) gets larger; at some point the largest glomeruli appear to split lengthwise, giving rise to two distinct structures.

Whether the glomerular increase results from addition of new central neurons that are the immediate targets of the olfactory afferents remains conjectural.

DISCUSSION

One of the attractive features of the olfactory system is that it remains largely unknown, if not unexplored. It is, therefore, frought with promise. I believe increasingly rapid progress can be made in comprehending primary olfactory processing - both at the periphery and within the CNS- by more intense utilization of crustacean model alternatives to the vertebrate systems studied so far. Decapod crustaceans are excellent alternative choices for several reasons. First, their olfactory sensory cell somata are both accessible and relatively large, ranging up to 15 micrometers; they are therefore within the size range suitable for electrophysiological investigation.

Since they reside within the cavity of the external antennular filaments, they can be readily exposedin situ with their business end intact. Such preparations are well suited for patch clamping, whole cell voltage clamping, or exposure to pharmacological agents while presenting the cells with their adequate stimulus (Anderson & Ache, 1985). Because crustacean olfactory sensory neuron populations are subdivided into manageable groups, each associated with an aesthetasc, their isolation and that of individual cells - for physiological, immunocytochemical, or molecular studies is more easily accomplished than it is with vertebrate counterparts.

One idea worth exploring is whether all such peripheral sensory ganglia in crustaceans are identical in their functional heterogeneity, essentially constituting repeat units. Perhaps the entire spectrum of olfactory capabilities of an animal is defined by the summed capacities of the individual sensory cells in any one ganglion.

While it is suspected that each sensory ganglion, through the properties of its individual neurons, is functionally heterogeneous, no experimental comparisons of cell spectra from different ganglia as yet have been performed.

Although the direct targets of crustacean olfactory afferents are thought to be unidentified fibers within the glomeruli, possibly originating in the globuli cell clusters intimately associated with the olfactory and accessory lobes of the deutocerebrum, we now lack a detailed knowledge of these connections. Does each olfactory sensory neuron terminate in just one glomerulus? Hanstrom (1924) believed that such was the case, arguing from Golgi stained material . Bethe, on the other hand, reported (1898) that sensory neurons branched within the olfactory lobe to supply many glomeruli. Our present data do not bear on this question, but if we assume that Hanstrom was correct, our results do provide evidence for broadly divergent, non-topographic central projections from the olfactory sensory ganglia.

How is non-topographic afferent projection involved in the integration of olfactory input? For the present we can only speculate. If each sensory ganglion represents the entire olfactory receptive field, as suggested above, each olfactory lobe glomerulus may act as a functional focus, where input is sharpened through summation of activity from other sensory cells having identical odorant sensitivities, and through interactions with other glomeruli serving sensory cells with similar, but non-identical, capabilities. Implicit in such conjecture is the assumption of functional convergence of input, such as occurs within the antennal lobe macroglomerular complex of male saturniid moths (Christensen et al, 1989). Electrophysiological studies are badly needed and will undoubtedly play a major role in shaping future models of olfactory processing, both at the level of the peripheral receptors (e.g., Ache et al, 1988; Johnson et al, 1988) and within the central nervous system (Arbas et al, 1988; Derby & Blaustein, 1988). A concerted effort on this front will be required to bring our understanding of electrical activity in the crustacean olfactory midbrain to a level comparable with that now enjoyed by the vertebrate visual system.

At the same time, anatomical approaches will be necessary to determine the changing relationships between periphery and central nervous system as an animal grows. Our studies have disclosed that the growing olfactory lobes elaborate increased numbers of individual glomeruli as new sensory ganglia appear with the incorporation of additional antennular segments. A continuing question of interest is how new olfactory sensory neurons are incorporated into the olfactory lobe. The elaboration of new glomeruli may play a functional role similar to the continual restructuring of the optic tectum found in some lower vertebrates, which continually add new retinal ganglion cells throughout their lives (e.g., Easter & Stuermer, 1984). These changes must be accounted in any theory of olfactory lobe function.

While I have emphasized recent work carried out in my laboratory on the crayfish olfactory system - a choice at least partially dictated by the dispersed nature of the crayfish aesthetasc array - most of the questions listed above can be attacked as well using other crustacean preparations. Indeed, as Barry Ache discerned many years ago, the spiny lobster, *Panulirus*, is an exemplary model system with which to probe olfactory receptor physiology. Behavioral responses to pheromones can be favorably studied in Callinectes and *Homarus* and, no doubt, in many other species. Brooding behavior in baby crayfishes may be evoked by maternal pheromones. Undoubtedly, interesting findings will emerge when comparative studies are made on the olfactory systems of predominantly terrestial crustaceans, such as Coenobita or Ligia. Thus, when one considers varieties of lifestyle, behavioral relevance, accessibility of neuronal elements, and developmental plasticity (not to mention esthetics), crustacean models for the study of olfactory mechanisms emerge as the logical choice.

Acknowledgements -

I thank Vinessa Alones for expert technical assistance in various aspects of this work. Laura Hurley is thanked for providing counts of olfactory lobe glomeruli. This work was supported by a grant from The Whitehall Foundation.

REFERENCES

Ache, B.W., Gleeson, R.A., Thompson, H.A. (1988) Mechanisms for mixture suppression in olfactory receptors of the spiny lobster. Chem. Senses, **13**: 425-434.

Anderson, P.A.V., Ache, B.W. (1985) Voltage- and current-clamp recordings of the receptor potential in olfactory receptor cells in situ. Brain Res.,**338**: 273-280. Bethe, A. (1898) Das Centralnervensystem von *Carcinus maenas*. Ein anatomische-
physiologischer Versuch. II. Theil. Arch. f. mikr. Anat., 51: 382-452.

Christensen, T. A., Mustaparta, H., Hildebrand, J.G.(1989) Discrimination of sex pheromone blends in the olfactory system of the moth. Chem. Senses, **14:** 463-477.

Derby, C. D., Blaustein, D. N. (1988) Morphological and physiological characterization of individual olfactory interneurons connecting the brain and eyestalk ganglia of the crayfish. J. Comp. Physiol., **163:** 777-794.

Easter, S. S., Steurmer, C.A.O. (1984) An evaluation of the hypothesis of shifting terminals in goldfish optic tectum. J. Neurosci., **4:** 1052-1063.
Hanstrom, B. (1925) The olfactory centers in crustaceans. J. Comp. Neurol., **38**: 221-250.
Johnson, B.R., Merrill, C.L.,Ogle, R.C., Atema, J.(1988) Response properties of lobster chemoreceptors: tuning of olfactory neurons sensitive to hydroxy-proline. J. Comp. Physiol., **162**: 201-211.
Mellon, DeF., Tuten, H.R., Redick, J. (1989) Distribution of radioactive leucine following uptake by olfactory sensory neurons in normal and heteromorphic crayfish antennules. J. Comp. Neurol., **280:** 645-662.
Sandeman, D.C., Luff, S.E., (1973) Structural organization of glomerular neuropile in the olfactory and accessory lobes of an Australian freshwater crayfish, *Cherax destructor.* Z. Zellforsch. Mikrosk. Ang., **142**: 37-61.
Sandeman, D.C., Denburg, J. (1976) The central projections of chemoreceptor axons in the crayfish revealed by axoplasmic transport. Brain Res., **115**: 492-496.

Frontiers in Crustacean Neurobiology
Advances in Life Sciences

PIGMENTS IN CRUSTACEAN COMPOUND EYES

Thomas W. Cronin

Department of Biological Sciences, University of Maryland Baltimore County, Catonsville, Maryland 21228 U.S.A.

INTRODUCTION

Like all photoreceptor organs, crustacean compound eyes produce pigments that interact with the light impinging upon them. Here, the term "pigment" refers to molecules that absorb light in the visual range, at wavelengths between about 330 and 700 nm. The two major classes of pigments in crustacean eyes are first the visual pigments, the photosensitive molecules that capture light and set in motion the complicated processes that signal its presence, and second the photostable pigments that must be present to regulate the light within the eye.

PHOTOSTABLE PIGMENTS.

Unlike vertebrate eyes, the dioptric elements of crustacean eyes are essentially transparent down to wavelengths of 350 nm or less (Cronin & Marshall, in press). Thus, any required filtering of light is performed by pigments located elsewhere. Crustacean compound eyes contain a complex assortment of secondary pigment cells with a great variety of pigment types (Autrum, 1981; Shaw & Stowe, 1982; Stavenga, 1989). Among these are melanins purines, ommochromes, pteridines, and carotenoids. These strongly colored pigments give crustaceans their characteristic eye coloration. Some secondary pigment cell classes contain reflecting pigments, which sometimes form true tapeta; in some crustacean compound eyes they assist in producing superposition images. The pigments of the secondary pigment cells also have active roles in vision, but as of yet we know little about these.

The function of pigments within the actual retinular cells is fairly well understood. The ommochromes possess broad and flat absorption spectra, well suited for controlling light intensity impinging on the photoreceptive membranes without altering the spectral content of that light. They form a cylindrical light- absorbing curtain of granules surrounding the rhabdom, optically isolating individual photoreceptors. They also play a dynamic role in photoreception, adjusting the light flux within the rhabdom by moving nearer to it in bright light and retracting away in dimmer light. This activity provides each ommatidium with its own self-regulating "pupil" to control its level of stimulation (review: Stavenga, 1979). The regulation is accomplished by changes in the aperture at the rhabdom's tip, and by the continuing absorption of light travelling along the borders of the rhabdom itself. By acting as lateral filters, these pigments can reduce the light intensity within the rhabdom, and narrow its spectral sensitivity, without greatly shifting the peak of the sensitivity maximum (Snyder et al., 1973). The activity of the intracellular pupil can be observed from outside the eye, which is useful for studing visual physiology (Cronin, 1989; Cronin and King, in press). The pigmentary migration is controlled by light intensity and involves the cytoskeleton, but we currently know neither the mechanism by which light energy is transduced to pigment movement nor that of the motor itself.

Besides pigment granules, crustacean retinular cells often contain oily vesicles of yellow, orange, or red pigments, probably carotenoids.

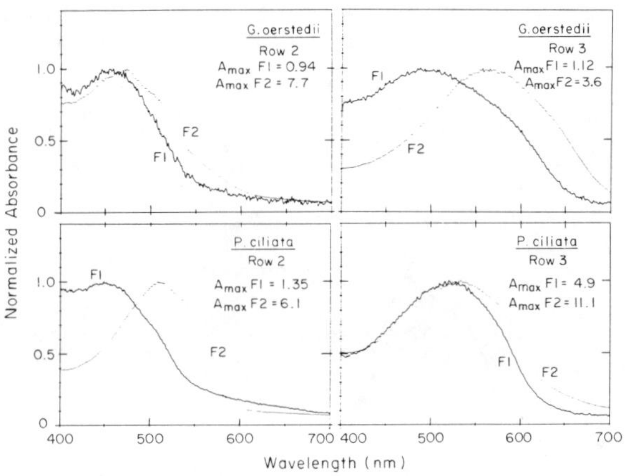

Fig. 1. Average absorption spectra of intrarhabdomal filters from eyes of the stomatopods Gonodactylus oerstedii and Pseudosquilla ciliata. Each curve is normalized to its peak, with the average maximum absorbance provided on the panel. The row numbers refer to the central band of ommatidia.

The most extreme cases of this occur in the stomatopods, where the colored material is injected into the rhabdom itself at 2 levels, to form intrarhabdomal filters (Fig. 1). These act in series with the visual pigments to shift, narrow, and multiply the spectral sensitivities of ommatidia in various parts of the eye (Marshall, 1988; Cronin & Marshall, 1989, in press). The arrangement produces the greatest diversity of spectral sensitivity mechanisms known for any retina.

CRUSTACEAN VISUAL PIGMENTS.

The visual pigments of crustaceans are found in the membranes of the rhabdomeral microvilli, where their mobility appears to be constrained, perhaps by cytoskeletal elements that extend into each microvillus

(Goldsmith & Wehner, 1977). Thus, their interactions with other membrane proteins, as well as with those of the cytoplasm, must be rather different than those of vertebrate visual pigments, which diffuse freely in the receptor membrane. In the microvillus, the absorption dipoles of the visual pigment molecules are roughly aligned with the microvillar axis, providing the elevated dichroic ratios that underlie crustacean polarized-light vision.

Crustacean visual pigments all have retinoid chromophores. Thus far, the only chromophores positively identified are retinal and 3-dehydroretinal (Suzuki et al., 1984; Zeiger & Goldsmith, 1989). However, very few species have been analyzed, and with the recent discoveries of novel chromophores in several other invertebrates (see Vogt, 1989) it would not be surprising if crustaceans also employ other retinoids. Crustacean opsins probably possess a high degree of homology with other opsins, particularly those of insects (review: Schwemer, 1989). In view of the tremendous diversity in spectral absorption properties of crustacean visual pigments (see below), it would be good to know quite a bit more about the primary structures of the opsins.

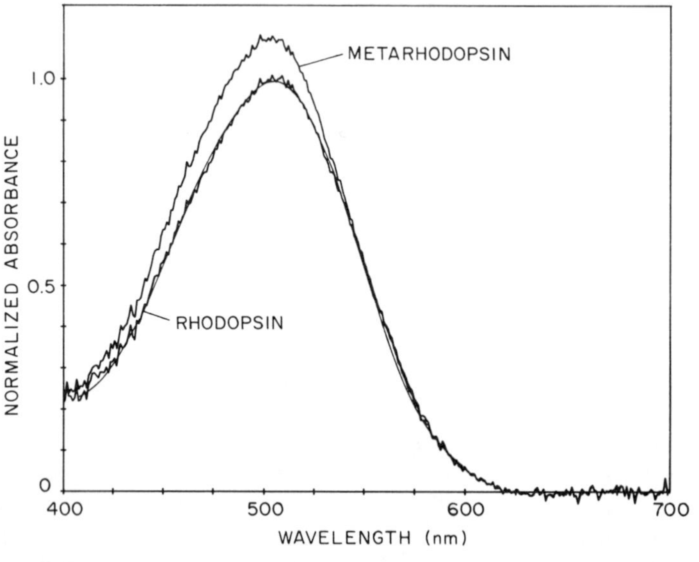

Fig. 2. Absorption spectra of the rhodopsin and metarhodopsin of the stomatopod Squilla empusa, normalized to the rhodopsin peak. The smooth curve fitted to the rhodopsin data is a Dartnall nomogram, a template derived for vertebrate rhodopsin.

In their photochemistry, crustacean visual pigments are also rather normal. For example, crayfish rhodopsin resembles vertebrate rhodopsin in both its molar extinction coefficient and its quantum efficiency for photoconversion (Cronin & Goldsmith, 1982). Spectral absorption curves of crustacean visual pigments closely resemble templates derived from vertebrate data (Lipetz & Cronin, 1988; Cronin & Marshall, 1989, in press). Like those of other rhabdomeric photoreceptors, crustacean visual pigments exist in 2 thermally stable forms (Fig. 2): the native pigment, with an 11-cis chromophore, and the photoproduct (metapigment), with an all-trans chromophore. Although the spectral locations of the visual pigments cover a broad range, the metapigments that have been identified all peak near 500 nm (a major exception is crayfish metaporphyropsin, which has a maximum at 537 nm; see Zeiger & Goldsmith, 1989). Since most of the visual pigments also peak between 490 and 510 nm, the general similarity of the metapigment's absorption to that of the visual pigment would tend to reduce the rate of photoregeneration and increase self- screening, neither of which would seem to be desirable. The metarhodopsins (though probably not metaporphyropsins), are autofluorescent (Cronin & Goldsmith, 1981). This property can be used to investigate both the photochemistry of the rhodopsin (Cronin & Goldsmith, 1982) and the physiology of photoreception itself (Cronin & Goldsmith, 1984; Cronin, 1985, 1989).

The thermal stability of the metapigment produces another conundrum. Once a steady-state mixture of pigment and product has been established in the rhabdomal membranes, there is no obvious way to restore a full load of the dark form of the visual pigment. One route to dark adaptation appears to be the synthesis of new photoreceptor membrane with new visual pigment molecules in it (review: Goldsmith & Bernard, 1985). While other, less drastic means of restoring full dark sensitivity may be available, there is as yet no evidence for their operation.

Also, used chromophore must continuously be converted back to the 11-cis form. Limited data suggest that in crayfish, at least, a pigment is present in the eyes which could assist in this process when irradiated with blue light (Cronin & Goldsmith, 1984). If such a retinochrome-like substance exists, it would represent a second class of photosensitive pigment present in crustacean eyes and vital for normal visual function (see Schwemer, 1989).

Virtually all crustaceans are aquatic, and relatively few species have been examined, but the spectral diversity of their visual pigments rivals that of the vertebrates. Visual pigments with rhodopsin-type spectra absorb maximally at wavelengths from 400 nm to beyond 550 nm, and crayfish porphyropsin peaks at 567 nm (Zeiger & Goldsmith, 1989)

Microspectrophotometric data obtained in my laboratory from isolated main rhabdoms (retinular cells 1 - 7) of 27 species of crabs and 6 species of stomatopods are illustrated in Fig. 3. The wavelength of maximum absorption in each individual scanned rhabdom was determined by a least-squares fit to a rhodopsin template (see Cronin & Marshall, in press), and results are displayed at 1-nm intervals. Most of the original data appeared in Cronin (1985), Cronin & Forward (1988), and Cronin & Marshall (in press).

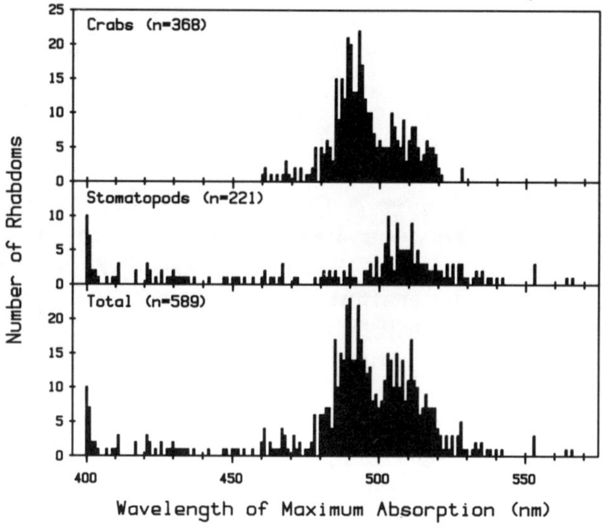

Fig. 3. Histograms of numbers of individual rhabdoms possessing visual pigments with wavelengths of maximum absorption from 400 to 570 nm. The number of rhabdoms included on each panel is given. See the text for further explanation.

The data show considerable scatter, partly because each analyzed spectrum is obtained by taking the difference between the absorption by the dark-adapted photoreceptor and that remaining after photobleaching the visual pigment. Thus, identification of the spectral location of the visual pigment is not so precise as in vertebrate photoreceptors, which usually require only a single direct scan. Nevertheless, some patterns emerge from this presentation. The crab visual pigments tend to cluster into 2 major classes, near 490 and 510 nm; the first peak is characteristic of brachyuran crabs and the second of hermit crabs. The stomatopod data cover a much greater range, often even in a single species, but also exhibit some clumping aroung 510±10 nm (the apparent peak at 400 nm results from the fact that this was the shortest wavelength analyzed, so rhabdoms with slightly shorter absorption maxima tended to fall into the 400-nm class). The total data set thus illustrates the same two preferred groupings, with a distinct valley between them near 500 nm. A similar plot of vertebrate rhodopsins would have its dominant peak at 500-502 nm (Dartnall & Lythgoe, 1965), so the crustaceans and vertebrates clearly differ in where they place their most common spectral classes. Of course, the crustacean pigments might not all be true rhodopsins, which could help explain the difference. Another difference between Fig. 3 and similar plots for vertebrate visual pigments is the absence in the crustacean case of obvious periodicity in the position of the maximum. Vertebrate rhodopsins have regular peaks at intervals of 6.7 nm (Dartnall & Lythgoe, 1965). Again, the crustacean data are less precise because of the methods used, and could include pigments with various chromophores. In any case, neither visual inspection nor analysis by autocorrelation or Fourier techniques reveals clear periodicity.

Unlike aquatic vertebrates, crustaceans of a given taxonomic group tend generally to possess similar visual pigments independent of habitat. Even the deep-sea forms have visual pigments peaking near 490 nm, a good 10 nm longer than deep-sea fish (Partridge et al., 1989). Stomatopods, with their intensely polychromatic retinas, possess similar suites of visual pigments in the various species. The current situation permits little generalizing about the ecology of these pigments.

In addition to the visual pigments of the main rhabdoms, many crustacean retinas have a visual pigment class absorbing at very short wavelengths, probably contained in the rhabdomere of the 8th retinular cell (Cummins & Goldsmith, 1981). Sensitivity to ultraviolet light is common among semiterrestrial or shallow- water crustacean species. Several ultraviolet-absorbing visual pigments from insect eyes have been identified (see Stavenga and Schwemer, 1984), but as of yet there is no published description of an analogous crustacean pigment.

Ultimately, the spectral sensitivity of a crustacean photoreceptor depends on the absorption spectrum and density of the visual pigment itself, combined with the effects of optical filters in series with the photoreceptor, lateral filtering by pigments of the retinular cells, self-screening by photoproducts or photostable pigments within the rhabdomeric membranes, and modification of light by the reflecting pigments or tapetum. In view of the profusion of colored materials in crustacean compound eyes, it is probably rare that the visual pigment's absorption spectrum completely determines the actual spectral sensitivity. In some cases, however, the sensitivity function can be explained by a single, unfiltered rhodopsin (Cronin and King, in press). In others, such as in the optically complex retinas of the central ommatidial bands of mantis shrimps, spectral sensitivity is only distantly related to absorption properties of the visual pigments (Cronin & Marshall, 1989, in press).

The structural and functional complexity of crustacean photoreceptors produces many unanswered questions concerning how they are used for analyzing environmental light. A recent surprising report suggests that in a deep-sea shrimp, the visual pigment might be used not for vision in the usual sense, but instead to detect long-wavelength radiation from nearby hydrothermal plumes (Van Dover et al., 1989). Without doubt, many other unexpected discoveries remain for researchers of crustacean vision.

ACKNOWLEDGEMENTS

This material is based on research supported by the National Science Foundation under Grants No. BNS-8518769, and INT-8814562. M.F. Land and N.J. Marshall provided much helpful discussion.

REFERENCES

Autrum, H. (1981) Light and dark adaptation in invertebrates. In Handbook of Sensory Physiology, Vol VII/6C. (ed. H. Autrum) pp.1-91. Berlin: Springer.

Cronin, T.W. (1985) The visual pigment of a stomatopodcrustacean, Squilla empusa. J. comp. Physiol. A **156:**679-687.

Cronin, T.W. (1989) Application of intracellular optical techniques to the study of stomatopod crustacean vision. J.comp. Physiol. A **164:**737-749.

Cronin, T.W. & Forward, R.B., Jr. (1988) The visual pigments of crabs. I. Spectral characteristics. J. comp. Physiol. A**162:**463-478.

Cronin, T.W. & Goldsmith, T.H. (1981) Fluorescence of crayfish metarhodopsin studied in single rhabdoms. Biophys. J. **35**:653-664.

Cronin, T.W. & Goldsmith, T.H. (1982) Quantum efficiency and photosensitivity of the rhodopsin-metarhodopsin conversion in crayfish photoreceptors. Photochem. Photobiol. **36**:447-454.

Cronin, T.W. & Goldsmith, T.H. (1984) Dark regeneration of rhodopsin in crayfish photoreceptors. J. gen. Physiol. **84:**63-81.

Cronin, T.W. & King, C.A. (in press) Spectral sensitivity of vision in the mantis shrimp, Gonodactylus oerstedii, determined using non-invasive techniques. Biol. Bull.

Cronin, T.W. & Marshall N.J. (1989) A retina with at least ten spectral types of photoreceptors in a mantis shrimp. Nature **339:**137-140.

Cronin, T.W. & Marshall, N.J. (in press) Multiple spectral classes of photoreceptors in the retinas of gonodactyloid stomatopod crustaceans. J. comp. Physiol.

A Cummins, D.R. & Goldsmith, T.H. (1981) Cellular identification of the violet receptor in the crayfish eye. J. comp. Physiol.**142**:199-202.

Dartnall, H.J.A. & Lythgoe, J.N. (1965) The spectral clustering of visual pigments. Vision Res. **5**:81-100.

Goldsmith, T.H. & Bernard, G.D. (1985) Visual pigments of invertebrates. Photochem. Photobiol. **42**:805-809.

Goldsmith, T.H. & Wehner, R. (1977) Restrictions on rotational and translational diffusion of pigment in the membranes of arhabdomeric photoreceptor. J. gen. Physiol. **70:**453-490.

Lipetz, L.E. & Cronin, T.W. (1988) Application of an invariant spectral form to the visual pigments of crustaceans:implications regarding the binding of the chromophore. Vision Res. **10**:1083-1093.

Marshall, N.J. (1988) A unique colour and polarisation vision system in mantis shrimps. Nature **333**:557-560.

Partridge, J.C., Shand, J., Archer, S.N., Lythgoe, J.N., & van Groningen-Luyben. (1989) Interspecific variation in the visual pigments of deep-sea fishes. J. comp. Physiol. A **164:**513-529.

Schwemer, J. (1989) Visual pigments of compound eyes - structure,photochemistry, and regeneration. In Facets of Vision (ed. D.G.Stavenga & R.C. Hardie) pp. 112-133. Berlin: Springer. Shaw, S.R. & Stowe, S. (1982) Photoreception. In The Biology ofCrustacea, Vol 3 (ed. D.C. Sandeman & H.L. Atwood) pp. 291-367. New York: Academic Press.

Snyder, A.W., Menzel, R., & Laughlin, S.B. (1973) Structure and function of the fused rhabdom. J. comp. Physiol. **87**:99-135.

Stavenga, D.G. (1979) Pseudopupils in compound eyes. In Handbook of Sensory Physiology, Vol VII/6A (ed. H. Autrum) pp. 357-439. Berlin: Springer. Stavenga, D.G. (1989) Pigments in compound eyes. In Facets of Vision (ed. D.G. Stavenga & R.C. Hardie) pp. 152-172. Berlin: Springer.

Stavenga, D.G. & Schwemer, J. (1984) Visual pigments of invertebrates. In Photoreception and Vision in Invertebrates(ed. M.A. Ali) pp. 11-61. New York: Plenum.

Suzuki, T., Makino-Tasaka, M., & Eguchi, E. (1984) 3-Dehydroretinal (vitamin A2 aldehyde) in crayfish eye. VisionRes. **24**:783-787.

Van Dover, C.L., Szuts, E.Z., Chamberlain, S.C., & Cann, J.R. (1989) A novel eye in "eyeless" shrimp from hydrothermal vents of the Mid-Atlantic Ridge. Nature **337**:458-460.

Vogt, K. (1989) Distribution of insect visual chromophores: functional and phylogenetic aspects. In Facets of Vision (ed.D.G. Stavenga & R.C. Hardie) pp. 134-151. Berlin: Springer.

Zeiger, J. & Goldsmith, T.H. (1989) Spectral properties of porphyropsin from an invertebrate. Vision Res. **29:** 519-527.

Frontiers in Crustacean Neurobiology
Advances in Life Sciences

ENERGY RELEASING METABOLISM IN THE COMPOUND EYES OF THE GHOST CRAB, *OCYPODE*

H. Langer, U. Knollmann and M. Delpiano

Lehrstuhl für Tierphysiologie, Fakultät für Biologie der Ruhr-Universität, Bochum, and Max-Planck-Institut für Systemphysiologie, Dortmund, Federal Republic of Germany

The large compound eyes are the most prominent sensory organs of ghost crabs. They allow a 380° visual field with stereoscopic parts in front and behind the animal. In these crabs, which live predominantly terrestrial on the shores of tropical oceans, the activity periods are controlled mainly by the tides independent from the day-night cycle, for they are feeding on the water-line -over day as like as during night - while the flood is coming up. Therefore, their eyes have to deal with extremely different light intensities. The ommatidia of *Ocypode* - as those of other crabs - are of the apposition type; therefore, they have only a limited range of light adaptation by movement of screening pigments. Much more prominent are changes in size of the rhabdoms (Fig. 1), which are composed of the rhabdomeres of seven long photoreceptor cells and of a short one which is located distally in contact with the dioptric apparatus. During the daily cycle, the amount of visual pigment contained in the eye changes by a factor of about 6; every evening, a large part of the visual pigment is newly synthesized (Henning and Langer, 1986). On the other hand, the very high intensity of sunlight over day (up to more than 150,000 lux on the surface of white coral sand in the beach) must cause a large turnover of the visual pigment within the rhabdomeres.

Therefore, we are interested in the energy releasing metabolism and its light dependence in these compound eyes. To learn about preferred metabolic pathways, maximal specific activities of enzymes involved in energy releasing reactions were determined in the eyes of the ghost crab and compared with those of the blowfly, which are also of the apposition type. The completely different ways of oxygen supply - by the hemolymph with hemocyanin in the crab and by tracheoles via air diffusion in the fly - could cause different preconditions for pathways of energy release, which might be mirror-imaged in the enzyme patterns. As seen in Table 1, *Ocypode* has relatively low capacity of the oxidative pathway (GPox, CS,

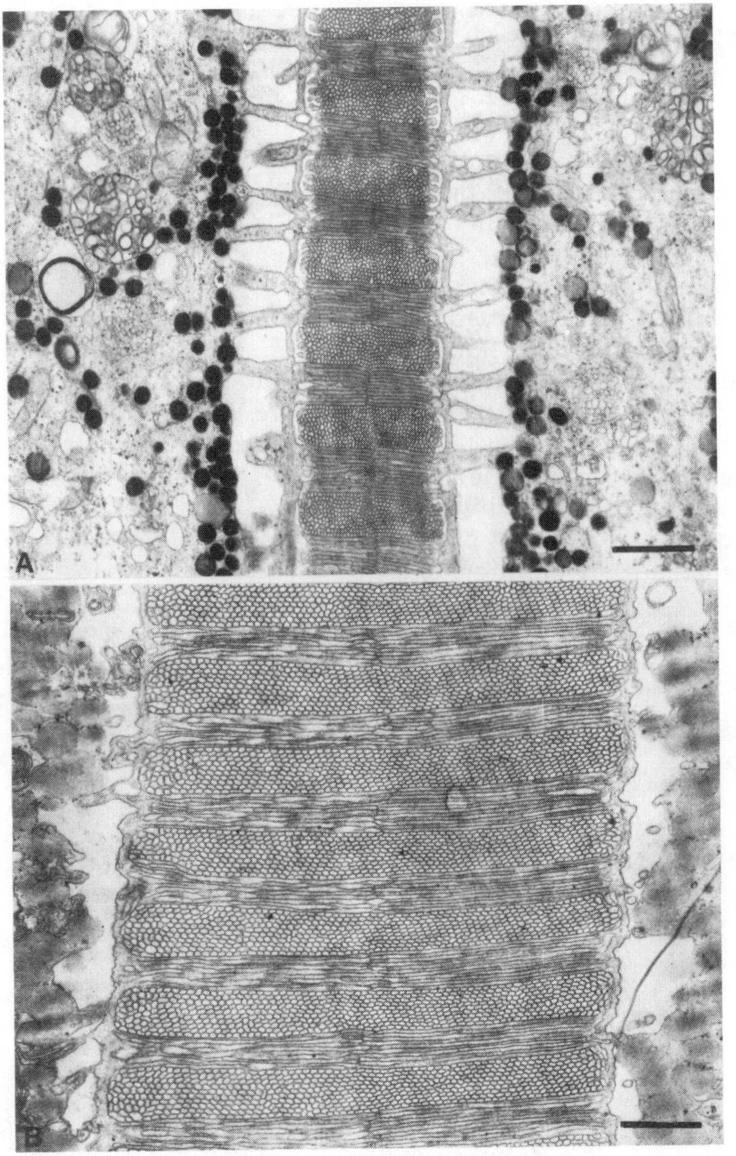

Fig. 1. Longitudinal sections through ommatidia near to the axis of the rhabdom from eyes (A) over day and (B) during night. The cross-section area in this part of the rhabdom - next to the nuclei of the large photoreceptor cells no. 1 to 7 - is in (B) about tenfold that in (A); the overall volume of the rhabdom changes from day to night-time by a factor of 8. Bar: 1 μm. - Preparation and electron micrographs by Dr. C.C. Meinecke/Bochum.

Ccox) in comparison to *Calliphora*. On the other hand, the glycolytic capacity (PH, LDH) is much higher in *Ocypode* than in *Calliphora*; in accordance, the molar ratio ArgP:ATP is 4:1 and 1:1, respectively (Langer et al., 1976).

In order to discover the actual metabolic situation of the tissue under day-light conditions more precisely, we determined the amounts of substrates and the end product of glycolysis (glucose, glycogen, and lactate) together with the `high-energy phosphates' (ATP, ADP, AMP) and the prevailing phosphagen (L-phospho-arginine) in the crab retinal tissue. One eye of the animal which served as a control was cut off at its joint to the carapax, quickly frozen in liquid nitrogen and freeze-dried. For analysis, only the retinal tissue - which could be separated easily from the other eye-constituents - was dissected. Out of the fronto-lateral area of the other eye, a bowl-shaped piece was cut, which contained the greatest part of the receptor cells, the crystalline cones and the adhering cornea. Care was taken to remove optical ganglia and gland tissue proximal to the basal lamina. This preparation was placed into a perspex chamber and superfused at 25°C with an air-equilibrated physiological saline of the following composition (concentrations in mmoles l^{-1}): NaCl 460, KCl 15, $MgCl_2$ 3.8, $MgSO_4$ 5.2, $CaSO_4$ 25, HEPES 10, $NaHCO_3$ 6; pH 7.3 (Cole, 1941). Aliquots of the outflowing superfusate were checked continuously for lactate delivered from the tissue. After superfusion the preparation was further treated as described above for the control.

Table 1. Specific activities of enzymes under optimal conditions in eyes of the ghost crab *Ocypode ryderi* and the blowfly *Calliphora erythrocephala*. Data are given in mU./mg total protein ±S.D.; n=8. (From Rivera and Langer, 1983).

	Ocypode	Calliphora
PH	31.1± 4.4	12.7± 2.4
HK	4.7± 1.0	16.8± 1.8
PFK	1.5± 0.1	4.7± 1.4
GADPH	169 ± 14	1010 ± 94
PK	161 ± 19	966 ± 97
G6PDH	24.0± 4.1	6.5± 1.4
LDH	342 ± 50	52.8± 7.6
GDH	11.6± 3.3	61.3± 9.6
GPox	1.6± 0.5	4.5± 0.4
CS	1.8± 0.6	268 ± 41
Ccox	6.3± 1.7	391 ± 50
Mg-ATPase	26.1± 3.2	186 ± 24
NaK-ATPase	4.2± 1.4	45.0± 6.7
ArgK	3470 ±340	1300 ±120

Tables 2 and 3 summarize the concentrations of the metabolites measured inside the retinal tissue and the calculated 'Atkinson Energy Charge' (AEC) for control and superfused retinas. No significant changes could be detected concerning the amounts of substrates of glycolysis and the energy state of the preparation, but the amount of lactate inside the tissue increased to about eightfold, and additionally a release of lactate from the tissue was found with a rate of 6.6 nmoles per mg dry weight and hour.

Table 2. Contents of adenine nucleotides and phosphagen and calculated energy charge in the retina of Ocypode ryderi. One eye frozen in liquid nitrogen immediately after removal from the animal and dissected after freeze-drying served as control. From the second eye of the same animal a preparation was made and incubated for 2 to 5 h in an open flow system (25°C, flow rate 1-4 ml/h). After this incubation the preparation was frozen and treated like the control. Values are given in nmol per mg dry weight ± S.D.; n=6

	Control retina	Incubated retina
Arginine phosphate	24.1±4.1	19.8±4.8
ATP	6.1±1.6	5.7±1.4
ADP	0.4±0.3	0.5±0.3
AMP	1.3±1.0	2.3±1.7
Energy charge (AEC)	0.85	0.71

Table 3. Contents of glycogen, glucose, lactate in and release of lactate from the retina of *Ocypode ryderi*. Treatment of controls and incubated preparations as described in Table 2. Values are given in nmol per mg dry weight ± S.D.; n=6.

	Control retina	Incubated retina
Glycogen	659 ±197	666 ±242
Glucose	21.8± 6.8	30.7± 18.0
Lactate	2.4± 2.3	18.9± 6.5
Rate of lactate release (nmol/mg dry weight·hour)		6.6± 1.9

The merely slight decrease in AEC even after superfusion periods of up to 5 hours seems to reflect the good viability of the tissue under the employed conditions; the lactate production obviously contributes to this viability by an appreciable amount. On the other hand, this lactate production occurring in spite of a good oxygen supply could be a consequence of diffusion limitations imposed by the tissue. Therefore, we measured - under similar superfusion conditions - the availability of oxygen with increasing tissue depth. This was done by impaling a double-barrelled microelectrode (Acker et al., 1983) through the basal lamina further downward to the cornea by means of a micromanipulator. This allowed measurements of oxygen partial pressure (P_gO_2) in 40 µm steps, while the second channel (DC) served to detect the surface of the tissue at the level of the basal lamina (assigned as zero-depth in Figs. 3 and 5). The partial pressure of oxygen in the surrounding superfusion-medium was continuously checked by a catheter electrode, as were pH (pH-electrode) and temperature (thermocouple). Fig. 2 gives a schematic representation of the superfusion-equipment used for these investigations.

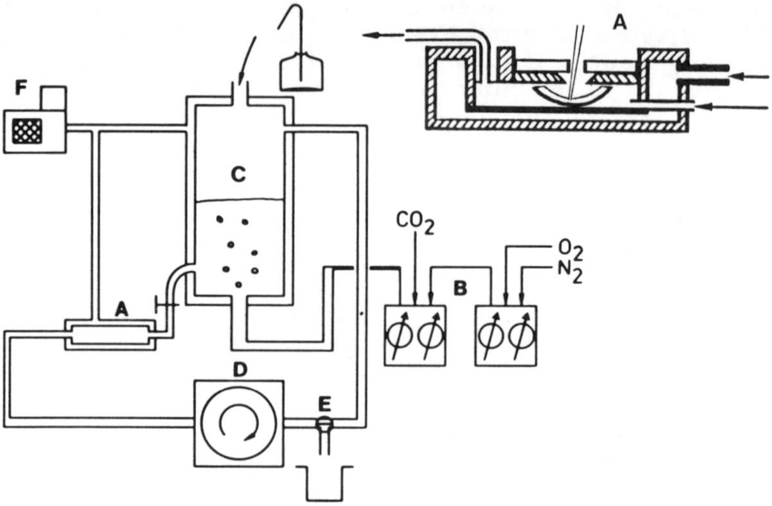

Fig. 2. Setup for the superfusion experiments. A, lucite temperature constant tissue chamber for the crab retina with O_2-sensitive microelectrode; B, gas-mixing pumps to equilibrate Cole's solution (1941) in reservoir C; D, peristaltic pump for promotion of circulation of the solution; E, stopcock for interruption of recirculation; F, thermostat. (From Delpiano, 1988).

As given in Fig. 3, we found a PO_2 profile with the P_gO_2 starting to decrease already above the tissue surface down to a stable value inside the tissue. This final P_gO_2-level as well as the steepness of this PO_2-gradient depend on the PO_2 of the superfusing medium. The oxygen supply in vivo must be very effective even up to the distal parts of the photoreceptor cells. This is evident from the position of the mitochondria: most of them are distally situated, and they have their highest concentration near to the end of the crystalline cone, were they are in close vicinity to the rhabdom (Fig.4).

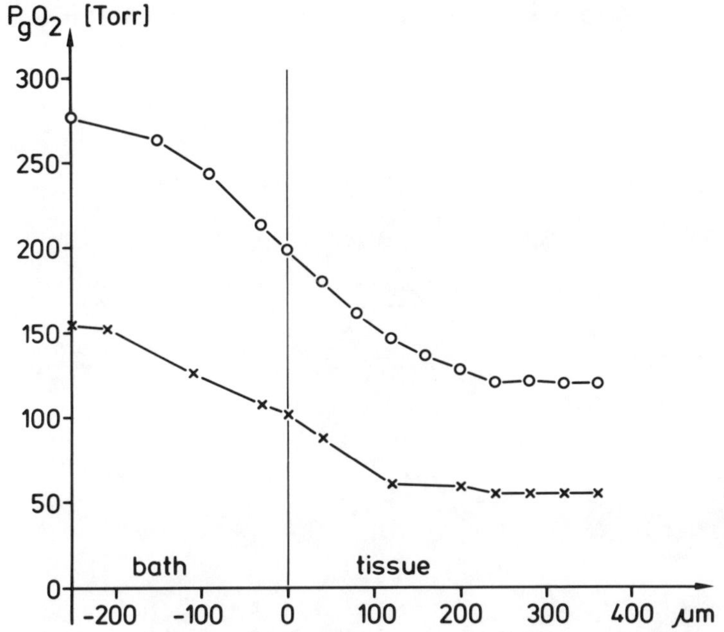

Fig. 3. Profiles of partial pressures of oxygen above and within the retinal tissue of the crab measured with PO_2 microelectrodes under different PO_2 in the medium (-**o**-, 280 Torr; -**x**-, 150 Torr) during superfusion. The abscissa gives the depth of puncture, the ordinate the PO_2 above and inside the tissue. 0 µm represents the tissue surface on the level corresponding to the basal lamina.

A profile similar to that of PO_2 could be detected for the extracellular pH, measured by a pH/DC microelectrode (Delpiano and Acker, 1985). From a pH of 7.3 within the bath the pH showed a decrease - also starting above the tissue surface - to a stable pH value of 7.15 inside the tissue (Fig. 5).

The P_gO_2 profile can be abolished by application of antimycin A (100 µmoles/l). From this effect it can be concluded that the PO_2 gradient is caused by oxygen consumption inside the tissue. The pH gradient obviously resembles production of acidic metabolites in and their release from the tissue, as mentioned above, presumably lactate. Since these measurements were carried out in a strongly oxygenated superfusion medium, which makes more oxygen available to the tissue than may be made by the hemolymph under physiological conditions, the presented results show that lactate production by the retinal tissue of the crab occurs in spite of a sufficient oxygen supply and consumption, i.e. is aerobic glycolysis.

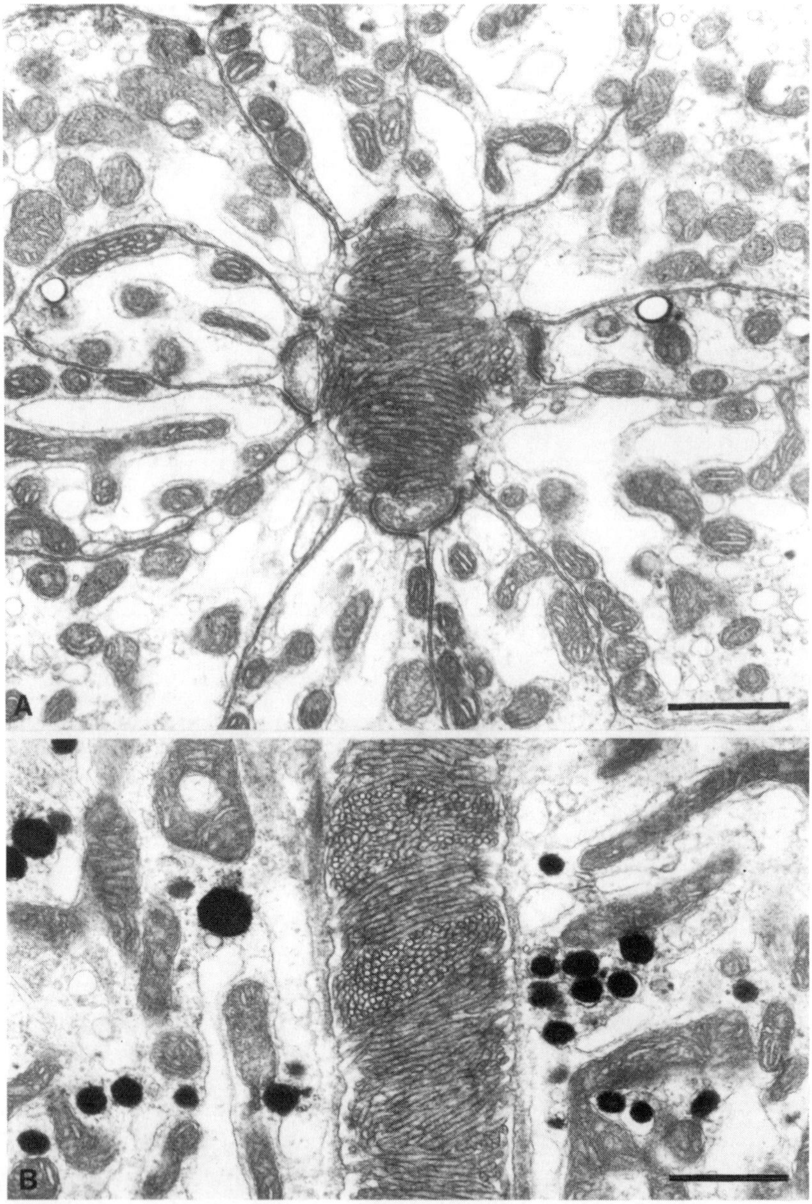

Fig. 4. Oblique (A) and longitudinal section (B) through the most distal region of the rhabdom from an eye during day-time. The rhabdom is built exclusively by the rhabdomeres of the four lobes of the short distal photoreceptor cell. The seven large photoreceptor cells have only cytoplasmic parts in this region. The rhabdom is surrounded by proximal processes of the four crystalline cone cells. Note the numerous and large mitochondria situated near to the rhabdom. Bar: 1 μm. - Preparation and electron micrographs by Dr. U. Henning/Bochum.

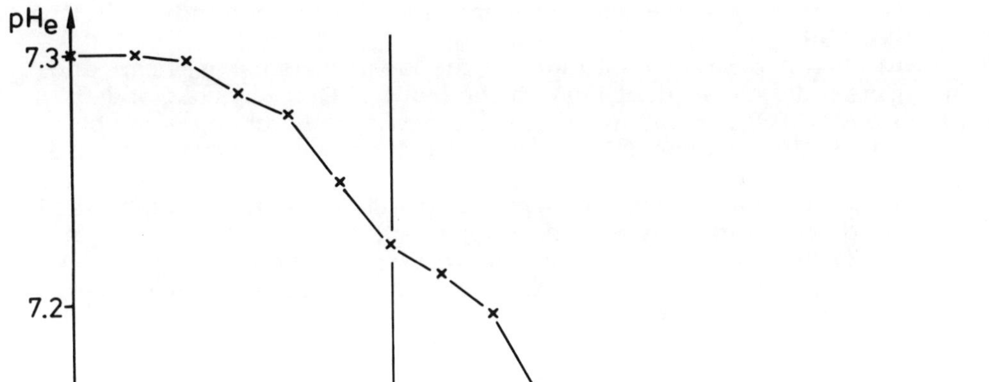

Fig. 5. pH profile outside and inside the tissue of the superfused retina of the crab measured with a double-barrelled pH-sensitive microelectrode at a PO_2 in the medium of 280 Torr. Details of diagram as in Fig. 3.

From these experimental results one can be sure that aerobic glycolysis occurs in the retinal tissues of the ghost crab, as like as it is known for the retina of mammals from investigations by Warburg and coworkers (1924). In this case the lactate production is thought to improve the oxygen supply to the retinal tissue via its Bohr-effect on hemoglobin. In the eyes of the crabs, however, there are no blood vessels in the retina; the oxygen is supplied from the central hemolymph space in the eye stalk by diffusion across the basal membrane. Although lactate could influence the hemolymph after diffusing backwards out of the retina, this would not make sense: It is known from the work by Morris and Bridges (1985) on the hemocyanin of Ocypode, which shows a normal "positive" Bohr effect ($\Delta \log P_{50}/\Delta pH$ averaged −0.67),that increasing hemolymph concentration of lactate not only leads to an increased oxygen affinity of the molecule but also reduces the figure of the measured Bohr-factor. Therefore, a hypothesis to explain this phenomenon cannot be offered at the present time.

REFERENCES

Acker, H, Holtermann G, Carlsson J, Nedermann T (1983) Methodological aspects of microelectrode measurements in cellular spheroids. Adv Exp Med Biol **159**: 445-462

Cole WH (1941) A perfusing solution for the lobster (Homarus) heart and the effects of its constituent ions on the heart. J Gen Physiol **25**: 1-6

Delpiano MA (1988) Possible meaning of different ionic changes in the carotid body during hypoxia. In: Acker H (ed) Oxygen sensing in tissues. Springer, Berlin, p 193

Delpiano MA, Acker H (1985) Extracellular pH changes in the superfused cat carotid body during hypoxia and hypercapnia. Brain Res **342**: 273

Henning U (1986) Der Turnover der Photorezeptormembran im Komplexauge der terrestrischen Krabbe *Ocypode ryderi*. Dissertation, Ruhr-Universität Bochum

Henning U, Langer H (1986) Untersuchungen zum Turnover der Photorezeptormembran im Auge der Krabbe *Ocypode ryderi*. Verh Dtsch Zool Ges **79**: 213-214

Langer H, Lues I, Rivera ME (1976) Arginine phosphate in compound eyes. J Comp Physiol 107: 179-184

Morris S, Bridges CR (1985) An investigation of haemocyanin oxygen affinity in the semi-terrestrial crab *Ocypode sarratan* Forsk. J Exp Biol **117**: 119-132

Rivera ME, Langer H (1983) Enzyme pattern of energy releasing metabolism in eyes and ganglia of the blowfly *Calliphora erythrocephala* and the crab *Ocypode ryderi*. Mol Physiol **4**: 265-277

Warburg O, Posener K, Negelein E (1924) Über den Stoffwechsel der Carcinomzelle. Biochem Z **152**: 309-344

Frontiers in Crustacean Neurobiology
Advances in Life Sciences

THE CRAYFISH MUSCLE RECEPTOR ORGAN (MRO):- MODEL FOR THE MEMBRANE, RECEPTOR, CIRCUIT, AND BEHAVIOURAL LEVELS

David L. Macmillan

Zoology Department, University of Melbourne, Parkville, Victoria 3052, Australia

SUMMARY

The crayfish muscle receptor organ is one of the classical preparations of neuroethology (Fields, 1976). Experiments on the receptors underpin much of our basic understanding of receptor function and the receptors still provide an outstanding model for contemporary questions about receptor physiology. We have been using them as models to examine the toxicology of ethanol and carbon monoxide at the receptor level. We have also been using them to examine the effects of neuromodulators on primary receptor output. Following their discovery, considerable work was done on receptor connectivity and its relation to complex behavioural interactions controlling the abdomen. A sound information base was established. Developments in technique have now opened up further opportunities for progress. We are examining the basis of two local reflexes.

INTRODUCTION

Crustacean muscle receptor organs (MROs) were first described in lobsters by Alexandrowicz (1951). Most reptantian decapods have these receptors associated with the dorsal musculature of the abdomen, and in some cases, of the thorax (Pilgrim, 1960). They occur as bilateral pairs, immediately beneath the dorsal surface, spanning the articulations between the dorsal abdominal plates. The obvious morphological difference between the two receptor cells and their insertions into associated muscle strands led Alexandrowicz to predict that they would have different response characteristics. Wiersma et al. (1953) subsequently showed that one receptor responds tonically to imposed stretch and the other phasically.

Because the cells are large (60 - 100 μm; Florey & Florey, 1955) they are easily penetrated with micro-electrodes and so were used early for investigations at the cell and membrane levels; for example, to establish the relationship between generator potentials, adaptation, and action potentials (Eyzaguirre & Kuffler, 1955a, b). Subsequent voltage clamping of the membranes of these two cells showed that the firing rate in both is controlled by fast Hodgkin-Huxley gating processes and complex slow inactivation mechanisms (Gestrelius & Gramp, 1983; Gestrelius et al., 1983). The marked difference in their response characteristics can be attributed at the organ and cell level to mechanical coupling and at the membrane level to the values of the kinetic parameters of the inactivation (Edman et al., 1987). These accessible attributes are further enhanced, from the experimental point of view, by up to three additional accessory efferent fibres that synapse directly onto the receptor cells (Alexandrowicz, 1951). These increase the K^+ permeability and hence reduce receptor excitability (Eyzaguirre & Kuffler, 1954; Jansen et al., 1971). The receptors are involved in a number of reflexes but the functional or behavioural significance of most of these has not yet been estabilished. Because of the brevity and rapid adaptation of the response from the phasic receptor, most work has been concentrated on the tonic system.

Impulses evoked by imposed stretch of the MROs activate a myotatic reflex in the same segment. This is mediated by at least one of the slow extensor motor neurones (SEMNs) which results in a contraction that unloads the MROs and reduces their level of excitation (Fields, 1966; Fields & Kennedy, 1965; Sokolove, 1973). In addition, the homonymous receptors are strongly inhibited by the accessory nerves (Eckert, 1961a; Nja & Walloe, 1975). Receptor activity produced by imposed stretch evokes similar inhibitory reflexes in other segments and inter-segmental influences are additive. The strength of the reflex falls away with distance from the segment of activation (Eckert, 1961a) and is biased in the anterior direction (Fields et al., 1967).

The myotatic reflex stabilises abdominal position against imposed movement when the animal is quiescent and also acts as part of a servo-loop to establish new centrally selected resting positions (Fields, 1966). The anterior bias of the inter-segmental reflex relates to centrally driven movements. Flexion of the abdomen would normally activate the myotatic reflex but because centrally driven flexion occurs from rear to front, the forward-biased inhibitory reflex turns it off ahead of the contraction (Page & Sokolove, 1972). The receptor muscles attached to the MROs share at least one excitatory motorneurone with the slow extensor muscles. During some voluntary extensions the muscles attached to the receptors are also activated so that no sensory discharge occurs unless shortening is impeded. In other cases an extension may be initiated by motorneurones that do not affect the MROs. This organization provides mechanisms for load-compensating or pure tension control (Eckert, 1961b; Fields et al., 1967). A substantial amount of information is also available on related abdominal postural control systems (Jellies & Larimer, 1985; Jones & Page, 1986).

Clearly the MROs have afforded experimental opportunities for analysis of a wide range of questions about receptors and their role in behaviour. They still provide excellent openings and this chapter describes some of the ways in which I and my colleagues are using them to address a number of problems at different levels.

RESULTS

Effects of alcohol. The short-term behavioural effects of alcohol intoxication are caused by changes in the activity of neurons and synapses which can dramatically alter their firing patterns under its influence (Sandler, 1980). The changes can be detected at a number of levels. The EEG, for example, has provided evidence of secondary and tertiary effects of intoxication at various brain loci in mammals but there remain problems in interpreting these data because of lack of basic information about the effect of ethanol at the neuronal level (Hunt & Majchrowicz, 1979). Although its effect has been studied in a number of invertebrate preparations, the significance of the findings is uncertain because the concentrations used would cause coma or death in intact animals (Hunt, 1985). Recent experiments have demonstrated that crayfish can provide a sound behavioural model for intoxication and that the function of some of their synapses is modified at physiological ethanol levels (Blundon & Bittner, 1988; Friedman et al., 1988). The common Australian crayfish *Cherax destructor* also shows behavioural modifications consistent with intoxication at low blood alcohol levels and we have used preparations of its MRO to measure the effect of ethanol on primary receptor neurons (Macmillan & Vescovi, 1989). The preparation consists of two MRO organs pinned out on Sylgard (Dupont) in a small perspex chamber illuminated from below. One end of each organ is attached to a pair of screw micro-forceps so that the amount of stretch, and hence the rate of receptor discharge, can be adjusted.

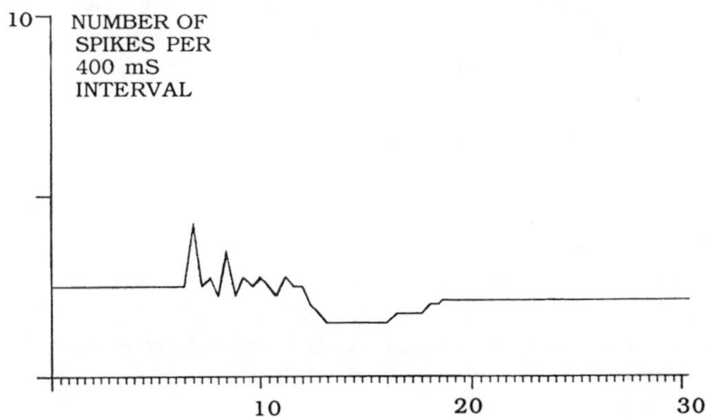

Fig. 1. The effect of 83 mM ethanol in saline on the firing rate of the tonic MRO of *Cherax destructor*.

One pair of forceps is connected to a pen motor driven by a function generator so that the MRO receives standard, intermittent ramp stretches. The bath is perfused with a smooth, non-turbulent flow of cold aerated saline from reservoirs containing different concentrations of ethanol, arranged to avoid a pressure wave when switching from one to another. The electrical activity from the receptors is recorded with suction electrodes attached close to the spike initiating zone. For the preliminary experiments described here receptor activity was monitored by counting the number of spikes per unit time. Even with this rather insensitive measure, we detected ethanol mediated changes in firing rate at concentrations of ethanol as low as 43 mM and clear dose-dependent frequency changes in the 80-120 mM range. Figure 1 shows a typical response: an initial significant dose-dependent frequency reduction followed by a partial recovery which is not complete, at least in the medium-term, until the ethanol is removed. This study is continuing with intracellular monitoring of spike initiation during ethanol challenge to determine how the activation and inactivation processes are affected.

Carbon monoxide toxicity. There is evidence that carbon monoxide (CO) poisoning causes more neural damage than an equivalent hypoxia produced by substitution of oxygen with other gases such as nitrogen. Investigators have encountered some difficulty in separating its primary toxic effects on neurons from those produced by hypoxia because of its affinity for oxygen transport molecules and interaction with parts of the respiratory chain (Piantodosi, 1987). The isolated MRO perfused with saline provides an opportunity to study the primary toxic effects of CO on single, identified, receptor neurons, in a situation in which blood-borne respiratory pigments are absent, or of no consequence to the poisoning episode (Parsons & Macmillan, 1989). Our experimental procedure was similar to that described above for ethanol testing except that the volume of the bath was reduced to a minimum and the pp of O_2, N_2 and CO in the perfusate controlled. Three saline solutions were passed over the preparation with a peristaltic pump. We found that the MRO organs are extremely resistant to hypoxia and continue to function electrically quite normally for about an hour, irrespective of the gas used to produce the hypoxia. After that time we found slowly developing reductions in spike number per stretch and even later, in spike amplitude, but these changes were again independent of the gas used (Parsons & Macmillan, 1989). We concluded that carbon monoxide has no toxic effect on the MROs of *Cherax* in addition to that attributable to hypoxia.

Neuromodulators. There is now wide interest in how neuromodulator substances alter the set-point and performance of different elements of crustacean neural and muscular systems (Bishop et al., 1987; Kravitz et al.,

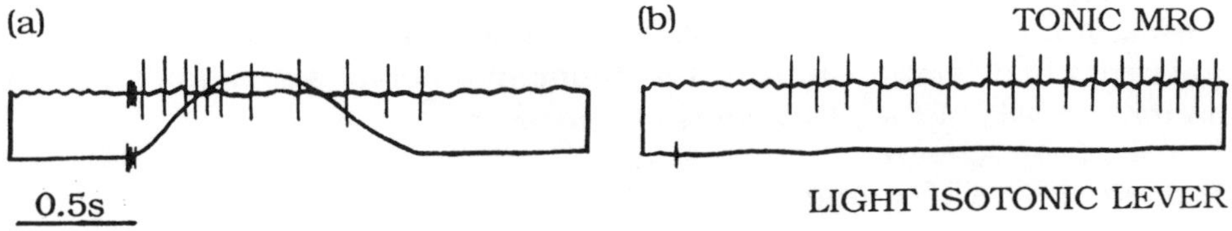

Fig. 2. Example of effect of 5-HT on tonic MRO excitability. (a) MRO activity induced by receptor muscle contraction following direct stimulation of the muscle. (b) Similar level of response evoked by 5-HT 10^{-4} in the bath without tension or length change.

1985; Mulloney et al., 1987). Recent evidence showing that neuromodulators can also alter the performance of a primary receptor cell is particularly intriguing because it raises the possibility that an animal's sensory environment can be altered in a functional way from within (Bush & Pasztor, 1989). The first report involves the oval organ of the lobster which combines spiking and non-spiking elements and we have now tested the generality of the finding by examining the effects of several neuromodulators on the purely spiking MRO receptors (Macmillan & Pasztor, 1988; Pasztor & Macmillan, 1988). Using a preparation similar to that used for ethanol studies, we found specific and different effects on tonic and phasic MROs for a number of common neuromodulators (Fig. 2) (Pasztor & Macmillan, 1989).

Abdominal reflexes. The use of intracellular dyes has opened up new possibilities for furthering our understanding of the reflex systems pioneered shortly after the discovery of the MROs (Bastiani & Mulloney, 1988a,b). We have examined the projections of the MROs in *Cherax* with similar results to those reported for *Procambarus*. The axons of both phasic and tonic MROs enter and bifurcate up and down the cord in the ganglion of entry. In *Cherax*, there appears to be more branching in the

ganglion of entry and in the next most anterior ganglion than in *Procambarus*. As these are the likely substrate for at least some of the known local reflex effects (Eckert, 1961a, b) we are presently concentrating on these relationships. Using dual dye filling we are staining pairs of slow extensor motorneurones and MRO central projections to locate the connections and interposed interneurons.

CONCLUSIONS

The crustacean MROs provide opportunities for experimenters at all levels of reduction. Large size and lack of connective tissue makes them attractive for receptor model studies. The complexity of the efferent innervation and large areas of exposed membrane surface mean that they are also likely to be very useful for the study of neuromodulator effects with patch clamp. With dye injection techniques, the body of information on components and relationships in the abdominal nervous system can be built upon for analysis of the MRO control systems.

Supported by ARC grants to the Author.

REFERENCES

Alexandrowicz, J.S. (1951) Muscle receptor organs in the abdomen of *Homarus vulgaris* and *Palinurus vulgaris*. *Quart. J. Micr. Sci.* **92**:163-199.

Bastiani, M.J. & Mulloney, B. (1988a) The central projections of the stretch receptor neurons of crayfish: Structure, variation, and postembryonic growth. *J. Neurosci.* **8**: 1254-1263.

Bastiani, M.J. & Mulloney, B. (1988b) The central projections of the stretch receptor neurons of crayfish: Segmental gradients of synaptic probability and strength. *J. Neurosci.* **8**:1264-1272.

Bishop, C.A., Wine, J.J., Nagy, F. & O'Shea, M. (1987) Physiological consequences of a peptide cotransmitter in a crayfish nerve-muscle preparation. *J. Neurosci.* **7**:1769-1779.

Blundon, J.A. & Bittner, G.D. (1988) Effects of acute and chronic ethanol exposure on crayfish behavior and synaptic transmission. *Neurosci. Abs.* **14**:83.1.

Bush, B.M.H. & Pasztor, V.M. (1989) Primary afferent responses of a crustacean mechanoreceptor are modulated by proctolin, octopamine and serotonin. *In press.*

Eckert, R.O. (1961a) Reflex relationships of the abdominal stretch receptors of the crayfish. I. Feedback inhibition of the receptors. *J. Cell. Comp. Physiol.* **57**:149-162.

Eckert, R.O. (1961b) Reflex relationships of the abdominal stretch receptors of the crayfish. II. Stretch receptor involvement during the swimming reflex. *J. Cell. Comp. Physiol.* **57**:163-197.

Edman, A., Gestrelius, S. & Grampp, W. (1987) Analysis of gated membrane currents and mechanisms of firing control in the rapidly adapting lobster stretch receptor neurone. *J. Physiol.* **384**:649-669.

Eyzaguirre, C. & Kuffler, S. (1954) Inhibitory activity in single cell synapses. *Biol. Bull.* **107**:310.

Eyzaguirre, C. & Kuffler, S. (1955a) Process of excitation in the dendrites and in the soma of single isolated sensory nerve cells of the lobster and crayfish. *J. Gen. Physiol.* **39**:87-119.

Eyzaguirre, C. & Kuffler, S. (1955b) Further study of soma, dendrite, and axon excitation in single neurons. *J. Gen. Physiol.* **39**:121-153.

Fields, H.L. (1966) Proprioceptive control of posture in the crayfish abdomen. *J. exp. Biol.* **44**:455-468.

Fields, H.L. (1976) Crustacean abdominal and thoracic muscle receptor organs. In *Structure and Function of Proprioceptors in the Invertebrates* (ed. P.J. Mill) pp. 65-114. London: Chapman & Hall.

Fields, H.L., Evoy, W.H. & Kennedy, D. (1967) Reflex role played by efferent control of an invertebrate stretch receptor. *J. Neurophysiol.* **30**:859-874.

Fields, H.L. & Kennedy, D. (1965) Functional role of muscle receptor organs in crayfish. *Nature* **206**:1235-1237.

Florey, E. & Florey, E. (1955) Microanatomy of the abdominal stretch receptors of the crayfish (*Astacus fluviatilis L.*). *J. Gen. Physiol.* **39**:69-85.

Friedman, R.N., Bittner, G.D. & Blundon, J.A. (1988) Electrophysiological and behavioural effects of ethanol on crayfish. *J. Pharmacol. Exp. Ther.* **246**:125-131.

Gestrelius, S. & Grampp, W. (1983) Impulse firing in the slowly adapting stretch receptor neurone of the lobster and its numerical simulation. *Acta Physiol. Scand.* **118**:253-261.

Gestrelius, S., Grampp, W. & Sjolin, L. (1983) Kinetics of the TTX Na^+ current in the slowly adapting lobster stretch receptor neurone. *Acta Physiol. Scand.* **118:**135-140.

Hunt, W.A. (1985) *Alcohol and Biological Membranes.* New York: The Guilford Press.

Hunt, W.A. & Majchrowicz, E. (1979) Alterations in neurotransmitter function after acute and chronic treatment with ethanol. In Biochemistry and Pharmacology of Ethanol (eds. E. Majchrowicz & E.P. Noble) pp. 167-185. New York: Plenum.

Jansen, J.R.S., Nja, A., Ormstad, K. & Walloe, L. (1971) On the innervation of the slowly adapting stretch receptor of the crayfish abdomen. An electrophysiological approach *Acta Physiol. Scand.* **81**:273-285.

Jellies, J. & Larimer, J.L. (1985) Synaptic interactions between neurons involved in the production of abdominal posture in crayfish. *J. Comp. Physiol.* A, **156**:861-873.

Jones, K.A. & Page, C.H. (1986) Postural interneurons in the abdominal nervous system of lobster: I. Organization, morphologies and motor programs for flexion, extension and inhibition. *J. Comp. Physiol.* A, **158**:259-271.

Kravitz, E.A., Beltz, B., Glusman, S., Goy, M., Harris-Warrick, R., Johnston, M., Livingstone, M., Schwartz, T. & King-Siwicki, K. (1985) The well modulated lobster. The roles of serotonin, octopamine and proctolin in the lobster nervous system. In *Model Neural Networks and Behavior* (ed. A.I. Selverston) pp. 339-360. New York: Plenum.

Macmillan, D.L. & Pasztor, V.M. (1988) Differing modulatory effects of proctolin, FRMF-amide, octopamine and 5-HT of the crayfish abdominal muscle receptor organ (MRO). *Proc. Aust. Physiol. Pharmacol. Soc.* **19**:180P.

Macmillan, D.L. & Vescovi, P.J. (1989) The effect of ethanol on the function of a crustacean sensory receptor. *In preparation.*

Mulloney, B., Acevedo, L.D. & Bradbury, A.J. (1987) Modulation of the crayfish swimmeret rhythm by octopamine and the neuropeptide proctolin. *J. Neurophysiol.* **58**:584-597.

Nja, A. & Walloe, L. (1975) Reflex inhibition of the slowly adapting stretch receptors in the intact abdomen of the crayfish. *Acta Physiol. Scand.* **94**:177-183.

Page, C.H. & Sokolove, P.G. (1972) Crayfish muscle receptor organ: role in regulation of postural flexion. *Science* **175**:647-650.
Parsons, D.W. & Macmillan, D.L. (1989) The effect of carbon monoxide on the function of a crustacean sensory receptor is no different to the effect of hypoxia. *In press.*
Pasztor, V.M. & Macmillan, D.L. (1988) Diverse modulatory effects of proctolin, FRMF-amide, octopamine and 5-HT on crayfish mechanoreceptors. *Soc. Neurosci. Abs.* **14:**153.16.
Pasztor, V.M. & Macmillan, D.L. (1989) Species and organ specificity in the response of crustacean primary sensory receptors to neuromodulators. *In preparation.*
Piantodosi, C.A. (1987) Carbon monoxide, oxygen transport, and oxygen metabolism. *J. Hyperbaric. Med.* **2**:27-44.
Pilgrim, R.L.C. (1960) Muscle receptor organs in some decapod Crustacea. *Comp. Biochem. Physiol.* **1**:248-257.
Sandler, M. (1980) *Psychopharmacology of Alcohol.* New York: Raven.
Sokolove, P.G. (1973) Crayfish stretch receptor and motor unit behavior during abdominal extensions. *J. Comp. Physiol.* **84**:251-266.
Wiersma, C.A.G., Furshpan, E. & Florey, E. (1953) Physiological and pharmacological observations on muscle receptor organs of the crayfish, *Cambarus clarkii* Girard. *J. exp. Biol.* **30**:136-150.

Frontiers in Crustacean Neurobiology
Advances in Life Sciences

CELLULAR BASIS OF MECHANICAL TRANSDUCTION IN THE ABDOMINAL STRETCH RECEPTOR OF THE CRAYFISH

Christian Erxleben

Department of Biology, University of Konstanz, Postfach 5560, D7750 Konstanz, Federal Republic of Germany

SUMMARY

Current passing through single stretch-activated ion channels was studied on the soma and primary dendrites of stretch receptor neurons of the crayfish *Orconectes limosus*. When the membrane of the patch was deformed by applying suction to the pipette, a marked nonlinear increase in single channel activity was observed. Two classes of mechanically gated channels were identified with similar conductance properties but different voltage range of activation and different sensitivity to membrane tension. The first type showed strong inward rectification and responded only weakly to membrane tension. The second type was largely voltage independent and more sensitive to membrane tension with an average value of 5.6 ± 2.2 (S.D., n=5) mm Hg for an e-fold change in suction. This channel was permeable to mono- and divalent cations. Current-voltage relationships were linear with slope conductances of 71 ± 11 (S.D., n=3) pS for K^+, 50 ± 7.4 (n=5) pS for Na^+, and 23 pS for Ca^{++}. The data suggest that this (second) channel is responsible for the mechanotransduction process in the stretch receptor neuron.

INTRODUCTION

Ever since the fundamental physiological properties of the abdominal stretch receptor organ of the crayfish were determined by Wiersma et al. (1953), this preparation has proven to be a useful model system for mechanoreception. The receptor organ is easily accessible and the neuron large enough for intracellular recordings. This makes it an ideal preparation to study the steps involved in the transformation of mechanical energy into a series of action potentials. Thus, the relationships between muscle tension, the generator potential and spike frequency, as well as mechanical filter properties and adaptation phenomena have been well characterized (see: Terzuolo and Knox, 1971).

For the initial step of transduction -the transformation of mechanical deformation into a receptor current- various mechanisms have been considered. Among those are: 1. changes in membrane capacity analogous to a 'condenser microphone' (Katz, 1951), 2. electrohydraulic excitability with the membrane acting as a 'wet piezoelectric device' (Teorell, 1971), and, 3. transduction by permeability changes due to the opening of ionic channels (Corey and Hudspeth, 1983, Edwards, 1983). The notion of mechanically gated ion channels was supported by the discovery of ion channels in the membrane of tissue-cultured skeletal muscle that respond to membrane tension (Guharay and Sachs 1984, Brehm et al. 1984). Similar types of stretch-activated channels were subsequently found in a variety of cells from plants, animal tissue and in bacteria (see: Sachs, 1988), but evidence for stretch-activated channels in a mechanoreceptor was lacking. Recently, we demonstrated mechanically gated channels in the abdominal stretch receptor neuron of the crayfish (Erxleben and Florey, 1988, Erxleben 1989). Some properties of these channels and their involvement in the transduction process and are presented in this paper.

METHODS

Receptor organs, consisting of a fast and slowly adapting receptor cell and the corresponding muscle fibers (Alexandrowicz, 1951), were isolated from the 2nd to 5th abdominal segments of Orconectes limosus. The preparation was pinned at the approximate in-situ length in a Sylgard 184 (Dow Corning) lined experimental chamber and submerged in a saline of 195mM NaCl, 5.4mM KCl, 13.5mM $CaCl_2$ and 2.6mM $MgCl_2$ with the pH adjusted to 7.4. Experiments were performed at ambient temperature (20 - 24°C).

To obtain Giga-Ohm seals, the preparations were treated locally with protease (10 mg/ml, type XIV Sigma). A polished pipette of about 25 μm opening was filled with saline containing protease and was positioned onto the receptor cell. An exposure of 5-10 minutes, depending on the extent of connective tissue, was sufficient to make the surface accessible for patch clamp recordings.

Single-channel currents were recorded with an EPC-7 (List Electronic) patch clamp amplifier. Recording techniques were those of Hamill et al. (1981). Membrane tension was controlled via a 100 μl syringe connected to the patch electrode holder and a calibrated pressure transducer (Hugo Sachs Elektronik). Data were either stored on magnetic tape or directly digitized by a 12 bit A/D converter (1401 labinterface, CED Cambridge) in connection with a PC (Tandon PCA 40).

RESULTS

Determination of the patch recording site. As the stretch receptor neuron is extensively covered by glial type cells (Tao-Cheng et al. 1981) it was crucial to determine whether patches were from such glial cells or from the receptor neuron itself. Ninety to 95% of all patches typically showed a voltage independent K^+ channel. In the whole-cell current-clamp mode obtained by rupturing the patch by a strong suction pulse on the pipette, the cells were found to be electrically inexcitable. These patches were thus determined to be from the glial cells.

Patches on the neuron were identified by the following criteria 1. In spontaneously active neurons, capacitive components of action potentials could be observed in the cell-attached configuration. 2. In the whole-cell mode, the corresponding intracellular action potentials could be recorded.

Increase in channel activity with suction. During seal formation, it became apparent that patches on the neuron contained channels which responded to suction on the pipette (fig. 1). Two types of stretch-activated channels were observed. They were indistinguishable on the basis of their ion selectivity or single channel conductance but differed in their sensitivity to membrane deformation and voltage range of activation.

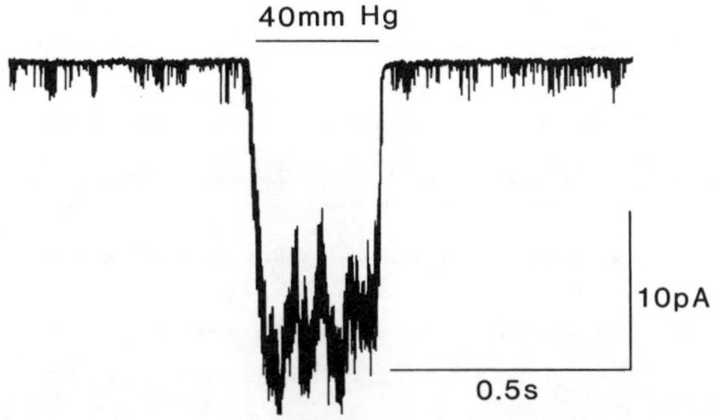

Fig. 1. Activation of an inward current by negative pressure. Cell attached patch with high K^+ solution in the pipette, patch potential at cell membrane potential. During the time indicated, suction was applied to the pipette. (from Erxleben, 1989)

The first type of channel was virtually inactive in the absence of suction to the pipette and showed at most a few bursts per minute. The probability of the channel being open increased with hyperpolarization. Because of its voltage range of activation and its rather low channel density the contribution of this channel to the generator current is expected to be small (Erxleben, 1989). It is therefore not discussed any further.

The second type of channel showed a weak positive voltage dependence and its average basal activity in the absence of suction was about an order of magnitude higher than that of the other channel. In general, a large number of channels were present in the patch.

Other types of channels, such as a delayed-rectifying K+ channel which was sometimes present in the same patch as the stretch-activated channels, did not respond to suction. In one particular experiment, the open probability of the stretch-activated channel increased some 55 fold from P_O= 0.0013 to P_O= 0.0718 while changing from 0 mm Hg suction to -21 mm Hg. In contrast, the open probability of the voltage-dependent K^+

channel did not change significantly (P_O= 0.28 at 0 mm Hg, P_O= 0.26 at -21 mm Hg). Furthermore, patches that originated from the glial cells never showed pressure sensitive channels.

Relationship between membrane tension and open-probability. Whereas the general effect of an increase in negative pressure is best demonstrated in a recording with many channels (fig. 1), patches with few, preferably just one channel are suited for a more quantitative description of the tension vs. open-probability relationship. For this purpose, activity of the stretch-activated channels was recorded over periods of several minutes at different levels of constant suction (Fig. 2).

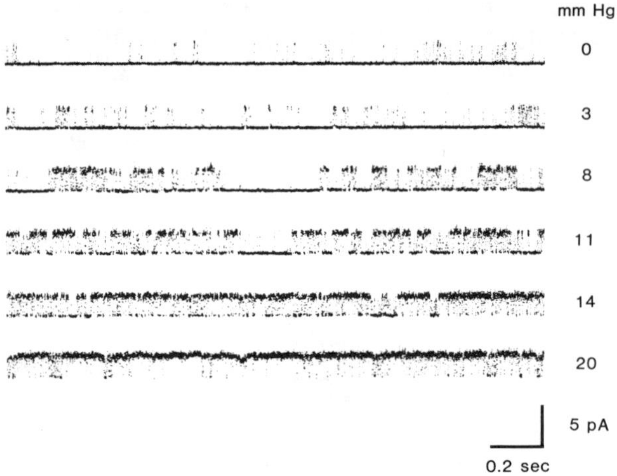

Fig. 2. Unitary currents through stretch-activated channels. Data from cell-attached patches with normal saline in the pipette. Holding potential was at the cell's resting potential. Nonconsecutive traces during constant suction levels as indicated. Inward current is shown as upward deflection.

With increasing suction, channel activity increased in a nonlinear fashion, reaching saturation at some 25 mm Hg (Fig. 3). At constant suction, mean channel activity remained constant. While the absolute open-probabilities varied between patches, the pressure sensitivities were remarkably similar. Sensitivities were calculated from a maximum likelihood fit to the data with Boltzmann type curves of the form:

(1) $$P_O = 1/[1+k*\exp(-\Theta*(p-p0)2)]$$

k is a pressure-insensitive term and Θ the sensitivity. p denotes the applied negative pressure in cm Hg an p0 is an offset pressure term. p0 is introduced to account for the preconditioning of the patch caused by the formation of the seal. The average sensitivity Θ was 0.711 ± 0.73 cm Hg^{-2} (n=5).

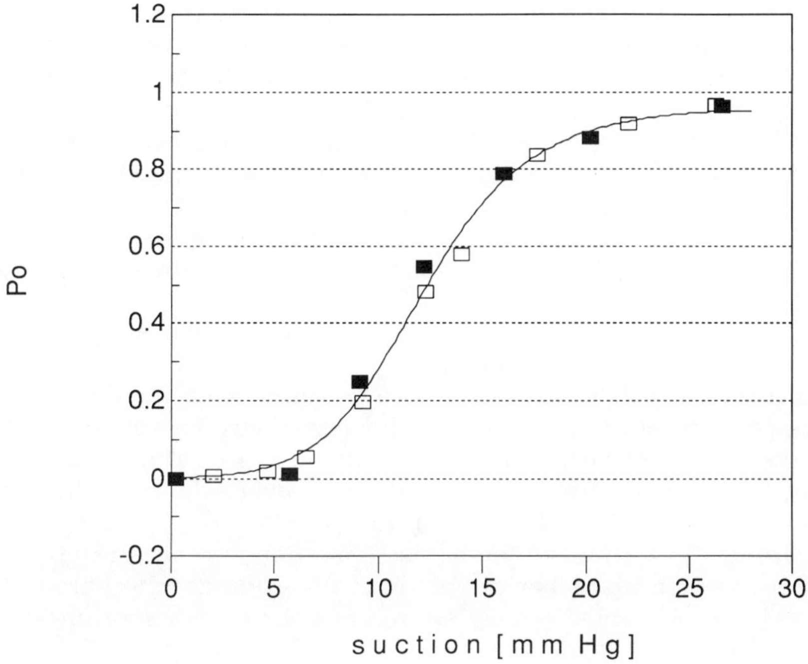

Fig. 3. Open probability vs. suction relationship of the stretch-activated channel. P_o is plotted vs. negative pressure. Open and closed squares are data from two series of measurements from the same cell-attached patch. The line is a fit to the datapoints with equ. 1. Parameters of the fit are:k=0.05, Θ=1.13 (cm $Hg)^{-2}$ and p0=2.87 cm Hg. Holding potential was at the cell's resting potential, high Na^+ solution in the pipette.

Single channel conductances. Voltage clamp data of the stretch-induced receptor current in the crayfish stretch receptor (Edwards et al. 1981) suggest that the mechanotransduction channel should not only be permeable to Na^+, the main charge carrier under physiological conditions, but also to K^+ and divalent cations such as Ca^{++}. Therefore, the ion-selectivity for the putative transduction channel was determined in cell-attached patches where Na+ in the pipette solution was substituted for by either K^+ or Ca^{++}. Both of these cations were also able to carry current through the channel. Current-voltage relationships were approximately linear. The slope conductance for K^+ was found to be highest with 71 ± 11 pS (S.D., n = 3) followed by 50 ± 7.4 pS (n = 5) for Na^+ and 23 pS for Ca^{++}.

Assuming an average resting potential of -70 mV, the extrapolated reversal potentials were about 0 mV.

DISCUSSION

The stretch-activated cation channel described in this paper fulfills the criteria for the mechanotranduction channel which has been postulated for crayfish stretch receptor neurons (Edwards, 1983). Besides the obvious sensitivity to membrane stretch, it has the low cation selectivity previously established for the receptor current in voltage clamp experiments (Brown et al. 1978; Edwards et al. 1981). The permeability of the channel for Ca^{++} is of particular interest in view of the involvement of a Ca-activated K^{+} current in the dynamic phase of the adaptation process (Ottoson and Swerup, 1985). The high external Ca^{++} concentration in the physiological saline (13.5 mM) is likely to lead to Ca^{++} influx through the SA channel and to subsequent activation of Ca^{++}-sensitive K^{+} channels. Adaptation at the single-channel level, such that the open probability decreases during sustained membrane deformation, can be excluded from the data.

It is tempting to speculate that the density of stretch-activated channels matches that of the stretch induced current measured under voltage clamp (Brown et al. 1978). The current data, however, do not allow such a comparison since the patches were from the soma of the receptor cell or, at best, from the primary dendrites. The density of stretch-activated channels is likely to be higher at the dendritic endings, the part of the cell which is actually deformed during stretch of the receptor neuron.

Channel gating. Two models have been proposed to account for the gating of mechano-tranduction channels. One is based on the kinetics of the receptor current of hair cells (Corey and Hudspeth, 1983) and a second on data from single stretch-activated channels in cultured chick skeletal muscle (Guharay and Sachs, 1984). While the former model views the stretch-activated channel as a displacement sensor with the gating energy depending on the first order of displacement, the latter assumes the gating energy to be a function of the membrane tension. As a consequence the models predict a linear relationship between either pressure or (pressure)2 and the natural logarithm of the open probability.

The data on the stretch-activated channels in the stretch receptor neuron presented here were fitted by the squared model. It should be mentioned, however, that in most experiments (6 out of 10) no significant difference was found between the two models. The difficulty of clearly distinguishing between the two models might result from nonstationary behavior of the channels which produces sufficient scatter. For perhaps the same reason, the issue of a linear or squared dependence on pressure is controversial in the literature (see Sachs, 1988).

This work was supported by the DFG (SFB 156/B1).

REFERENCES

Alexandrowicz, J.S. (1951) Muscle receptor organs in the abdomen of Homarus vulgaris and Palinurus vulgaris. Quart. J. microscop. Sci. 92:163-200.

Brehm, P., Kullberg, R. and Moody-Corbett, F. (1984) Properties of non-junctional acetylcholine receptor channels on innervated muscle of Xenopus laevis. J. Physiol. **350:**631-648.

Brown, H.M., Ottoson, D. and Rydqvist, B. (1978) Crayfish stretch receptor: an investigation with voltage-clamp and ion-sensitive electrodes. J. Physiol. **284**:155-179.

Corey, D.P. and Hudspeth, A.J. (1983) Kinetics of the receptor current in bullfrog saccular hair cells. J. Neurosci. **3:**962-976.

Edwards, C. 1983. The ionic mechanisms underlying the receptor potential in mechanoreceptors. In The Physiology of Excitable Cells (ed. A.D. Grinnell & W.J. Moody, Jr.). New York. Alan R. Liss, Inc. 497-503.

Edwards, C., Ottoson, D., Rydqvist, B. and Swerup, C. (1981) The permeability of the transducer membrane of the crayfish stretch receptor to calcium and to other divalent cations. Neurosci. **6**:1455-1460.

Erxleben, C. (1989) Stretch-activated current through single ion channels in the abdominal stretch receptor organ of the crayfish. J. gen. Physiol. in press.

Erxleben, C. and E. Florey. (1988) Stretch-activated single ion channels in the crayfish stretch receptor neuron. Pflüger's Arch. **411:**R155.

Guharay, F. and Sachs,F. (1984) Stretch-activated single ion channel currents in tissue-cultured embryonic chick skeletal muscle. J. Physiol. **352**:685-701.

Hamill, O.P.,Marty, A., Neher, E., Sakmann, B. and Sigworth, F. (1981) Improved patch-clamp techniques for high-resolution current recordings from cells and cell-free patches. Pflüger's Arch. **391**:85-100.

Katz, B. (1950) Depolarization of sensory terminals and the initiation of impulses in the muscle spindle. J. Physiol. **111:** 261-282.

Ottoson, D. and Swerup, C. (1985) Ionic dependence of early adaptation in the crustacean stretch receptor. Brain Res. **336:**1-8.

Sachs, F. (1988) Mechanical transduction in biological systems. CRC Crit. Rev. Biomed. Eng. 16:141-169.

Tao-Cheng, J-H., Hirosawa, K. and Nakajima, Y. (1981) Ultrastructure of the crayfish stretch receptor in relation to its function. J. comp. Neurol. **200**:1-21.

Teorell, T. (1971) A biophysical analysis of mechano-electrical transduction. In Principles of receptor physiology, (ed. W.R. Loewenstein) pp. 291-339. Berlin: Springer.

Terzuolo, C.A. and Knox, C.K. (1971) Static and dynamic behavior of the stretch receptor organ of crustacea. In Principles of receptor physiology, (ed. W.R. Loewenstein) pp. 500-522. Berlin: Springer.

Wiersma, C.A.G., Furshpan, E. and Florey, E. (1953) Physiological and pharmacological observations on muscle receptor organs of the crayfish, *Cambarus clarkii* Girard. J. exp. Biol. **30:** 136-150.

EXTERNAL SENSORS AND THE DORSAL ORGAN OF CRUSTACEA

M.S.Laverack

Gatty Marine Laboratory, St Andrews, Scotland KY16 8LB

SUMMARY

The Crustacea , along with other arthropods, provide ideal material for a study of sense organs. The dorsal organ is used as an example of a recently recognised sensor offering new opportunities for research.

INTRODUCTION

Crustacea usually possess a number of instars or larval stages, often juveniles of adult form but immature, and adults that may grow continuously over a protracted lifetime or grow to a finite size. Throughout this period, often of many years duration, the animals add sensory apparatus and possibly also lose some components (Laverack 1988). There is opportunity therefore to

1. study sensors in larval animals, that may be the primary portions of a long lasting system or alternatively may exist only for the lifetime of the larva and then disappear (e.g. after site selection in barnacles or of a host in parasitic forms)
2. investigate the individual discrete sense organs with one or few neurone components in very localised places
3. examine the addition and differentiation of new sensors during the life of the animal (and also of course during regeneration where this takes place)
4. determine the impact of additional sensory neurones on the central nervous system with the development of new synapses, and consequent alterations in neuropile arrangements.
5. isolate and characterise individual sensors within sensillae.

The Crustacea possess a finite number of sites, both internal and external, at which sensory cells can be identified but the expectation that all may eventually be characterised may, however, be more apparent than real . Various difficulties arise in any attempt at generalisation and the extreme variability in number of moults , larval stages, and final sizes means that careful consideration has to be given to life cycles and the age of the animal at the time of examination (Laverack 1988). Sensors that can be identified and typified at the early developmental stages (e.g.nauplius, zoea) and those found in the juveniles and adults may be very different.

Sensors may be classified in relatively few categories but the numbers of each type varies greatly from place to place on the body, and from sense organ to sense organ. Difficulties of interpretation and discrimination arise when more than one type of sensor is located within a single sense organ or sensillum. There are also problems when sensors are present at one stage and not another. Function is still not easily determined from a study of structure alone, but neither is it easy to detect which nerve cell does what in a multiply innervated organ just on the basis of physiological response. We have little information for example on the site of magnetic perception in Crustacea (Lohmann 1987).

In the past a number of studies have reported the apertures found in crustacean exoskeletons (.e.g.Mauchline and Ballantyne 1975 ; Mauchline 1977) after removal of soft tissues. Such pores, often species specific in pattern, represent the sum of numerous glands that exude material on to the surface plus many surface setae. Not all setae are innervated (Bender, Gnatzy and Tautz 1984). Therefore although a map of pores may be informative as to possible sensory input areas these have to be confirmed by other methods such as scanning electron microscopy, histology, transmission EM, electrophysiology etc.

The majority of Crustacea are aquatic, being freshwater, marine, estuarine and littoral creatures with few representatives living truly terrestrial lives. In most cases, therefore , consideration has to be given to the chemical and physical conditions surrounding the animal and which are monitored by the sensory apparatus (Atema 1984,1988). Little work has focussed on the implications of ionic composition and gaseous content for example, and how these might be monitored. Changes in respiratory rates and reponses to alterations in gaseous regimes are well documented (Taylor 1984 ; Taylor and Whiteley 1989) but the sensors that detect change are not yet recognised.

Among the many and varied types of receptor that exist is a characteristic array on the dorsal surface. Although noted by Barrientos and Laverack (1984) and Laverack and Barrientos (1985) as being undescribed it has become obvious that this organ has been seen in a number of crustacean orders. It exists in a rather uniform fashion in copepods (Nishida 1989), euphausids (Mauchline 1977), decapod larvae (Pohle and Telford 1981 , Laverack and Barrientos 1984) shrimps (Laverack and Crombie 1987), mysids (Mauchline 1977, Schram 1986), Notostraca (Schram 1986), Cladocera (Frey 1959). Even pentastomids (Osche 1963) have a dorsal organ. A dorsal organ, or something very similar, has also been described for the fossil Trilobita (Stormer 1931) and Kazachartha (Schram 1986). Whether this organ is ubiquitous and homologous throughout the Crustacea , however, remains to be seen.

Known distribution of the organ is patchy ; in Decapoda the Reptantia (Palinura, Astacida, Brachyura etc) possess the organ in larval stages (see

Pohle and Telford 1981 ; Laverack and Barrientos 1985, Nishida and Kittaka pers comm). Amongst Natantia (*Crangon crangon,* Laverack and Crombie 1988) the organ is found at all stages including adults. In copepods Nishida (1989) reports it's presence only in some males and associates it with mate selection.

The basic organisation of the dorsal organ is of a glandular cell (single in all known cases except copepods) in a group with several (often four) sensory areas, arranged in a characteristic fashion (Fig 1 A, D, E) . Although variations (in number of components and in display) may be found on this pattern the central gland and the peripheral sensors seem consistent.

The glandular region of copepods is composed of two cells with external secretions, and in one case association with the cuticle (Nishida 1989). In pentastomids the dorsal organ gland also appears secretory (Osche 1963). In Decapoda the glandular cell has quite a different structure, possessing a brush-border microvillous lumen suggestive of an ion regulating cell (Laverack and Barrientos 1986; Laverack and Ritchie unpublished). So far as is known there is no connection between this cell and the adjacent sensory cells, but the possibility remains of a functional link.

The sensory apparatus is of great interest and intriguing anatomy. Very little fine structural information has yet accrued but two major lines have been followed. Scanning EM work shows areas of flattened cuticle that may or may not possess pores or nipples in the centre (Pohle and Telford 1981, Nishida 1989, Laverack 1988, Laverack and Crombie 1988). On such findings it has been proposed that these are chemoreceptors. It has not been clear, however, that the pores penetrate the cuticle, nor that 'nipples' (Fig 1 B, F) are exposed dendrites from within. Nishida (1989) finds that the sensory ending (only one in male copepods) forms an expanded plate at the surface with a thin cuticular layer across the dendritic ending. Laverack and Barrientos (1985) and Laverack (1988) comment on the 'spongy' nature of the cuticle in the larval representatives of Decapoda.

RESULTS

Recent investigations by Laverack and Ritchie (unpublished but see succeeding figures) have concentrated on the system in *Crangon crangon*, a species in which the organ persists throughout life and which demonstrates 'nipples' at the plate. Figure 2 A - F show some details of these organs, in which the major features are the

i. electron dense flocculent material that surrounds the dendritic endings,

ii. the extremely long and somewhat eccentric rootlets central to the very short ciliary body of the sensory cell

iii. the expanded and inflated appearance of the dendritic endings in the cuticular pocket below the surface,

iv. the fine extensions of the dendrites into a small projection of the cuticle , termed the 'nipple', but with no detectable exposure to the external medium,

v. the very thin (approx 0.21μ) cuticular covering lying above the dendrites vi.there are four dendrites in all.

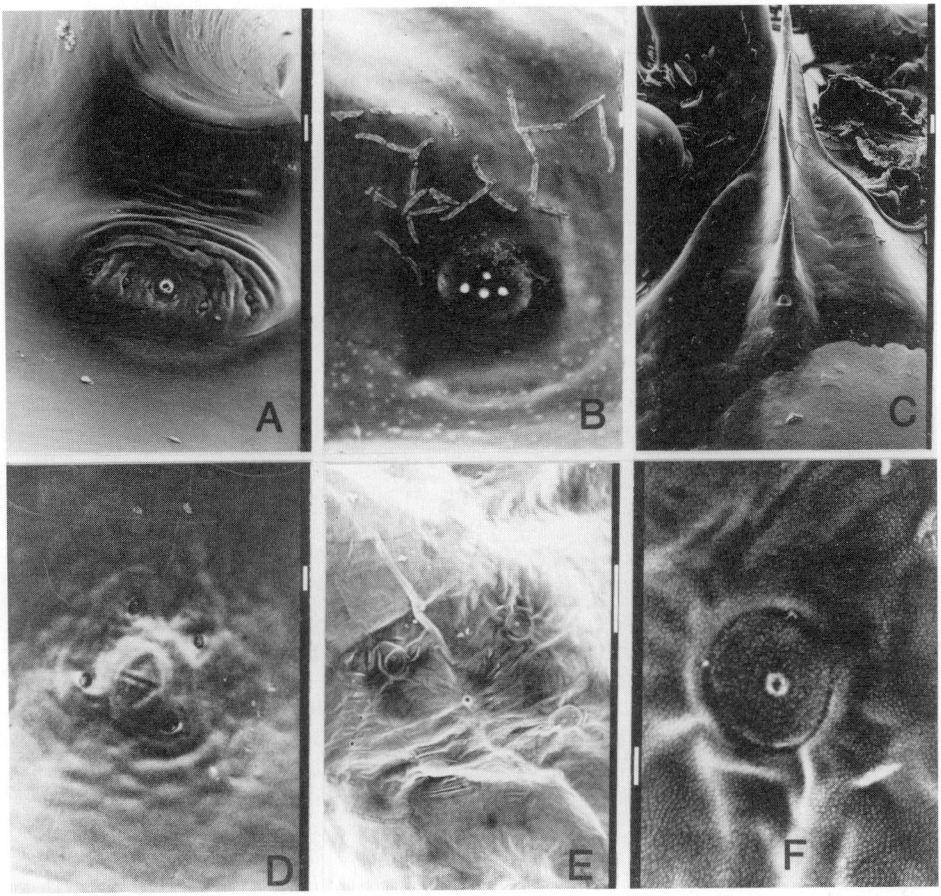

Fig. 1
1. Dorsal organ from various Crustacea
A. *Crangon crangon* ; the whole organ that resides ventral to the dorsal rostral spine.
B. *Crangon crangon* ; a sensory plaque together with the four prominent nipples protruding from the surface.
C. *Thoralus cranchii* ; dorsal organ lies behind the rostral spines
D. *Panulirus argus* ; dorsal organ of the stage 10 phyllosoma larva
E. *Sesarma (=Aratus) elegans* ; the whole organ
F. *Sesarma (= Aratus) elegans* ; detail of a sensory plaque.
Scales ; A,C,D,E bar= 10 μ ; B, F bar = 1 μ

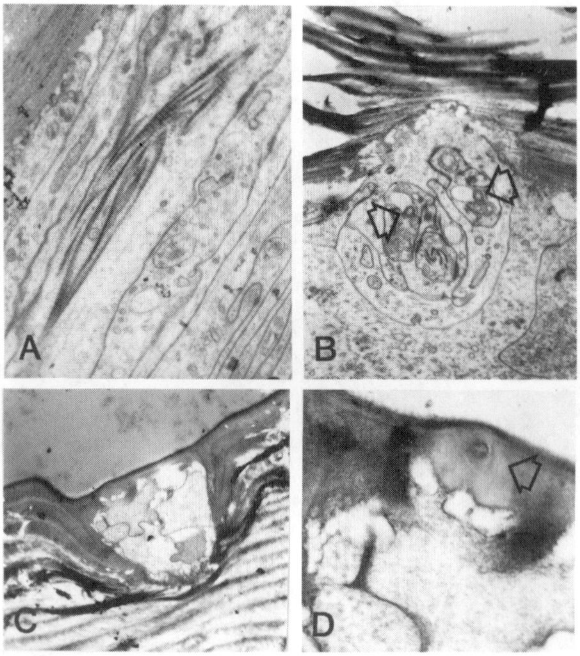

Fig. 2. *Crangon crangon*
Transmission electron micrographs of the dorsal organ
A. T.S. primary dendrite showing axial rootlet of the cilium
B. the ciliary body region (arrows)
C. the four distal dendritic regions, showing the lumen of the cuticular cavity surrounding the expanded balloon-like dendrites and the extreme thinness of the cuticle at the surface of the plaque,
D. the distal region of the dendrites showing (arrow) the small nipple that is visible in SEM views of the external surface.

DISCUSSION

These findings do not resolve the difficulties of interpretation of function and no physiology has yet been carried out. The likelihood of two real alternatives still exist though my personal view has shifted in emphasis.

1. A chemoreceptive function may be indicated by
   A. the presence of a superficial plate
   B. the possible penetration of the plate by dendritic endings
   C. by the thin nature of the covering cuticle that may be highly permeable to external sapient substances
   D. by the occasional presence of pores
   E. by the ecological significance of such organs occurring only in male copepods
2. A mechanoreceptive function may be shown by

A.the apparent 'stretching' of the thin cuticle across a circular aperture as in a tympanum
B. the extreme thinness of the plate, in some examples, and the 'spongy'nature of others, possibly allowing flexibility
C. the linkage of dendrites to the plate
D. the long rootlet structure typical of many mechanoreceptors (Altner and Prillinger 1980)
E. the expanded appearance of the dendrites within a rigid capsule formed by the surrounding cuticle
F. the flocculent substance investing the dendrites

My initial thoughts on this organ were in terms of a specific chemoreceptor, and this is the proposal also made by Nishida (1989) . The TEM analysis of *Crangon crangon*, however, makes the alternative more attractive. Various reports exist in the literature of a pressure sense in Crustacea. Swimming in response to alterations in hydrostatic pressure (depth) has been observed in a number of species (e.g.Rice 1964). One or two attempts to explain such sensitivity have been made (e g Digby 1961) but without convincing evidence as to physiology or anatomy of presumptive sensors (Digby 1964).

The innervation of the sensory plaques in decapods shows that the sensory neurones end in modified cuticle (either 'spongy' or very thin), are specialised (ramifying in larval cuticle, or inflated in shrimp and copepod), with structures associated with mechanoreception internally (long rootlets) and a cup shaped cuticular lumen surrounding the entire apparatus. If one assumes that modified cuticle can be deformed by external pressure (as in a tambour, or a compressible resilient sponge) this may be sufficient to stimulate the attendant sense cells. There is no direct evidence for this yet but it is being actively sought. If this hypothesis is correct it may help to explain a hitherto "mysterious " sense in Crustacea.

REFERENCES

Altner, H. and Prillinger, L. (1980) Ultrastructure of invertebrate chemo-, thermo- and hygro-receptors and its functional significance. Int .Rev. Cytol. 67 : 69 -132.

Atema, J. (1984) Chemoreception in the sea; adaptations of chemoreceptors and behaviour to aquatic stimulus conditions. Symp.Soc.Exp. Biol.39 : 387 - 423

Atema, J. (1988) Distribution of chemicals in the sea. In Sensory Biology of Aquatic animals . (Eds J. Atema, R.R.Fay , A.N.Popper and W.N.Tavolga) pp 29 - 56 . Springer-Verlag, New York

Barrientos ,Y. and Laverack, M.S. (1985) The larval crustacean dorsal organ and its relationship to the trilobite median tubercle. Lethaia 19, : 309 - 313

Bender, M., Gnatzy,W.and Tautz, J.(1984) The antennal feathered hairs in the crayfish ; a non-innervated stimulus transmitting system. J. Comp. Physiol . 154A : 45 - 47

Calman,W. T. (1906) Crustacea. In a Treatise on Zoology ,Vol 9 (Ed Ray Lankester). A and C Black, London

Digby, P.S.B. (1961) Mechanism of sensitivity of hydrostatic pressure in the prawn *Palaemonetes varians* Leach. Nature 191 : 366 - 368
Digby, P.S.B. (1964) Semi-conduction and electrode processes in biological material 1 Crustacea and certain softbodied forms. Proc. Roy.Soc. Lond. B 161 : 504 - 525
Frey, D.G. (1959) Phylogenetic significance of head pores of the Chydoridae. Int.Rev. ges. Hydrobiol. 44 : 27 -50
Hanstrom, B. (1947) The brain, sense organs, and the incretory organs of the head in Crustacea Malacostraca. Lunds Univ. Arssk 2 (43) Nr 9
Laverack, M.S. (1988) Larval locomotion, sensors, growth and their implication for the nervous system. Symp.Zoo.Soc.Lond. 59 :103 - 122
Laverack, M. S. and Barrientos, Y. (1986) Sensory and other superficial structures in living marine Crustacea. Trans.Roy.Soc.Edin. Earth Sci. 76 : 123 - 136
Laverack, M.S.and Crombie,B. (1988) The dorsal organ of the natantian crustaceans *Crangon crangon, Thoralus cranchi* and *Pandalus montagui* ; an SEM study. Zool.Anz 220 :17 - 24
Lohmann, K. (1987) Geomagnetic field detection by the Western Atlantic spiny lobster, *Panulirus argus.* Mar. Behav. Physiol. 12 :1 -17
Mauchline, J.(1977) The integumental sensilla and the glands of pelagic Crustacea. J. Mar. Biol. Ass.,U.K. 57 : 973 - 994
Mauchline, J. and Ballantyne, A.R.S. (1975) The integumental organs of amphipods. J.Mar.Biol.Ass.,U.K.55 : 345 - 355
Nishida, S. (1989) Distribution, structure and importance of the cephalic dorsal hump; a new sensory organ in calanoid copepods. Marine Biol. 101 : 173 - 185
Osche, G. (1963) Die systematische stellung und phylogenie der Pentastomidea, embryologische und Vergleichende anatomische studien an *Reigenhardia sternae.* Z. Morph. Okol. Tiere. 52 : 487 - 596
Pohle, G. and Telford, M. (1981) The larval development of *Dissodactylus crinitichelis* Moreira 1901 (Brachyura, Pinnotheridae) in laboratory culture. Bull. Mar. Sci., 31 : 753 - 773
Rice, A.L.(1964) Observations on the effects of changes of hydrostatic pressure on the behaviour of some marine animals. J. Mar. Biol. Ass., U. K. 44 :163 - 175
Schram, F. (1986) Crustacea. Oxford Univ. Press , Oxford. 606pp.
Størmer, L. (1930) Scandinavian Trinucleidae, with special reference to Norwegian species and varieties. Norsk Videns - Akad Oslo Mat. Naturv. Kl **4** 1-111
Taylor, E.W. (1984) Control and coordination of gill ventilation and perfusion. Symp. Soc. Exp. Biol. 39 : 123-161
Taylor,E.W. and Whiteley, N. M. (1989) Oxygen transport and acid-base balance in the haemolymph of the lobster *Homarus gammarus,* during aerial exposure and resubmersion. J. Exp. Biol. 144 : 417 - 436

Frontiers in Crustacean Neurobiology
Advances in Life Sciences

RECORDING FROM SENSORY CELLS IN THE STATOCYST OF *ASTACUS*

Gunter Lemmnitz* and Heinz G. Wolff**

* Zoologisches Institut und Zoologisches Museum, Universität Hamburg, Martin-Luther-King-Platz 3, D-2000 Hamburg 13, Federal Republic of Germany
** Zoologisches Institut der TU Braunschweig, Physiologie, Pockelsstr. 10a, D-3300 Braunschweig, Federal Republic of Germany

SUMMARY

In the statocyst of *Astacus leptodactylus*two sets of sensory hairs on the ventral floor were compared with regard to the directionality of their receptor responses: the crescent-shaped hair group in the middle region of the cyst (crescent group) and the transversally arranged single row of hairs in the posterior region of the statocyst (transverse group). Whereas all transverse-group hairs are morphologically polarized to the posterior, the crescent-group hairs are polarized mainly to the anterior, to the medial and to the posterior - depending on their location within the crescent. Deflection of transverse-group hairs to the posterior as well as deflection of many crescent-group hairs to the medial caused a distinct and long-lasting tonic discharge in the statocyst nerve. It was shown that different tilts during circular rotation of the statocyst about its roll axis can be well discriminated by responses of many crescent-group receptors. In contrast, a similar discrimination of tilts about the pitch axis could be achieved only by responses of transverse-group cells.

INTRODUCTION

The decapod crustaceans can orient themselves well with respect to gravity. This ability is achieved by statocyst input which controls diverse responses like uropod steering movements or compensatory eyestalk movements (Yoshino et al., 1982; Stein, 1975). In the crayfish statocyst, the sensory hairs of two ventrally arranged sets of receptors extend into the cyst lumen and make contact with the statolith body (Prentiss, 1901; Panning, 1924; Takahata & Hisada, 1979): the approximately eighty hairs of the so-called crescent group, which form a semicircle on the lateral floor of the statocyst, and the aproximately nine hairs of the so-called transverse group, which form a single transversally arranged row in the posterior region of the cyst.

The crescent-group hairs are well-examined: Schöne & Steinbrecht (1968) found a morphological polarization of these hairs, recognizable by a fulcrum-like structure on one side of the hair base. Takahata & Hisada

(1979) showed, that in the *Procambarus* statocyst all these hair receptors are polarized towards the center of the crescent. The transverse group however was scarcely examined up to now. Furthermore, responses of differently arranged hair receptors in various regions of the statocyst to circular rotations were not known. In the present study, the polarization of transverse-group receptors as well as their responses to diverse tilts are examined and compared to the properties of different crescent-group receptors. An attempt is made to find out the function of the transverse group, which is lacking in other decapods like the lobster.

METHODS

Experiments were carried out on 15 individuals of the crayfish *Astacus leptodactylus*obtained commercially and maintained in laboratory tanks. For morphological studies, scanning electron microscope (SEM) photographs of the ventral statocyst floor and of single sensory hairs were made. For physiological experiments, the anterior part of the cephalothorax with a statocyst dorsally opened was secured in a chamber filled with ringer solution (modified according to Van Harrefeld, 1936). The chamber was then sealed round about, avoiding air bubbles.

During rotations 360° about the longitudinal (roll) and transverse (pitch) axis of the horizontally arranged statocyst, the receptor responses could be recorded from the medial (crescent group) and lateral (transverse group) bundle of the statocyst nerve using a suction electrode. Rotations were performed in steps of 45° with 3 r.p.m. Each 45° movement was followed by an intermission of 30 s. After the rotations the statolith was washed out. The following successive deflection of all sensory hairs of the statocyst floor with a glass needle allowed the localizing of those receptors responsible for the previously recorded response to rotations. The nerve activity and the stimulus signal (from a potentiometer or a waveform generator) were monitored on an oscilloscope and computer-analysed.

RESULTS

Morphological classification of sensory hairs. After removing the statolith the sensory hairs of the ventral statocyst floor were accessible (Fig.1). According to Schöne & Steinbrecht (1968), the location of the fulcrum-like structure within the hair base (Fig.2) and the bend of the hair shaft were used to determine the direction of morphological hair polarization. In the crescent group, all hairs seem to be polarized towards the center of the crescent. Closer examination of scanning electron micrographs however indicated an irregular polarization mainly in the anterior region (Fig. 3): Here many hairs are not polarized in a posterior direction, but in a more medial or lateral direction (arrows in Fig.3).

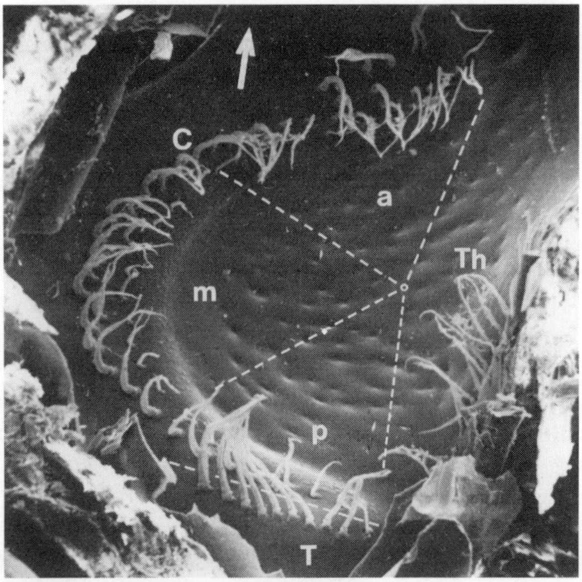

Fig. 1. Scanning electron micrograph of the ventral hair field of a left statocyst. Arrow: anterior direction. Broken lines: subdivision of the crescent group into an anterior (a), a middle (m) and a posterior (p) sector. Scale bar 500 µm C, crescent group; T, transverse group; Th, thread hairs (not involved in perception of gravity).

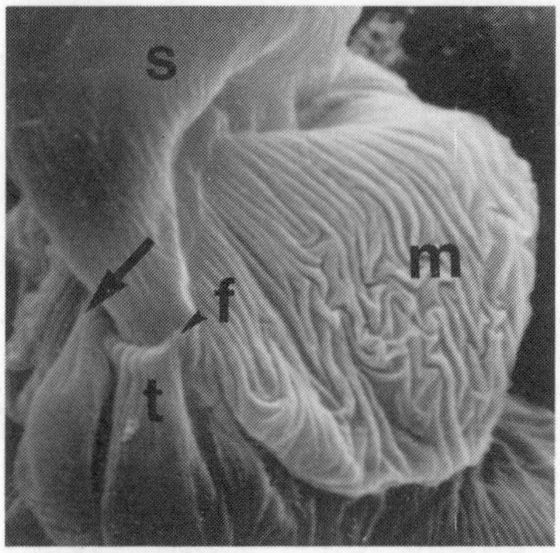

Fig. 2. Single base of a sensory hair (Scanning electron micrograph) The hair shaft (s) turns round a fulcrum (f), which is formed by a process of the shaft and the tooth (t) of the base. Scale bar 5 µm. m, membrane.The arrow indicates the direction of the morphological polarization.

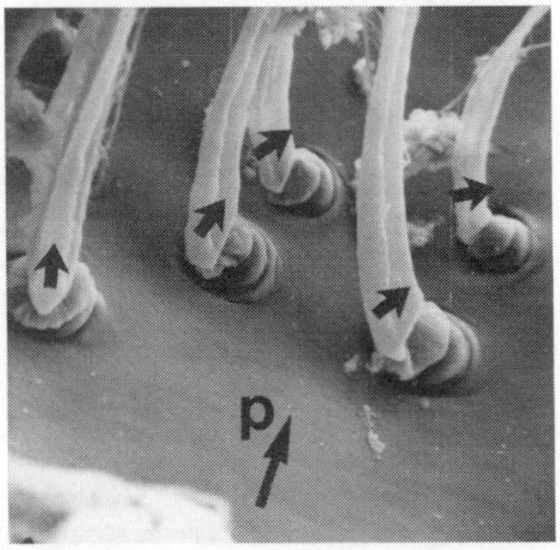

Fig. 3. Scanning electron micrograph of some hairs in the anterior sector of the crescent group. The hairs are polarized in different directions (short arrows). p, posterior direction.

Because of the semicircular hair arrangement, there is a continuous transition of the polarization in the crescent group. Nevertheless, it proved to be useful to subdivide this group roughly into three sectors: the anterior sector (Fig.1 "a"), within which the hairs are polarized to the posterior as well as to the more lateral and the more medial, the middle sector (Fig.1 "m"), where the hairs point mainly in a medial direction, and the posterior sector (Fig.1 "p"), where the hairs are polarized preferentially to the anterior. Within the transverse group, all hairs are longer than in the crescent group (up to 450 μm) and strictly polarized to the posterior. Thus this direction is much better represented in the transverse group than in the crescent group.

Physiological polarization of hair cells. Recordings from the lateral bundle of the statocyst nerve revealed that the responses of transverse-group cells are similar to the well-known activity of crescent-group receptors. If a single hair was artificially deflected by means of a glass needle, a tonic and/or phasic response occured (Fig.4). In most of the examined crescent-group cells, a mainly tonic response could be elicited by hair deflection either towards the center of the crescent or towards more medial directions (Fig.4A). Based on recordings from a large number of cells a distinct and long-lasting tonic response to posterior hair deflection was found only in transverse-group cells (Fig.4B).

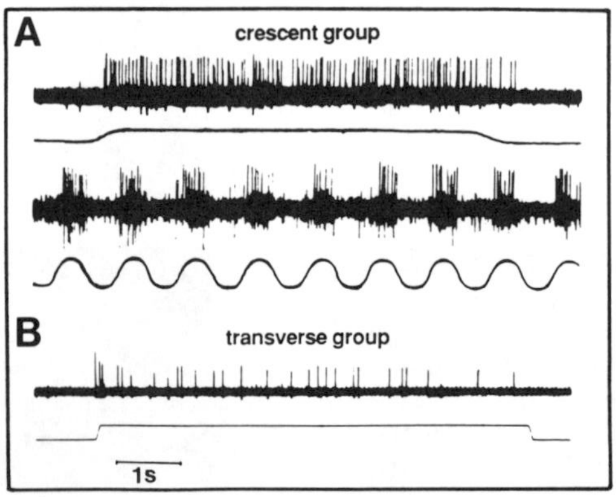

Fig. 4. Activity in the statocyst nerve (upper traces) in response to artificial deflection of single statocyst hairs (lower traces). Deflection amplitude: ca. 15°. (A) Responses from the anterior crescent sector to posterior-medial hair deflection. (B) Response of a transverse-group receptor to posterior hair deflection.

Responses of cells in different hair sectors to tilts. Stepwise 360° rotations elicited phasic and tonic responses in the statocyst nerve. Successive deflection of each of the sensory hairs after the rotations

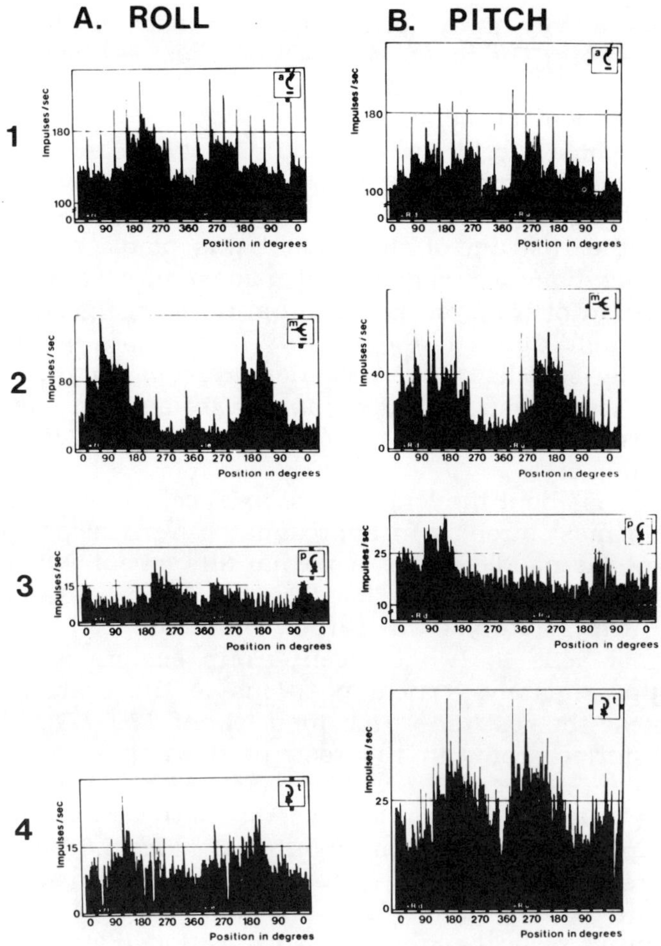

Fig. 5. Spike frequencies of responses to diverse tilts as a function of the degree of tilt. Each of the diagrams shows the activity from one of the hair field sectors in response to a clockwise and counterclockwise rotation in 45° steps. The hair field sectors are numbered 1-4 from anterior to posterior. Inset figures: scheme of the hair arrangement with rough location and main polarization of the involved receptors (arrow) and with the axis of rotation (beam). Broken line on the bottom: white parts reflect the stops at the diverse tilts, black parts the 45° rotations. (A) Rotation about the longitudinal axis of the statocyst. (B) Rotation about the transverse axis. a, anterior crescent sector; le, leftward rotation; m, middle crescent sector; p, posterior crescent sector; ri, rightward rotation; R.d., rotation starting with rostrum moving downwards; R.u., rotation starting with rostrum moving upwards; t, transverse group.

revealed, that this activity always originated from neighbouring cells of one of the hair field sectors. The tonic parts of the responses became visible in the intermission phases of the rotation. Thus they reflected only the tilts between the 45° rotations of the statocyst.

Two types of responses to tilts were found: One type showed a maximum tonic discharge in approximately vertical positions of the cyst, that means the statocyst was lying on its medial or on its lateral side, or - turning about the other axis - the rostrum of the animal was pointing downwards or upwards. The other type of response had a maximum activity in a more upside-down position of the cyst. A minimum discharge generally occured at tilt angles, which differed about 180° from those with maximum response. Especially in cells of the posterior crescent sector, the minimal activity was much lower than the activity in upright position (Fig.5:3). Other receptors like those of the anterior crescent sector lowered their discharge rate only slightly (Fig.5:1).

In case of rotations about the longitudinal axis, cells of all crescent-group sectors responded most strongly in approximately vertical positions of the statocyst: cells of the middle sector at medial tilts (about 90°, Figs.5,6:A2) and cells of the anterior and posterior sector at lateral tilts (about 270°, Figs.5,6:A1+A3). If the statocyst was turned about the transverse axis, the tonic responses of cells in two crescent-group sectors also reached a maximum in approximately vertical positions of the cyst: those of the anterior sector near the rostrum-up position (about 270°, Figs.5,6:B1) and those of the posterior sector in the rostrum-down position (about 90°, Figs.5,6:B3).

The examined cells of the middle sector however responded most strongly in the upside-down position (about 180°, Figs.5,6:B2). Recordings from the transverse-group cells also showed both types of responses: In the case of rolls about the longitudinal axis, the tonic parts of the frequencies reached a maximum near the upside-down position (Figs.5,6:A4). In the case of rotating about the pitch axis, the maximum occured in the rostrum-up position and a distinct minimum in the rostrum-down position (Figs.5,6:B4).

DISCUSSION

If a horizontally arranged crayfish is rotated about the roll or pitch axis, all sensory hairs inserted in the statolith mass are deflected in the same direction by statolith displacement. The elicited responses of the involved receptor cells sum up to a complex pattern which can be recorded from the statocyst nerve and even from statocyst interneurones in the ventral nerve cord (Takahata & Hisada, 1982). The contribution of each of the three neurons per sensory hair (Schöne & Steinbrecht, 1968) to the pattern is not clear. However, studies on the lobster (Patton, 1969) suggested that the phasic and tonic parts of the response are elicited by different receptors. We mainly have analysed the tonic activities occurring at different tilts because they seemed to be the only responses clearly related to the degree of tilt.

The responses to tilts depend not only on the axis the animal is turned about but also on the exact group of axons contained within the electrode. Since the registered nerve activity displayed in Fig.5 always originated from neighbouring cells of one of the defined hair field sectors, the responses could be correlated to a predicted movement of the hair shaft during the rotation.

Fig.6 summarizes schematically the tonic responses to tilts. Only receptors of the middle crescent sector and of the transverse group showed - depending on the axis of rotation - either a maximum activity in an upside-down position (Fig.6:B2,A4) or a maximum as well as a minimum activity in vertical positions of the statocyst (Fig.6:A2,B4). In the first case (maximum in upside-down position), the hairs were deflected perpendicularly to their polarization plane - eliciting a mainly phasic response. However, if the rotated statocyst approached its upside-down position, the hairs moved towards their polarization plane and the tonic parts of the responses increased. In the second case (maximum at vertical

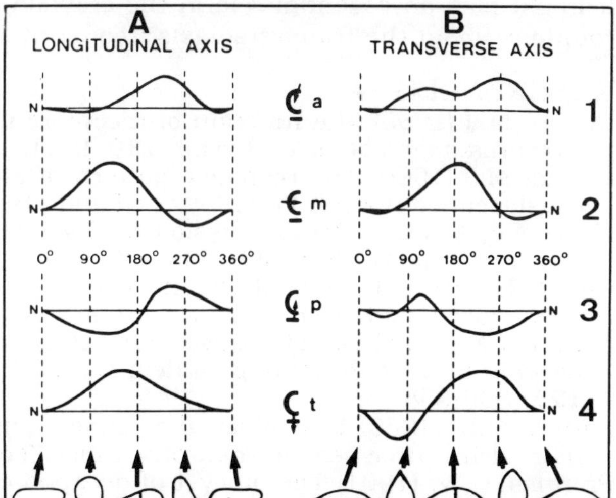

Fig. 6. Tonic responses from all hair field sectors to tilts. Displayed are normalized and simplified schematic curves of only the tonic frequencies of the responses to tilts. Each curve was calculated from 2-5 responses. Symbols on the bottom: schematic drawings of a transverse section (on the left) and of a longitudinal section (on the right) of the statocyst with an outlined sensory hair. N, "normal" activity in upright position of the statocyst. Compare with Fig.5 for further explanations.

tilts),the hairs were deflected either in their preferred direction - eliciting a maximal response, or away from it - eliciting a minimal response. The examined cells of the other sectors always showed a maximum tonic activity in approximately vertical positions (Fig.6:1,3). This kind of response was probably caused by a diverging polarization of these cells with respect to the axes of rotation, that is, these hairs were not deflected within either their preferred plane or a plane perpendicular to it.

In most of the recordings, the activity in the upright position was lower than in the upside-down position. This effect possibly resulted from the laterally tilted statocyst floor (Kinzig, 1919), which causes a lateral displacement of the statolith in the upright position of the cyst.

The analysis of diverse receptor responses to tilts produced a striking result: whereas a distinct discrimination between rightward and leftward tilts was possible for the receptors of all crescent sectors, a similar discrimination between rostrum-down and rostrum-up tilts could be achieved only by transverse-group cells (compare 90° with 270° in Fig.6A,B).

According to these findings, the crescent-group allows good perception of tilts specifically about the roll axis and probably about axes intermediate between the roll and pitch axes. The transverse group however permits tilts about only the pitch axis to be well perceived. This ability suggests to be an important and probably the main function of the separate transverse group. It might play an essential role in the crayfish escape reaction, during which rotations about the transverse axis frequently occur.

REFERENCES

Cohen, M.J.(1955) The function of receptors in the statocyst of the lobster *Homarus americanus*. J.Physiol. **130**: 9-34.

Cohen, M.J.(1960) The response pattern of single receptors in the crustacean statocyst. Proc.Roy.Soc.Lond. (Biol.) **152**: 30-48.

Harreveld, A. van (1936) A physiological solution for freshwater crustaceans. Proc.Soc.Exp.Biol.Med. **34:** 428-432.

Kinzig, H. (1919) Untersuchungen über den Bau der Statocysten einiger dekapoder Crustaceen. Verh.Naturhist.-med.Ver.Heidelberg N.F. **14**: 1-19.

Panning; A. (1924) Die Statozyste von *Astacus fluviatilis* (*Potamobius astacus* Leach) und ihre Beziehung zu dem sie umgebenden Gewebe. Z.Wiss.Zool. **123**: 305-358.

Patton, M.L. (1969) Physiological evidence indicating that decapod statocyst hairs drive three sensory neurons. Amer.Zool. **9**: 1097.

Prentiss, C.W. (1901) The otocyst of decapod crustacea: its structure, development and functions. Bull.musc.Comp.Zool. Harvard **36:** 167-254.

Schöne, H. & Steinbrecht, R.A. (1968) Fine structure of statocyst receptor of *Astacus fluviatilis*. Nature (London) **220**: 184-186.

Stein, A. (1975) Attainment of positional information in the crayfish statocyst. Fortschr.Zool. **23**: 109-119.

Takahata, M. & Hisada, M. (1979) Functional polarization of statocyst receptors in the crayfish *Procambarus clarkii* Girard. J.Comp.Physiol. **130**: 201-207.
Takahata, M. & Hisada, M. (1982) Statocyst interneurons in the crayfish *Procambarus clarkii* Girard. J.Comp.Physiol. **149**: 287-300.
Yoshino, M., Takahata, M. & Hisada, M. (1980) Statocyst control of the uropod movements in response to body rolling in the crayfish. J.Comp.Physiol. **139:** 243-250.

Frontiers in Crustacean Neurobiology
Advances in Life Sciences

THE ACOUSTIC RESPONSE THRESHOLD OF THE NORWAY LOBSTER, *NEPHROPS NORVEGICUS* (L.) IN A FREE SOUND FIELD.

Christine Goodall[1], Colin Chapman[2] and Douglas Neil[1]

[1] Neurobiology Laboratory, Dept.of Zoology, University of Glasgow, [2] D.A.F.S. Marine Laboratory, Aberdeen

SUMMARY

The behavioural responses of *Nephrops norvegicus* (L.) to acoustic stimuli have been investigated under laboratory and free field conditions. In the laboratory a distinct set of postural motor responses elicited, by sound frequencies of 20-180Hz, was identified. This set of responses was then exploited during free field experiments conducted in a Scottish sea loch to determine the acoustic response threshold. *Nephrops* were found to be displacement rather than pressure sensitive with a response threshold of 0.888µm which was independent of frequency within the range 20-200Hz.

INTRODUCTION

Vibration sensitivity has been studied extensively in decapod crustaceans. Along with morphological studies the main approach to the problem has been the use of recordings made from neurones in semi-intact preparations held in small experimental tanks. Consequently we now have an extensive picture of both the morphological characteristics of the setae and other cuticular structures, eg statocysts, which are used to detect such stimuli (Derby, 1982 ; Farmer, 1974; Thomas, 1973), and the sensory properties of the underlying afferent neurones and vibration sensitive interneurones (Breihaupt and Tautz, 1988; Tautz and Sandeman, 1984; Wiese, 1987; Reichert et al. 1982, Tautz and Hamm, 1986).

Two aspects of vibration sensitivity in crustaceans which have received less attention are their behavioural responses (Tautz, 1987; Heinisch and Wiese, 1987), and the measurement of their response thresholds in the favourable acoustic conditions of a free sound field. It is important to utilize such conditions for the measurement of acoustic thresholds because of the mismatch between the acoustic impedances of air and water. This means that sound does not propagate from one medium to another easily and will be reflected by any air-water interface. Consequently the acoustic conditions in small laboratory tanks are anomalous due to the proximity of reflecting boundaries (Parvulescu, 1964, Hawkins, 1981). For a relatively small sound pressure, generated under these conditions the particle displacement component of a sound may be very large. These effects may be minimized by conducting experiments in conditions approximating to a free sound field in the sea.

The determination of auditory thresholds in fish has been achieved by the use of cardiac conditioning methods (Chapman and Sand, 1974; Chapman and Hawkins, 1973; Hawkins, 1981). Although this has been attempted in the Crustacea (Offut, 1970) it has serious limitations; the heartbeat of crustaceans is irregular and the heart may stop or miss beats for no obvious reason making the determination of response thresholds very difficult. Sensory thresholds have been determined in several crustaceans however, using neuronal recordings (Wiese, 1976; Tautz and Sandeman, 1980) and although these have been measured in non-ideal stimulus conditions, they provide some useful comparisons.

We have adopted a novel approach in attempting to measure the behavioural response threshold of *Nephrops* to sound in free field conditions. In the course of a larger study (Goodall, 1988) a set of postural motor responses was identified in *Nephrops* which are reliably driven by water borne sound. We first characterized these responses to different sound frequencies under controlled laboratory conditions and then we utilized these un-conditioned responses to investigate sound reception by the animal. We have been able to meet the further requirement of a free sound field by making use of an off-shore floating laboratory facility owned by the Department of Agriculture and Fisheries for Scotland.

MATERIALS AND METHODS

Preliminary laboratory-based experiments . Eight male *Nephrops* were used in the experiment. Each was clamped by the thorax in a normal standing position (10° head up) in a glass walled tank (1.0x0.38x0.32m) so that all of the appendages and the abdomen were free to move but the animal was unable to undergo displacement in any direction. Sound stimuli in the frequency range from 20-300Hz were generated by a Dyna-Empire J9 sound projector suspended in the tank. The J9 was driven by a 25W Derritron power amplifier.

Experiments were recorded using a closed-circuit video system and tapes were analysed frame by frame using an interface which overlaid cross hairs onto the image. After alignment, co-ordinate points could be entered directly to a microcomputer. This allowed the position of the abdomen to be monitored throughout the 30 second stimulus period.

Field-based threshold measurements . Measurements were made in a free sound field in Loch Thurnaig, part of Loch Ewe, on the west coast of Scotland. The laboratory was situated on a pontoon moored in the Loch, the depth of water under the pontoon was 30m.

Four specimens of *Nephrops* (carapace length 43-55mm) which had been creel caught in the Loch, were again clamped by the thorax and attached below the lid of a perforated perspex box which was mounted on a PVC frame. Also mounted on this frame were a low light sensitive underwater TV camera, which viewed from the side the animal standing in the box and a calibrated hydrophone placed directly above the box to monitor the sound signals and ambient sea noise.

The frame and a J9 loudspeaker were suspended from a horizontal metal bar and lowered to a depth of 12m. The distance of the J9 from the animal could be varied. Tests were carried out at random time intervals using pure tones from 20-200Hz. The hydrophone signal was amplified and filtered using a Brookdeal amplifier and measured using a narrow band frequency analyzer and level recorder (Bruel and Kjaer Types 2107 and 2305).

Thresholds were determined using a 'staircase' method. At each frequency the tone stimulus was attenuated by 5dB steps until a response no longer occurred. The stimulus amplitude was then sequentially increased by 5dB and attenuated by 5dB until the threshold was confirmed. Blank tests were carried out randomly throughout the experiment by attenuating the signal by 30dB. The threshold at each frequency was determined from a plot of the percentage of positive responses at each sound pressure level (SPL). The SPL at which 50% of positive responses occurred was taken as the threshold.

RESULTS

Laboratory experiments; behavioural responses of Nephrops to different sound frequencies. Nephrops showed distinct and reliable responses to certain sound frequencies. The most striking component of this response was abdominal extension (Fig. 1) which was preceded by a small extensory movement of the anterior abdominal segment.

Fig. 1. Diagram of abdominal extension in a tethered *Nephrops* in response to a sound stimulus of 30Hz. The time course is 0.72 seconds.

For tone frequencies of 20-80Hz (Fig. 2) these responses occurred concurrently at the stimulus onset and were accompanied by leg movements, swimmeret beating and antennal and claw waving. Stimuli of 30Hz occasionally led to tail flipping. From 80-180Hz (Fig. 2) there was a marked delay between the stimulus onset and the onset of full abdominal extension although the initial abdominal movement and leg movements often occurred in this delay period. Within this frequency range negative responses were not uncommon and above 180Hz abdominal extension was never seen.

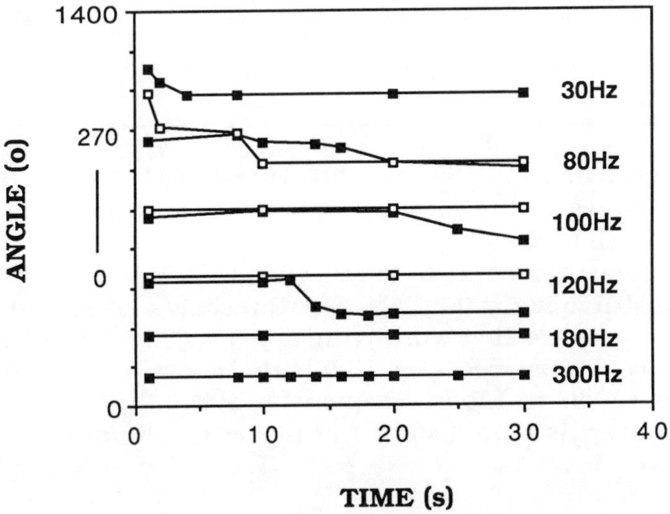

Fig. 2. Plot of change in angle (degrees) of the posterior three abdominal segments of *Nephrops* with reference to the stationary thorax over time (seconds) during sound stimuli of different frequencies presented in the laboratory. Closed squares indicate the most frequently seen response, open squares indicate responses seen less frequently.

Field experiments; the response threshold. Previous experiments to test the responses of freely moving *Nephrops* to acoustic stimuli in Loch Torridon had yielded negative results with the J9 at distances of 0-10m from the animals (Goodall, 1988). In the present set of experiments sounds were initially presented with the J9 exactly 1m from the animals. Stimuli were in the frequency range known to cause abdominal extension (20-200Hz) and were presented at very high stimulus amplitudes (+50 to +60db re 1μbar). No responses were shown by the animals in any of these tests.

When the J9 was moved to a distance of 0.09m from the animal however, very clear responses were observed. These responses were identical in form to those seen in the laboratory and described above. The fact that responses were produced at 0.09m and not at 1m, even though the SPL were the same in each case strongly suggests that *Nephrops* are sensitive to the particle motion component of the stimulus rather than the sound pressure.

Thresholds were subsequently determined with the J9 at a distance of 0.09m from the animal. They were initially expressed in terms of sound pressure to which the hydrophone was sensitive but were subsequently converted to particle displacement using the following equation (Chapman and Sand, 1973)

$$d = \frac{P}{2\pi\rho cf} \sqrt{[1 + (\lambda / 2\pi r)^2]} \qquad (1)$$

where d=displacement (cm), P=sound pressure (μbar), f =frequency (Hz), ρc= acoustic impedance of the medium, λ = wavelength (cm), r= distance from the sound source (cm).

The threshold measurements in terms of both SPL and displacement were plotted against frequency (Fig. 3). The thresholds expressed in terms of SPL were positively correlated with frequency (Fig. 3.A). At 40Hz the SPL required to produce a response was +32db re 1μbar while at 200Hz the required SPL was +60db re 1μbar. Frequencies above 200Hz could not be tested because the signals were distorted at higher amplitudes.

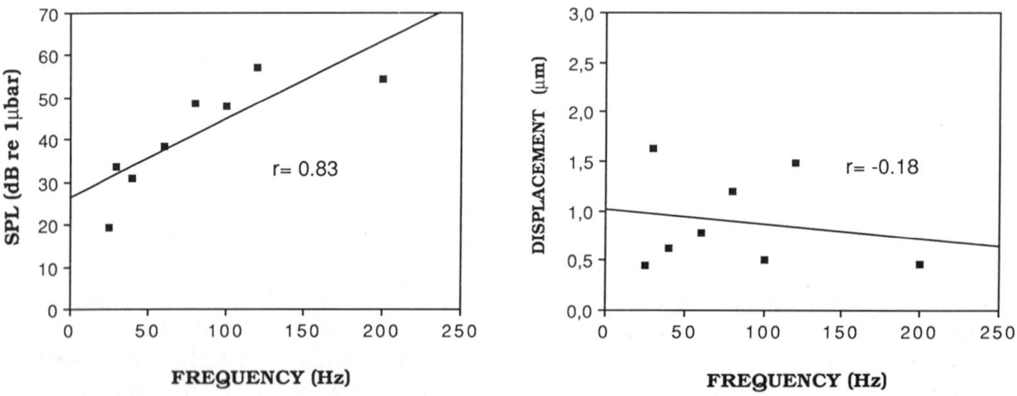

Fig. 3. **A**. The acoustic response threshold of *Nephrops* expressed in terms of sound pressure. The plot shows sound pressure level (SPL, dB re 1μbar) against frequency (Hz). A linear regression line has been fitted to the data ($r= 0.83$, $P< 0.05$). Sound source distance 0.09m **B**. The acoustic response threshold of *Nephrops* expressed in terms of displacement. The plot shows displacement (μm) against frequency (Hz). ($r=-0.18$, N.S.)

The slope of the line for particle displacement against frequency (Fig. 3.B) was not significantly different from zero. Under these circumstances the mean value of the data gives an estimate of the average threshold level at 0.888μm. The displacement threshold was therefore independent of frequency.

DISCUSSION

This study has characterized a set of behavioural responses of *Nephrops* to different sound frequencies under controlled laboratory conditions. Subsequent work has helped to reveal the neuronal basis for these responses (Goodall et al., 1990). This set of responses has then been used to investigate sound reception by *Nephrops* in the sea and has allowed the determination of the unconditioned response thresholds. The main conclusions drawn from the data are that *Nephrops* are sensitive to particle motion rather than sound pressure and that within the frequency range 20-200Hz the displacement threshold of 0.888μm is independent of frequency. This value is comparable with sensory thresholds measured physiologically under laboratory conditions in other crustaceans, for example, the crayfish *Procambarus clarkii* has a threshold value of 0.1-0.6 μm at 100Hz (Wiese, 1976; Tautz and Sandeman, 1980). The behavioural threshold for this species could be higher bringing it closer to that of *Nephrops*.

Hearing thresholds for some fish species have been calculated under free sound field conditions. Those of salmon, cod and flatfish fall in the range $0.5\text{-}5 \times 10^{-4}$ μm to 5×10^{-4}Chapman & Sand, 1974). The difference in sensitivity, of several orders of magnitude, between the thresholds of fish and crustacean species has led Hawkins and Myrberg (1983) to question whether crustacean systems should be called 'auditory'.

It is interesting to speculate whether *Nephrops* are sufficiently sensitive to detect and respond to sound sources in their natural environment. From the data obtained here and in previous experiments (Goodall, 1988) it seems unlikely that *Nephrops* would be able to detect any naturally occurring far field sound or indeed many near field stimuli. In the present experiments positive responses were only produced when the J9 was very close to the restrained animals and no responses could be elicited when the source was 1m away. Furthermore no responses were observed in freely moving animals with the J9 at 10m or closer (Goodall, 1988). The most likely explanation of this, borne out by the present study, is that the particle displacements associated with the sounds generated in the above experiments were below the detection threshold.

It is possible that the displacement sensitive system of *Nephrops* is analogous to the lateral line system of fish. The lateral line responds primarily to water movement and has been claimed to respond to low frequency near field sound (Sand, 1981). The lateral line is most sensitive to frequencies of 50-100Hz with a displacement threshold of 0.1-0.5µm comparable to the frequency range and sensitivity of *Nephrops.* The lateral lines of fish may be used to detect the presence of other fish during schooling (Blaxter, 1981) and it is possible that *Nephrops* may use their arrays of cuticular sensillae (Goodall, 1988, Farmer, 1974) to detect the displacement produced by fish as the latter swim through the water.

ACKNOWLEDGMENT

The authors would like to thank Dr A.D. Hawkins for his advice and comment on the manuscript. We would also like to thank Mr P. MacLachlan for his assistance on site at Loch Ewe and Mr. C. Shand for operating the TV equipment. This work was supported by SERC studentship No. 8551104 to CAG.

REFERENCES

BLAXTER, J.H.S. (1981). The swimbladder and hearing. *In Hearing and Sound Communication in Fishes.* (eds. W.N. Tavolga, A.N. Popper & R.R. Fay) pp. 61-72. New York Springer Verlag

BREIHAUPT, Th. &TAUTZ, J. (1988) Vibration sensitivity of the crayfish statocyst. *Naturwissenschafen.* **75**: 310-312

CHAPMAN, C.J. & HAWKINS, A.D. (1973). A field study of hearing in the cod, *Gadus morhua* (L.). *J. Comp. Physiol.* **85**: 147-167.

CHAPMAN, C.J. & SAND, O. (1974). Field studies of hearing in two species of flatfish, *Pleuronectes platessa* (L.) and *Limanda limanda* (L.) (Family Pleuronectidae) *Comp. Biochem. Physiol.* **47A**: 371-385.

DERBY, C. (1982) The structure and function of cuticular sensillae of the lobster *Homarus americanus. J. Crust. Biol.* **2**: 1-21.

FARMER, A.S. (1974). The functional morphology of the mouthparts and pereiopods of *Nephrops norvegicus. J. Nat. Hist.* **8:** 121-142.

GOODALL, C.A. (1988). The sensory detection of water borne vibrational stimuli and their motor effects in the Norway lobster, *Nephrops norvegicus* (L.). Ph. D. Thesis. University of Glasgow.

GOODALL, C.A., NEIL, D.M. & CHAPMAN, C.J. (1990). Restricting a locomotory response to water borne vibrational stimuli leads to the expression of a behavioural hierarchy in the Norway lobster, *Nephrops norvegicus* (L.) In *Studies in Neuroscience* (eds. B.M.H. Bush & A. Roberts) pp. 00-00. Manchester University Press. (In Press)

HAWKINS, A.D. (1981). The hearing abilities of fish. In *Hearing and Sound Communication in Fishes* (eds. W.N. Tavolga, A.N. Popper & R.R. Fay) pp. 109-137. New York, Springer Verlag.

HAWKINS, A.D. & MYRBERG, A.A. Jnr. (1983). Hearing and sound communication underwater. In *Bioacoustics, A Comparative Approach* (ed B. Lewis) pp. 347-405.

HEINISCH, P. & WIESE, K. (1987). Sensitivity to movement and vibration of water in the North Sea shrimp *Crangon crangon* (L.) *J. Crust. Biol.* **7**: 401-413.

OFFUT, G.C. (1970). Acoustic stimulus perception by the American lobster *Homarus americanus. Experentia* **26**: 1276-1278.

PARVULESCU,A. (1964). Problems in propagation and processing. In *Marine Bioacoustics.* (ed. W.N. Tavolga) pp. 87-100. Oxford, Pergammon Press.

REICHERT, H., PLUMMER, M., HAGIWARA, G., ROTH, R. & WINE, J.J. (1982). Local interneurones in the terminal abdominal ganglion of the crayfish. *J. Comp. Physiol.* **149**: 145-162.

SAND, O. (1981). The lateral line and sound reception. In *Hearing and and Sound Communication in Fishes.* (eds. W.N. Tavolga, A.N. Popper & R.R,. Fay) pp. 459-480. New York, Springer Verlag.

TAUTZ, J. (1987). Water vibration elicits active antennal movements in the crayfish *Orconectes limosus. Anim. Behav.* **35:** 748-754.

TAUTZ,J. & HAMM, I. (1986). Interneurones sensitive to water vibrations in the second abdominal ganglion of the crayfish. *J. Exp. Biol.* **126**: 525-529.

TAUTZ, J. & SANDEMAN, D.C. (1980). The detection of water borne vibration by sensory hairs on the chelae of the crayfish. *J. Exp. Biol.* **88:** 351-356.

THOMAS, W.J. (1970). The setae of *Austropotomobius pallipes* (Crustacea: Asticidae). *J. Zool.*, Lond. **160**: 91-142.

WIESE, K. (1976). Mechanoreceptors for near field water displacements in crayfish. *J. Neurophysiol.* **39:** 816-833.

WIESE, K. (1987). The representation of hydrodynamic parameters in the CNS of the crayfish, Procambarus. In *The Sensory Biology of Aquatic Animals.* (eds. J. Atema, R.R. Fay & A.N. Popper) pp. 665-682. New York, Springer Verlag.

Frontiers in Crustacean Neurobiology
Advances in Life Sciences

THE SENSITIVITY OF CRAYFISH MECHANORECEPTORS TO HYDRODYNAMIC AND ACOUSTIC STIMULI

Thomas Breithaupt and Jürgen Tautz

Fakultät für Biologie, Universität Konstanz, Postfach 5560, D-7750 Konstanz, Federal Republic of Germany

SUMMARY

Three basic types of hydrodynamic and acoustic receptors can be distinguished in crayfish: specialized sensory hairs on the body surface, mechanoreceptors sensing the deformation of the antennal flagella, and statocysts. Since crustaceans are not equipped with air filled cavities, reception of the pressure component of sound is unlikely. Threshold curves of the different receptor systems show highest sensitivity at frequencies below 150 Hz, which is in accordance with the dominance of low frequencies in the velocity spectrum of biotic hydrodynamic events.

INTRODUCTION

Behavioral studies on water vibration reception in decapod crustaceans indicate that these animals perceive hydrodynamic stimuli (e.g. Tautz, 1987; Heinisch & Wiese, 1987). Various identified cuticular receptors respond to medium vibrations (Fig. 1). These include free standing sensory hairs (Laverack, 1962; Wiese, 1976; Tautz & Sandemann, 1980), specialized joint receptors on/in the antennal flagellae (Tautz et al., 1981; Sandeman, 1989), the statocysts (Taylor, 1968) and proprioreceptors in the joints of antennae and other body appendages (Taylor, 1967).

In this article we will rediscuss electrophysiologically determined threshold curves obtained by different authors for crayfish hydrodynamic receptors (Wiese, 1976; Tautz & Sandeman, 1980; Tautz et al., 1981; Breithaupt & Tautz, 1988; Plummer et al., 1988). The data are interpreted by taking into account the physical forces of adequate natural stimuli, as has been proposed before by Kalmijn (1988) for the hydrodynamic receptors in fish.

Aspects of mechanoreception in water

In contrast to terrestrial animals, aquatic organisms have about the same density as the surrounding medium (density of water: 1000 kg/m3; crayfish: 1100 kg/m3). As a consequence, the animal's body follows large volume oscillatory movements of the surrounding water, unless the animal stays firmly attached to the substrate. The driving force is the pressure difference which builds up between opposite ends of the body. These whole body movements stimulate the statocysts as well as sensory hairs and the joint receptors of the antennal flagellae and other body appendages. Local disturbances covering smaller water volumes, e.g. small eddies and turbulances, should not be efficient in moving the whole body of a decapod crustacean. External sensory hairs and the antennal flagellae are more likely to be stimulated by these events.

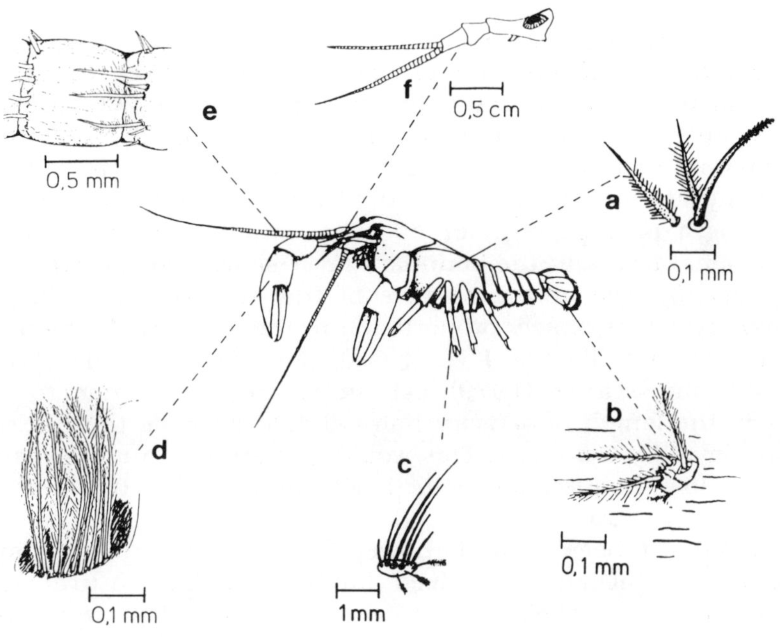

Fig. 1. crayfish hydrodynamic receptors: a. carapace sensory hairs (redrawn after Mellon, 1963); b. telson sensory hairs (unpubl.); c. sensory hairs on the second paraeopod (redrawn after Riemay, 1980); d. cheliped hair pit organ (redrawn after Tautz & Sandeman, 1980); e. feathered procumbent and upright smooth hairs on the second antenna (redrawn after Tautz et al., 1981); f. schematic view of first antenna showing the position of the statocyst inside the basal segment (unpubl.).

Can crustaceans hear?

If hearing is defined as the reception of the pressure component of sound this question has to be negated. Only the presence of air filled spaces inside aquatic animals, e.g. the swimbladder of fish, allows the reception of small pressure variations.

Behavioral tests on the American lobster confirm that these animals do not respond to the pressure component of sound (Goodall et al., this volume), but that they do react to the particle velocity in the near field of a sound source.

As far as crustaceans have been found to respond to changes in the hydrostatic pressure, the threshold of response initiation (for an amphipod: 500 to 1000 Pa; Enright, 1962) was by far above the level of natural occuring acoustic signals (level of very intense underwater sound, e.g. snapping shrimp: 60 Pa at less than 15 cm range; Fish, 1964).

Mechanoreceptive subsystems

Sensory hairs. Thousands of sensory hairs cover the exocuticle of decapod crustaceans, ranging in size from 20 to 2000 μm and being chemoreceptive or mechanoreceptive or both (Derby, 1982). The hydrodynamic hair receptors considered here are very softly articulated in the body surface and usually feathered (Wiese, 1976; Fig 1 b,d).

Hair length is important for effective coupling to medium oscillations since frictional forces in the boundary layer slow down the water motion, its velocity beeing zero at the surface of the animal. The thickness of the boundary layer is inversely proportional to the stimulus frequency (Fletcher, 1978). For laminar flow at 1 Hz it is 0,4 mm (20°C), while at 100 Hz it is only 0,04 mm. Tautz (1979) estimated that, in order to work most effectively, the length of sensory hairs should override the thickness of the boundary layer by 2-6 times. This would give an optimum hair length of 1 to 3 mm for low frequencies (e.g. 1 Hz) and 0,1 to 0,3 mm for higher frequencies (e.g. 100 Hz).

It has not yet been proved, however, that the boundary layer on the surface of crustaceans is indeed laminar during natural stimulation. Roughness of the exoskeleton can cause turbulent flow, which reduces the boundary layer and may thus stimulate even short hair sensillae at low frequencies.

When displaced directly by a stimulator and studied electrophysiologically, all hair receptors on the telson of *Procambarus clarkii* show similar response thresholds over a broad range of frequency (Wiese, 1976; Fig. 2). Thus, the sensory cell reacts to the displacement of the hair shaft. However, stimulation of the hairs via water oscillations (which resembles the natural stimulus) results in a response of the sensory neurons proportional to the velocity of the water movement (Fig. 3c). This reflects the properties of stimulus coupling between hair shaft and surrounding fluid. The hairs are driven by viscous forces that are proportional to the velocity of the oscillating water flow.

Fig. 2. Electrophysiologically determined response thresholds of afferent fibers of hair receptors on the telson of *Procambarus clarkii.* The hairs were displaced by a needle connected to the hair tip (after Wiese, 1976).

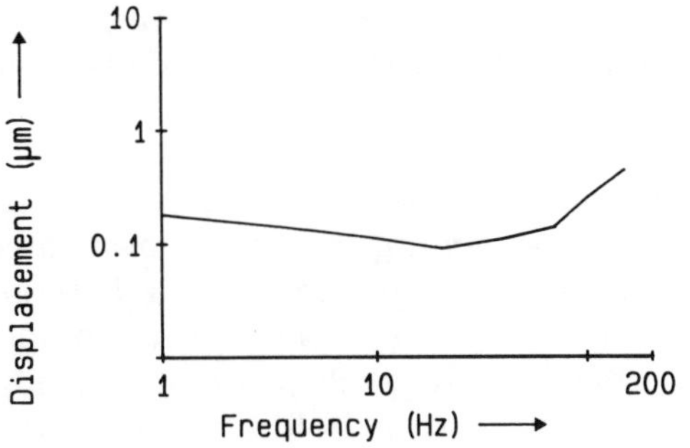

Fig. 3. Electrophysiologically determined velocity thresholds for afferent fibers of telson hair receptors (c) and a mechanosensory interneuron postsynaptic to these fibers (a,b). Stimulation by oscillatory water movement. The interneuron is excited at low frequencies (a) and inhibited at high frequencies (b) (c. after Wiese, 1976; a.,b. after Plummer et al., 1986).

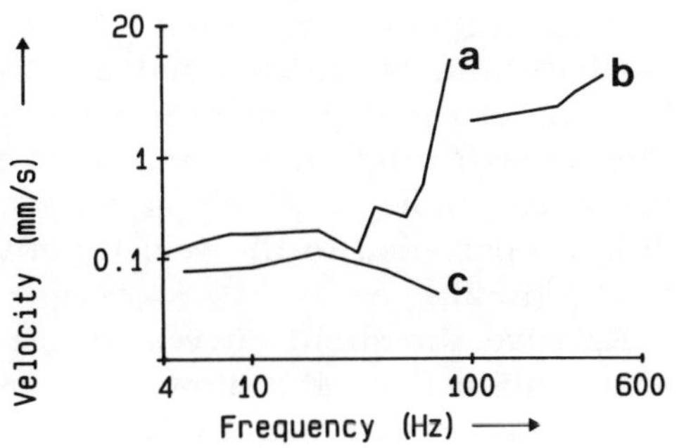

Fig. 4. Electrophysiologically determined acceleration thresholds for afferent fibers of hair pit organs on the chelae of Cherax destructor (a. after Tautz & Sandeman, 1980), for external joint receptors on the antennal flagella of Astacus leptodactylus (b. after Tautz et al., 1981), and for the statocyst of *Orconectes limoses* (c. after Breithaupt & Tautz, 1988). Stimulation either by oscillatory water movements (a,b) or direct oscillation of the statocyst (c). The threshold curve for antennal receptors gives only relative values.

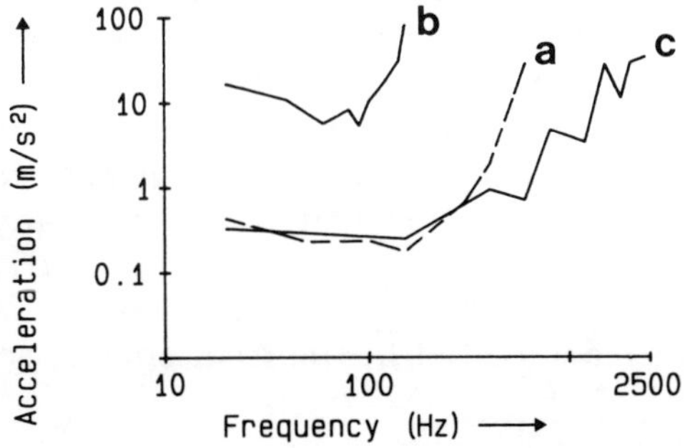

The threshold curve (Fig. 3) recorded from a mechanosensory interneuron in the 6th abdominal ganglion of *Procambarus clarkii*, which is postsynaptic to these hair receptors, show similar properties in the low frequency range (Fig. 3a). At higher frequencies (>50 Hz) the threshold first increases while the interneuron is inhibited above 100 Hz (Fig. 3b). This is a typical example for a low pass interneuron. Other mechanosensory interneurons possess broad band or high pass filter characteristics (Plummer et al., 1986), thus demonstrating the importance of frequency analysis in the processing of hydrodynamic signals.

Response thresholds of the hair pit organs on the chelae , stimulated by water vibration, are independent of frequency up to 150 Hz only with respect to the acceleration of the stimulus (Fig. 4a). The most likely interpretation of this behavior is that in contrast to tailfan receptors the sensory cells of the hair pit organs are velocity sensitive. As a consequence the hair receptor responds proportional to the first derivate of water velocity, i.e. to acceleration.

Antennal flagellum. Even very weak water vibrations make the flagellum oscillate and excite external or internal joint receptors responding to the bending of the flagellar articulations (Tautz et al., 1981; Sandeman, 1989). The forces acting on a given point of antennal flagella result from both the pressure gradient, which is proportional to acceleration, and the viscous drag proportional to the velocity of water moving past the antenna (Masters et al., 1982).

Relative threshold curves (mean of 8 receptors) drawn with respect to acceleration (Fig. 4b) show increasing sensitivity from 20 to 90 Hz and a steep decrease in sensitivity at higher frequencies. The smallest threshold displacement found for a single receptor was 0,2 m/s2 at 105 Hz. This can be explained by the resonance frequency of the antennal flagellum at 100 Hz (Tautz et al., 1981).

Frequency range of natural stimuli

Recent studies have focussed on wave stimuli caused by moving fish (Kalmijn 1988, Breithaupt et. al. 1989). Water disturbances produced by fish are of great importance for aquatic crustaceans since fishes represent potential predators or prey (Rahel & Stein, 1988).

The main spectral energy of many waves produced by moving fish, frogs or crustaceans are below 10 Hz. In some situations, however, (e.g. struggling fish) turbulences occur, which cause higher components (up to at least 70 Hz) in the frequency spectrum (Breithaupt et al., 1989).

Conclusions

All spectral threshold curves of hydrodynamic receptors of decapod crustacea show a broad minimum at frequencies below 150 Hz, when referred to the adequate stimulus parameter. Thus they are adapted to the low frequency nature (<100 Hz) of naturally occuring signals. Besides frequency, the spatial dimension of hydrodynamic events and hydrodynamic receptors are of importance for the stimulation of different types of receptor systems.

ACKNOWLEDGEMENT
The authors would like to thank C. Rose for assistance in the drawings and B.Schmitz and R.Uhl for critically reading the manuscript.

REFERENCES

BREITHAUPT, Th. & TAUTZ, J. (1988) Vibration sensitivity of the crayfish statocyst. Naturwissenschaften **75:** 310-312.

BREITHAUPT, Th., BLECKMANN, H. & TAUTZ, J. (1989) The time course and spectral energy distribution of hydrodynamic flow fields caused by moving fish, frog, and crayfish. In: Dynamics and Plasticity in Neuronal Systems, (ed. N. Elsner & W. Singer) p. 266. Stuttgart: Thieme.

DERBY, C. (1982) Structure and function of cuticular sensilla of the lobster Homarus americanus. J.Crust.Biol. **2**: 1-21.

ENRIGHT, J.T. (1962) Responses of an amphipod to pressure changes. Comp.Biochem.Physiol. 7: 131-145.

FISH, M.P. (1964) Biological sources of sustained ambient sea noise. In: Marine Bio-acoustics, (ed. W.N. Tavolga) pp. 281-299. New York: Pergamon Press.

FLETCHER, N.H. (1978) Acoustical response of hair receptors in insects. J.Comp.Physiol. 127: 185-189.

HEINISCH, P. & WIESE, K. (1987) Sensitivity to movement and vibration of water in the north sea shrimp Crangon crangon L. J.Crust.Biol. **7**: 401-413.

KALMIJN, A.J. (1988) Hydrodynamic and acoustic field detection. In: Sensory Biology of Aquatic Animals, (ed. J. Atema, R.R. Fay, A.N. Popper & W.N. Tavolga) pp. 83-130. New York: Springer.

LAVERACK, M.S. (1962) Responses of cuticular sense organs of the lobster Homarus vulgaris (Crustacea). I. Hair-peg organs as water current receptors. Comp.Biochem.Physiol. **5**: 319-325.

MASTERS, W.M., AICHER, B., TAUTZ, J. & MARKL, H. (1982) A new type of water vibration receptor on the crayfish antenna. II. Model of receptor function. J.Comp.Physiol. 149: 409-422.

MELLON, D. (1963) Electrical responses from dually innervated tactile receptors on the thorax of the crayfish. J.Exp.Biol. **40**: 137-148.

PLUMMER, M.R., TAUTZ, J. & WINE, J.J. (1986) Frequency coding of waterborne vibrations by abdominal mechanosensory interneurons in the crayfish, *Procambarus clarkii.* J.Comp.Physiol. **158:** 751-764.

RAHEL, F.J. & STEIN, R.A. (1988) Complex predator-prey interactions and predator intimidation among crayfish, piscivorous fish, and small benthic fish. Oecologia **75**: 94-98.

RIEMAY, H. (1980) Zur Kenntnis mechanorezeptiver Cuticularsensillen auf den Pareiopoden von *Orconectes limosus* Raf. Zool.Jb.Physiol. 84: 226-230.

SANDEMAN, D.C. (1989) Physical properties, sensory receptors and tactile reflexes of the antenna of the Australian freshwater crayfish *Cherax destructor*. J.Exp.Biol. **141:** 197-217.

TAUTZ, J. (1979) Reception of particle oscillation in a medium - an unorthodox sensory capacity. Naturwissenschaften **66**: 452-461.

TAUTZ, J. (1987) Water vibration elicits active antennal movements in the crayfish *Orconectes limosus*. Anim. Behav. **35:** 748-754.

TAUTZ, J. & SANDEMAN, D.C. (1980) The detection of water borne vibration by sensory hairs on the chelae of the crayfish. J.Exp.Biol. **88**: 351-356.

TAUTZ, J., MASTERS, W.M., AICHER, B. & MARKL, H. (1981) A new type of water vibration receptor on the crayfish antenna. I. Sensory physiology. J.Comp.Physiol. **144**: 533-541.

Taylor, R.C. (1967) Functional properties of the chordotonal organ in the antennal flagellum of a hermit crab. Comp.Biochem.Physiol. **20:** 719-729.

TAYLOR, R.C. (1968) Water vibration reception: A neurophysiological study in unrestrained crayfish. Comp.Biochem.Physiol. **27**: 795-805.

WIESE, K. (1976) Mechanoreceptors for near field water displacements in crayfish. J.Neurophysiol. **39**: 816-833.

Frontiers in Crustacean Neurobiology
Advances in Life Sciences

SENSITIVITY TO VIBRATION AND TURBULENCE OF WATER IN CONTEXT WITH SCHOOLING IN ANTARCTIC KRILL *EUPHAUSIA SUPERBA*.

K.Wiese and H.P.Marschall*

Zoologisches Institut und Zoologisches Museum der Universität, Martin Luther King Platz 3, D-2000 Hamburg 13, FRG and *Alfred Wegener Institut für Polar- und Meeresforschung, Columbusstrasse, D-2850 Bremerhaven, FRG

SUMMARY.

The spectrum of water-turbulence generated by *Euphausia* is dominated by the beat frequency (modulation 2-10 Hz) of pleopods. Records from sensory axons of the antennule nerve revealed a uniform value of particle velocity (0.006 cm/s) effective at threshold of sensory cell activity correlated to the vibratory stimulus(0.5-50 Hz). The characteristic floating posture behavior was calibrated by focussing water vibration onto the animals carapace. Water vibrations (70-150Hz) justabout eliciting the behavior showed a uniform value of particle acceleration (40 cm/s). A potential role of the two systems monitoring water displacement in intraspecific communication during schooling is discussed.

INTRODUCTION

Euphausia superba (Fig.1A) is exceptional among eucarid (Decapoda and Euphausiacea) crustaceans because of its pelagic life (Marr 1962; Mauchlin and Fisher 1969) which enforces continuous action of the swimmerets (pleopods) and because this animal seasonally forms large schools in which individuals swim neatly arranged in parallel and at times as close as an estimated 5 cm distance from each other (Hamner et al. 1983; Hamner 1984). The sensory modality which enables krill to swim in close formation at considerable speed (15-20 cm/s: Kanda et al. 1982) has become a matter of debate, because all hitherto made attempts to prove the use of photophores in intraspecific communication have been unsuccessful (Grinell et al. 1988). On the other hand *E. superba* produces a strong propulsion jet (U.Kils 1982) modulated by the beat of pleopods, a formidable strong signal to potentially guide follower conspecifics during schooling (Hamner 1984), provided that E.s. is sufficiently sensitive to this particular kind of water turbulence.

Measurements of sensitivity to medium displacement have been reported from crayfish (sensors of the telson: Plummer et al. 1985; sensors on the claw: Tautz and Sandeman 1980; isolated second antennas: Tautz et al.1981). Earlier work by Ebina and Wiese (1984) has compared sensitivity to flow signals as seen in the activity of mechanosensory interneurons versus such displayed in behavior of *Procambarus*. Laverack (1962a) found cuticular sensilla in lobsters sensitive to flow and Luther and Maier (1963) observed loss of orientation to flow direction in shrimps *Crangon* when the lateral flagella of antennules were ablated.

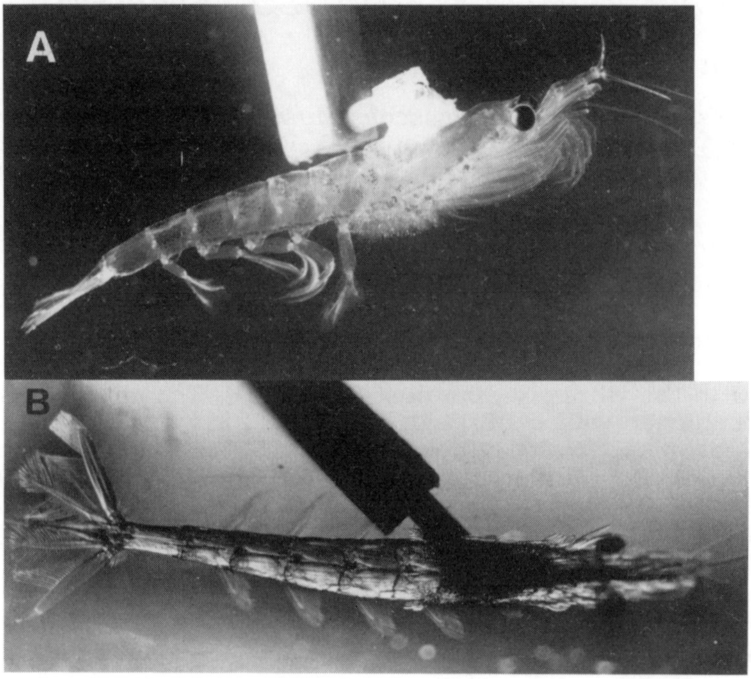

Fig.1 *Euphausia superba* in tethered condition. Size of the animal from tip of the antennule to end of the tail-fan: 60 mm; A: swimming; note the good size swimmerets and their articulation way below the sternum of abdominal segments. B: in floating posture, motionless, with the exopodites of pleopods and the uropods of the tailfan spread to slow sinking. Photograph taken through a mirror underneath the cuvette.

Despite of all these measurements of crustacean sensitivity to water displacement, there still is no sufficient information on sensitivity to low frequency vibration (below 20Hz) and especially to flow which could be extrapolated to characterize corresponding sensitivity in *E.s.* For that reason we report below about measurements of the exact sensory capacity of *Euphausia* with respect to water-flow and - vibration.

METHODS.

Live specimens of *Euphausia superba* were taken from the colony maintained at the Alfred Wegener Institute at Bremerhaven, where they are fed on a diet of laboratory-raised phytoplankton which is dominated by *Thallassiosira-*, *Chaetoceros-* and *Nitzschia*-species (Marschall 1990 in preparation). The technique to calibrate a behavior displayed in response to water vibration has been described in earlier work (Wiese, Wollnik, and Jebram 1980). The vibratory signal of the medium was produced by multiplication of a trapezoid voltage pulse of 1 sec duration with a continuous sine wave.This signal was amplified and drove the speaker-system with the connected aluminum tube and sphere (diameter 10 mm; dipol source). At frequencies 1-20Hz rise and fall times were set to 300 ms each, at frequencies 40 Hz and above the rise and fall times were set to 100 ms. The electrophysiological recording from the antennular nerve used conventional microelectrode amplifier equipment and glass insulated metal electrodes of about 2 um tip diameter and 0.5 -2 Megohm resistance.

RESULTS.

Laser-Doppler-Anemometer records (method see: Michelsen, Larsen, 1978) and frequency analysis of the propulsion jet of *Euphausia* show, that the center frequency of the spectrum of the generated turbulence corresponds to the beat frequency of the pleopods without significant higher frequency components (Fig.2).

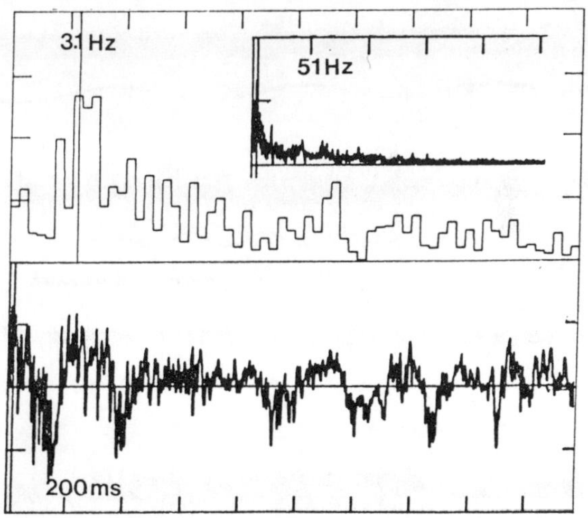

Fig.2 Laser-Doppler-Anemometer record of turbulence generated by the swimmerets of *Euphausia*; low section: actual recording of particle velocity (uncalibrated) in parallel to the long axis of the body, 10mm below the tailfan of a tethered swimming animal, pleopode movement 3Hz.
upper section: FFT-spectrum analysis of the velocity recording shown below. x-axis: 2.5 Hz/Div, bin width 0.35 Hz., y-axis: normed to 1.0; center frequency 3.1 Hz; inset: same spectrum at larger scale(51 Hz/div.) showing no obvious contributions by frequency bands other than that around fc.

Euphausia pleopods in normal swimming beat at 2-10 Hz frequency (Kils 1982), all higher speeds of locomotion are obtained by escape- (tail-flip-) swimming. Conspecifics swimming in the swarm can notice 2-10 Hz displacement signals prospectively only by specialized flow sensors, in arthropods a function of antennae (locusts: Gewecke 1975), in crustaceans often a function of the antennular flagella (e.g.Schopmann 1977). For that reason electrophysiological recording from sensory axons in the antennules were made while a dipol source (oscillating sphere) was operated in measured distance in front of the flagellum. Fig.3 shows a latero-ventral view of the head of E.s. with the insertion point of the glass-insulated metal electrode marked by x.

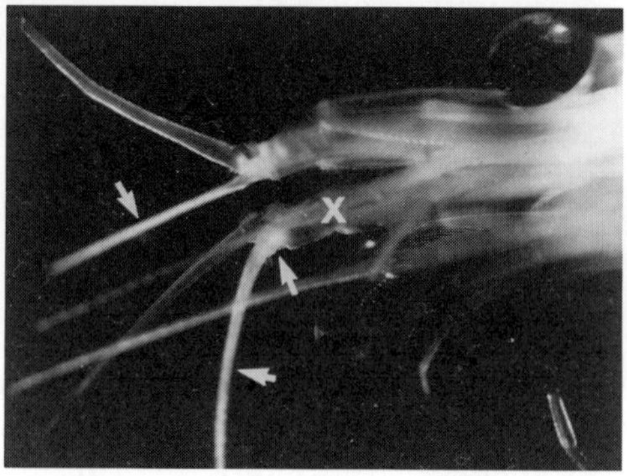

Fig.3 Antennular flagella in *Euphausia superba* as seen from ventro-laterally. Deflections and extensions of the whitish flagella (arrows) around a hinge(arrow) at the base, are monitored by a scolopal organ. Site of insertion of recording electrode marked by x. Calibration bar: 1 mm.

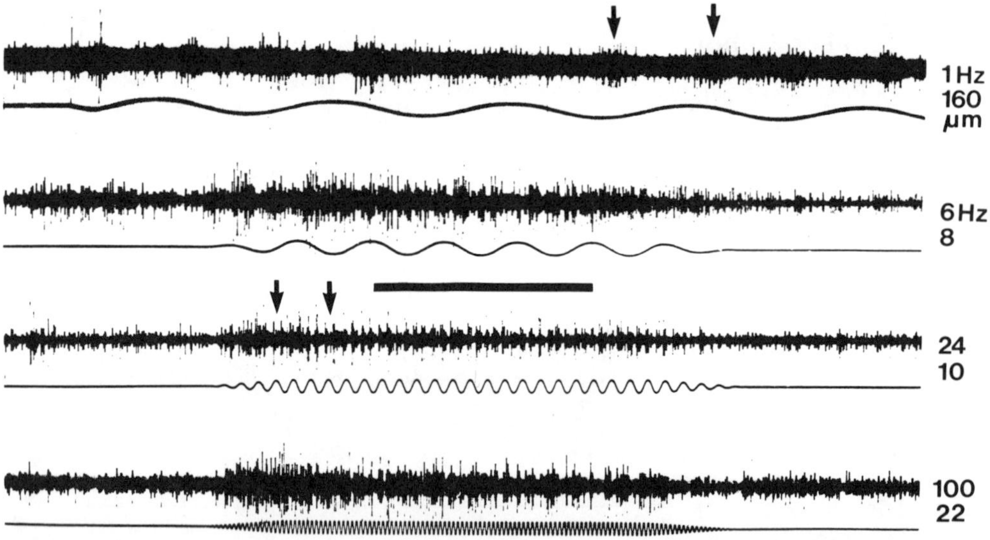

Fig.4 Sample records of responses of sensory axons from the scolopalorgan of the protopodite-flagellar hinge (Fig.3 arrow) when stimulated with water vibrations (odd values of displacement originate from calculation of attenuation between oscillating sphere and flagellum. Note the two response bursts per cycle of oscillation (arrows and at 24 Hz). Calibration bar: 0.5 s

Sample records of the sensory activity observed are shown in Fig.4. Though the background activity is rather strong (probably due to the open water surface just 20 mm above the flagellum), a very important feature of the neuronal response to the vibratory stimulus is visible: two responses to each cycle of the vibration are recorded (see sample at 24 Hz stimulus frequency). Deflecting and extending of the flagella by a wire probe revealed, that a movement in the hinge between the ventrally directed flagellum and the basipodite of the antennule fired the axons recorded. Histology and the information provided by Wyse and Maynard(1965) indicate that the recorded sensory cells belong to a scolopalorgan monitoring movement -both flexion and extension- in this hinge. In contrast, very few sensory cells responded to movement of the horizontally held other flagellum.

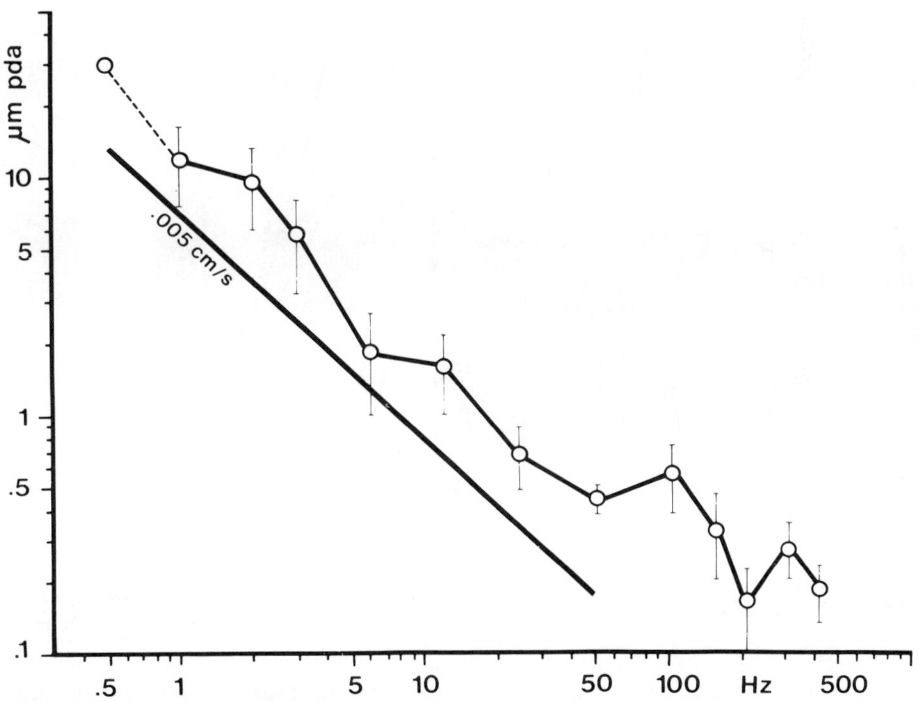

Fig.5 Thresholds of displacement required to produce barely audible (audiomonitor of recording) responses correlated to the stimulus (threshold criterion). Five series of measurements, using three animals were evaluated ; vertical bars give standard deviations drawn in symmetrically to the average (log.scale!). The isovelocity line marked 0.005 cm/s connects corresponding displacement values at various frequencies and demonstrates velocity dependence of the sensor system.

Attenuation of the measured movement of the sphere(dipol source) in calibrated steps leads to a situation where each stimulus presentation produces a justabout noticeable correlated neuronal response. Using this situation as threshold criterion, and calculating additional attenuation of the vibration due to the distance between center of the sphere and a point half length of the antennular flagellum, a curve of water displacements was obtained which justabout activated sensory cells suprathreshold at different frequencies of vibration (Fig.5). The characteristics of the obtained curve of threshold displacements in the range 1-50 Hz is, that with a ten-fold increase of stimulus frequency the threshold-displacement found is reduced to one tenth. This rule holds in the tested frequency range 0.5Hz-50Hz and testifies that this sensor system is designed for the parameter **velocity** ($A_0 \times \pi \times$ frequency) of water displacement

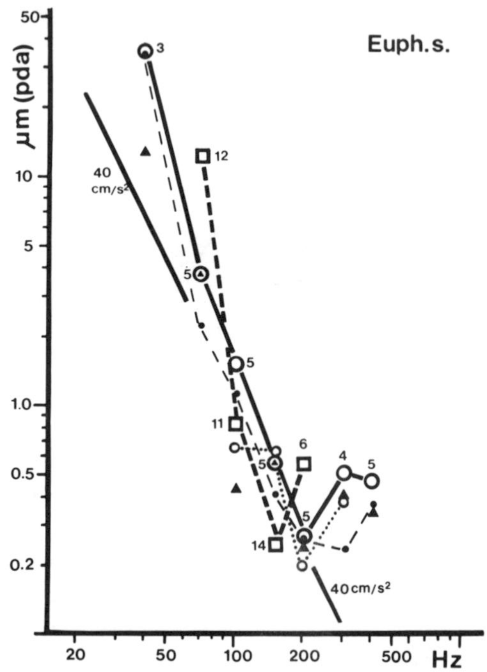

Fig.6 Thresholds of displacement triggering the weakest form of floating posture reflex in *Euphausia* when vibration is focused onto sensilla of the carapace. 5 animals stood the long series of threshold measurements during a continuous session. In the frequency range 70-150 Hz all the threshold displacements when converted provide a uniform 40 cm/s^2 in the parameter acceleration.

In the past much work has been invested to explore the physiological properties of hair type sensilla on the skeleton of crayfish, especially those on the telson, because they constitute the sensory input to the escape reflex circuitry (e.g. Plummer et al. 1985). These sensilla exist in *Euphausia* as well. To explore their role in the animals sensitivity to water turbulence we calibrated the easy to observe floating posture (Kils 1982) reflex of *Euphausia* (Fig.1B). The attenuation of displacements generated by the oscillating sphere (10 mm diameter) with increasing distance (d= A_0 x

R^3/r^3; d: displacement at point of obs.; R: radius of sphere; r: distance from center of sphere; van Bergeijk 1967) is that dramatic, that the displacement stimulus generated in the direction of the movement of the sphere can be focused onto the flanks of the carapace. Calculation allows to calibrate the stimulus(displacement) at any measured distance from the source. By simply moving away the dipol source til the stimulus produces only a short stop of pleopods (threshold criterion), a curve of threshold displacements minimally required to elicit the floating posture reflex was obtained (Fig.6). The characteristics of this threshold curve is, that, in the frequency range 40 to 100 Hz, a doubling of frequency reduces the value of threshold displacement to one eigth of the original value at reference frequency. This again is signalling **acceleration** ($A_o \times \pi \times$ frequency$)^2$) the effective stimulus parameter in this sensor- and trigger system Averages of these 5 measurements. and the corresponding standard deviations are shown in Fig.7, right side.

DISCUSSION.

From our experiments and from literature we draw the conclusion, that the propulsion jet generated by *Euphausia* has a strong flow component (evaluation of cinematographic records (Kils 1982: 7cm/s at 3 Hz pleopod beat frequency) and a turbulent component the center frequency of which corresponds to the frequency of actual pleopod beat. In the context of these statements a clasp coupling between endopodites of pleopods of *Euphausia* (Kils 1982) has to be mentionned which acts to synchronize movement of the pair of pleopods and to make the pair, together with exopodites, form a large scoop during powerstroke. The increased load of water as compared to the load of an individual pleopod slows the repetition of strokes to a maximum of 10 Hz, mostly however lower, beatfrequency.

The ventrally directed flagella and their proprioceptors (Wyse and Maynard 1965) at the basal hinge have turned out sufficiently sensitive to low frequency turbulence and flow (0.006 cm/s) to monitor both components of flow signals produced by conspecifics.

The increased range of flow signals (attenuation by $1/r$: Schlichting 1982) as compared to the displacements generated by the oscillating sphere (attenuation by $1/r^3$: van Bergeijk,1967), makes medium flows excellent carriers of communication signals in the spatially limited world of small animals, which nevertheless can afford the modest energy expense of flapping(pumping) body appendages (Markl 1973,1983). Selfprotecting jets of extended rectangular cross-section as likely produced by the ribbon- or scarf-shaped (Hamner 1984) formation of a school of antarctic Krill attenuate even more slowly according to the estimate 1/ square oot of r, modified by the force impulse of the stroke of the pleopod (Schlichting 1982).

Let us assume that *Euphausia* can easily produce flow speeds of 10 cm/s. Behavioral responses, turning of animals headon into water currents as slow as 1mm/s have been observed in preliminary experiments in a flow channel (threshold of behavioral responses to flow in baby-crayfish: 1 mm/s; Ebina, Wiese 1984).

The discrepancy between sensitivity of the flow sensor (0.006 cm/s) and the threshold of behavior (0.1 cm/s) is presently attributed to either noise production by the movement of the animals body during swimming or/and to the possibility that efferent inhibition (in mechanosensory pathways of crayfish: Kirk 1985, with all earlier lit.) are reducing centrally the sensitivity to water vibration during swimming.

Using a figure of 10 cm/s of flow speed produced by *E.s.* and 1mm/s flow speed responded to behaviorally, a 100 cm distance (applying the rule 1/r) between signal source and receiver can be bridged. Applying the rule 1/square root of r, a range estimate of 100 meters can be envisaged. Whereas the flow itself corresponds to the carrier in a system of communication, the specific signal (characterizing the producer) is the modulation of the flow by the beat of the pumping appendages. Expectation is, that the modulation lasts longer and extends for a longer distance into the flow path as the force impulse (Schlichting 1982) applied by the driving appendage increases.

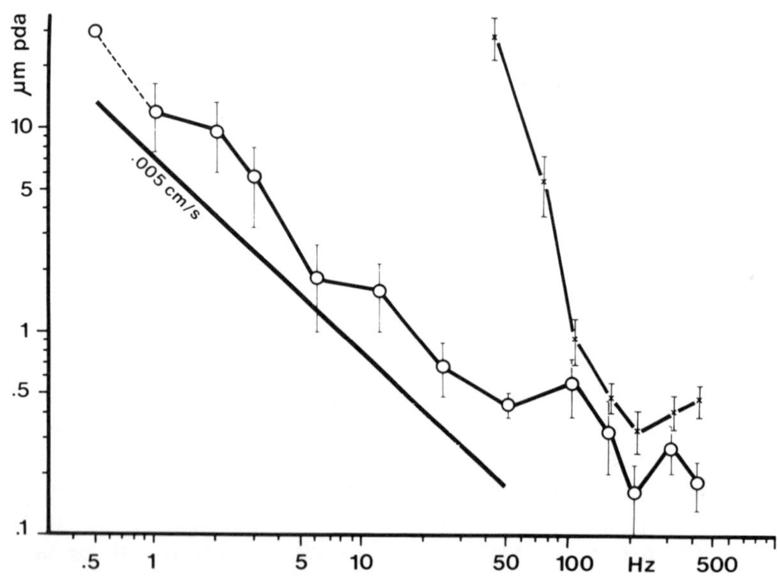

Fig.7 Sensitivities to water displacement, both velocity- and acceleration-dependent systems, of *Euphausia* shown in combination. Curve at the right side gives the averages of the measurements of Fig.6, vertical bars are standard deviations, plotted symmetrically to the average.

The theoretically possible range (estimate:100 m) of the flow signal trailling a school of *E.s.* gives interesting perspectives for the process of recruitment to schools and for detection of krill schools by predators. Precise range measurements of both the flow and the modulation component in the open ocean have now to be done.

In contrast to the situation found in flow signals, displacements of high acceleration as required to effectively drive sensilla on the carapace have a range of only a few millimeters (attenuation by $1/r^3$). The isoacceleration line in Fig.5 visualizes, that the floating posture reflex has a threshold depending on a fixed value of acceleration ($40 cm/s^2$). Such rather strong acceleration is typically produced by contact of the hard body skeleton with some other hard object,e.g. claw of an attacker or a metal probe: comp. Wine and Krasne 1972) or by the tailflip of a neighboring conspecific or by the dive of the penguin from the rim of the shelf ice or in the presence of big and strong, fast swimming organisms. In all, we are led to assume, that the acceleration dependent system is an alarm system, not a channel used in general communication.

Current ideas on the reasons for formation swimming focus on the need of energy conservation during the extended travelling of *Euphausia* to richer pastures of phytoplancton. For instance we assume that a vortex in the turbulent flow at fixed distance behind a swimming animal could provide better effectivity of swimmeret action in producing propulsion as compared to not defined places somewhere in the flow path. Confirmation or rejection of this hypothesis is expected from flow field visualizations (Ebina, this volume) presently made.

Acknowledgements:

The authors want to thank Prof.G.Hempel for the support he provided to advance this project, Dr.J.Tautz, T.Breithaupt, University of Konstanz, helped with LDA measurements, DFG provided the equipment used (DFG Az. Wi363/10-1), Drs.W. Kirchner, Würzburg, and J.Tautz commented on an earlier version of this manuscript and Mrs.S.Marschall made the final draft.

REFERENCES

Bergeijk, W.van (1967) Introductory comments on lateral line function.In: Cahn,P.(ed.) Lateral line detectors. Indiana university Press, Bloomington, pp.73-81

Ebina,Y., Wiese,K. (1984) A comparison of neuronal and behavioral thresholds in the displacement sensitive pathway of the crayfish *Procambarus*. J.exp. Biol. **108**: 45-55

Gewecke, M.(1975) The influence of the air current sense organs on the flight behavior of Locusta migratoria. J comp. Physiol. **103:** 79-95

Grinnell, A.D., Narins, P.M., Awbrey,F.T., Hamner, W.M., Hamner P.P.(1988) Eye-photophore coordination and light following in krill, *Euphausia superba*. J. exp. Biol. **134**: 61-77

Hamner, W.M.(1984) Aspects of schooling in *Euphausia superba*. J.Crust.Biol.**4**: 67-74

Hamner W.M.,Hamner P.P, Strand S.W. Gilmer, R.W.(1983) Behavior of Antarctic krill *Euphausia superba*: chemoreception, feeding, schooling and molting. Science **220**: 433-435

Kanda,K., Tagaki, K., Seki, Y. (1982) Movement of the larger swarms of antactic krill *Euphausia superba* population off Enderby Land during the 1976-77 season. J.Tokyo Univ. Fish **68**: 25-42

Kils,U.(1982) Swimming behavior, swimming performance and energy balance of Antarktic krill, *Euphausia superba*. Biomass Scient.Ser. **3**: 1-121

Kils,U.(1983) Swimming and feeding of antarctic krill *Euphausia superba*. In: Berichte zur Polarforschung (AWI) Sonderheft 4, S.B.Schnack (ed.) Alfred Wegener Institut, Bremerhaven 1983 pp.130-155.

Kirk,M.D. (1985) Presynaptic inhibition in the crayfish CNS: Pathways and synaptic mechanisms. J.Neurophysiol. 54:1305-1325

Markl,H.(1973) Leistungen des Vibrationssinnes bei Wirbellosen Tieren. Fortschr. Zoologie **21**: 100-120

Markl,H.(1983) Vibrational communication. In: Huber,F., Markl, H (eds.) Neuroethology and behavioral physiology. Springer Verlag, Berlin Heidelberg New York pp.332-353

Marr, J.W.S.(1962) The natural history and geography of the antarctic krill (*Euphausia superba* DANA). Discovery Rep. *32*:33-464

Marschall, H.P.(1990) Rapid growth of krill under laboratory conditions. Polar Biol.,in prep.

Mauchline,J. Fisher L.R. (1969) The biology of the Euphausiids. Adv. Mar. Biol. **7**: 1-454

Michelsen,A., Larsen,O.N. (1978) Biophysics of the ensiferan ear. I.Tympanal vibrations in bushcrickets (Tettigoniidae) studied with Laser Vibrometry. J.comp.Physiol.123: 193-203.

Plummer, M.R., Tautz J., Wine J.J.(1985) Frequency coding of water borne vibrations by abdominal mechanosensory interneurons in the crayfish, *Procambarus clarkii*. J.comp. Physiol. A **158**: 751-764

Schlichting, H.(1982) Grenzschicht-Theorie. 8.Auflage. Verlag G.Braun, Karlsruhe pp.749-778.

Schopmann, A.(1977) Movement dependent position changes of the antennular flagellum of *Palaemon xiphias*.J.comp. Physiol.**117**: 267-275.

Tautz,J. (1979) Reception of particle oscillation in a medium- an unorthodox sensory cpacity. Naturwissenschaften **66**: 452-461

Tautz,J. Sandeman D.C. (1980) The detection of water borne vibration by sensory hairs on the chelae of the crayfish.J.exp. Biol. **88**: 351-356

Wiese, K., Wollnik, F., Jebram, D.(1980) The protective reflex of *Bowerbankia* (Bryozoa): Calibration and use to indicate movements of the medium beneath a capillary surface wave. J. comp. Physiol **137**: 297-303

Wine,J.J., Krasne F.B.(1972) The organization of escape behaviour in the crayfish. J.exp. Biol. **56:** 1-18

Wine,J.J., Krasne,F.B. (1982) The Cellular Organization of Crayfish Escape Behavior. In: The Biology of Crustacea, Vol.4 D.Bliss (ed.), Academic Press, New York, London pp. 242-292

Wyse G.A., Maynard, D.M. (1965) Joint receptors in the antennule of *Panulirus argus* Latreille. J.exp. Biol. **42**: 521-535

Frontiers in Crustacean Neurobiology
Advances in Life Sciences

PICTURE(VIDEO-)ANALYSIS AS A TOOL TO VISUALIZE FLOW PATTERNS PRODUCED BY SWIMMING *EUPHAUSIA*.

Yoshio Ebina

Zoologisches Institut und Zoologisches Museum der Universität Hamburg, Martin Luther King Platz 3, D-2000 Hamburg 13,FRG and Department of Electrical Engineering, Yamaguchi University, UBE, 755 Japan

SUMMARY

A method to visualize flow patterns is described which uses time correlations calculated from time differences of pixel brightness in video records of floating particles. The parameter time difference of pixel brightness is recommended as very effective to show the degree of turbulence in flow signals.

INTRODUCTION.

In context with the phenomenon of formation-swimming of antarctic Krill (schooling) it has been hypothesized (Wiese, Marschall 1990, this volume) that the water flow produced by swimming *Euphausia* possibly turns turbulent at a certain distance from the beating pleopods (=swimmerets). Flow sensors connected with the antennules of *Euphausia* possibly detect the first of vortices and locking onto this signal keep the animal- as is typically seen in schooling- at a fixed distance behind the conspecific. The reason for doing so is possibly the conservation of energy, because pleopod paddles presumably propel the animal more effectively if the surrounding medium(set into motion by the conspecifics swimming in front) was not moving 180 degrees away from the desired direction of swimming, but would instead move 90 degrees sidewards as in a vortex.

As a first step to examine the situation, videorecords of light reflecting particles moving with the propulsion jet of *Euphausia* were processed using a method of video picture analysis developed in earlier work (H.Miike, K.Ochiai, H.Hashimoto, Y.Ebina 1985). Though the questions raised in context with schooling of *Euphausia* are still far from being answered, this opportunity is used to demonstrate the method in a biological experiment.

METHODS.

Experiment: A specimen of *Euphausia superba* taken from the colony maintained at the Alfred Wegener Institute für Polar- und Meeresforschung, Bremerhaven, was attached to a holder by cyanacrylate glue and positioned in an upper corner of an aquarium of 35x45x35 cm (width, length, height) to have the diagonal of the tank as an undisturbed flow path. Experiments were done in a cold room of 0 deg. Celsius. White, light reflecting plastic particles of about 0.1 mm size and of a specific weight of 1.04 were added to the seawater to visualize the propulsion jet produced by *Euphausia*. Fig.1 schematically shows experimental set up and the system used for analysis.

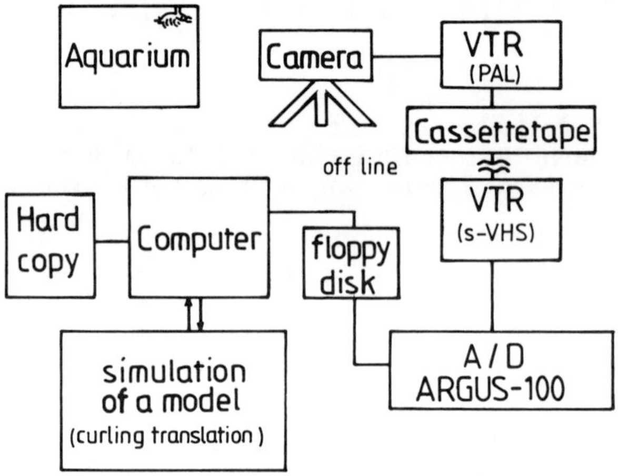

Fig.1 Block-diagram of apparatus used in recording and analysis. Processing of recorded data in these experiments included a conversion from european PAL- to SECAM-norm.

The analogue data of 120 frames(sampled at 15±1.2Hz) taken by the camera(National Panasonic WV-1850) were recorded on VTR-cassette-tapes. At a rate of 3.7- about corresponding the beat frequency of the swimmerets of the animal at the time of the recording- frames were sampled and digitized using the ARGUS-100 (Hamamatsu-Photonics Ltd) system and stored on floppy disks. Fig.2a shows the experimental situation.

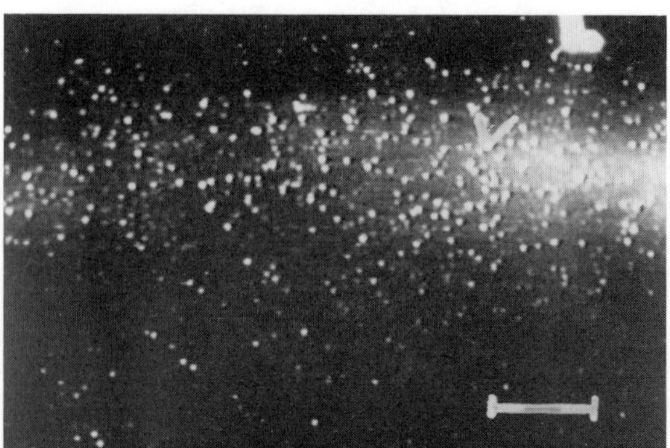

Fig.2a Photograph of the view recorded by video camera. Shown are the position of the holder (upper right) carrying the tethered animal of 3.5 cm body length (pleopod beat frequency 3.7 Hz). Two light sources illuminate the suspension of particles. The mark indicates position of the distal end of the field of 128x 128 pixels subjected to analysis.Flow velocity at this position was 1.4 cm/s in the recorded situation. Calibration bar: 5 cm

The suspended particles matched the specific weight of the seawater very well because, as tested in a resting body of water, the suspended particles took about 15 minutes to assemble at the water surface.

Picture analysis: A detailed description is given in the reference quoted above. Designations and equations used to calculate parameters used in visualization are as follows:
The brightness or intensity of pixels at the coordinates (i,j) are represented by $SS(i,j)_t$. The suffix t means the frame number (total of that is NN, NN=120, or 100 in this paper). The time differences between $SS(i,j)_t$, and $SS(i,j)_{t-1}$ are represented as:

$$ST(i,j)_t = SS(i,j)_t - SS(i,j)_{t-1} \quad (1)$$

Several parameters are calculated from $ST(i,j)_t$

$$\text{Averages: } \langle ST(i,j)\rangle = (1/NN)\sum_{t=1}^{NN} ST(i,j)_t \quad (2)$$

Auto-correlation function (in this paper we use the word "variance" instead of auto-correlation at lag-time 0):

$$\langle ST(i,j)^2\rangle = (1/NN)\sum_{t=1}^{NN} (ST(i,j)_t - \langle ST(i,j)\rangle)(ST(i,j)_t - \langle ST(i,j)\rangle) \quad (3)$$

Mutual-correlation function at lag-time 0:

$$\langle MST(i,j{:}k,l)\rangle = (1/NN)\sum_{t=1}^{NN} (ST(i,j)_t - \langle ST(i,j)\rangle)(ST(k,l)_t - \langle ST(k,l)\rangle) \quad (4)$$

respectively.

RESULTS.

Analysis of a simulation of turbulence by a simple mathematical model
The following situation was assumed: The trajectories of particles make several microscopically small curlings, remaining macroscopically in the same place. In this situation, two extremes (i,ii) were considered:
i) curling or a rotational mode of motion around a center point with the angular velocity of rotation given by the uniform random number function.
ii) a translational mode of motion in one direction (parallel to i-axis) and with random velocity given by the random uniform number function.
The two extremes nevertheless show some aspects of turbulences because distributions of both the translational velocity and the angular velocity of

rotation are important characteristics of turbulent flow. In the model investigation, the dimensions of the picture to be analyzed were made 60x60 pixels and the total number of frames was limited to 100. Several values of angular and translational velocity were examined. In the correlation functions (variance, mutual correlations, together with averages) obtained, large values of angular velocity were found to be a measure of strong turbulence. In the case of translational movements, two sorts of modes of motion were calculated: at right angle and in parallel to the i-axis. The assumption, that turbulences were probably stronger in the direction parallel to the i-axis was verified by the variance and mutual correlation pictures. To conclude, the larger the angular velocity introduced into this model, the larger was the variance of the parameters of ST. This suggests that the parameters recommended here are most suitable to visualize turbulence of flow.

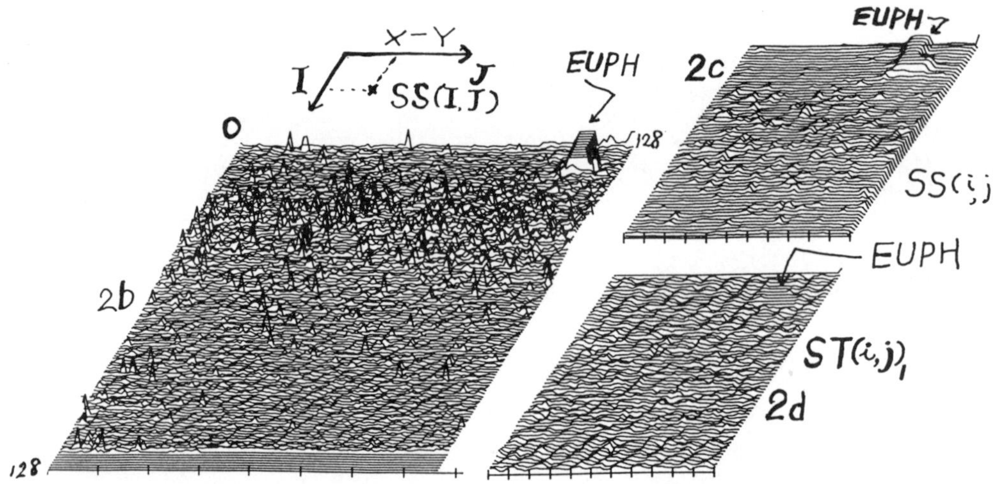

Fig.2b-d: b) Stereoplot of digital images of views as shown in Fig.2a. Peaks indicate light reflected from a floating particle. The center coordinates if the picture are Ic=64 and Jc=64. The position of *Euphausia* is seen at the top right; c) Stereoplot of the digital image of a quarter (64x64 pixels) of the area shown in Fig.2b; center coordinates are Ic=32, Jc=96. The height of the wavy lines indicates the brightness of light refelected from particles; d) Stereoplot of temporal brightnes differences(="time differences") obtained by subtraction of brightnesses of pixels in two consecutive frames in the same area as shown in Fig.2c; see text for details. Center coordinates: Ic=32, Jc=96; sampling time 0,066 s. Picture size 64x64 pixels.

Analysis of experimental data. Records of flow generated by *Euphausia* were made to demonstrate the effectivity of the parameters variance of temporal changes (in the following text referred to as"time differences") of brightness and of variance of brightness and of the parameters correlation of time differences and correlation of brightness in the task of visualization of flow events.

Fig.2b shows a frame of 128x128 pixels of the digitized picture taken in the situation shown in Fig.2a. The vertical excursions of the lines shown indicate the brightness of light reflected from a suspended particle Further analysis was restricted to one quarter of the field shown, an area 64x64 pixels right next to the position of the animal. Whereas Fig.2c shows again the brightness of particles (or pixels) in this smaller area, Fig. 2d shows the stereoplot of the parameter time difference ST in the same area in consecutive pictures analyzed. The tethered animal always reflecting light continously from the same spot of the analyzed area, produces a zero-response in this parameter (see the area of absolutely parallel, horizontal lines in the position of the animal). The time difference parameters ST(i,j) express the net changes occuring and the correlation functions of the changes become larger as the turbulences occuring become significant. Evidence that this statement is justified is provided by calculation of the parameters from digital pictures taken at different sampling times. The events around the position cf the swimming *Euphausia* are described by these parameters as shown in Fig.3A and B.

Sampling time in Fig.3A is 0.066 s, in Fig.3B 0.6 s. The aspect of flow of a particle is visible in Fig.3AB a:ST2. In the parameter variance of brightness (Fig.3ABc:SS2) this event is not showing. The display of averages of brightness d:SS clearly shows the position of *Euphausia*, the plot of averages of time differences b:ST does not and is difficult to interpret. Note that the scale of the vertical axis (normalization factor) in a: and b: is changed.

Figs.4 A,B,C show displays of variance of ST(i,j) and SS(i,j) at a site closer to and more (as compared to the site analyzed in Fig.3, see center coordinates Ic and Jc) towards the rear of the swimming *Euphausia*. Sampling times are 0.66, 0.2 and 0.6 s in 4A,B, and C respectively. Increasing the sampling time the variances become larger (note scales) and flow and turbulence patterns appear. In the displays of variance of brightness the visualization of flow and turbulence is less clear described. The suggestion is made that averages of brightness are more useful to the purpose of description of flow than the variances of brightness.

The results shown in Figs.3 and 4 confirm, that a parameter computed from time differences of pixel brightness, the variance of time differences of brightness, reliably traces the flow of individual particles and can express the degree of turbulence in the flow pattern.

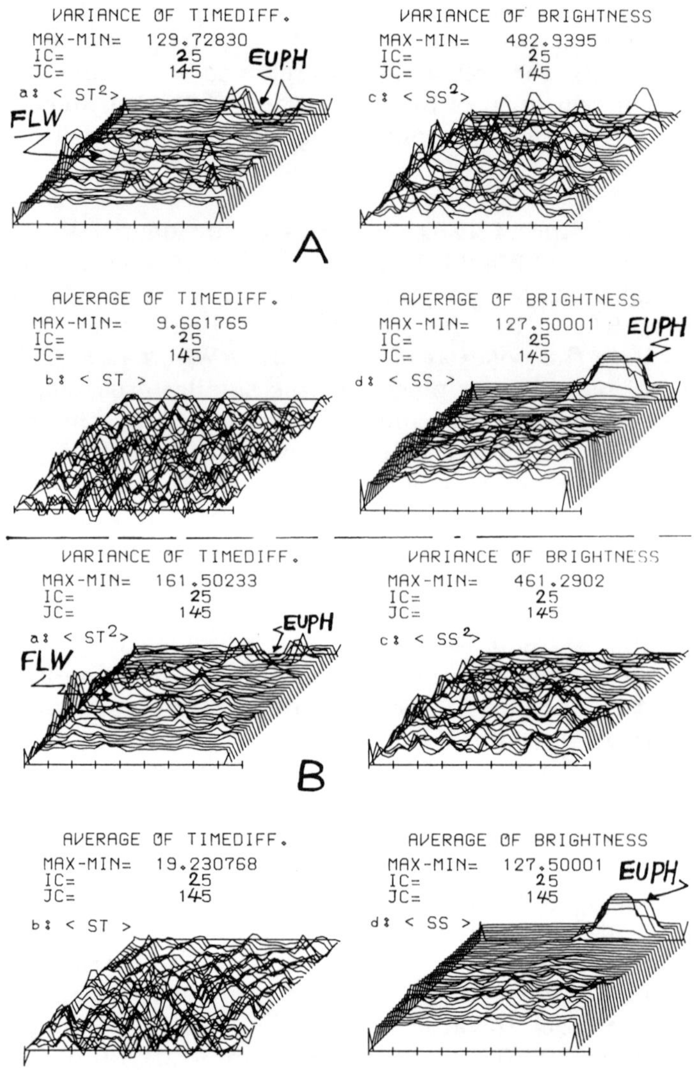

Fig.3 Two dimensional display of the parameters "variance " and "average" of ST("TIMEDIFF") and SS("brightness"). MAX-MIN marks the normalization factor, Ic and Jc are center coordinates of area analyzed.Size of pictures:40x40 pixels. *Euphausia* is shown as zero signal in ST- and as prominent peak in SS-plots; flow of particles is indicated at the places marked by FLW; A: parameters calculated from 120 frames taken with sampling time of 0.066 s and B: parameters calculated from 40 frames only taken with the sampling time of 0.6 s.

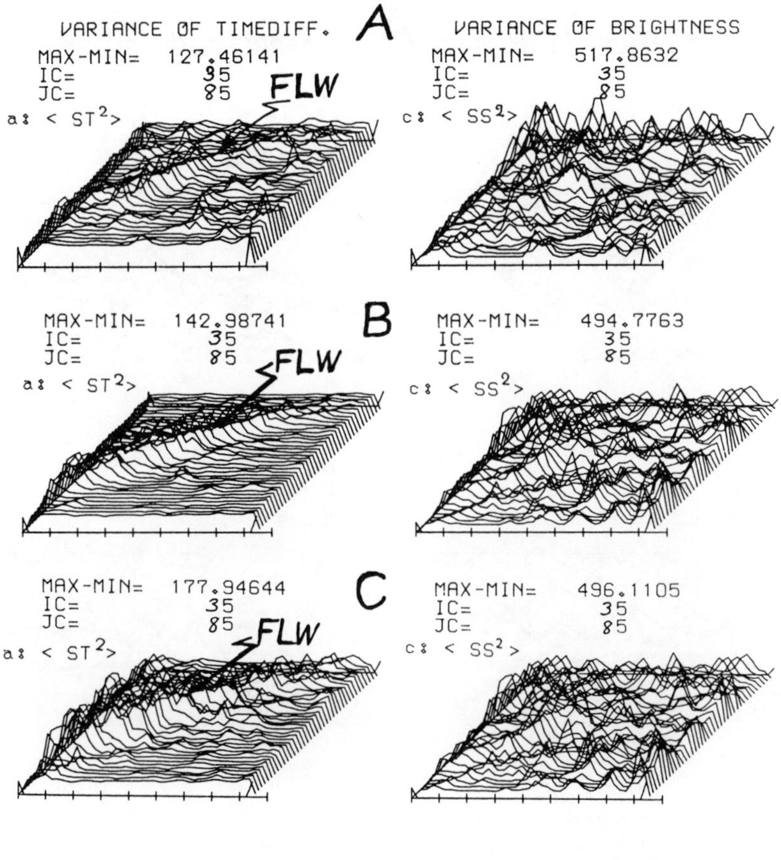

Fig.4 Two dimensional display of variance of time differences in brightness ST and brightness SS. Picture size is 40x40 pixels. Designations as in Fig.3. A: parameters calculated from 120 frames taken with the sampling time 0.066 s; B: parameters calculated from 120 frames taken with sampling time 0.2 s; C: parameters calculated from 40 frames taken with sampling time of 0.6 s.

The author expects that the degree of spatial correlation of turbulent flow might be reflected by the mutual correlation functions MST or MSS, sample-displays of which are shown in Fig.5A-C.

The parameters were computed from 15 neighbouring points around the central one (Ic/Jc). The picture size analyzed is 31x 31 pixels. The degree of spatial correlation is traced in the curves passing the central pixel (bold lines in the displays of MST and MSS). Because different center point locations were chosen (see coordinates Ic and Jc in A,B,C), the Fig.5 documents different spatial correlation in different areas of turbulent flow.

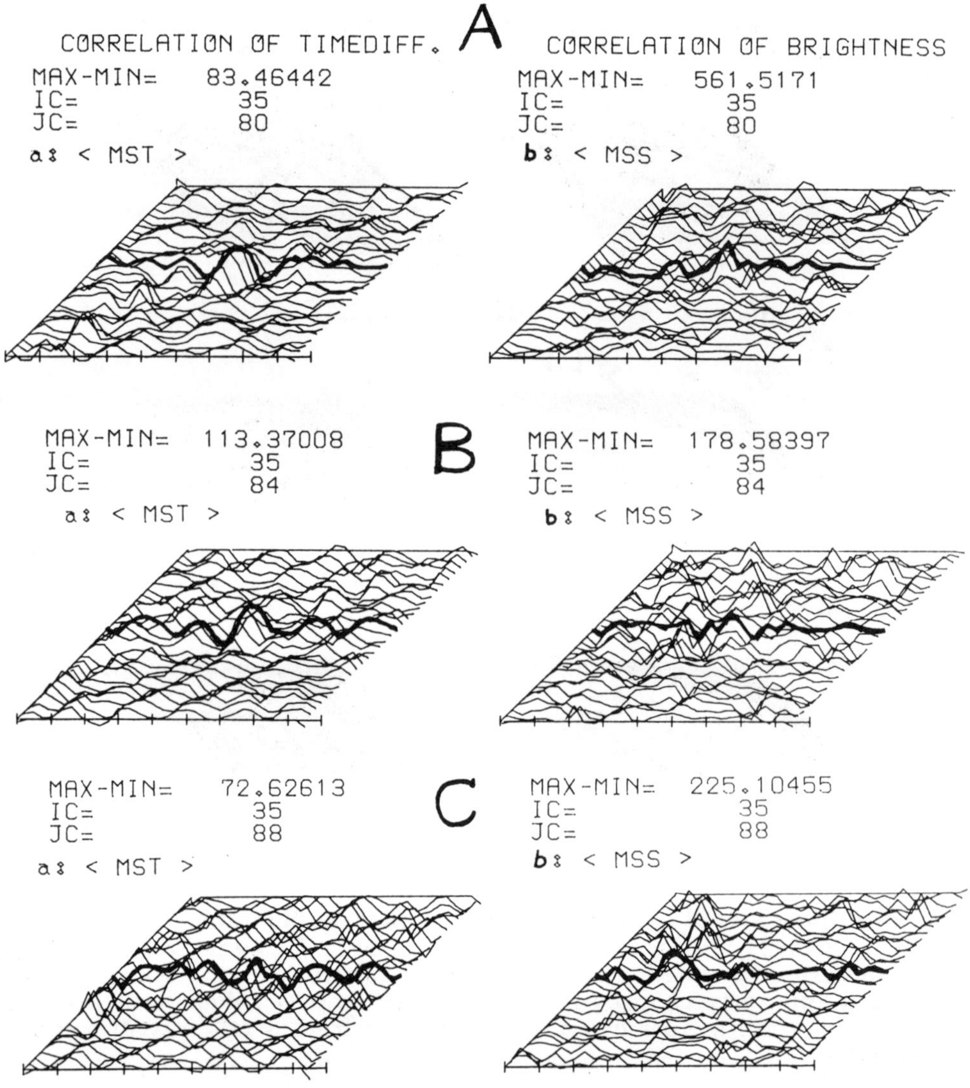

Fig.5 Two dimensional display of mutual-correlation functions of time difference (ST) and brightness (SS) parameters. Size of picture 31x31 pixels; the central line j=16 is shown in bold . Computations from 120 frames taken with 0.2 s sampling time; Figures A-C represent slightly shifted areas of analysis Jc=80,Jc=84 and Jc=88 at Ic=35.

DISCUSSION.

Though this study has not yet supplied the information required to explain schooling in Euphausia, it nevertheless demonstrates the power of picture analysis in the visualization of flow patterns around swimming antarctic krill.

Earlier work on the technique of dynamic image processing (H.Miike, S.Ikemoto, K.Ochiai, H.Hashimoto and Y.Ebina 1984) has focussed on the parameter difference in brightness of pixels in order to visualize turbulent movement. The now additionally adopted parameter ST (i,j,)t has definite advantages, based on the following facts:

By using the temporal change of brightness (=time differences of brightness) instead, only the net changes are used. This results in the fact, that in the presence of a signal the computed parameters variance and correlation become large with respect to background. Another even more essential point is, that the cross term effect becomes very large if strong turbulence induces dramatic changes in pixel brightness in frames taken at time t and time t-1. Hence, correlation parameters presumably provide additional information on the quality of tubulence in flow patterns.

Acknowledgements:

The author is much obliged to Mr. Yasuo Miwa for his efficient help with calculations and to K.Wiese for hospitality during his stay at the University of Hamburg.

REFERENCES:

Wiese,K., Marschall, H.-P. (1990) Sensitivity to vibration and turbulence of water in context with schooling in antarctic Krill *Euphausia superba*. In: Frontiers in Crustacean Neurobiology, K.Wiese, W.-D.Krenz, J.Tautz, H.Reichert, B.Mulloney (eds.), Birkhäuser Verlag Basel, Boston, Berlin this volume

Miike,H., Ikemoto,S., Ochiai,K. Hashimoto,H., Ebina,Y.(1984) New dynamic image processing technique for the analysis of texture movement. Jpn.J.Appl.Phys. **23:** L379-L381

Miike,H., Ochiai,K., Hashimoto,H., Ebina Y.(1985) Digital image processing study on dynamics of dissipative structure in nematic liquid crystal. J.Phys.Soc.Jpn. **54**: 1724-1729

Frontiers in Crustacean Neurobiology
Advances in Life Sciences

PRESYNAPTIC INHIBITION OF PRIMARY AFFERENT SYNAPSES IN THE CRAYFISH

Mark D. Kirk[1] and C. K. Govind[2]

[1]University of Missouri at Columbia, Division of Biological Sciences, Lefevre Hall, Columbia, MO 65211 USA

[2]University of Toronto, Life Sciences Division, Scarborough College, 1265 Military Trail, Scarborough, Ontario, CANADA M1C 1A4

SUMMARY

Presynaptic inhibition of primary mechanoafferents in the crayfish abdomen, elicited during giant axon-mediated escape, protects primary afferent synapses from depression which would result from reafference during the tailflip. As in vertebrates, this inhibition is associated with primary afferent depolarization (PAD) ostensibly produced by a GABA-mediated increase in chloride conductance. We have physiologically and morphologically characterized the inhibitory interneurons (PADIs) directly responsible for producing PAD and presynaptic inhibition, identified elements of the pathways excited by the giant escape command cells which recruit the PADIs, and are currently studying the ultrastructure of synapses between the PADIs and afferent terminals.

INTRODUCTION

The first unequivocal evidence for a decrease in transmitter release caused by presynaptic inhibition came from a crustacean model system, the crayfish opener neuromuscular junction where Dudel & Kuffler (1961) showed that firing the opener inhibitor approximately 2 msec prior to firing the opener excitor dramatically inhibited the excitor's input to the muscle. This work provided a rigorous foundation for subsequent studies of presynaptic inhibition in other invertebrates and vertebrates (Schmidt, 1971; Levy, 1977; Ryall, 1978; Krasne and Bryan, 1973; Shapiro et al., 1980; Atwood et al., 1984). Here we discuss the efferent control of tactile receptors in the crayfish abdomen, specifically presynaptic inhibition of primary afferent synapses that occurs during giant axon mediated escape responses.

The dorsal surface of the crayfish telson (and remaining abdomen) is covered with hairs sensitive to nearfield water displacement and direct touch (Kennedy, 1971, 1974; Wiese, 1976; Plummer, 1984). Each of these mechanoreceptive hairs is innervated by up to two primary afferent sensory neurons (mechanosensory afferents, MSAs) which project into the last abdominal ganglion (i.e., the sixth). Here they synapse onto ascending mechanosensitive interneurons (MSIs) (Calabrese, 1976; Kennedy, 1971; Wiese et al., 1976; Sigvardt et al., 1982). A select group of these MSIs are innervated by the more phasic MSAs which respond to high frequency water vibrations and/or direct touch; these MSIs form the afferent circuit eliciting the Lateral Giant (LG) escape reflex (Zucker, 1972a). When the LGs fire, they recruit fast flexor motoneurons, thereby causing a rapid tail flexion which comprises the initial response to threatening stimuli directed at posterior regions of the animal (Fig. 1) [for a complete description of afferent and efferent pathways involved in LG and medial giant (MG) mediated tailflips, see Wine & Krasne, 1982; Wine, 1984].

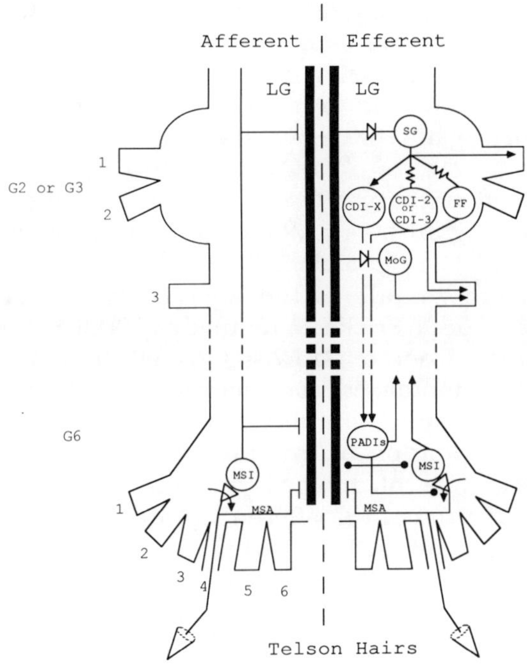

Fig. 1. Key elements in the afferent and efferent pathways of the lateral giant (LG) escape system found in the 2nd (G2) or 3rd (G3) and 6th (G6) abdominal ganglia [see text and Kirk (1985) for details]. Solid arrows indicate axonal projections or direct connections, dashed arrows indicate possible polysynaptic connections. Abbreviations in this and subsequent figures: CDI-2 or CDI-3, corollary discharge interneurons in the 2nd or 3rd ganglion; CDI-X, unidentified corollary discharge interneuron(s); FF, nongiant fast flexor motoneuron; MoG, giant fast flexor motoneuron; MSA, mechanosensory afferent; MSI, mechanosensory interneuron; PADI, PAD-producing inhibitory interneuron; SG, segmental giant. Adapted from Kirk (1985).

The excitatory chemical synapses made by the primary afferents onto first order MSIs are labile and with repeated activation exhibit extreme depression due to a decrease in quantal content (Krasne, 1969; Zucker, 1972b). This synaptic depression is an advantageous sensory adaptation underlying behavioral habituation to repeated non-threatening stimuli. However, such depression of the MSA synapses could be maladaptive under certain conditions. For instance, if activated due to centrally programmed ballistic abdominal movements, the resulting depression would leave the animal unable to respond to subsequent threatening stimuli. To prevent unwanted self-induced habituation, the crayfish has evolved a mechanism to *protect* these synapses from depression during giant mediated tailflips; the primary afferent synapses are inhibited presynaptically at a delay following a spike in either of the giant escape command neurons, and this inhibition protects the afferents from depression (Krasne & Bryan, 1973; Bryan & Krasne, 1977a,b). Inhibition and protection is observed in the intact animal, strongly supporting its presence during actual escape behavior (Wine et al., 1975).

Presynaptic inhibition of primary afferent synapses in the crayfish sixth abdominal ganglion following an LG or MG spike is associated with primary afferent depolarization (PAD), a depolarization of the afferents produced by inhibitory interneurons presynaptic to the afferent terminals (Kennedy et al., 1974; Kennedy et al., 1980; Fricke & Kennedy, 1983). Previous studies suggest that PAD results from a GABA-mediated increase in chloride conductance and that this increased conductance shunts action potential currents, thus decreasing spike amplitudes in the afferent terminals (Kennedy et al., 1974). Inhibition of synaptic release presumably ensues from a consequent decrease of inward calcium current. Therefore, presynaptic inhibition may protect the afferent synapses from depression by preventing transmitter depletion, although this has yet to be tested. Other reports of presynaptic control of synapses in crayfish CNS have appeared (Sillar & Skorupski, 1986; Skorupski & Sillar, 1986; Wang-Bennet & Glantz, 1985; Glantz et al., 1985; Paul, 1989). Below we briefly describe our studies of the pathways and synaptic mechanisms producing PAD and presynaptic inhibition of primary afferent synapses during LG and MG mediated escape behavior.

METHODS

PHYSIOLOGY. All experiments were performed on the crayfish *Procambarus clarkii.* Originally, intracellular and extracellular recordings and stimulations as well as sucrose gap recording of PAD were obtained in the isolated abdominal nerve cord as described previously (Kirk & Wine, 1984; Kirk, 1985; see Fig. 3). Recently, to obtain intracellular recordings from afferent terminals and identify the associated sensory hair, we have used a reduced version of the isolated tailfan preparation. In our new isolated telson preparation we detached the uropods at their basal joints, leaving the telson free of associated uropod sensory and motor structures. The telson remained attached to the abdominal nerve cord via nerve roots 4 and 5, which innervate most of the hairs on one half of the rostral telson (Calabrese, 1976). With the dorsal surfaces of the telson and sixth ganglion uppermost, we recorded intracellularly from primary afferent terminals at their entrance to the sixth ganglion neuropil. We then used a fine stainless steel needle to probe individual telson hairs to identify the position and structure of the hair subtended by the impaled afferent. When studying PAD and IPSPs in identified sensory neurons, intracellular recordings from afferent terminals were often made with microelectrodes filled with 3 M KCl which allowed intracellular Cl^- injections to increase the peak depolarization of PSPs mediated by increased Cl^- conductance.

CELLULAR MORPHOLOGY AND IMMUNOCYTOCHEMISTRY. Intracellular dye injections (iontophoresis and/or pressure injection) were made with electrodes containing lucifer yellow or Horseradish Peroxidase (HRP). For light microscopy, the preparations were viewed in wholemount or sectioned material (Kirk, 1985). To test for GABA-like immunoreactivity, we used a rabbit primary antibody to GABA purchased from Chemicon (Cat. No. AB131) with an FITC tagged goat anti-rabbit secondary antibody (Sigma), and viewed frozen sections (16-20 microns thick) of the nerve cord with an epifluorescence microscope.

ELECTRON MICROSCOPY. To investigate the input and output synapses involving primary afferent terminals in the sixth abdominal ganglion, we intracellularly injected HRP into afferent terminals. The fourth root, with an attached sliver of neuropil containing the terminals of the fourth root afferents was then developed using DAB (Muller & McMahan, 1976; Wang-Bennet & Glantz, 1985), fixed with glutaraldehyde, and embedded in plastic. Ultrathin sections were viewed with an electron microscope (Govind et al., 1988).

RESULTS

First we will summarize the pathways leading to PAD and presynaptic inhibition of primary afferent synapses in the sixth ganglion, then present our morphological and physiological results on the primary afferent depolarizing interneurons (PADIs) which are the final common inhibitory interneurons for presynaptic inhibition produced following LG and MG spikes. Then we will present our immunocytochemical studies into the transmitter phenotype of the PADIs as well as the ultrastructure of putative PADI synapses impinging on the primary afferent terminals.

In addition to causing fast flexor motor output, an impulse in the giant axons recruits an extensive recurrent inhibitory network having many actions including inhibition of LG itself, inhibition of extensor excitor motoneurons at short latency (for short duration), inhibition of the giant flexor motoneuron (MoG), inhibition of the fast flexor muscles by firing the flexor peripheral inhibitor at long latency, inhibition of MSIs postsynaptically, and inhibition of primary afferent synapses presynaptically (Wine & Krasne, 1982). Onset of PAD and presynaptic inhibition is delayed by 10-12 msec following an LG action potential to peak at the time of maximal flexor activation. The duration of PAD and presynaptic inhibition are similar, lasting about 100 msec, (although the inhibition sometimes outlasts observable PAD, Kennedy et al., 1974).

The latency to PAD and inhibition is due to the polysynaptic nature of the pathway activating the PADIs. PADIs fire multiple spikes at long latency following activation of the LG (Fig. 2B). When the LG fires, it excites the segmental giants (SGs) which in turn excite numerous elements in the escape circuit including corollary discharge interneurons (CDIs). Two CDIs (CDI-2 and CDI-3, in the second and third abdominal ganglia respectively) have been uniquely identified (Kramer et al., 1981). CDIs recruited in the second and third abdominal ganglia are the interneurons primarily responsible for firing the PADIs. However, CDI-2 and CDI-3 produce only minor direct excitation of PADIs (Kirk, 1985); therefore, most of the input to PADIs is from unidentified CDIs (CDI-X in Fig. 1) activated by the SGs in the second and third ganglia (Fig. 2C).

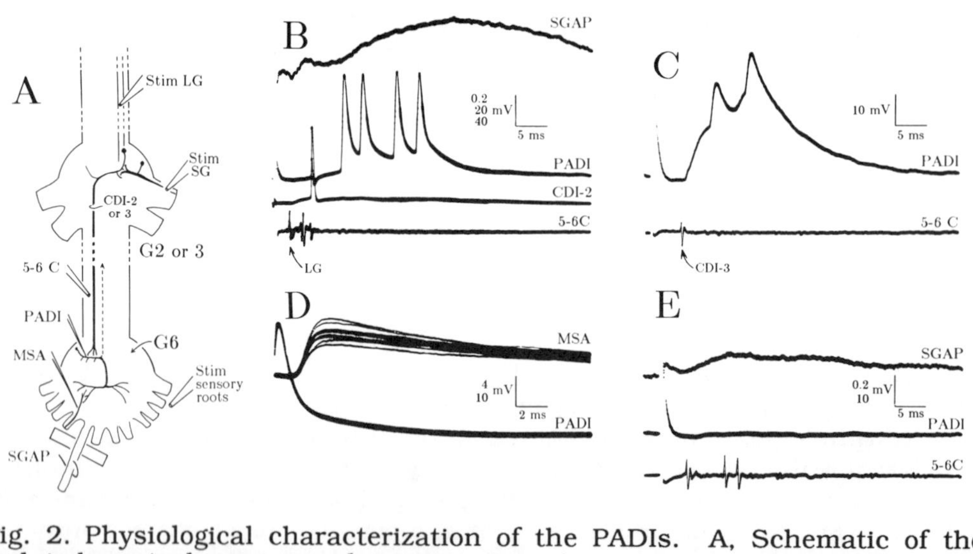

Fig. 2. Physiological characterization of the PADIs. A, Schematic of the isolated ventral nerve cord preparation showing sites of recording and stimulation. B, Response to LG stimulation. C, Response to stimulation of the ipsilateral SG in G3. CDI-3 is recruited by the stimulus as recorded on the dorsal surface of the 5-6 connective, but longer latency input is responsible for firing the PADI. D, Driving PADIs directly produces short and constant latency unitary PAD with fluctuating amplitudes. E,

PAD is produced in fourth root afferents (recorded using a sucrose gap) and sensory interneurons are fired (5-6C) in response to stimulation of the adjacent fifth sensory root. However, the PADI receives only minor subthreshold input.

PAD is also produced in fourth root afferent terminals upon stimulation of adjacent afferent nerves (Kennedy et al., 1974); however, the PADIs are not activated by stimulation of sensory roots in the abdomen (Fig. 2E), indicating a least some separation in the LG/MG- and sensory-evoked PAD (Kirk, 1985).

That PADIs cause PAD and presynaptic inhibition directly via monosynaptic contacts with the afferent terminals is supported by the following results. Firing the PADIs with intracellulary injected current causes unitary PAD at short and constant latency (Fig. 2 D) capable of following PADI impulses one-for-one even at frequencies greater than 100 Hz (Kirk and Wine, 1984; Kirk, 1985). In addition when a PADI and afferent terminal are simultaneously dye-filled, the axonal terminals of the PADI are contiguous at several sites with branches of the afferent as observed at the light level, a requirement for monosynapticity (Kirk, 1985).

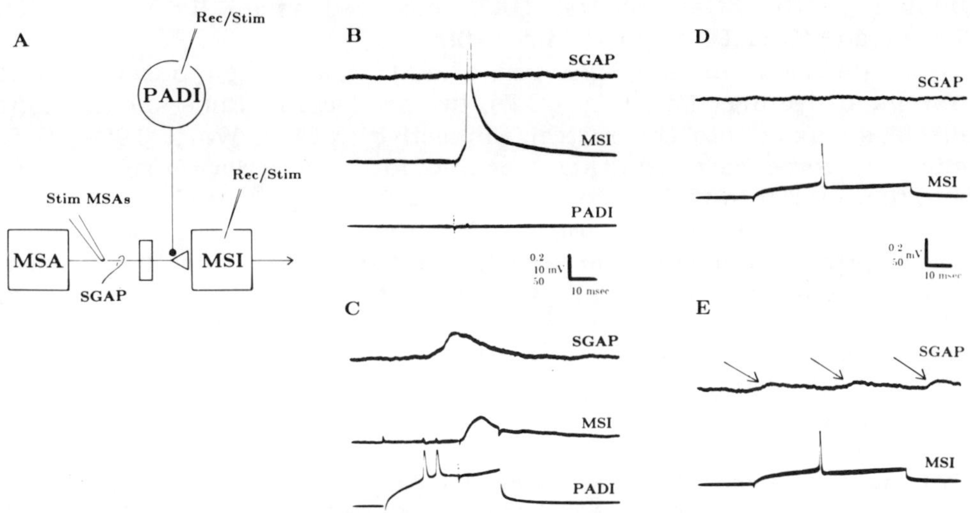

Fig. 3. PADIs produce presynaptic inhibition of primary afferent synapses. A, Schematic of the sites of recording and stimulation. B, Stimulation of the sensory branch of the 2nd root produces an EPSP and action potential in Interneuron C. C, Firing a doublet of action potentials in a PADI cause summating unitary PAD recorded with the sucrose gap and reduces the EPSP amplitude in Interneuron C below threshold. The PADI produced no observable IPSPs in Interneuron C. D and E, No evidence for a remote postsynaptic conductance change was found in Interneuron C when driving a PADI. D, Interneuron C was fired directly with injected current. E, Paired firing of the PADI did not influence the integration time to spike threshold in Interneuron C. From Kirk (1985).

PAD appears to be caused by an increased conductance to chloride (Kennedy et al., 1980); unitary PAD (as with LG/MG-elicited PAD) is increased in amplitude upon intracellular Cl^- injection into the afferent terminal (Kirk, 1985). Furthermore, the sign and amplitude of PAD is dependent on extracellular chloride concentration (Kennedy et al., 1980). Another intriguing aspect of the unitary PADs is that they fluctuate in amplitude with repetitive stimulation; in fact, successive unitary PADs appear to vary in discrete steps (Fig. 2D) suggestive of quantal fluctuations. Direct presynaptic inhibition of primary afferent synapses by PADIs can be unambiguously demonstrated using the sixth ganglion primary MSI Interneuron C (Zucker, 1972a) or 6C1 (Sigvardt et al., 1982). Directly firing a PADI with injected current so that peak PAD coincides with the arrival of primary afferent input to Interneuron C causes inhibition (Fig. 3B,C) without causing an observable postsynaptic conductance increase (Fig. 3D,E) (Kirk, 1985).

Firing the PADIs does produce IPSPs in another primary MSI, Interneuron A (Zucker, 1972a), thereby producing both pre- and post-synaptic inhibition in this case (Kirk, 1985). PADIs also cause recurrent inhibition in the LGs (Roberts, 1968) observed as an IPSP in the LG following an MG or LG impulse (Kirk, 1985).

Three different anatomical types of PADI have been observed with intracellular dye-injections (Fig. 4C,D), two are local neurons and the third projects an axon into the rostral connective (Kirk & Wine, 1984; Kirk, 1985). All three have dendrites localized to the anterior-dorsal neuropil where they overlap with CDI axon terminals. The PADI axonal terminals are located in caudal-ventral neuropil where they overlap with the terminal fields of primary afferents traveling in ganglionic roots one through five. These afferents are from receptors of both the telson and uropods (Calabrese, 1976). The terminals of the PADIs also interdigitate with dendrites of the LGs (Fig. 4F) consistent with their direct inhibition of this command cell mentioned above. The axons of projecting PADIs are found in the ventral medial region of the anterior connective as observed in cross sections (Fig. 4E).

PAD may be mediated by the action of GABA on the afferent terminals as bicuculline and picrotoxin decreased PAD and GABA application depolarized the afferents (Kennedy et al., 1980). We have evidence for GABA-like immunoreactivity using a polyclonal antibody specific for GABA. Our preliminary results reveal GABA-like immunoreactivity in the sixth ganglion ventral neuropil (data not shown) and in axons located in the ventral-medial region of the anterior connective (Fig. 5). An overall distribution of GABA-like immunoreactivity in the crayfish abdominal nerve cord consistent with our results has been recently demonstrated (Mulloney & Hall, 1988).

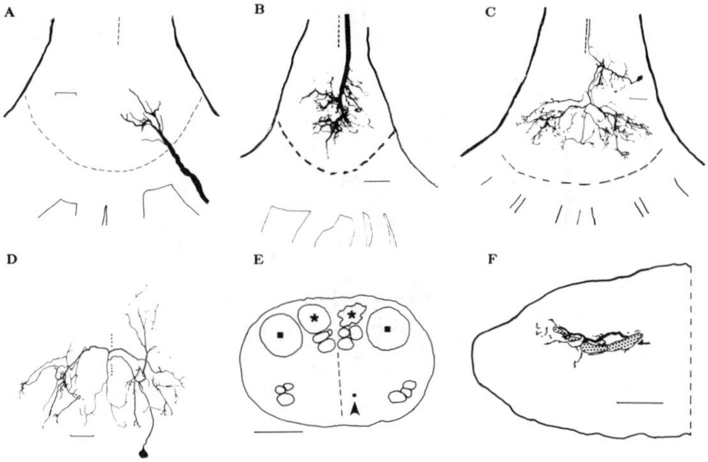

Fig. 4. Cellular morphology of primary afferent terminals, CDI terminals, and PADIs. A, 3rd root primary afferent terminal. B, CDI-3 terminal. C, PADI with axon that projects into the anterior connective. D, A second type of PADI with cell body located caudally and no projecting axon. E, Cross section of the 5-6 connective showing the position of a PADI axon (arrowhead). The empty profiles of several large axons [including the LGs (black squares) and MGs (stars)] are illustrated for orientation. F, One half of the sixth ganglion in cross section illustrating the overlap of PADI terminals and the LG dendrite (dots). Calibration bars: A, C-F; 100 microns, B; 200 microns. Adapted from Kirk (1985).

To investigate the synaptic morphology underlying presynaptic inhibition, we are currently examining the fine structural relationships between the terminals of primary afferents and PADIs in the sixth ganglion. Impaled afferent terminals were labeled using HRP-filled microelectrodes after their sensory responses and the telson hair they innervated were documented, and examined with the electron microscope. Both output and input synapses of the conventional chemical types with synaptic vesicles, characterize the labelled primary afferents. The identity of contributing elements of such synapses may be revealed with labeling of both primary afferent and PADI. These results corroborate earlier findings of input and output synapses on presumed primary afferent terminals when the entire fourth root was backfilled with cobalt (Lee, 1983).

DISCUSSION

A of number of parallels exist between presynaptic inhibition in the CNS of crayfish and vertebrates (Kennedy et al., 1980); in both: 1) presynaptic inhibition appears to be directed mainly at primary afferents, 2) presynaptic and postsynaptic inhibition occur together, 3) presynaptic inhibition outlasts its postsynaptic counterpart, 4) presynaptic inhibition is correlated

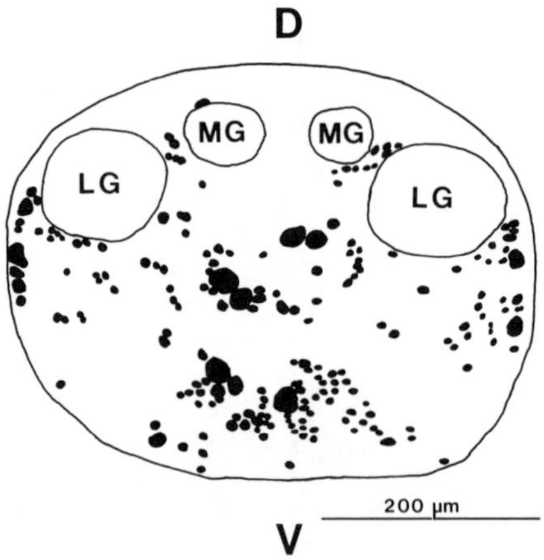

Fig. 5. Reconstruction of GABA immunoreactivity in the 5-6 connective shown in cross section. Immunoreactive axonal profiles are filled in black. Note several small axons in the ventral-medial region. The giant axon profiles are included in outline for orientation. D, dorsal; V, ventral.

with PAD, 5) GABA is the putative transmitter producing PAD (although this needs confirmation), and 6) presynaptic and postsynaptic inhibition is mediated by the same inhibitory interneurons (Solodkin et al., 1984; Kennedy et al., 1980; Kirk, 1985). These parallels show that the crayfish is an excellent model system to study presynaptic inhibition of primary afferent synapses and PAD.

In addition to the LG/MG pathways described here several other pathways are known to recruit PAD in the fourth root afferents, including pathways recruited by leg proprioceptors (Fricke & Kennedy, 1983), adjacent sensory roots (Kennedy et al., 1974), and the muscle receptor organs (MROs, Wine & Krasne, 1982). We found that the identified PADIs are not excited by sensory root shock; although Kennedy et al. (1974) suggested that sensory root-evoked and LG/MG-mediated PAD shared some common final elements. If these pathways do share some final common presynaptic inhibitors, they are not the PADIs we have identified to date. Additionally, a PAD-producing interneuron excited by sensory root shock but not by firing the giant axons has been observed (Kirk, 1985). However, PADIs may be shared by other pathways activated under circumstances other than LG/MG-elicited escape behavior such as the pathways evoked by leg proprioceptors recruited during walking (Fricke & Kennedy, 1983) or pathways active during nongiant-mediated swimming (Kramer & Krasne, 1984) as well as unknown sensory or motor pathways. To understand the organization and coordination of networks mediating PAD and presynaptic inhibition, it will be important to further identify the pathways presynaptic to the PADIs, to determine the rostral outputs of the projecting PADIs, and to identify the final common inhibitory elements mediating presynaptic inhibition under other conditions.

Our goal in studying the crayfish CNS is to understand the pathways and the cellular and molecular mechanisms responsible for PAD and presynaptic inhibition. With easy access to the large diameter fourth root primary afferent terminals and because individual afferents elicit large unitary EPSPs in identifiable MSIs, it will be possible to apply voltage and patch clamp techniques as well as intracellular microinjections to study the biophysics and molecular physiology of presynaptic inhibition of primary afferent synapses, something that may never be possible in more complex vertebrate systems.

ACKNOWLEDGEMENTS: Thanks to Dr. Bill Eldred for help with the GABA immunocytochemistry, to Joanne Pearce for the electron microscopy, and to Dr. Paul Katz for criticizing the manuscript.

REFERENCES

Atwood, H.L., Stevens, J.K., & Marin, L. (1984) Axoaxonal synapse location and consequences for presynaptic inhibition in crustacean motor axon terminals. *J. Comp. Neurol.* **225**: 64-74.

Bryan, J.S. & Krasne, F.B. (1977a) Protection from habituation of the crayfish lateral giant fiber escape response. *J. Physiol.(London).* **271**: 351-368.

Bryan, J.S. & Krasne, F.B. (1977b) Presynaptic inhibition: the mechanism of protection from habituation of the crayfish lateral giant fiber escape response. *J. Physiol. (London).* **271**: 369-390.

Calabrese, R.L. (1976) Crayfish mechanoreceptive interneurons. I. The nature of ipsilateral inputs. *J. Comp. Physiol.* **105**: 83-102.

Dudel, J. & Kuffler, S.W. (1961) Presynaptic inhibition at the crayfish neuromuscular junction. *J. Physiol. (London).* **155**: 543-562.

Fricke, R.A. & Kennedy, D. (1983) Inhibition of mechanosensory neurons in the crayfish. II. Presynaptic inhibition of primary afferents by a central proprioceptive tract related to walking. *J. Comp. Physiol.* **153**: 443-464.

Glantz, RM., Wang-Bennett, L. & Waldrop, B. (1985) Presynaptic inhibition in the crayfish brain. I. Inhibition of a central synapse and synaptic events in the presynaptic terminals. *J. Comp. Physiol.* **156**: 477-487.

Govind, C.K., Kirk, M.D., & Pearce, J. (1988) Highly active neuromuscular system in developing lobsters with programmed obsolescence. *J. Comp. Neurol.* **272**: 437-449.

Kennedy, D. (1971) Crayfish interneurons. *Physiologist* **14**: 5-30.

Kennedy, D. (1974) Connections among neurons of different types in crustacean nervous systems. In *The Neurosciences: Third Study Program*, (ed. F.O. Schmitt and F.G. Worden) pp. 379-388. Cambridge, Mass., M.I.T. Press.

Kennedy, D., Calabrese, R., & Wine, J.J. (1974) Presynaptic inhibition: primary afferent depolarization in crayfish neurons. *Science.* **186**: 451-454.

Kennedy, D., McVittie, J. Calabrese, R., Fricke, R.A., Craelius, W., & Chiapella, P. (1980) Inhibition of mechanosensory interneurons in the crayfish. I. Presynaptic inhibition from giant fibers. *J. Neurophysiol.* **43**: 1495-1509.

Kirk, M.D. (1985) Presynaptic inhibition in the crayfish CNS: pathways and synaptic mechanisms. *J. Neurophysiol.* **54**: 1305-1325.

Kirk, M.D. & Wine, J.J. (1984) Identified interneurons produce both primary afferent depolarization and presynaptic inhibition. *Science.* **225**: 854-856.

Kramer, A.P. & Krasne, F.B. (1984) Crayfish escape behavior: production of tailflips without giant fiber activity. *J. Neurophysiol.* **52**: 189-211.

Kramer, A.P., Krasne, F.B., & Wine, J.J. (1981) Interneurons between giant axons and motoneurons in crayfish escape circuitry. *J. Neurophysiol.* **45**: 550-573.

Krasne, F.B. (1969) Excitation and habituation of the crayfish escape reflex: the depolarizing response in lateral giant fibers of the isolated abdomen. *J. Exp. Biol.* **50**: 29-46.

Krasne, F.B. & Bryan, J.S. (1973) Habituation: regulation through presynaptic inhibition. *Science.* **182**: 590-592.

Lee, S.C. (1983) Fine structure of synapses of the sensory portion of the circuit for lateral giant fiber mediated escape reactions of crayfish. *Ph.D. Dissertation.* University of California at Los Angeles.

Levy, R.A. (1977) The role of GABA in primary afferent depolarization. *Prog. Neurobiol.* **9**: 211-267.

Muller, K.J. & McMahan, U.J. (1976) The shapes of sensory and motor neurones and the distribution of their synapses in ganglia of the leech: a study using intracellular injection of horseradish peroxidase. *Proc. R. Soc. Lond. B.* **194**: 481-499.

Mulloney, B. & Hall, W.M. (1988) A map of the GABAergic neurons in segmental ganglia and the stomatogastric system of the crayfish. *Neurosci. Abstr.* **14**: 382.

Paul, D. (1989) Nonspiking stretch receptors of the crayfish swimmeret receive an efference copy of the central motor pattern for the swimmeret. *J. Exp. Biol.* **141**: 257-264.

Plummer, M.R. (1984) Frequency coding of waterborne vibrations by the crayfish. *Ph.D. Dissertation,* Stanford University.

Roberts, A. (1968) Recurrent inhibition in the giant-fiber system of the crayfish and its effect on the excitability of the escape response. *J. Exp. Biol.* **48**: 545-567.

Ryall, R.W. (1978) Presynaptic inhibition. *Trends Neurosci.* **1**: 164-166.

Schmidt, R.F. (1971) Presynaptic inhibition in the vertebrate central nervous system. *Ergeb. Physiol. Biol. Chem. Exp. Pharmakol.* **63**: 20-101.

Shapiro, E., Castellucci, V.F., & Kandel, E.R. (1980) Presynaptic inhibition in *Aplysia* involves a decrease in the Ca^{+2} current of the presynaptic neuron. *Proc. Natl. Acad. Sci. USA.* **77**: 1185-1189.

Sigvardt, K.A., Hagiwara, G., & Wine, J.J. (1982) Mechanosensory integration in the crayfish abdominal nervous system: structural and physiological differences between interneurons with single and multiple spike initiating sites. *J. Comp. Physiol.* **148**: 143-157.

Sillar, K.T. & Skorupski, P. (1986) Central input to primary afferent neurons in crayfish, *Pacifastacus leniusculus*, is correlated with rhythmic motor output of thoracic ganglia. *J. Neurophysiol.* **55**: 678-688.

Skorupski, P. & Sillar, K.T. (1986) Phase-dependent reversal of reflexes mediated by the thoracocoxal muscle receptor organ in the crayfish, *Pacifastacus leniusculus*. *J. Neurophysiol.* **55**: 689-695.

Solodkin, M., Jimenez, I., & Rudomin, P. (1984) Identification of common interneurons mediating pre- and postsynaptic inhibition in the cat spinal cord. *Science.* **224**: 1453-1456.

Wang-Bennet, LT. and Glantz, RM. (1985) Presynaptic inhibition in the crayfish brain. II. Morphology and ultrastructure of the terminal arborization. *J. Comp. Physiol.* **156**: 605-617.

Wiese, K. (1976) Mechanoreceptors for near-field water displacements in crayfish. *J. Neurophysiol.* **39**: 816-833.

Wiese, K., Calabrese, R.L., & Kennedy, D. (1976) Integration of directional mechanosensory input by crayfish interneurons. *J. Neurophysiol.* **39**: 834-843.

Wine, J.J. (1984) The structural basis of an innate behavioral pattern. *J. Exp. Biol.* **112**: 283-319.

Wine, J.J. & Krasne, F.B. (1982) The cellular organization of escape behavior. In *The Biology of Crustacea*, (ed. D.E. Bliss) pp. 241-292. Academic: New York.

Wine, J.J., Krasne, F.B., & Chen, L. (1975) Habituation and inhibition of the crayfish lateral giant fiber escape response. *J. Exp. Biol.* **62**: 771-782.

Zucker, R.S. (1972a) Crayfish escape behavior and central synapses. I. Neural circuit exciting lateral giant fiber. *J. Neurophysiol.* **35**: 599-620.

Zucker, R.S. (1972b) Crayfish escape behavior and central synapses. II. Physiological mechanisms underlying behavioral habituation. *J. Neurophysiol.* **35**: 621-637.

Frontiers in Crustacean Neurobiology
Advances in Life Sciences

LOCOMOTION MODULATES THE SENSITIVITY OF MECHANOSENSORY INTERNEURONS IN FRESHWATER CRAYFISH

Iris Hamm and Jürgen Tautz

Fakultät für Biologie, Universität Konstanz,
Postfach 5560, D-7750 Konstanz, Federal Republic of Germany

SUMMARY

In freshwater crayfish resting or walking on a treadmill 12 different identified mechanosensory interneurons have been recorded intracellularly in order to investigate the influence of the state of activity of the crayfish on the responsiveness of these neurons to water stimuli directed onto the tailfan of the animal. First, the background activity of these neurons is influenced by the state of activity of the crayfish, which allows to group the neurons into three classes (no change, increase, decrease of activity while walking). Second, additional stimulation of tailfan hair receptors by water movements, results in a complex across-the-fiber-pattern within the interneuron population, which might allow the distinction between self-induced stimulation by the relative water movement produced during walking and external stimulus sources.

INTRODUCTION

Spezialised sensory hairs on the surface of a crayfish are sensitive to water vibrations. These water vibrations can be elicited by an external source or by the locomotion of the animal or by both. It thus becomes an important task for the crayfish to distinguish self-produced from foreign-produced stimulation of the hair sensilla. This problem, however, is not limited to the crayfish and its mechanosensory system, but is true for most other sensory systems in different other animals as well.

One solution to the problem is efferent control of the afferent activity. However, the mechanisms, on which this phenomenon is based upon, is not clear in most of the cases. Two possibilities are discussed: modulation either by proprioceptors or by corollary discharge of neuronal units, which are activated before or during locomotion (Gallistel 1980).

MATERIAL AND METHODS

Freshwater crayfish of the species *Orconectes limosus* were fixed with the dorsal carapace to a holder and placed inside a tank, which was divided into two chambers. In one chamber (filled with freshwater) the animal was standing on a treadmill (two independent moveable wheels), on which it

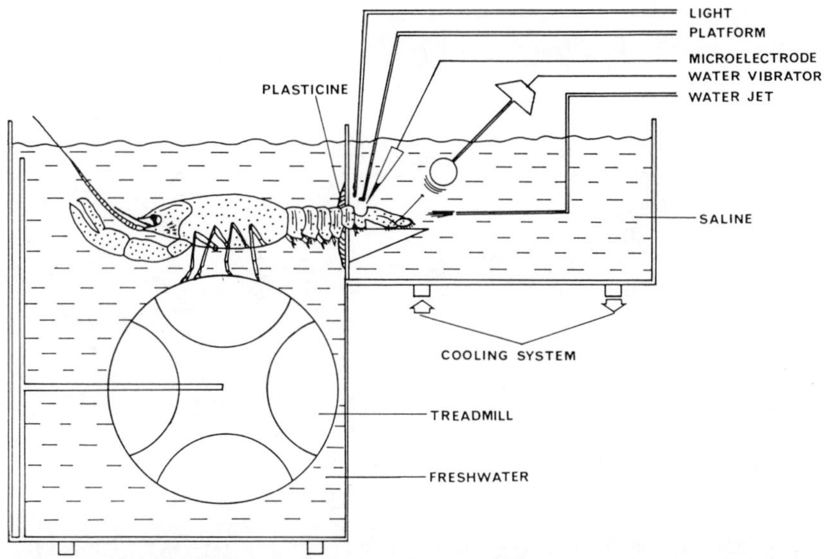

Fig.1: Experimental set up showing the crayfish sitting on a treadmill. The tailfan is mechanically isolated from the main tank.

could walk forwards or backwards. The tailfan was resting on a platform in the other chamber separated by a wall fitting tightly around the abdomen (Fig.1). It was shown in control experiments that the water vibrations caused by locomotion of the crayfish were not transmitted into the "tailfan" chamber. The hair receptors on the tailfan were thus exclusively stimulated by water vibrations and water jets controlled by the experimenter. The last abdominal ganglion was dissected from the dorsal side and the electrical activity was recorded intracellularly from interneurons stained subsequently with lucifer yellow.

Mechanosensory interneurons were studied under different activity states of the crayfish and different stimulus conditions:

a. animal resting, not stimulated.
b. animal walking, not stimulated.
c. animal resting, stimulated by water movements directed to the tailfan.
d. animal walking, stimulated as in c.

RESULTS AND DISCUSSION

12 different identified interneurons ascending from the last abdominal ganglion (Sigvardt et al.1982) were investigated a number of times each. The morphology of these neurons is shown in Fig.2. The somata are either located posteriorly or anteriorly in the last abdominal ganglion. The dendritic arborizations are typically contralateral to the soma of the cell.

If the electrical activity of a neuron during locomotion of the crayfish is compared with the neuronal activity during rest the investigated cells can

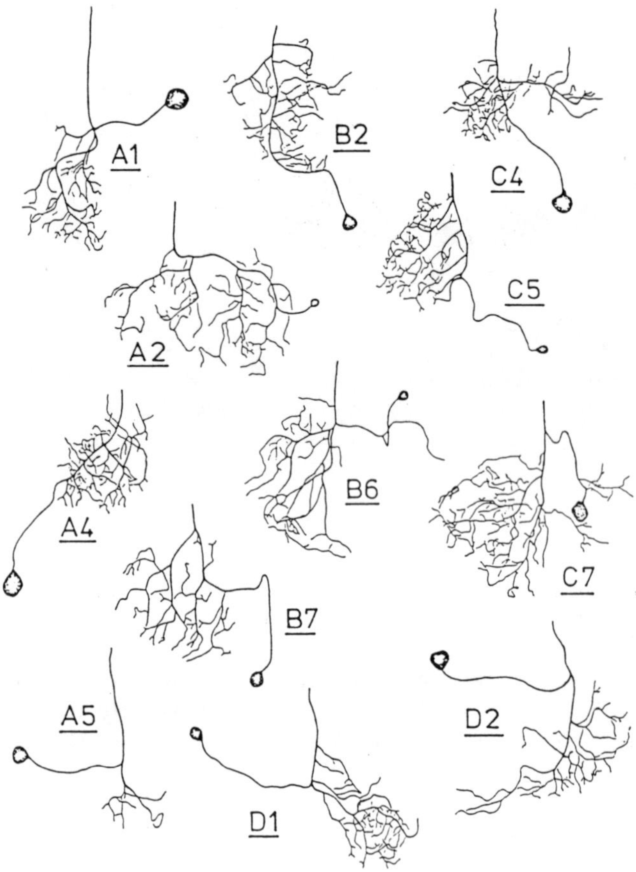

Fig.2: Morphology of the identified interneurons investigated. Nomenclature after Sigvardt et al. (1982).

be grouped into 3 classes: 1. Neurons not changing their state of activity (A1,A2,A5,B7,C4), 2.Neurons increasing their activity during locomotion (B2,B6,C5,C7,D1,D2), 3.Neurons decreasing their activity during locomotion (A4).

Recordings from sensory neurons projecting into the last abdominal ganglion allowed to control for stimulus artefacts onto the sensory hairs of the tailfan possibly produced by walking. As a result, these sensory neurons were not activated by crayfish locomotion but were highly sensitive to water jets and oscillations directed to the tailfan.

The sensitivity of the interneurons to water movements directed onto the tailfan also changes with the state of activity of the animal. Each of the 3 classes mentioned above can be further subdivided (Table 1).

Table 1: Change of responsiveness of the interneurons to water movement stimuli in walking crayfish as compared to resting ones. In backets: "+" increase in response strength, "-" decrease in response strength, "=" no change in response strength.

Class 1: A1(=), A2(-)(see Fig.3), A5(=), B7(=), C4(=).

Class 2: B2(-), B6(+), C5(+), C7(+), D1(+)(see Fig.4), D2(=).

Class 3: A4(-).

Thus, when looking at the overall activity of the investigated fibers a complex across-the-fiber-pattern occurs, which is different in a resting animal compared to a walking one. This pattern can be the basis for the distinction between external stimulus sources from self-produced hair stimulation.

3

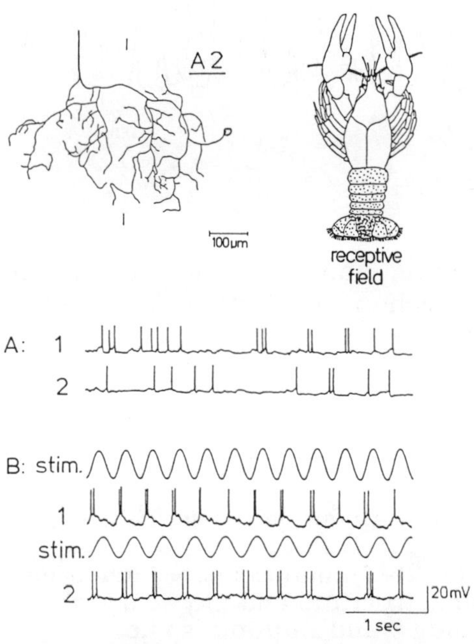

4

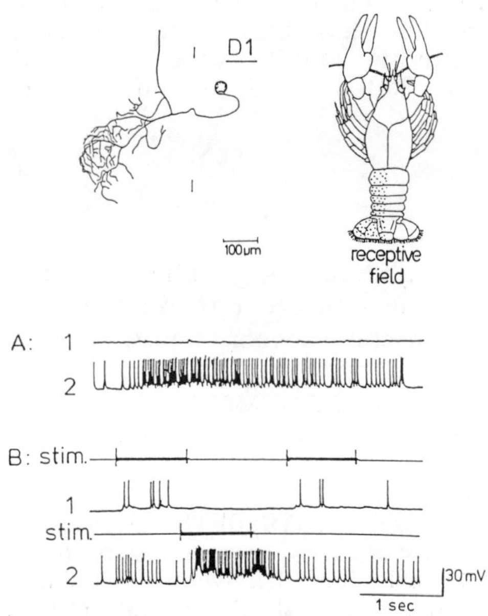

Fig.3: Morphology, receptive field and electrical activity of neuron A2. A: No stimulation of the tailfan. Activity at rest (1) and while walking (2). B: Response to water oscillations while resting (1) and walking (2).

Fig.4: Morphology, receptive field and electrical activity of interneuron D1. A: No stimulation of the tailfan. Activity at rest (1) and while walking (2). B: Response to water jets while resting (1) and walking (2).

In order to test for the origin of these modulations in some preparations the ventral cord was cut anterior to the last abdominal ganglion. After severance of the ventral cord in no case a difference between the discharge pattern during locomotion and that during rest was noticed (e.g.Fig.5). Thus, the modulation of background activity and of responsiveness to water movements is caused by neurons descending in the ventral cord into the last abdominal ganglion. These descending neurons now have to be identified in order to unravel the exact mechanism of efferent control of the mechanosensory input..

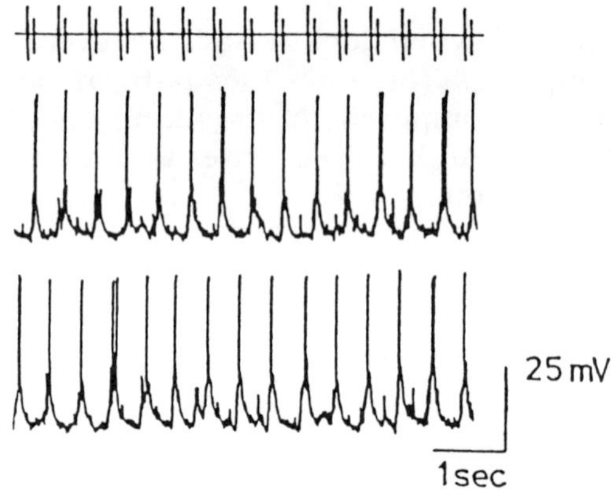

Fig.5: Response of the interneuron D1 (see also Fig.3) to water jets onto the tailfan in crayfish with the ventral cord severed anterior to the last abdominal ganglion. Top: Stimulus. Middle trace: Animal at rest. Bottom trace: Animal walking.

ACKNOWLEDGEMENT
We thank B.Schmitz for valuable suggestions to the manuscript.

REFERENCES

Gallistel,C.R. (1980) The organization of action: a new synthesis. Hilldale, New Jersey: Lawrence Erlbaum Ass.

Sigvardt, K.A., Hagiwara,G. & Wine, J.J. (1982) Mechanosensory integration in the crayfish abdominal nervous system: structural and physiological differences between interneurons with single and multiple spike initiation sites. J.comp.Physiol.**148**: 143-157.

Frontiers in Crustacean Neurobiology
Advances in Life Sciences

SYNAPTIC MECHANISMS OF A DUAL CHANNEL CONTRAST DETECTION SYSTEM IN THE CRAYFISH OPTIC LOBE

R. Glantz and C. Pfeiffer-Linn

Department of Biochemistry and Cell Biology
Rice Univesity, Houston, TX 77251

SUMMARY

The sustaining and dimming fibers (SF, DF) of the crayfish optic lobe constitute a dual channel contrast detection system and mediate the dorsal light reflex. The receptive fields and dynamic properties of SFs and DFs are shaped by dendritic geometry and interactions among presynaptic columnar and multicolumnar neurons (amacrine and tangential cells) of the laminaand medulla externa . The visual response of each multicolumnar neuron reflects the antagonistic interaction of two postsynaptically acting neurotransmitters. These transmitters (Ach, GABA, Glutamate) are contained in columnar interneurons.

INTRODUCTION

Many visual systems possess a massively parallel architecture capable of processing a number of stimulus parameters simultaneously. The cellular organization however is still far from clear. The visual pathway which subserves the crayfish optomotor system transmits both dynamic and steady-state information to optomotor neurons. Recently it has been shown that the motor neurons which control vertical and rotational eye displacements are under the control of identified tonic ON visual interneurons, the sustaining fibers (SF), (Glantz, et al., 1984). Each optomotor neuron receives monosynaptic excitatory input from a small cluster of SFs and disynaptic inhibitory input from a second SF cluster. The receptive fields of the two clusters of SFs are arranged so that each motorneuron is excited by illumination of a particular corneal location (e.g. posterior rim or the central axis of the left eye) and inhibited by illumination of a complementary corneal location (e.g. anterior rim, central axis of the right eye).

The SF excitatory receptive fields are in turn determined by the location of the planar SF dendrite in the medulla externa, i.e. second optic neuromere, (Kirk et al., 1983), and reflects the intersection of the retinotopic columnar projection and the orthogonal SF dendrite (Fig. 1). Illumination to corneal locations outside the SF excitatory field produces lateral inhibition. The SFs are exquisitely sensitively to movement and to the rotation of the e-vector of polarized light. The medulla externa also contains a second class of principal output cell, the tonic OFF dimming fibers (DF), (Fig. 1). The SFs and DFs constitute a dual channel, contrast encoding system.

Recently we have begun to examine the nonspiking interneurons of the lamina ganglionaris (first optic neuromere) (Wang-Bennett and Glantz, 1987a,b) and the medulla externa (Waldrop and Glantz, 1985; Pfeiffer and Glantz, 1989) in an effort to understand how the SF and DF receptive fields are organized. I will illustrate our approach by summarizing some recent results on two classes of broad field medullary interneurons, the tangential cells and amacrine neurons, their relationship to the SFs and DFs and the roles of two putative neurotransmitters, acetylcholine (Ach) and g-amino butyric acid (GABA).

RESULTS

The distribution of Ach and GABA were assessed immunocytochemically with polyclonal antibodies to transmitter-protein conjugates (Wang-Bennett et al, 1989). Ach is highly concentrated in the medulla externa and interna and only barely detectable in the lamina or external chiasm. Within the medulla, Ach-like reactivity is principally found in the columnar transmedullary monopolar neurons (Fig. 1 TM). There appears to be one cholinergic transmedullary neuron in each medullary column. GABA-like reactivity is found in the external chiasm where it is distributed among columnar neurons and reactivity is most intense where the lamina neurons enter the distal medulla (Pfeiffer and Glantz, 1989) (Fig. 1 LM). GABA-like reactivity is also found in columnar medullary neurons.

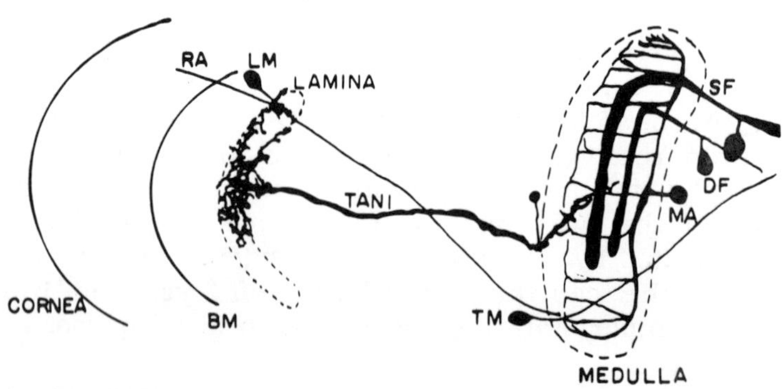

Fig. 1 Structure and location of six classes of visual interneurons in the crayfish lamina and medulla externa Dorsal view. RA, receptor axons; BM, basement membrane; LM, lamina monopolar neuron; Tan 1, tangential cell; TM, transmedullary monopolar neuron; MA, medullary amacrine cell; SF, sustaining fiber; DF, dimming fiber.

Tangential cells are well known in crustacean and insect optic lobes (Strausfield and Nassel, 1980) and are thought to provide a centrifugal feedback signal (Shaw, 1985) from medulla to lamina. One class of tangential cell (Tan1)has a narrow dendrite in the medulla externa and a bistratified terminal in the lamina. The Tan1 response to a pulse of illumination consists of a graded hyperpolarization which decays to a somewhat smaller steady-state value (Wang-Bennett and Glantz, 1987b). Tan1 cells have large receptive fields and are not subject to surround inhibition. Functionally, Tan1 appears to be a component of the afferent pathway to the SFs. When hyperpolarized with extrinic current, Tan1 elicits excitation in SFs. Furthermore, Tan1 is highly sensitive to a rotating e-vector as previously observed in the decapod SFs (Leggett, 1976). The Tan1 response to e-vector rotation is a function of angular velocity and the direction of rotation (unpublished observations).

Tan1 is hyperpolarized by Ach (0.1 to 10μM) (Fig. 2) (and nicotine, 10nM) and the response to Ach persists following synaptic blockade with 20 mM $CoCl_2$ (Pfeiffer and Glantz, 1989). The Ach response shares many features with the visually-elicited hyperpolarizing synaptic potential (PSP) including the reversal potential, sensitivity to extracellular chloride concentration and picrotoxin (a chloride channel blocker). Both the hyperpolarizing PSP and the Ach-response exhibit a nicotinic ganglionic pharmacological profile; they are about 100x more sensitive to ganglionic antagonists such as pempidine and mecamylamine than to d-tubocurarine. Muscarinic agents such as atropine are ineffective even at a 1mM concentrations.

Tan1 responds to GABA with a depolarization (Fig. 2) associated with a decrease conductance to Cl^- (Pfeiffer and Glantz, 1988). The GABA response persists following synaptic blockade. Both the GABA response and the repolarizing phase of the visually elicited PSP are selectively blocked by the GABA A receptor blocker, bicuculline. In the presence of bicuculline the peak hyperpolarization of the PSP is increased which suggests that GABA is normally acting concurrently with Ach to shape the Tan1 PSP.

The medullary amacrine cells (Fig. 1, MA) are nonspiking local interneurons with large transverse dendrites that intersect the columnar projection in the medulla externa. They respond to illumination with a graded depolarizing PSP (Fig. 2) which rapidly decreases to a smaller steady-state value (Waldrop and Glantz, 1985). When depolarized with extrinsic current, the amacrine cells inhibit the light-elicited discharge of SFs and excite the DFs. The inhibition acts presynaptically with respect to SFs and has all of the features of the surround inhibitory mechanism. Extrinsic hyperpolarization of amacrine cells enhances the light elicited SF discharge as one might expect following the removal of a tonic source of inhibition.

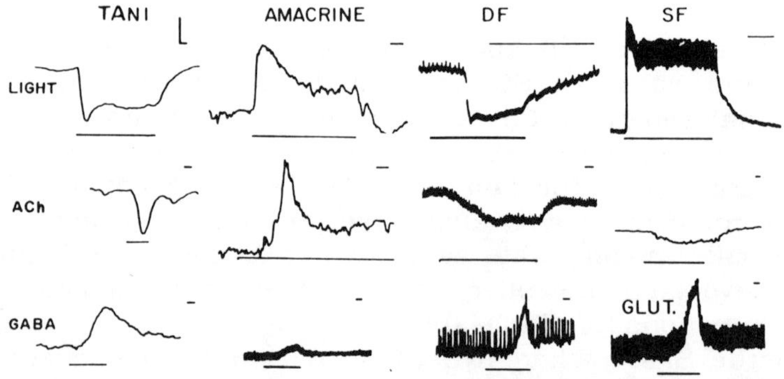

Fig.2 Light and agonist-elicited responses of four classes of visual interneurons. Scale in upper left is 10 mV and 200 ms. Vertical scale is common to all panels and 200 ms time scale is in upper right of each panel. Light or agonist pulse timing is indicated by line beneath each physiological trace. Succcessive rows indicate responses to light, Ach and GABA except in last panel of bottom row which is a glutamate response.

Amacrine cells are depolarized by Ach (Pfeiffer and Glantz, 1989) and the depolarization has the same reversal potential and pharmacological profile as the visually elicited PSP. It is interesting to note that the amacrine cell Ach receptor (AchR) like that of Tan1 exhibits a nicotinic ganglionic pharmacological profile. The GABA response (Fig. 2) is associated with an increased membrane conductance and a reversal potential that is 2 to 5 mV above the resting potential. These results suggest that the amacrine cell visual response, like that of Tan1, is shaped by the concurrent actions of Ach and GABA. In each case Ach conveys the net effect of illumination and the action of Ach is modulated by GABA postsynaptically.

The DFs have the same pharmacological profile as Tan 1 (Fig. 2); they are hyperpolarized by light and Ach which inhibits the dark-discharge and they are depolarized by GABA (Fig. 2). The SFs are unique in this group in that Ach opposes the light elicited response (Fig. 2) and hyperpolarizes the cell. The excitatoryt transmitter for the SF is glutamate (Fig. 2).

DISCUSSION

These results have implications in three contexts: i) the transmitter receptors; ii) the presynaptic elements which release Ach and GABA; and iii) the synaptic organization of the visual pathway in the medulla externa.

In tangential cells, a nicotinic AchR is coupled to a chloride channel while in amacrine cells, an AchR with identical pharmacology is associated with a cationic conductance. In Aplysia, AchRs are also coupled to chloride and cationic conductances (Blankenship et al, 1971) but the receptor associated with each type of conductance has a different pharmacological profile (Kehoe, 1972). In crustacea, a nicotinic AchR is associated with a cationic channel in crabs and lobster foregut muscle. Furthermore, a certain percentage of GABA receptor-chloride channels complexes of crayfish neuromuscular junctions can also be activated by Ach (Zufall et al, 1988). Thus the Tan1 and amacrine cell AchRs appear to be members of a wider family of crustacean AchRs.

The Tan1 GABA receptor has much in common with the well known GABA receptor of the crustacean neuromuscular junction including sensitivity to bicuculline and picrotoxin and an association with a chloride channel. The unusual future of Tan1 is that GABA causes a decreased conductance to Cl^-. Again there is a precedent for this phenomenon in the action of glycine on some GABA receptors of the crustacean neuromuscular junction (Finger, 1983).

The actions of Ach and GABA in Amacrine neurons are very similar to prior reports of their actions in crustacean muscle both as regards pharmacological profile and the associated ionic channel activity.

Cholinergic Transmedullary Monopolar Neurons . Ach mimics the actions of the light-elicited PSPs in both Tan1 and Amacrine neurons and the physiology of the PSPs implies that Ach is released by medullary columnar neurons during a light pulse. Independent measurements fully support these inferences: a) Ach is localized in transmedullary monopolar cells with immunocytochemistry; (Wang-Bennett et al, 1989), b) the transmedullary cells are depolarized by a pulse of illumination; and c) a light-dependent Ach release has been directly detected in the medulla externa (data not shown) with a chemilluminescent assay.

GABAergic Neurons. The physiology and pharmacology of the light-elicited PSPs in Tan1 and Amacrine cells suggest that GABA is released concurrently with Ach or perhaps after a slight delay during a light pulse. The immunocytochemistry indicates that GABA is contained in the axons of lamina monopolar cells which are transiently hyperpolarized by light (Wang-Bennett and Glantz, 1987) and putatively in transmedullary neurons which are depolarized by light pulses. Thus a light pulse should cause a transient reduction in GABA release from lamina axon terminals. This inference suggests two alternative sources for the GABA acting on Tan1 and the Amacrine cells during a light pulse. One possibility is that the GABA is released by the lamina monopolar neuron terminals but after a delay which is associated with the transient hyperpolarizing light response. In this hypothesis, release is associated with the repolarizing phase of the monopolar cell light response. The second possibility is that GABA is released from depolarizing columnar medullary neurons.

Synaptic Organization of the Medulla Externa. Previous physiological studies indicate that the SF excitatory receptive field is based upon the intersection of the SF medullary dendrites and the retinotopic columnar projection. Furthermore, the SF EPSP is mediated by glutamate (Fig. 2). Thus we infer that there is at least one glutamatergic transmedullary neuron in each column of the retinotopic projection. When a pulse of light falls on an area of the cornea, excitation of retinular cells and lamina monopolar cells transmit the signal to the medulla externa and the transmedullary neurons at a corresponding medullary location are depolarized. The glutamatergic transmedullary cells excite the SFs (Fig. 3) and the cholinergic neurons hyperpolarize tangential cells and DFs (Fig. 3) (Pfeiffer and Glantz, 1989) and depolarize the Amacrine neurons. Each Amacrine cell has a broad receptive field and appears to deliver its inhibitory effects to a broad field of medullary columnar neurons. The inhibition follows excitation by about 10 ms (Glantz and Nudelman, 1976) and our evidence suggests that it is mediated by GABA, (Pfeiffer and Glantz, 1988). The inhibition is expressed on both glutamatergic and cholinergic transmedullary cells (Fig. 3). As a result of this inhibition, SFs outside of the stimulus zone experience a net inhibition of their excitatory inputs (surround inhibition) and the DFs experience a net reduction of their hyperpolarizing cholinergic input (surround excitation or disinhibition). Thus a small number of amacrine cells, three classes of transmedullary neurons (similar but for their transmitters) and three transmitters provide the basis for the dual channel (SF and DF) contrast encoding scheme.

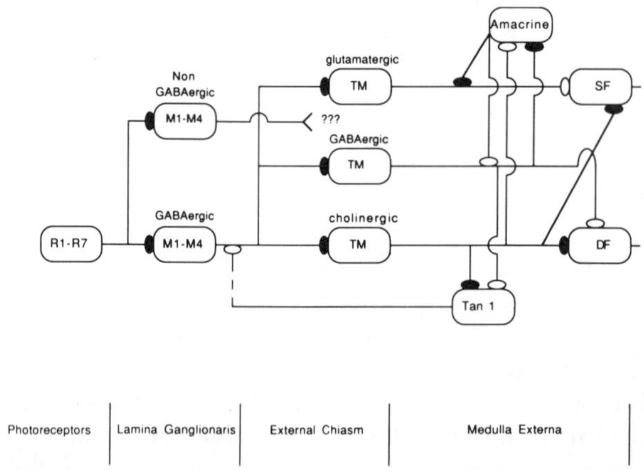

Fig. 3Proposed network organization for lamina and medullary neurons based upon immunocytochemistry and neuropharmacology. Abbreviations as in Fig. 1.

As noted previously, tangential cells are hyperpolarized by light and extrinsic hyperpolarization of Tan1 elicits indirect excitation of SFs. Tan1 sensitivity to a rotating polarizer suggests a strong input from lamina ganglion cells M3 and M4 (Nassel and Waterman, 1977). These results all imply that Tan1 is part of the circuitry that converts the stationary polarization sensitivity (PS) of the photoreceptors to the dynamic PS of SFs. But there are several conundrums. Tan1 cells have a broad receptive field (>90°) but their medullary dendrites are quite narrow (<30°). Although the Tan1 light-elicited PSP is mediated by Ach it cannot be driven exclusively by cholinergic transmedullary cells which have narrow projections. Thus there is likely to be a broad field cholinergic process in the distal medulla that we have not yet identified. Furthermore, it is not clear how Tan1 with its efferent centrifugual processes in the lamina modulates the SF light response. Presumably, the hyperpolarization of Tan1 releases a lamina neuron from inhibition which in turn either excites or disinhibits the excitatory pathway to the SF. The Tan1 transmitter is also unknown. A few (<15) large somata in the medullary cell body area, that could belong to Tan1 cells, exhibit Ach-like immunoreactivity and a few similar cells exhibit GABA-like immunoreactivity.

References

Blankenship, J., M. Wachtel and E. Kandel (1971). Ionic mechanisms of excitatory, inhibitory, and dual synaptic actions mediated by an identified interneuron in abdominal ganglion of Aplysia. J. Neurophysiol. **34**:76-91.

Finger, W. (1983). Effects of glycine on the crayfish neuromuscular junction. I. Glycine operated inhibitory postsynaptic channels and a glycine effected decrease in membrane conductance. Pflug. Arch. **397**:121-127.

Glantz, R.M., H.B. Nudelman, and B. Waldrop (1984). Linear integration of convergent visual inputs in an oculomotor reflex pathway. J. Neurophysiology. **52**:1213-1225.

Kehoe, J. (1972). Three acetylcholine receptors in Aplysia neurons. J. Physiol. **225**:115-146.

Kirk, M., Waldrop, B. and glantz, R.M. (1982). The crayfish sustaining fivers I. Morphological representation of visual receptive fields in the second optic neuropil. J. Comp. Physiol. **146**:175-179.

Leggett, L. (1976). Polarized light-sensitive interneurons in a swimming crab. Nature. **262**:709-711.

Nassel, D. and Watermen, T. (1977). Golgi EM evidence for visual information channelling in crayfish lamina ganglionaris. Brain Res. **130**:556-563.

Pfeiffer, C. and Glantz, R.M. (1988u). Evidence that GABA is a neurotransmitter in the crayfish medulla. Soc. for Neurosci. Abst. **14**:382.

Pfeiffer, C. and Glantz, R.M. (1989). Cholinergic synapses and the organization of contrast detection in the crayfish optic lobe. J. Neuroscience. **9**:1872-1882.

Strausfeld, N. and Nassel, D. (1980). Neuroarchitecture of brain regions that subserve the compound eyes of crustacea and insects. IN: Handbook of Sensory Physiology. Vol. 8, Pt. 6B, p. 1-132. Springer Verlag, New York.

Waldrop, B. and Glantz, R.M. (1985). Nonspiking local interneurons mediate surround inhibition in crayfish sustaining fibers. J. Comp. Physiol. 156:763-774.

Wang-Bennett, L. and Glantz, R.M. (1987a). The functional organization of the crayfish lamina ganglionaris. I. Nonspiking monopolar cells. J. Comp. Physiol. **161**:131-145.

Wang-Bennett, L. and Glantz, R.M. (1987b). The functional organization of the crayfish lamina ganglionaris. II. Large field spiking and nonspiking cells. J. Comp. Physiol. **161**:147-160.

Wang-Bennett, L., Pfeiffer, C., Arnold, J. and Glantz, R.M. (1989). Acetylcholine in the crayfish optic lobe: concentration profile and cellular localization. J. Neuroscience. **9**:1864-1871.

Zufall, F., Ch. Franke and H. Hett (1988). Acetylcholine activates a chloride channel as well as glutamate and GABA. J. Comp. Physiol. **163**:609-620.

Frontiers in Crustacean Neurobiology
Advances in Life Sciences

VISUALLY ELICITED ESCAPE IN CRABS

Hans-Ortwin Nalbach

Max-Planck-Institut für biologische Kybernetik,
Spemannstrasse 38, D-7400 Tübingen 1, Federal Republic of Germany

SUMMARY

A review is given on field and laboratory studies, including intracellular recordings from the optic lobes, on the visually elicited escape response of a mangrove and a rocky shore crab. The crabs flee when the angular size of an approaching object has expanded by a critical value. Neurons which respond specifically to this stimulus were encountered in the lobula (internal medulla). Illusiory expansion produced by rotating spirals evokes no reaction. The results suggest a hypothesis on the underlying mechanism for looming detection. The direction of the crab's escape can be understood as a compromise between a tendency away from the approaching object and towards a probable shelter since it can be described by a weighted vectorial summation of both components.

INTRODUCTION

Detailed knowledge on visual capacities of decapod crustaceans is hitherto restricted to the optomotor system. Here, the analysis has revealed much detail about the higher order neural circuitry and the motor system (Neil 1982). Furthermore, the logical scheme of the circuitry is well understood from the cybernetical viewpoint, namely of the optokinetic eye movements (Nalbach 1989). These compensatory eye movements, backed up by proprioceptive input from statocysts and leg mechanoreceptors, are thought to improve aquisition of visual information. Available studies on higher order visual functions, however, either are aimed to give insight into the behavioural repertoire of the species, or they analyse the functional role of visually guided behaviour, e.g. during orientation within the habitat (Herrnkind 1983) or in social communication (Salmon and Hyatt 1983). Only sparce information exists, however, on the relevant parameters of the visual stimuli which the animals exploit. And consequently, there is no knowledge about neural processing of such visual information in decapod crustaceans.

A still easy to access but complex visually elicited behaviour of decapod crustaceans is their escape and defense reflex. Both behavioural patterns can be elicited by an approaching object. I studied the escape reaction of semiterrestrial crabs since these animals possess a highly developped visual system. Their habit of breathing in open air offers an opportunity to study their behaviour quantitatively in the field as well as in the laboratory, and furthermore facilitates electrophysiological recordings from an intact animal.

RESULTS

The critical stimulus parameters. Every person that wants to observe crabs in the field knows about the alertness of these attentive creatures. I studied the critical stimulus parameters which elicit flight in the semaphore crab, *Heloecius cordiformis*, which is closely related to the famous fiddler crabs and replaces them along the fringes of mangroves of the southeastern coast of Australia. These crabs live in large colonies and take refuge in individual selfdug burrows. When a person (starting from about 50 m initial distance) approaches a crab foraging at the border of a colony it stops feeding and rushes towards its burrow when the image of the person has expanded to a critical angular size. It waits in the entrance of its burrow with the eyes erected until the person's image has grown to a second critical size. Now the crab will disappear. The velocity of approach does not influence these critical values (Fig. 1 A).

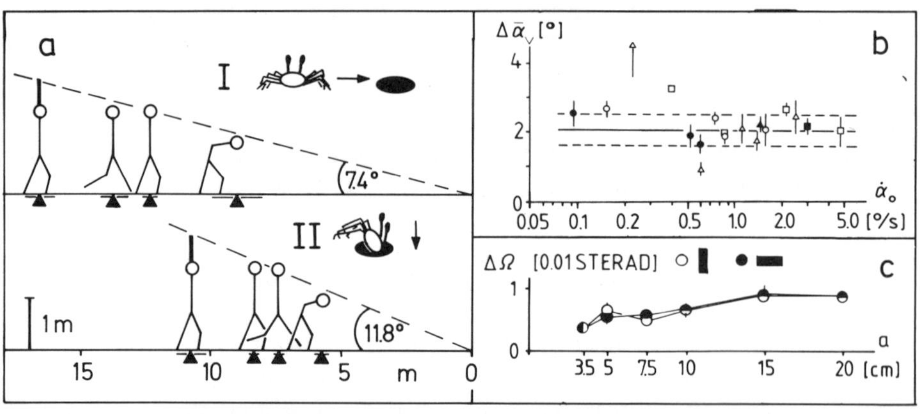

Fig. 1 A. Field experiments with a person walking (75 cm/s) or running (390 cm/s) towards a semaphore crab which first escapes towards its burrow and then disappears underneath the surface. B. Critical expansion to elicit escape of *Heloecius* walking on a ball. Experiments with disks of diameters 3.5 cm (open circles) to 20 cm (filled squares), linear velocities 6 76 cm/s and hence a range of inital expansion velocities (°/s). Dashed lines indicate standard deviation from the mean. C. Critical expansion in solid angle with rectangular plates either horizontally or vertically elongated (length a), the other edge 3.5 cm wide.

These results were confirmed and expanded in laboratory studies which allow for more controlled stimulus conditions. The crabs were tethered above an aircushioned Styrofoam ball which they rotated by their walking movements. From the turns of the ball the intended path of the crab was reconstructed. This setup was placed in an arena surrounded by white walls to provide a homogeneous background in front of which objects approached the crabs from maximal distance 108 cm.

Similar to the observation in the field experiments, the semaphore crabs tried to escape the approaching disk typically in two spurts. Here I present quantitative data calculated from the delay between stimulus onset and onset of the first spurt. From the results obtained in experiments with circular disks of different diameters and different initial distances it becomes evident that it is not the angular size of the object that is decisive for initiation of an escape. The "critical" angular size of the disk increases in proportion to the initial angular size of the disk and is widely independent of the disk velocity except at very low velocities when often no escape was elicited (Fig. 1 B). Hence the critical stimulus parameter to initiate an escape is the increase in angular size. The critical increase in angular size does not vary markedly with the direction of approach, neither in azimuth nor in elevation (Nalbach 1987).

The image of circular disks expands at similar rates horizontally as well as vertically. In order to obtain information about the angle which is evaluated by the crab I used rectangular plates, elongated either horizontally or vertically. The crabs flee when the solid angle of the plate has expanded by a critical value, independent of the orientation of the object (Fig. 1 C).

This result leads to the correct interpretation of the outcome of the field experiments. Since in these experiments the initial distance of the approaching person was always about 50 m, the results (Fig. 1 A) are equally compatible with the interpretation that also in the field the crabs flee when the image of the approaching object has increased by a critical solid angle.

Repeating the experiments with a rock crab, *Pachygrapsus marmoratus*, a crab from a three dimensionally complex habitat in contrast to *Heloecius* which lives on mud flats, led to the same result (Nalbach 1987). Thus, the critical stimulus parameter for initiation of escape is independent of the ecological conditions of the crabs and hence of the design of their eyes (Zeil et al. 1986).

Illusiory expansion produced by rotating spirals was completely ignored by the crabs. This is remarkable since this stimulus readily induces landing in flies (Braitenberg & Taddei-Ferretti 1966) which typically react to approaching objects (Borst & Bahde 1988).

Direction of escape. After detecting an approaching object the crab tries to escape. Slowly walking species on soft mud may rapidly dig into the substratum (Nalbach 1987), fast runners far away from their refuge erratically may change their course (Vannini 1980). Usually, however, the crab will run into a particular direction. When disturbed during foraging, *Heloecius* always dashes towards its individual burrow. When crabs are transferred to a remote place, however, or when they walk on the aircushioned ball, they run more or less straight away from the approaching disk. They are able to determine the direction of the approach monocularly although they deviate systematically from the precise 180° course. This deviation is more pronounced in *Pachygrapsus* than in *Heloecius* (Fig. 2).

In *Pachygrapsus*, the direction of escape can be calculated by a weighted vectorial summation of a tendency away from the approaching object and towards the side of the blinded eye. Therefore, it can be concluded that the deviation from the straight course is not a consequence of a miscalculation which might arise because the information from one eye is missing in this situation. From field observations (Drzewina 1908) it is known that *Pachygrapsus* has a strong photonegative tendency. In their natural habitat, this strategy will lead them under protective rocks. The tendency of the monocular crabs to deviate towards the side of their blinded eye, therefore, can be interpreted as this preference of a course towards the dark. With such a model of weighted vectorial summation of two tendencies one away from the approaching object and one towards a preferred goal also the direction of visually elicited escape of the blue swimming crab, Callinectes sapidus (Woodbury 1986), can be quantitatively described (Nalbach 1987).

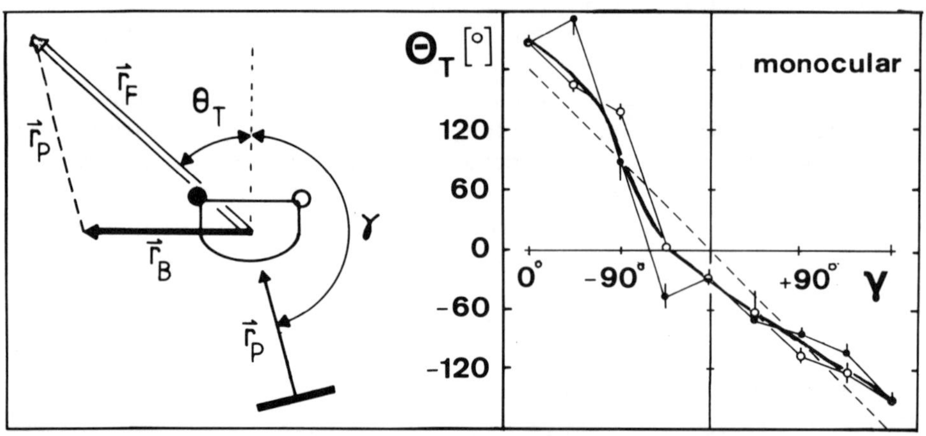

Fig. 2. Weighted vectorial summation of a predator induced tendency (rP) and an internal bias (rB) leading to a tendency of flight (rF) relative to the animals body axis. Data obtained from 2 left and 1 right eye blinded *Pachygrapsus* (drawn as if left eye blinded), heavy line calculated with /rB/:/rP/ = 0.58.

Electrophysiological recordings from the optic lobes. As a first step to understand the neural circuitry underlying the detection of an approaching object it seemed to be worthwhile to examine successively the visual ganglia within the eye stalk. With such a study it was intended to determine the probable anatomical location of the expected 'looming' detector cells (Nalbach, unpubl.). Related knowledge is provided by extracellular recordings from the optic nerve of crayfish during visually elicited defense reflex (Glantz 1977). In these studies is was demonstrated that the activity of 'jittery movement detectors' is integrated giving rise to a response delay which corresponds to the increase in angular size of the approaching object. Thus, the critical stimulus parameter evaluated to elicit escape in crabs and defense reflex in crayfish is the same.

Heloecius provides an appropriate preparation for this study. Its visual ganglia are linearly aligned in the distal part of the eye stalk (Fig. 3). They can be penetrated sequentially downwards from a small hole cut into the cuticular cap covering the tip of the eye. The eye stalk was glued in its natural orientation to the micromanipulator setup which also carried the glass micropipettes for intracellular recording and staining with cobalthexaminechloride. The crab was suspended by a rod glued to its carapace above a sprung table which allowed for walking movements. The eye was exposed to a lightguide, handheld disks and movement in depth provided by a similar apparatus as in the behavioural experiments reported above.

Light on/off was the only stimulus to elicit responses in cells of the lamina and was also the most effective stimulus to depolarize cells in the external medulla. Here, from 29 neurons 18 responded to light on/off stimuli only, 5 also depolarised during movement of the handheld disks oscillating tangentially to the eye within the receptive field of the large tangential cells. Quantitative results were obtained from 6 cells which, in addition, responded to a circular disk approaching towards or retreating from the eye.

The delay from onset of disk movement until the cell begins to depolarise, and thus the "critical" increase in angular size of the approaching disk, depends on diameter and velocity of the disk (Fig. 3 B). Therefore, the relevant stimulus parameters represented by theses neurons is different from those underlying the escape response (see Fig. 1).

From the 9 cells penetrated in the lobula (internal medulla) none responded exclusively to light on/off stimuli which always evoked only weak, often rapidly fading transient depolarisations. They all responded to disks moving tangentially to the eye, and for 5 cells, in addition, motion of the disks in depth was an effective stimulus (Fig. 3 A).

The onset of depolarisation of two of the lobula cells was independent of diameter and velocity of the approaching disks. Thus, the delay of these cells depends on the increase in angular size of the looming object (Fig. 3 B) which is the same critical stimulus parameter as for the escape response. Furthermore, these cells have a restricted receptive field and thus could encode the direction of approach.

One of the important cues to identify the jittery movement fibres as part of the crayfish defense reflex is that both behavioural and neural response habituate during repetitive stimulation and that responsiveness recovers when the disk approaches towards a new area of the eye (Glantz 1977).

A similar phenomenon of local habituation was observed in the escape response of crabs (Fig. 4 A) and the looming cells in the lobula (Fig. 4 B).

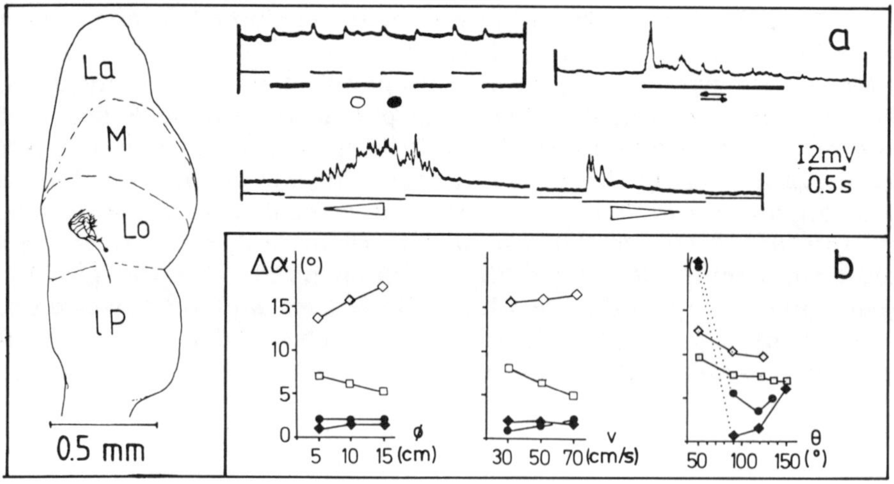

Fig. 3. A. Camera lucida drawing of a whole mount preparation of the optic ganglia in *Heloecius* (Lamina, Medulla, Lobula, lateral Protocerebrum) showing a 'looming' cell, and sample records obtained under light stimuli, a disk oscillating tangentially to the eye, and an disk moving in depth. B. Critical expansion, calculated from the delay between onset of disk movement and depolarisation of 2 cells in the external Medulla (open symbols) and 2 cells in the Lobula, as function of disk diameter, velocity and direction of approach in azimuth (0°: frontal).

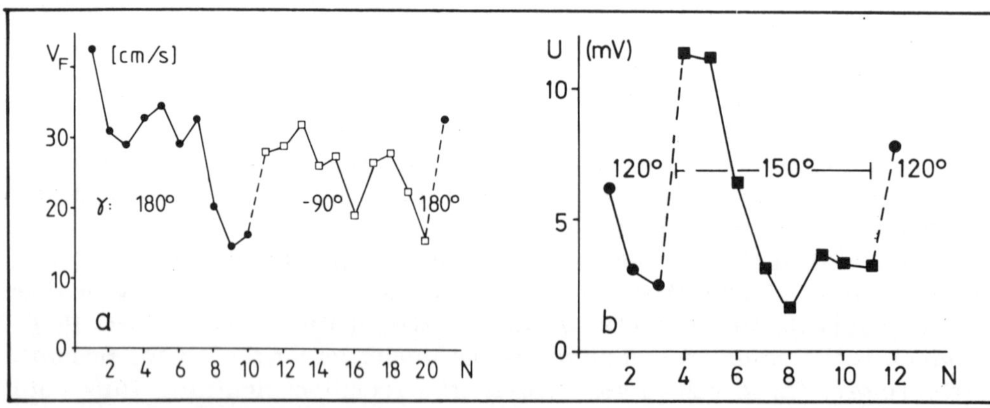

Fig. 4. Local habituation of (A) the escape reaction (*Pachygrapsus*) and (B) the responsiveness of a lobula looming cell (*Heloecius*), indicated by decrease in flight velocity or maximal depolarisation during repetitive stimulation every 10 s and recovery when the disk approaches from a new direction (velocity 35 cm/s or 70 cm/s).

DISCUSSION

I would like to conclude this overview with a hypothesis on a wiring scheme which might underly the crabs mechanism to detect the approach of an object and to initiate an escape response. The basic idea is that expansion is unambiguously determined by the increasing contour line of the approaching object over time. Hence, the number of ommatidia which are stimulated by the moving border increases proportionally. The number of activated border detectors decreases over time when the object contracts; the number remains constant during illusiory expansion produced by a rotating spiral and by borders travelling tangentially to the eye.

To extract this information, local directioninsensitive movement detectors could be spatially integrated resulting in a signal proportional to the number n(t) of stimuluted ommatidia. In a next step, from this signal the output of the hypothetical pool cell, delayed by an intervall d, is subtracted resulting in a signal proportional to the change in number of stimulated local detectors: Dn(t) = n(t)n(td). Temporal integration, possibly via low pass filters (Borst & Bahde 1988), eventually results in suprathreshold level of excitation and an escape response is gated. Since the change of the number of stimulated local detectors is proportional to the instantaneous change in contour length of the object, temporal integration of Dn(t) results in a signal proportional to the change in solid angle of the object. And this exactly is the critical stimulus parameter to elicit an escape response in crabs or a defense reaction in crayfish.

REFERENCES

Borst, A. & Bahde, S. (1988) Spatiotemporal integration of motion A simple strategy for safe landing in flies. Naturwissenschaften **75**: 265-267.

Braitenberg, V. & Taddei Ferretti, C. (1966) Landing reaction of Musca domestica induced by visual stimuli. Naturwissenschaften **53**: 155.

Drzewina, A. (1908) Les reactions adaptives chez les crabes. Bull. Int. gen. Psychol. 8: 235-256.

Glantz, R.M. (1977) Visual input and motor output of command interneurons of the defense reflex pathway in the crayfish. In Identified neurons and behavior of arthropods, (ed. G.Hoyle) pp.259-274. New York:Plenum.

Herrnkind, W.F.(1983) Movement patterns and orientation. In The biology of crustacea, Vol. 7, (ed. F.J. Vernberg & W.G. Vernberg) pp. 41-105.New York: Academic Press.

Nalbach, H.O. (1987) Neuroethologie der Flucht von Krabben (Decapoda: Brachyura). University of Tübingen: Doctorial Thesis.

Nalbach, H.O. (1989) Three temporal frequency channels constitute the dynamics of the optokinetic system of the crab, *Carcinus maenas* (L.). Biol. Cybern. **61**: 59-70.

Neil, D.M. (1982) Compensatory eye movements. In The biology of crustacea, Vol. 4, (ed. D.C. Sandeman & H.L. Atwood) pp. 133-163. New York: Academic Press.

Salmon, M. & Hyatt, G.W. (1983) Communication. In The biology of crustacea, Vol. 7 , (ed. F.J. Vernberg & W.G. Vernberg) pp. 140. New York: Academic Press.

Vannini, M. (1980) Notes on the behaviour of Ocypode ryderi Kingsley (Crustacea, Brachyura). Mar. behav. Physiol. **7:** 171-183.

Woodbury P.B. (1986) The geometry of predator avoidance by the blue crab, *Callinectes sapidus* Rathbun. Anim. Behav. **34:** 28-37.

Zeil, J., Nalbach, G. & Nalbach, H.O. (1986) Eyes, eye stalks and the visual world of semiterrestrial crabs. J. comp. Physiol. **159**: 801-811.

Frontiers in Crustacean Neurobiology
Advances in Life Sciences

NEURAL BASIS FOR OLFACTORY DISCRIMINATION IN THE SPINY LOBSTER

Charles Derby, Peter Daniel, Jacqueline Fine-Levy
and Marie-Nadia Girardot

Department of Biology, Georgia State University, Atlanta, Georgia 30303, U.S.A.

SUMMARY

The peripheral olfactory system of the spiny lobster has been used as a model for understanding principles of neural coding of the quality and intensity of chemical stimuli. The code for natural odorant mixtures in this population of olfactory receptor cells is probably a population code rather than a labeled line code because these cells are broadly tuned to these mixtures and do not appear to belong to discrete cell types based on their response profiles to these mixtures. Furthermore, stimulus quality and intensity seem to be discriminated by independent components of the neuronal population response, suggesting the existence of separate codes for these two stimulus attributes: stimulus quality by the across neuron pattern (ANP), and stimulus intensity by the absolute response magnitude (ARM). Support for this conclusion comes from the observation that the pattern of behavioral discrimination of these mixtures closely parallels that of neural discrimination by ANPs.

INTRODUCTION

This chapter describes our efforts to explain how chemosensory nervous systems code the quality and intensity of chemical stimuli. Two general theories have been proposed to account for coding of the quality of chemical stimuli: the labeled line code and the across neuron pattern code. The labeled line coding hypothesis implies that each quality is coded by the exclusive activation of a type of cell with a distinct and narrowly tuned response profile. A labeled line system therefore would *require* that the population of cells be composed of many discrete cell types, with as many cell types as there are discriminable qualities. The across neuron pattern coding hypothesis holds that each stimulus quality is coded by a distinctive pattern of activity across a population of broadly tuned cells, called an across neuron pattern or ANP. This coding system would not require discrete cell types, although some differences in response spectra across cells is necessary for discrimination by ANPs. The ANP is only one feature of the population response which could be used in the coding of stimulus attributes. Another feature of the population response is the total amount of activity across the neurons, called the absolute response magnitude or ARM.

Few studies have addressed the question of how a population of chemoreceptor cells can simultaneously code stimulus quality and stimulus intensity, and these studies have been limited almost exclusively to mammalian gustation. We are using the spiny lobster *Panulirus argus* as a model system for understanding how an olfactory system accomplishes these necessary coding tasks. Our approach is to use behaviorally relevant but synthetic chemical mixtures in studies of the lobsters' behavioral discriminatory abilities and of the way in which potential neural codes could provide information necessary to allow the observed behavioral discriminations. We are also using responses of a population of olfactory receptor cells to test (i) the labeled line coding hypothesis by searching for discrete cell types based on response profiles to these mixtures and (ii) the population coding hypothesis by examining how ANPs and ARMs discriminate stimulus quality and stimulus intensity.

METHODS AND RESULTS

Mixtures. The stimuli used in all experiments are artificial mixtures of crab, mullet, oyster, and shrimp, whose compositions are based on chemical analyses of tissue extracts of food of spiny lobsters (Carr & Derby, 1986). All mixtures are composed of the same 41 amino acids, nucleosides and nucleotides, quaternary ammonium compounds, and organic acids, and they have the same total molar concentration, but they differ in the relative amounts of the individual components.

Behavioral Discrimination. Naive spiny lobsters (*Panulirus argus*) respond to these mixtures with typical appetitive feeding behaviors such as searching, grabbing, and antennular flicking (Daniel & Derby, 1988; Fine-Levy et al., 1988, 1989). To allow expression of the behavioral ability of the lobsters to discriminate among these four mixtures, we have used two conditioning paradigms: habituation, a non-associative technique (Daniel & Derby, 1988); and differential aversive conditioning, an associative technique (Fine-Levy et al., 1988, 1989). Habituation, defined as failure of an animal to respond to 10 consecutive presentations of a mixture, was achieved within 3 hr by presenting that mixture every 5 min. Aversive conditioning was performed by pairing an aversive stimulus (a "pseudopredator") with one of the four mixtures (designated the conditioned mixture) twice per day for 5-7 days. The associative procedure resulted in the development of aversions, expressed as passive and/or active avoidance. The conditioned changes in responsiveness of lobsters in the two paradigms were quantified as "habituation index" and "aversion index" (Fig. 1). Comparison of the habituation index or aversion index values for the conditioned mixture versus the three non-conditioned mixtures gives us a measure of the ability of lobsters to discriminate the mixtures: the non-conditioned mixture with an index value most similar to that for the conditioned mixture is most poorly discriminated from the conditioned mixture.

Results are shown for animals conditioned to crab mixture using aversive conditioning (Fig. 1A) or habituation (Fig. 1B). In both cases, lobsters discriminate crab mixture from the other three mixtures. But the discrimination of crab from shrimp is least distinct, while the discrimination of crab from mullet is the most distinct. Other behavioral results (Fine-Levy et al., 1988, 1989, Fine-Levy & Derby, 1989) indicate that the discrimination of mixture quality is accurately performed independent of mixture intensity.

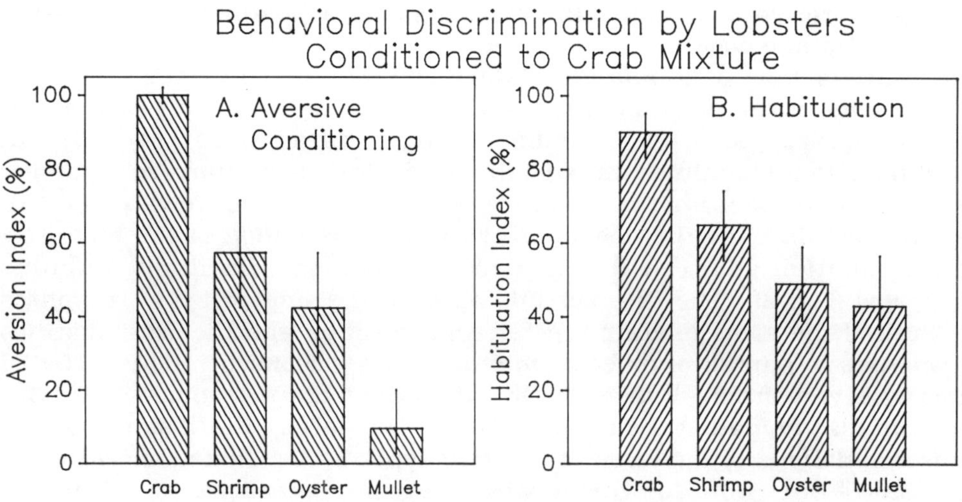

Fig. 1. Comparison of behavioral discrimination for animals conditioned to crab mixture, from results of (A) aversive conditioning and (B) habituation. Lines represent standard error of group means (N=3 lobsters in [A] and N=5 lobsters in [B]). From Fine-Levy et al., 1989.

Neural Discrimination. Toward understanding neural mechanisms of olfactory discrimination, we have examined the responses of 30 olfactory receptor cells in the antennules of spiny lobsters to the same four artificial mixtures, each at three log-step concentrations (Girardot & Derby, 1988, 1989a, 1989b).

To examine whether a labeled line code might be used in the discrimination of these mixtures, we have searched for receptor cells that are narrowly tuned to any of the four mixture types or that can be statistically categorized as belonging to a discrete cell type based on their responses to these mixtures. Narrowly tuned cells, defined either qualitatively as responding solely or predominantly to only one of the mixture types, or quantitatively based on a breadth of responsiveness metric, were not found (Girardot & Derby, 1988). The existence of discrete cell types was examined using multidimensional scaling analysis and cluster analysis of the computed Euclidean distances between cells because these techniques are based on quantitative, objective, and non-arbitrary criteria. These techniques failed to identify unequivocally discrete cell types, but rather suggested a continuum of cellular response profiles (Girardot & Derby, 1989b). Cells are not grouped into four clusters according to the most effective mixture for each cell or according to any other single identifiable property of their response profiles to the mixtures (Girardot & Derby, 1989b). The lack of narrowly tuned cells and the lack of cell types for the mixtures suggest that the code for the quality of these behaviorally relevant odorants in this system is a population code rather than a labeled line code.

To evaluate how a population code might be used by these olfactory receptor cells in the discrimination of the quality and intensity of the four odorant mixtures, these same neural data were reanalyzed. Multidimensional scaling was again used, but this time to examine Euclidean distances between *stimuli* rather than between *cells*. To quantitatively describe the degree of neural discrimination of the mixtures, a discrimination index (DI) was derived from the resulting stimulus coordinates (Fig. 2). The DI takes into account the similarities in responses to stimuli of the same mixture type or concentration and the dissimilarities in responses to stimuli of different mixture types or concentrations. The DI values can vary from -1 to +1. Discrimination occurs when DI>0, with maximum discrimination occurring at DI=1. DIs based on ANPs are positive for discriminations of mixtures of different types at the same concentration (Fig. 2A1) but not for discriminations of mixtures of different concentrations of the same type (Fig. 2A2). DIs based on ARMs are positive for discriminations of mixtures of different concentrations (Fig. 2B2) but not for discriminations of mixtures of different types (Fig. 2B1). The results indicate that mixture quality and intensity can be discriminated by separate components of the response of the population of neurons: quality by ANPs, and intensity by ARMs.

That ANPs can be used by the peripheral olfactory nervous system of spiny lobsters to code for mixture quality is supported by parallel results in the behavioral discrimination and neural discrimination experiments. The behavioral data indicate that spiny lobsters discriminate between crab and shrimp mixtures relatively poorly. But they discriminate relatively well between crab and either mullet or oyster, between mullet and oyster, between mullet and either crab or shrimp, and between oyster and either crab or shrimp (Fine-Levy et al., 1989). The neural discrimination data indicate the same relative similarities among mixtures based on ANPs (Girardot & Derby, 1988, 1989b). Furthermore, the fact that conditioning experiments indicate that behavioral discriminations between different mixture types can be made relatively independent of changes in mixture concentration (Fine-Levy et al., 1988, 1989, Fine-Levy & Derby, 1989) suggests that stimulus quality is encoded in the nervous system independent from stimulus intensity.

The abilitity of lobsters to discriminate among these four mixtures is a reflection and consequence of differences in the compositions of the mixtures. Statistical analysis of the compositions of the mixtures (Daniel et al., 1988) shows that crab and shrimp mixtures are compositionally more similar to one another than they are to mullet and oyster mixtures, and mullet and oyster mixtures are compositionally relatively dissimilar to one another and to crab and shrimp mixtures. Small pools of chemicals, often less than 10, are responsible for the dissimilarities in the compositions of any two mixtures. We therefore predict that the observed differences in ANPs generated by the mixtures, as in Figure 2, are largely due to only a handful of the 41 components of the mixtures.

DISCUSSION

From our behavioral and neural data for artificial mixtures, we have formulated a working model as to mechanisms by which the olfactory system can discriminate quality and intensity of chemical stimuli. Stimulus quality can be coded using one feature of the neuronal population response -- the across neuron pattern (ANP), while stimulus intensity can be coded using a second feature of the population response -- the absolute response magnitude (ARM). This model of course does not preclude the possibility that other codes, such as temporal or spatial codes, might also be used. Support for the validity of our model comes from responses to a second set of mixtures -- natural food extracts (Girardot & Derby, 1988, 1989a, 1989b). We are presently testing this model further with behavioral and neural data for a set of 7 single compounds and their binary mixtures. We are also using this new data set to examine the effects of mixture interactions on discrimination. Mixture interactions, defined as instances in which responses to mixtures are not accurately predicted from the measured responses to the individual components of the mixtures, can change the information about the nature of chemical stimuli which is carried by chemosensory neurons. As a result, mixture interactions could have significant effects on ANPs and ARMs, which in turn would affect behavioral detection and discrimination of stimuli in a theoretically predictable fashion (Derby et al., 1988). Thus, our experiments with binary mixtures and their components should provide us with a means both to test our model of mechanisms of neural coding responsible for behavioral discrimination of stimulus quality and intensity and to test effects of mixture interactions on such coding and discrimination.

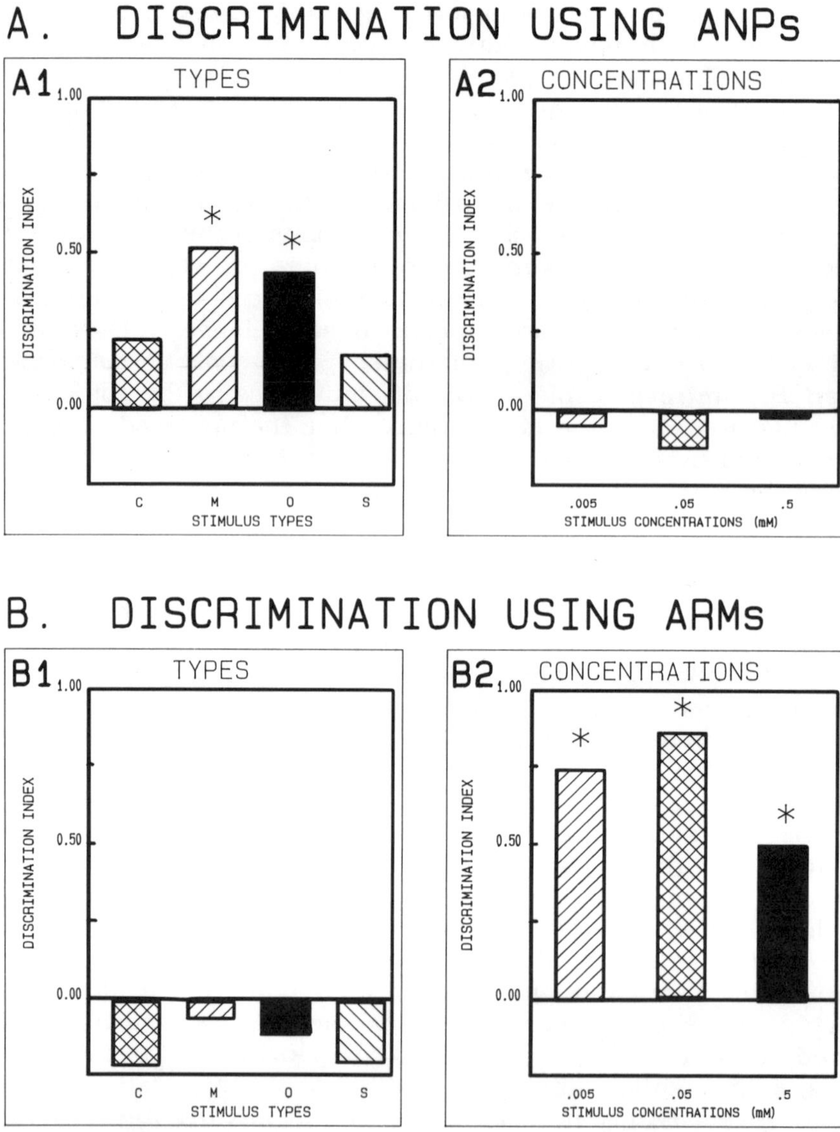

Fig. 2. Discrimination of mixture types and concentrations by (A) ANPs and (B) ARMs. C=crab, M=mullet, O=oyster, S=shrimp. * = the within-type or within-concentration distances are significantly smaller than the between-types or between-concentrations distances, respectively (Mann-Whitney U-test, $P<0.05$). Modified from Girardot and Derby, 1989a).

Independence of codes for chemical quality and intensity could have behavioral significance, in that the ANP and ARM might have different functions during an animal's interaction with its chemical environment (Girardot & Derby, 1989a). According to this hypothetical scheme, activation of a specific ANP is linked to the identification of a stimulus or set of related stimuli and to the production of a behavior or behaviors *specific* to that ANP. For example, a "food-ANP" would elicit appetitive feeding behaviors, and a "predator-ANP" would elicit avoidance. The ARM would be important in determining the magnitude of the behavioral response. For example, a given appetitive feeding behavior -- antennular flicking, searching, or grabbing -- would be initiated and maintained if the ARM is suprathreshold for that behavior; the threshold for ARMs for the various appetitive behaviors may differ, however, with antennular flicking being released by low ARMs and grabbing being released only by high ARMs. Additionally, the response intensity of each behavior would be a function of intensity of the ARM.

REFERENCES

Carr, W.E.S. & Derby, C.D. (1986) Behavioral chemoattractants for the shrimp, *Palaemonetes pugio*: identification of active components in food extracts and the involvement of mixture interactions. *Chem. Senses* **11**: 49-64.

Daniel, P.C. & Derby, C.D. (1988) Behavioral olfactory discrimination of mixtures in the spiny lobster (*Panulirus argus*) based on a habituation paradigm. *Chem Senses* **13**: 385-395.

Daniel, P.C., Fine-Levy, J.B. & Derby, C.D. (1988) Resolving mixture differences: compositional and behavioral analyses. *Chem. Senses* **13**: 682.

Derby, C.D., Girardot, M.-N., Daniel, P.C. & Fine-Levy, J.B. (1988) Olfactory discrimination of mixtures: behavioral, electrophysiological, and theoretical studies using the spiny lobster *Panulirus argus*. In *Perception of Complex Smells and Tastes* (ed. D.G. Laing, W.S. Cain, R.L. McBride & B.W. Ache) pp. 65-81. Sydney: Academic.

Fine-Levy, J.B., Girardot, M.-N, Derby, C.D. & Daniel, P.C. (1988) Differential associative conditioning and olfactory discrimination in the spiny lobster *Panulirus argus*. *Behav. Neural Biol.* **49**: 315-331.

Fine-Levy, J.B., Daniel, P.C., Girardot, M.-N. & Derby, C.D. (1989) Behavioral resolution of quality of odorant mixtures by spiny lobsters: differential aversive conditioning of olfactory responses. *Chem. Senses* **14** (in press).

Fine-Levy, J.B. & Derby, C.D. (1989) Effect of stimulus intensity on discrimination of odorant mixtures by spiny lobsters in an associative learning paradigm. *Soc. Neurosci. Abstr.*, Vol. **15** (in press).

Girardot, M.-N. & Derby, C.D. (1988) Neural coding of quality of complex olfactory stimuli in lobsters. *J. Neurophysiol.* **60**: 303-324.

Girardot, M.-N. & Derby, C.D. (1989a) Neural discrimination of quality and intensity of odorant mixtures by independent components of the receptor cell population response. (Manuscript submitted).

Girardot, M.-N. & Derby, C.D. (1989b) Peripheral mechanisms of olfactory discrimination of mixtures by the spiny lobster: no cell types but different functions for cells in the population. (Manuscript submitted).

Frontiers in Crustacean Neurobiology
Advances in Life Sciences

SPIKING LOCAL INTERNEURONS RELATED TO THE EQUILIBRIUM RESPONSES IN THE CRAYFISH BRAIN

Hideki Nakagawa and Mituhiko Hisada

Zoological Institute, Faculty of Science, Hokkaido University, Sapporo 060, Japan

SUMMARY

The spiking local interneurons related to the righting response and the compensatory eye movement within the crayfish brain were analyzed both in physiology and in morphology. Fourteen local brain (propriocerebral) interneurons which respond to the statocyst stimulation were successfully characterized in this study. They are classified into 4 subclasses of vplc-B, vplc-U, vupc-B and vupc-U according to their soma positions and neurite arborization in the protocerebrum. Both vplc-B and vupc-B groups include the neurons which show either excitatory or inhibitory responses to the statocyst stimulation. The vplc-U neurons show inhibitory responses and the vupc-U neurons show excitatory responses respectively. Only the neurons which are excited by the statocyst stimulation showed postsynaptic effects of changing the activities of the oculomotor neurons and/or the descending interneurons.

INTRODUCTION

In crayfish, disturbances of body posture brought out either by an animal's own activity or by the external forces are detected by various sense organs of balance: statocysts, proprioceptive organs and eyes. Almost all of body appendages are recruited to produce corrective righting reactions and, in addition, the eyestalks respond with compensatory movements. The peripheral mechanisms underlying these equilibrium responses are relatively well studied (for review see Neil, 1985). But the integrative mechanism of each sensory signal necessary to produce the appropriate motor output remains to be studied more fully, though some attempts have already been initiated (Fraser, 1975; Silvey & Sandeman, 1976; Takahata et al, 1985). There also remains an almost unexplored area of the central mechanism of interrelation between these two equilibrium related responses and, further still, of interaction between the equilibrium responses and other types of behavioral output (Takahata & Hisada, 1986a,b; Neil & Miyan, 1986; see Rowell, 1988). Elucidation of these central mechanism will help our understanding of how one particular behavioral output is selected and brought out among several possible ones, and how the adaptive adjustments of the effector output are performed. As a preliminary to this elucidation, we have been cataloging the statocyst related interneurons both at the circumesophageal commissure for the descending interganglionic neurons (Nakagawa & Hisada, 1989; see also Hisada & Neil, 1985) and in the deutocerebrum itself for the local brain interneurons (propriocerebral interneurons). The present paper will give the descriptions of the latter group of interneurons of particularly spiking type we have found. Besides the morphological and physiological characterization of the interneurons, interrelation between the descending statocyst pathways and the compensatory oculomotor pathways (see Neil, 1982) via these local interneurons will be referred to.

MATERIALS AND METHODS

Adult crayfish, *Procambarus clarkii* Girard, of either sex of 8 to 11 cm in body length were used. The details of dissection procedure has been described elsewhere (Nakagawa & Hisada, 1989).

A small hook probe was placed in contact with a group of hairs in the lateral region of sensory hair crescent by a micromanipulator. The probe was mounted on a loud-speaker which was driven by a waveform generator. The hairs were usually deflected sinusoidally by about 60 um to simulate the lateral body tilt. Inward deflection of the hairs simulate the lowering of the contralateral side of the animal.

To monitor the output signals of the equilibrium response occurring in simulation in the contralateral side. Spike activity was recorded from the optic nerve motor bundle (oculomotors) and the circumesophageal connective (descending statocyst interneurons) on the side contralateral to the stimulated statocyst.

For intracellular recording and staining, glass microelectrodes filled with 3% solution of Lucifer Yellow (DC resistance, 120-180 megohm) were employed. The statocyst-related neurons were sought in the deutocerebral region of the brain. Following the examination of both the response to the mechanical stimulation of the statocyst and the postsynaptic effect on the oculomotor and the descending neurons, the dye was injected iontophoretically with hyperpolarizing current of 10 nA for 15 min. Neurons in the brains were photographed with a fluorescence microscope after fixation and clearing and drawn from projected slides.

RESULTS

Physiological recordings and morphological stainings enough to characterize the neurons were obtained of 14 local brain interneurons.

All the local interneurons reported here belong to the spiking ones. Features common to these interneurons are that they respond to the statocyst stimulation of artificial hair bending with phaso-tonic or tonic responses and that in morphology they spread their neurites mainly in proto- and deutocerebrum. Their soma lie either in the ventral paired lateral cluster (vplc) or in the ventral unpaired posterior cluster (vupc) regions (nomenclatures after Tautz & Tautz, 1983), and their neurite arborizations in the protocerebrum are either bilateral (B) or unilateral (U). Thus they fall into four groups of vplc-B, vplc-U, vupc-B and vupc-U according to the soma position and the laterality of neurite arborization. None of these interneurons has bilateral neurite arborization in the deutocerebral region where the majority of statocyst afferents are known to terminate (Yoshino et al. 1983) (Fig. 1).

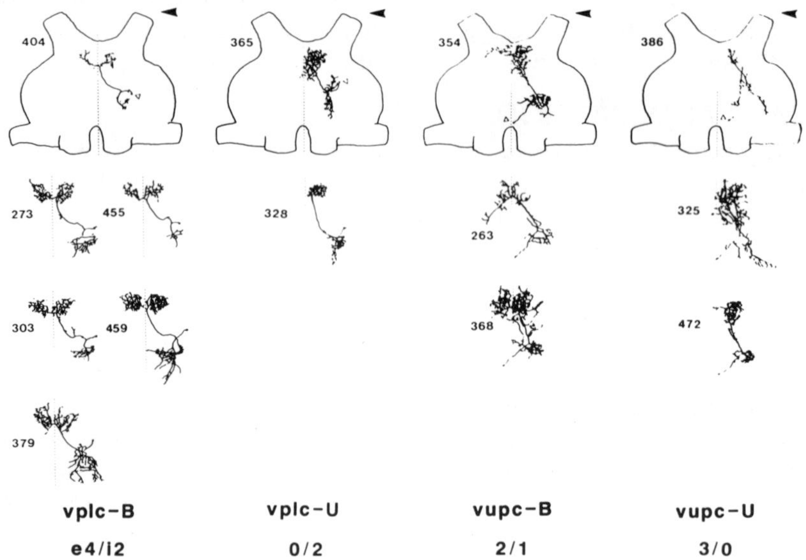

Fig. 1 Morphology of the characterized statocyst-related spiking local interneurons. Arrowheads indicate the side of statocyst stimulation. The neurons are classified by the soma postitions and the laterality of the protocerebral branches. The numbers of interneurons showing excitatory and inhibitory responses (upper and lower respectively) are presented below. Open triangles show soma positions.

All the interneurons in vupc-U group receive excitatory input from the statocyst ipsilateral to their deutocerebral branches, while those in vplc-U receive inhibitory input. Two bilateral groups of both vplc-B and vupc-B, are found to be of mixed populations of the interneurons showing either excitatory or inhibitory response to the statocyst stimulation. The interneurons found to have output effects to the oculomotor and/or the descending neurons are exclusively of those showing excitatory responses to the statocyst stimulation (Fig.2). Four neurons of the vplc-B group which are almost indiscernible each other in morphology (Fig. 1) are found to receive either excitatory (273, 459) or inhibitory (303, 404) input from the statocyst (Fig.2).

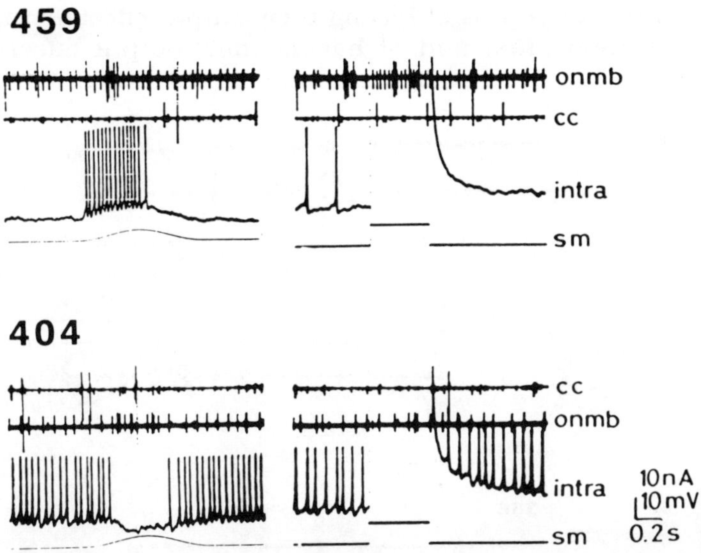

Fig. 2 Physiology of interneuron 459 and 404. Left panels show the responses of the interneurons to the deflection of the sensory hairs in the right statocyst. Right panels show the effects of depolarizing current injection (10nA) into the interneurons. onmb, optic nerve motor bundle; cc, circumesophageal connective; intra, intracellular recording at the right deutocerebrum. sm, stimulus monitor, left: inward deflection of sensory hairs, right: injection of depolarizing current. 459 is excited and 404 is inhibited by the hair deflection. In 459, depolarizing current injection increases spike frequency of the oculomotor neurons but not in 404.

Identification of the individual neurons and estimation of the numbers of each type of neurons in the brain is, thus, impossible at this stage.Artificial stimulation of the statocyst hairs usually produces both the oculomotor and the descending nerve activities, but the latter tends to be unstable (Fig. 3A). Stimulation of the descending interneurons S1 had no effect on the oculomotor activity by injection of depolarizing current through the microelectrode (Fig.3B). Other three descending statocyst interneurons tested (S3, S6 and S7; Nakagawa & Hisada, 1989) also did not affect the oculomotor activity. The descending neurons are thus not the part of the oculomotor pathway.

Depolarizing current was injected into the interneurons to see the output effects. As stated before, the interneurons found to have output effects are limited among those of showing excitatory responses to the statocyst stimulation. Excluding the dubious ones, five out of a total of nine interneurons with excitatory responses showed the output effects to the oculomotor and/or the descending neurons. These interneurons can be subdivided into two groups of having their output effects on the oculomotor neurons only (386, 459) and of having their output effects on both the oculomotor and the descending neurons (354, 379, 472) (Fig.3C).

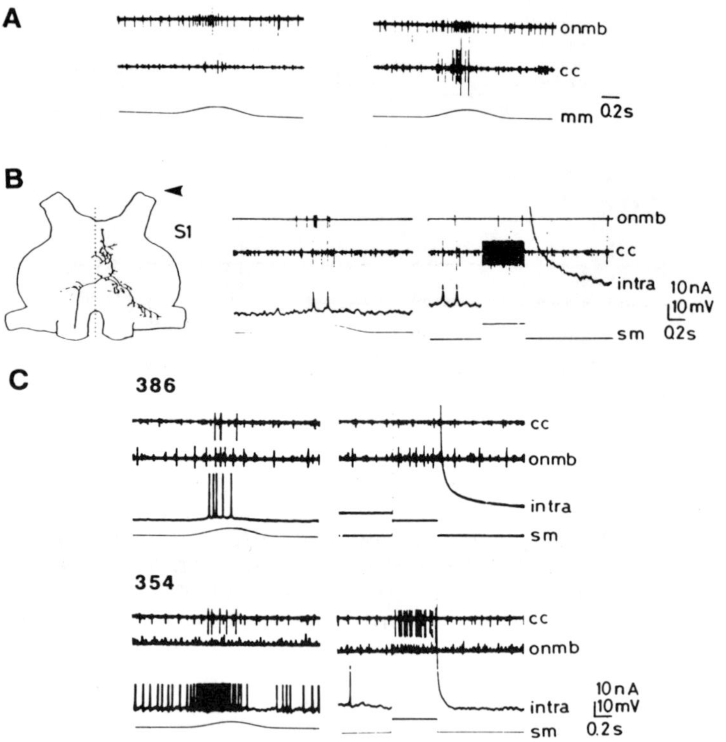

Fig. 3 A: The responses of oculomotor neurons and descending statocyst interneurons to statocyst sensory hair deflection of the right statocyst. mm, mechanical stimulus monitor. Upward excursion indicates the inward movement of the sensory hairs. Note that oculomotor neurons and descending statocyst interneurons are not necessarily activated at the same time. B: Morphology and physiology of a descending statocyst interneuron S1. Left panel shows the response of S1 to statocyst sensory hair deflection. S1 shows the excitatory response to the inward hair deflection. Right panel shows the effect of depolarizing current injection into S1. No detectable change of the oculomotor activity is observed during the current injection. C: Physiology of two local spiking interneurons 386 and 354, experimental conditions and data presentation are the same with those in B. Both neurons show excitatory responses to the inward statocyst hair deflection. Current injection into 386 increases the spike frequency of the oculomotor neurons, while current injection into 354 increases both those of the oculomotor and the descending neurons. Abbreviations and symbols are the same as in the previous figures.

DISCUSSION

All of the spiking local interneurons described here have branches that extend into the optic lobe and medial part of the deutocerebrum. These branching areas principally overlap with those of descending statocyst interneurons (Nakagawa & Hisada, 1989). The statocyst sensory afferents are known to terminate in both sides of the deutocerebrum (Yoshino et. al., 1983). Therefore, it is possible that interneurons with unilateral deutocerebral branches as those described in this paper receive input signals from the statocysts of both sides. However, all the local interneurons found in this study with responses to the statocyst stimulation were those of responding to the stimulation of the ipsilateral statocyst. This indicates that the local neurons receive the input only from the statocyst ipsilateral to their deutocerebral branches.

In the optic lobes of the protocerebrum, the bilateral groups of these interneurons, vplc-B and vupc-B, extend their neurite branches across the midline. There is no interneuron found which projects to the contralateral optic lobe only. Whether the interneurons with bilateral branches in the optic lobe receive the visual input signals at both sides remains to be examined.

Of all the neural connections hitherto reported about the statocyst related response in the decapod crustaceans, only certain motoneurons were found to have inhibitory connections, and the central integrative mechanism was thought to be mainly consisted of excitatory ones (Takahata et. al., 1985; Neil & Miyan, 1986; Hisada & Neil, 1985). However, of 14 currently characterized local interneurons 5 interneurons were found to show inhibitory responses to the statocyst stimulation. We also found a few units of the statocyst afferents which responded to the statocyst hair stimulation with suppression of its own spiking activity. Moreover, some identified descending statocyst interneurons which are excited by ipsilateral statocyst stimulation are centrally inhibited by contralateral statocyst stimulation. These findings suggest that inhibitory connections are also involved in the central mechanisms of the statocyst related responses (in preparation).

The local interneurons dealt in the present study showed four morphologically distinguishable structural categories, and two types of responses to the stimulation of the ipsilateral statocyst, excitatory and inhibitory. Only in the neurons showing excitatory responses to the statocyst stimulation, the postsynaptic effects on the oculomotor and/or the descending interganglionic interneurons could be observed. In this aspect, they can further subdivided into two groups. The first group is the neurons which are presynaptic to the oculomotor interneurons and not to the descending neurons. The second is presynaptic to the descending interneurons and, in addition, premotor to the oculomotor system.

However, as in the input connections from the statocyst, it appears to be impossible, at least at this stage, to relate this difference in the output connections with their morphology. This parallel presence of the singular and the common channels to the oculomotor and the descending pathways may reflect the necessity of controlling the two equilibrium responses, the eyestalk compensatory and the righting responses either simultaneously in strong coordination or independently with fine tuning to the need of behavioral context.

REFERENCES

Fraser, P. J. (1975) Free hook hair and thread hair input to fiber 5 in the mud crab, *Scylla serrata*, during antennule rotation. J. comp. Physiol. **103**, 291-313.

Hisada, M. & Neil, D.M. (1985) The neuronal basis of equilibrium behaviour in decapod crustaceans. In Coordination of Motor Behaviour, (ed. B.M.H. Bush & F. Clarac) pp. 229-248. Cambridge: Cambridge University Press.

Nakagawa, H. & Hisada, M. (1989) Morphology of descending statocyst interneurons in the crayfish *Procambarus clarkii* Girard. Cell Tissue Res. **255**, 539-551.

Neil, D.M. (1982) Compensatory eye movements. In The Biology of Crustacea, Vol 4, (ed. D.C. Sandeman & H.L. Atwood) pp. 133-163. New York: Academic Press.

Neil, D.M. (1985) Multisensory interactions in the crustacean equilibrium system. In Feedback and Motor Control in Invertebrates and Vertebrates, (ed. W.J.B. Barnes & M.H. Gladden) pp. 277-298. London: Croom Helm Ltd.

Neil, D. M. & Miyan, J. A. (1986) Phase-dependent modulation of auxiliary swimmeret muscle activity in the equilibrium reactions of the Norway lobster, *Nephropus norvegicus* L. J. exp. Biol. **126**, 157-179.

Rowell, C. F. H. (1988) Mechanisms of flight steering in locusts. Experientia. 44, 389-395.

Silvey, G. E. & Sandeman, D. C. (1976) Integration between statocystsensory neurons and oculomotor neurons in the crab *Scylla serrata*. III. The sensory to motor synapse. J. comp. Physiol. **108**, 53-65.

Takahata, M. & Hisada, M. (1986a) Sustained membrane potential change of uropod motor neurons during the fictive abdominal posture movement in crayfish. J. Neurophysiol. **56,** 702-717.

Takahata, M. & Hisada, M. (1986b) Local nonspiking interneurons involved in gating of the descending motor pathway in crayfish. J. Neurophysiol. **56**, 718-731.

Takahata, M., Yoshino, M. & Hisada, M. (1985) Neuronal mechanisms underlying crayfish steering behaviour as an equilibrium response. J. exp. Biol. **114**, 599-617.

Tautz, J. & Tautz, R. M. (1983) Antennal neuropile in the brain of the crayfish : Morphology of neurons. J. comp. Neurol. **218,** 415-425

Yoshino, M., Kondoh, Y. & Hisada, M. (1983) Projection of statocyst sensory neurons associated with crescent hairs in the crayfish *Procambarus clarkii* Girard. Cell Tissue Res. **230,** 37-48.

Frontiers in Crustacean Neurobiology
Advances in Life Sciences

EQUILIBRIUM CONTROL BY STATOCYST ACTIVATED INTERNEURONES

Peter J. Fraser

Zoology Department, Aberdeen University,
Tillydrone Avenue,Aberdeen, AB9 2TN, Scotland, UK.

SUMMARY

The statocyst of the crab is specialized for angular acceleration detection, with a fluid filled sack formed intohorizontal and vertical canals. Receptor hairs respond to fluid movements so that the statocyst mechanically abstracts componentsof angular acceleration in orthogonal planes. Equilibrium interneurones are multimodal interneurones which clearly code onedirection of angular acceleration in one of three orthogonal planes. The interneurones are active preceding and during walking and swimming. The output of the interneurones to a sinusoidal angular acceleration varies with temperature, and during the excited state which accompanies locomotion. The excited state may be simulated by perfusion of the cerebral artery with salinecontaining serotonin or octopamine. The set of equilibrium interneurones codes any direction of angular acceleration in terms of the relative activity in each cell. Although there are necessarily no connections between the cells, a form of multiplicative gain control exists, so that during a gain change,the activity levels of the separate cells change so as to preserve the coded direction.

INTRODUCTION

In early studies, Wiersma and his coworkers introduced the idea of the 'excited state' during which the thresholds and activity levels in many interneurones are altered, revealing the presence of central pathways (Wiersma and Yamaguchi, 1967). The cells were designated 'activity fibres'. Little is known of the basis for this property or its functional role. Equilibrium interneurones in crabs which receive input from fluid activated receptors in the statocyst located in the base of the antennule (Fig. 1) have many features in common with activity fibres, and show marked gain changes. The questions are: when does gain change and what happens to the direction coding properties of the cells during such gain changes? The crab statocyst consists of an invaginated sack in the base of the antennule (Fig. 1). The sack is further convoluted into a horizontal and a vertical canal (Sandeman and Okajima, 1972; Fraser, 1982). Fluid movements due to inertial forces during angular accelerations are sensed by free hook hair and thread hair receptors inside the statocyst (Fig. 2a & b). These receptors fire to one direction of fluid movement. They project monosynaptically to the equilibrium interneurones. Their output shows little adaptation, although their gain does change markedly with temperature (Fig. 3a; Fraser, 1989).

Equilibrium interneurones are known as a set of eight large interneurones with cell bodies and dendrites in the brain and axons descending in the oesophageal connectives which run through the fused thoracic and abdominal ganglia, with large axonal branches to thoracic neuropiles containing leg motor neurones (Fraser, 1974; 1975a,b; 1977).

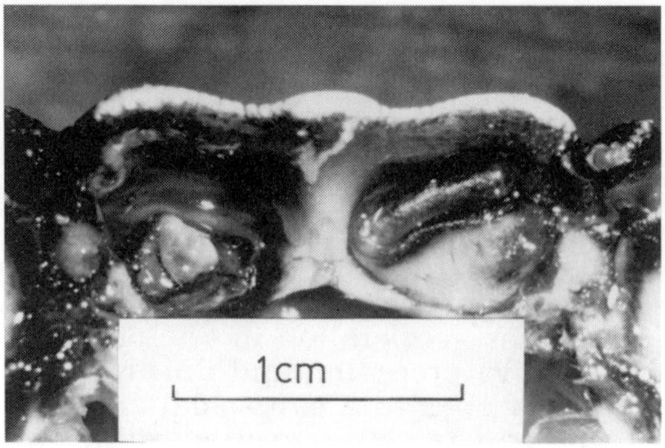

Fig. 1. Ventral view of *Carcinus* showing right antennule dissected to reveal the statocyst inside. Right and left vertical canals liein planes at approximately 45° and 225° to the saggital plane respectively.

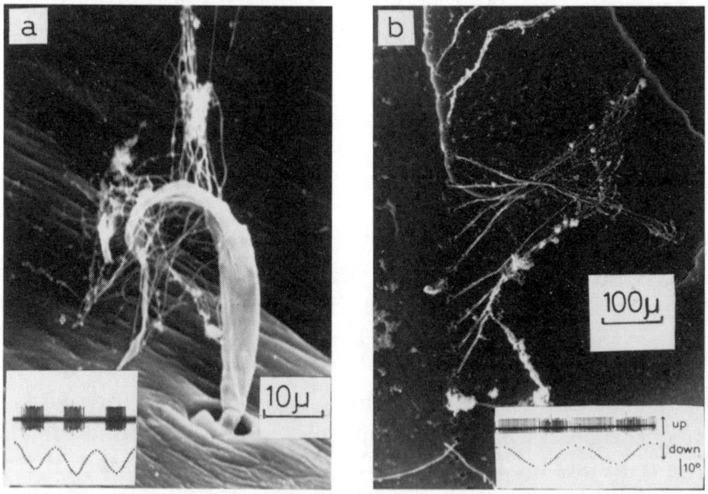

Fig. 2a. Scanning electron micrograph of *Carcinus* free hook hairreceptor, with inset showing a typical single unit responding to sinusoidal oscillation of c. 1 Hz.

2b. Similar scanning e.m. of the line of thread hairs on the sensory cushion (see Sandeman and Okajima, 1972).

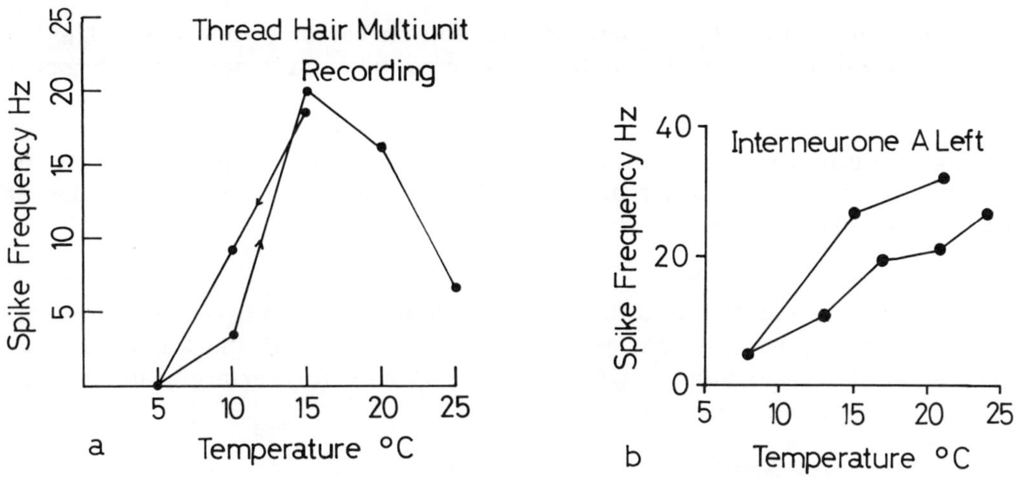

Fig. 3. Average spontaneous activity in (a) multiunit thread hair recording and (b) response from cell 5 left to 1 Hz cycle, during descending and ascending temperature changes.

They receive input from thread hair and free hook hair receptors such that each cell codes one direction of a single component of angular acceleration in one of three orthogonal planes (Fig. 4). The cells also receive input from leg joint proprioceptors and have sustained activity preceding and during swimming and walking (Fraser et al, 1987).

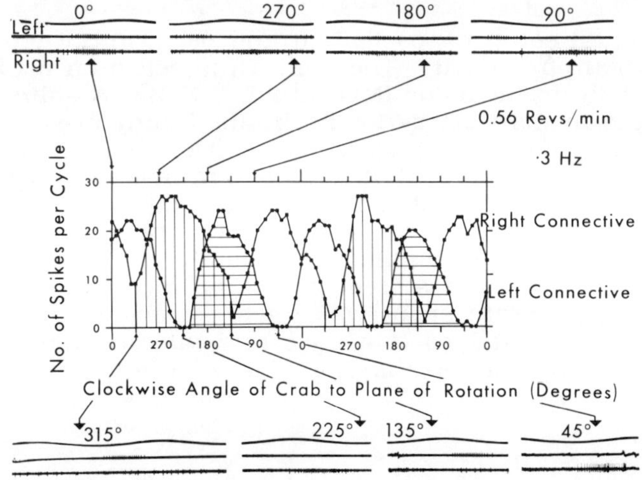

Fig. 4. Directionality of cells A in left and right connectives to oscillation in different vertical planes. The cells respond tohead up rotation in the plane of the contralateral statocyst vertical canal, and show a cosine function with respect to the angle of the plane of oscillation (From Fraser, 1975a).

In terms of their statocyst input, the function seems clear; the cells abstract orthogonal components of angular accelerations. Thew hole signal may be reconstituted by recombination of such vector components. The leg joint proprioceptor inputs can be considered to complement the statocyst input for angular accelerations against the resistance of the legs. The role of the 'activity' properties of the cells is less clear. I present evidence of changed gain in the equilibrium interneurones under a variety of circumstances, and consider the effect of such gain changes on the ability of the set of cells to code direction.

METHODS

Continuous oscillation and brain perfusion was effected as shown in Fig. 5. Interneurone spike frequencies were calculated per oscillation cycle and sent to an expanded Sinclair QL microcomputer for further analysis.

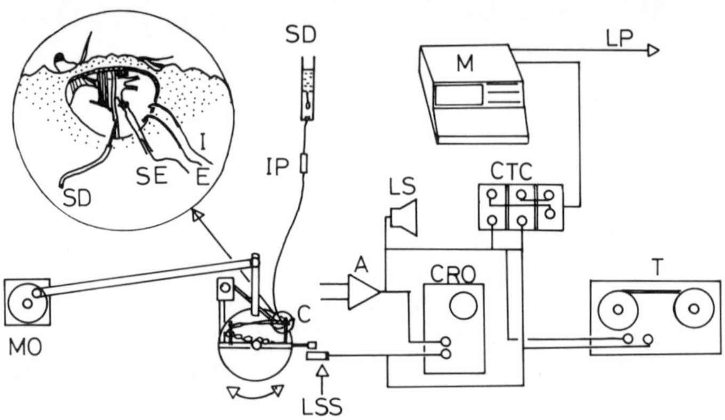

Fig.5. Experimental setup for oscillation and perfusion of crab brain while recording interneurone activity. The crab (C) is setup on a tilting platform driven sinusoidally by a motor (MO) at.25 - .3 Hz. A saline drip (SD) is inserted into the median artery to the brain. Interneurone responses are recorded from one cut oesophageal connective with a suction electrode (SE). Earth (E) and indifferent (I) electrodes are inserted nearby. Serotonin or octopamine was injected into the saline through an injection port (IP). Oscillation cycles were monitored by flag interruption of a light source and sensor (LSS). Signals were amplified (A), monitored on oscilloscope (CRO) and audioampifier (LS), and stored on a tape recorder (T). Signals were replayed through separate spike triggers to separate channels of a Z80 Counter timer circuit attached to a Nascom 3 microcomputer programmed in machine code to record spike and oscillation cycle times.

RESULTS

It was easy to record and separate activity in cells A, C and D in one connective. Cells A and D repond to head up and head down angular acceleration in the plane of the contralateral statocyst vertical canal whereas cell C responds to head down angular acceleration in the plane of the ipsilateral statocyst vertical canal. Thus cell C codes a plane at right angles to that coded byA and D. Usually cell A has least activity, cell C next and cell D most activity. During changing temperature, gain changes in the same way as for sensory neurones (Fig. 3b), but effects are usually less marked. During long term oscillation experiments, activity levels are usually constant for long periods with rather sudden, spontaneous changes in gain as expressed as output to a constant sinusoidal stimulation. Usually all three neurones show coincident increases or decreases. Figure 6 shows a record with fairly high variation in gain to emphasize this covariance. Abrupt changes in gain are often associated with struggling movements.

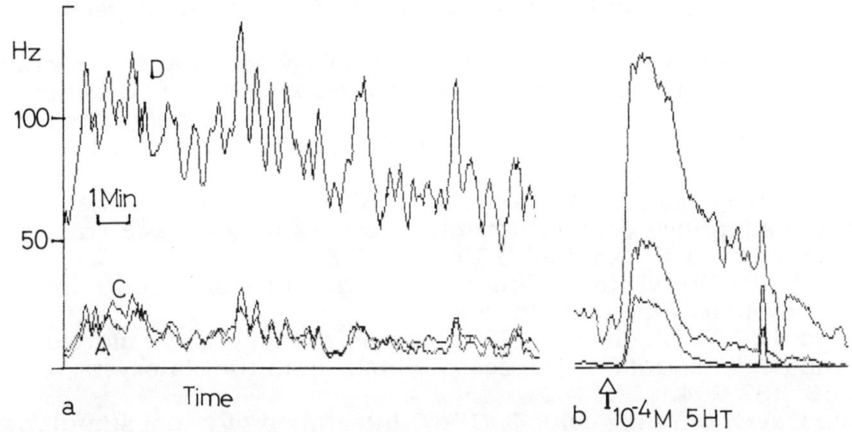

Fig. 6.(a) Spike frequencies in cells A, C and D in right connective recorded every oscillation cycle during a constant .3Hz sinusoidal oscillation, showing that the gain varies nearly always (but not invariably) in a similar way in all three cells. Abrupt changes in gain which occur spontaneously can be reproduced by perfusion of the brain with serotonin (b) and octopamine. Serotonin is ten times more sensitive than octopamine and above threshold effects occur to 10^{-8}M serotonin.

DISCUSSION

There are two separate reasons for increasing the discharge of an equilibrium interneurone. First, the larger the component of angular acceleration in the appropriate plane, the greater the expected spike discharge in the cell. In simple terms we might think that the cell would use it's entire operational range simply to code directions and magnitudes more accurately. The activity function is different, it precedes action and seems to have abehaviour switching role. Considering the interneurone outputs as separate orthogonal vector components and recombining them shows that the coded direction remains constant over a wide range of gain (Fraser, 1989b). It is suggested here that blood borne serotonin could act to affect such multiplicative gain in this distributed system of neurones.

REFERENCES

Fraser, P.J. (1974) Interneurones in crab connectives (*Carcinus maenas L.*): directional statocyst fibres. J. exp. Biol. **61**:615-628.

Fraser, P.J. (1975a) Free hook hair and thread hair input to fibre 5 in the mud crab, *Scylla serrata*, during antennule rotation. J. comp. Physiol. **103**: 221-313.

Fraser, P.J. (1975b) Three classes of input to a semicircular canal interneuron in the crab *Scylla serrata* and a possible output. J. comp. Physiol. **103**, 291-313.

Fraser, P.J. (1977) How morphology of semicircular canals affects transduction, as shown by response characteristics of statocyst interneurones in the crab *Carcinus maenas* (L.). J. comp. Physiol. **115:** 135-145.

Fraser, P.J. (1982) Semicircular canal morphology and function in crabs. In *The Vestibular System Function and Morphology* , (Ed. T. Gualtierotti) pp. 206-224. New York: Springer.Fraser, P.J. (1989a) Effects of temperature on statocyst afferents of the crab Carcinus maenas. J. Thermal Biol. In Press.

Fraser, P.J., Bevengut, M. & Clarac, F. (1987) Swimming patterns and the activity of identified equilibrium interneurones in the shore crab, *Carcinus maenas*. J. exp. Biol. **130**: 305-330.

Fraser, P.J. (1989b) Vector coding and multiplicative gain control in the nervous system of the crab. In Press.

Sandeman, D.C. & Okajima, A. (1972) Statocyst induced eye movements in the crab *Scylla serrata*. I. The sensory input from the statocysts. J. exp. Biol. **58**: 187-204.

Wiersma, C.A.G. & Yamaguchi, T. (1967) Integration of visual stimuli by the crayfish central nervous system. J. exp. Biol. **47**: 409-443.

Frontiers in Crustacean Neurobiology
Advances in Life Sciences

GIANT BRAIN NEURONS OF THE CRAYFISH: THEIR FUNCTIONAL ROLES IN THE COMPENSATORY OCULOMOTOR SYSTEM

Tsuneo Yamaguchi and Yoshinori Okada

Department of Biology, Faculty of Science, Okayama University, Okayama 700, Japan

SUMMARY

Three pairs of nonspiking giant interneurons (G1, G2, and G3; NGIs) of the crayfish brain respond with depolarizing and hyperpolarizing graded potentials to illumination of the contra- and ipsilateral eyes, respectively. These NGIs also respond with depolarizing and hyperpolarizing graded potentials to body tilts in roll to the ipsi- and contralateral sides, respectively. In the bilaterally statocystectomized animal, none of the NGIs responds to the body tilts in darkness, while in the presence of a discrete light source shining the dorsal side of the body all the NGIs elicit depolarizing and hyperpolarizing potentials in response to the body tilts to the ipsi- and contralateral sides, respectively. Depolarizing the NGIs with injected current increases the firing rate of ipsilateral eye-down and contralateral eye-up motor neurons mediating the eye-stalk movements. Hyperpolarizing the NGIs has the opposite effect.

INTRODUCTION

Crayfishes show compensatory eye-stalk movements in response to visual and geotactic stimuli (e.g. Wiersma & Yamaguchi, 1967; Wiersma & Oberjat, 1968; Okada & Yamaguchi, 1985). These eye-stalk movements are controlled mainly by three sets of functionally identified motor neurons innervating the eye-stalk muscles; clockwise and anticlockwise motor neurons responding only to horizontal rotations of the animal or surround, head-up and head-down motor neurons reacting to rotations along the transverse axis, and eye-up and eye-down motor neurons responding to rotations on the longitudinal axis. The main inputs for the first set originate only in visual stimuli, whereas those for the remaining two sets originate in both visual and geotactic stimuli.

Recently, the five pairs of nonspiking giant interneurons (NGIs) have been identified in the protocerebrum of the crayfish brain : G1,G2, and G3 are contained in one cluster, G4 and G5 are separate (Okada & Yamaguchi, 1988). These NGIs are postsynaptic to fourth-order visual interneurons (sustaining fibers [SFs]; Wiersma & Yamaguchi, 1966; Kirk et al., 1982; Yamaguchi et al., 1984). In the present paper we will describe that G1, G2, and G3 respond not only to visual stimuli, but also to geotactic stimuli, and that these NGIs connect functionally to the eye-up and eye-down motor neurons to act as premotor neurons in the oculomotor system.

MATERIAL AND METHODS

Experiments were performed on the crayfish (*Procambarus clarkii*), measuring 10-12 cm from rostrum to telson. Removal of the statocyst was done by cutting one of the antennules or both at their bases. The animal thus statocystectomized was kept for few days, till the injured part was sealed by healing and then subjected to the experiments. The animal was suspended with a clamp which held the carapace while all appendages were fixed with elastic threads. The clamp holding the animal was then mounted on a tilt device with a manipulator for insertion of a microelectrode into a NGI. This device, which could be driven by a pulse motor, allowed the mounted animal to be tilted around the transverse or longitudinal axis of the body, though the angle of body tilt was usually small to prevent from dislodging the microelectrode. Electrical recordings, intracellular staining, and visual stimuli were made as described previously (Okada & Yamaguchi, 1988).

RESULTS

Morphological features of NGIs. All three pairs of NGIs, G1, G2, and G3, have no demonstrable axons, but do have large dendritic processes (200-700 μm in length) that run in a bundle just above the protocerebrum bridge

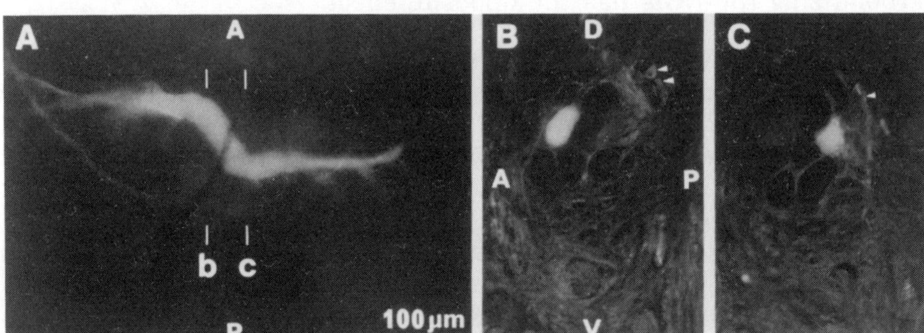

Fig. 1. Differential staining of a SF (left O38) and an NGI (right G3). (A) Dorsal view of whole-mount preparation. The O38 and G3 were stained differentially with ethidium bromide and Lucifer yellow, respectively. (B) Sagittal section of the preparation through the midline. (C) Sagittal section at a distance of 80 μm from the midline. The levels of sections in B and C correspond to those marked with b and c in A, respectively. Note that the SF extends its branchlets toward the cluster at the point where they encircle the cluster, and that the unstained processes of other members of the cluster can be seen. Arrow heads in B and C indicate the axon of SF.

across the midline. These dendritic processes have short thick primary branches: the higher-order branches contralateral to the somata have numerous varicosities at or near their endings, while those ipsilateral to their somata have dendritic, spine-like small processes. The somata are located near the distal end of the optic tract and are connected to their dendritic processes by thin primary neurites that have no side branches. The somata of paired NGIs lie in the opposite optic tract, and their dendritic processes are closely intertwined.

Differential staining of an NGI and a SF showed that the axon of the SF running down through the optic tract from the medulla externa approximately parallels the cluster within the protocerebrum and that long, fine branches extend, especially on the contralateral side, to surround the cluster. In some well- stained preparations, differentially stained branches in and around the cluster had the appearance of contacts between them (Fig. 1).

Responses of NGIs to illumination and body tilt. The potentials generated by NGIs were recorded from their dendritic processes. The resting membrane potential ranged from -30 to -60 mV but fluctuated frequently in the absence of a stimulus (Figs. 2, 3). All NGIs responded with depolarizing and hyperpolarizing graded potentials to illumination of contralateral and ipsilateral eyes, respectively (Fig. 3A,B). The amplitude of these potentials was related to the intensity of illumination. Depolarizing an NGI with injected current resulted in an increase of the ipsilateral response and a decrease of the contralateral response. Hyperpolarizing the NGI had the opposite effect. Both the ipsilateral and contralateral responses had different reversal potentials. Assuming that the membrane potentials of NGIs are shifted from the resting potential in proportion to the intensity of injected current, the reversal potentials of ipsilateral and contralateral responses were estimated to be about -45 mv and -18 mV, respectively.

Depolarizing potentials in G1, G2, and G3 were preceded by action potentials in the contralateral SFs. Hyperpolarizing potentials in these NGIs were preceded by action potentials in homologous ipsilateral SFs. The average time lag between the inflection of depolarizing or hyperpolarizing potential and the SF action potential was 1.8 ms.

On the other hand, all the NGIs, G1, G2, and G3, also responded with graded potentials to the body tilt in roll as well as to illumination, but scarcely responded to the body tilt in yaw. That is, the body tilts on the longitudinal axis to the ipsi- and contralateral sides evoked the depolarizing and hyperpolarizing potentials In NGIs, respectively (Fig. 2A). The larger the angle of body tilt was and the higher the velocity of body tilt was, the larger the amplitude of response occurred. In intact animals,the presence of a single light shining the dorsal part of the body had a small influence on the response elicited by body roll, except for the onset of light (Fig. 2A).

In unilaterally statocystectomized animals, all the NGIsresponded with depolarizing and hyperpolarizing potentials to the body tilts in darkness. However, in the unilateral animal of which the ipsilateral statocyst was removed, the amplitude of depolarizing potential, which was elicited by the body tilt to the ipsilateral side, was larger in the presence of a single light source shining the dorsal side of the body than in darkness (Fig. 2D). In the unilateral animal of which the contralateral statocyst was removed,

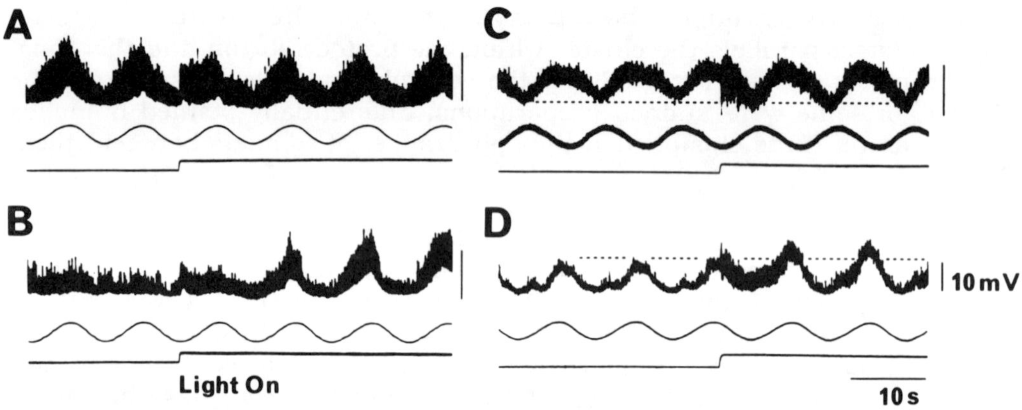

Fig. 2. Response of NGIs to a sinusoidal body tilt in roll through ±4°. The animals were sinusoidally tilted on the longitudinal axis, starting in the horizontal position in darkness. (A) Right G1 of an intact animal. (B) Right G1 of a bilaterally statocystectomized animal. (C) Left G3 of an unilaterally statocystectomized animal of which the contralateral (right) statocyst was removed. (D) Right G1 of an unilaterally statocystectomized animal of which the ipsilateral (right) statocyst was removed. In each record, the upper, middle, and lower traces represent the response of an NGI, body tilt (upward movement, left-side up tilt), and illumination (upward deflection, light on of a single light source locating above the body), respectively. In C and D, the dotted lines indicate the the levels of responses elicited by body tilts in darkness.

the amplitude of hyperpolarizing potential, which was elicited by the body tilt to the contralateral side, was larger in the presence of a single light than in darkness (Fig.2C).

In bilaterally statocystectomized animals, all the NGIs did not show any response to the body roll in the darkness, exceptfor the spontaneous occurrence of postsynaptic potentials. However, in the presence of a single light, all the NGIs responded well with depolarizing and hyperpolarizing potentials to the body tilt (Fig. 2B).

Functional connection between NGIs and motor neurons The two sets of motor neurons (head-up, head-down, eye-up, and eye-down motor neurons), which are controlled mainly by statocyst input, are under the the excitatory and inhibitory influence of light on the limited visual field or whole eye surface of either eye (e.g. Fig.3A,B; Wiersma and Yamaguchi, 1967). Depolarization or hyperpolarization of an NGI with injected current had no effect on the head-up and head-down motor neurons. As shown in Fig. 3B, however, the change in membrane potential of an NGI produced a noticeable effect on the firing frequency of eye-up and eye-down motor neurons: depolarizing the NGI resulted in an increase of the firing frequency of both the ipsilateral eye-down motor neurons and the contralateral eye-up motor neurons, while hyperpolarizing the NGI did in a decrease of their firing frequency.

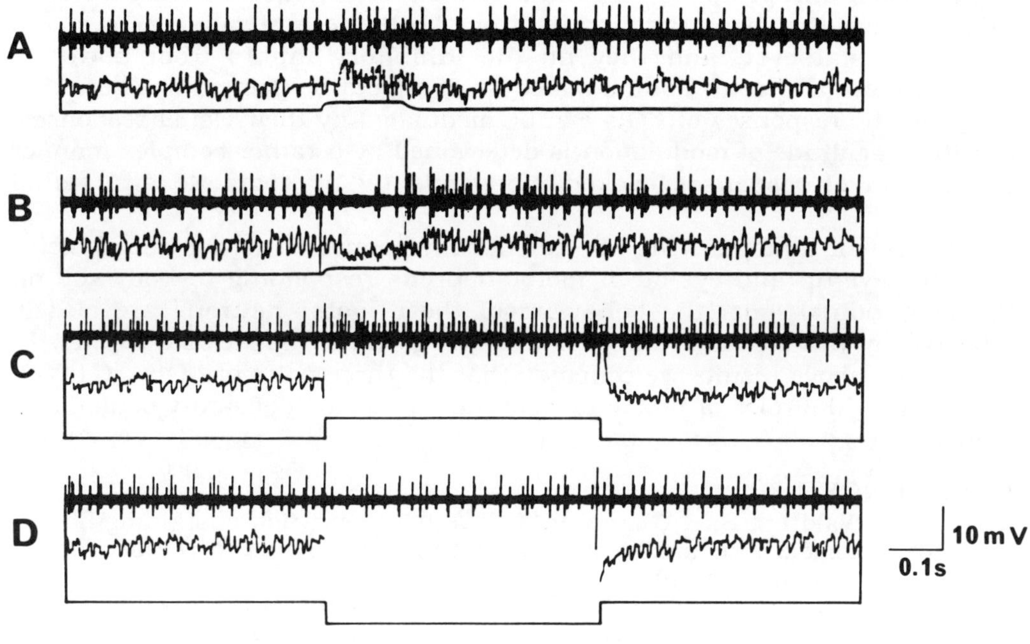

Fig. 3. Simultaneous recordings of a right NGI (G1) and two right eye-down motor neurons. (A) Responses to illumination of the right eye. (B) Responses to illumination of the left eye. (C) Effect of depolarizing current injection (+30 nA) through the GI on the eye-down motor neurons. (D) Effect of hyperpolarizing current injection (-30 nA) through the G1 on the eye-down motor neurons. In A-D, the upper and middle traces show the extracellular recording from the eye-down motor neurons and the intracellular recording from the G1, respectively. In A and B, the lower trace represents the monitor of illumination (upward deflection, light on), and in C and D it represents the monitor of current injection. The animal was held in the horizontal position during the period of experiments.

DISCUSSION

The above-mentioned results apparently indicate that the NGIs, G1, G2, and G3, receive the geotactic input as well as the visual input. Morphological and physiological relationships between these NGIs and SFs reveal that the NGIs are the neurons postsynaptic to the SFs running down from the medulla externa in the optic lobe, and suggest the presence of direct connections between the NGIs and SFs. According to Yoshino et al. (1983), primary statocyst sensory neurons enter the brain at the two discrete bundles, and one terminate in the ipsilateral paraolfactory lobe and the other in the contralateral paraolfactory lobe. Therefore. the geotactic input must be conveyed through unidentified interneurons from the primary statocyst sensory neurons to the NGIs.

The visual and geotactic responses of NGIs clearly demonstrate that the NGIs receive the excitatory inputs from both the contralateral eye and ipsilateral statocyst, and they do the inhibitory inputs from both the ipsilateral eye and contralateral statocyst. It should be pointed out here that the geotactic responses of NGIs can be modulated by their visual responses, but the magnitude of modulation is determined by a rather complex manner of addition of responses evoked independently by geotactic and visual inputs.

It is evident that the NGIs are functionally connected to one set of motor neurons, eye-up and eye-down motor neurons responding to body roll on the longitudinal axis: the behaviors of these motor neurons are closely reflected by the responsiveness of NGIs to geotactic and visual inputs. In view of the above results we conclude that the three pairs of NGIs , G1, G2, and G3 play the roles of premotor neurons on the compensatory oculomotor system.

REFERENCES

Kirk, M.D., Waldrop, B. & Glantz, R.M. (1982) The crayfish sustaining fibers. I. Morphological representation of visual receptive fields in the second optic neuropil. J.Comp.Physiol., 146:175-179.

Okada, Y. & Yamaguchi, T. (1985) Eyestalk movements in the crayfish, Procambarus clarkii. Comp.Biochem.Physiol., 81:157-164.

Okada, Y. & Yamaguchi, T. (1988) Nonspiking giant interneurons in the crayfish brain: morphological and physiological characteristics of the neurons presynaptic to visual interneurons. J.Comp.Physiol., 162:705-714.

Wiersma, C.A.G. & Oberjat, T. (1968) The selective responsiveness of various crayfish oculomotor fibers to sensory stimuli. Comp.Biochem.Physiol., 26:1-16.

Wiersma, C.A.G. & Yamaguchi, T. (1966) The neuronal components of the optic nerve of the crayfish as studied by single unit analysis. J.Comp.Neurol., 128:333-358.

Wiersma, C.A.G. & Yamaguchi, T. (1967) Integration of visual stimuli by the crayfish central nervous system. J.Exp.Biol., 47:409-431.

Yamaguchi, T., Okada, Y., Nakatani, K. & Ohta, N. (1984) Functional morphology of visual interneurons in the crayfish central nervous system. In Animal Behavior: Neurophysiological and Ethological Approaches, (ed. K. Aoki et al.) pp.109-122. Berlin, Heidelberg, New York, Tokyo: Japan Sci. Soc. Press/Springer.

Yoshino, M., Kondoh, Y. & Hisada, M. (1983) Projection of statocyst sensory neurons associated with crescent hairs in the crayfish Procambarus clarkii Girard. Cell. Tiss. Res., 230:37-48.

Frontiers in Crustacean Neurobiology
Advances in Life Sciences

CODING OF MECHANICAL STIMULI IN CRUSTACEANS - WHAT AND WHY?

Jürgen Tautz

Fakultät für Biologie, Universität Konstanz, Postfach 5560, D-7750 Konstanz, Federal Republic of Germany

SUMMARY

Sensory systems are not perfect instruments for the measurement of physical quantities but are shaped by natural selection to serve the needs of the animal. Thus in order to understand fully the perceptive capabilities of animals one has to ask the biological relevance in addition to the questions, "what is perceived" and "how is it done". Vibratory communication in fiddler crabs and the directionality of mechanosensory interneurons in crayfish are used to investigate two theses on the match between stimulus coding capabilities in animals and their physical environment.

INTRODUCTION

Behavioral decisions of animals are based on information transmitted through sense organs and processed in the central nervous system (CNS). However, sensory organs are not perfect instruments for the measurement of physical states and events but rather are detectors that have been shaped by natural selection to help organisms survive and reproduce (Schleidt 1985).

To fully understand the perceptive abilities of an animal we must study the mechanisms of sensory reception and processing of the received signals in the CNS (proximate causes) as well as the biological relevance of the ability under investigation (ultimate causes).

Crustaceans are excellent objects for this broad approach as their physiology is very accessible to investigation and their much different ecological needs in even closely related species emphasizes the search for biologically relevant stimuli.

Here two thesis concerning the match between perceptive abilities and the environment of animals will be formulated:

Thesis 1: Receptors receiving communicatory signals are adapted by natural selection to specific properties of these signals and not to maximal use of the transmission channel.

Thesis 2: The central nervous system reorganizes information from receptors and constructs biologically relevant new entities.

The first thesis will be investigated using the vibratory communication in fiddler crabs; the directionality of an identified mechanosensory interneuron in the crayfish is considered relative to the second thesis.

METHODS

1. Vibratory communication in fiddler crabs:

The transmission through sand of the drumming signals produced by male fiddler crabs (*Uca pugilator*) during courtship were measured at the side of the sender by accelerometers and a Laser-Doppler-vibrometer. The spectral sensitivity of vibration receptors in the legs of female fiddler crabs at the receiver side was determined by extracellular recordings from the leg nerve while vibrating the whole leg with controlled stimuli.

2. Directionality of mechanosensory interneurons in the crayfish:

The preparation consisted of the isolated tailfan of the freshwater crayfish *Orconectes limosus* and the abdominal ventral cord attached to it. Recordings were made intracellularly from two identified interneurons: the caudal photoreceptor (CPR) and the local directional selective (LDS) interneuron. Stimuli were water jets of 1 s duration and a velocity of 0.4 m/s directed onto the tailfan from different directions.

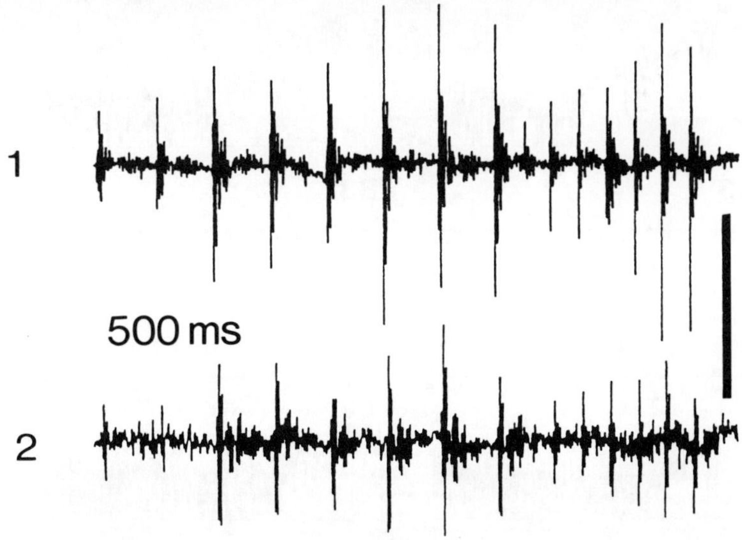

Fig. 1. A complete drumming series produced by a male fiddler crab, measured 6 cm (1) and 20 cm (2) from the signalling male. Calibration: 1 m/sec^2.

*The experiments were part of the PhD thesis of B.Aicher, Universität Konstanz (Aicher 1987)

RESULTS AND DISCUSSION

1. Vibratory communication in fiddler crabs:*

During courtship behavior the male fiddler crabs drum against the sand with their large chela. They produce series of single beats with a repetition rate of up to 40 per second (Figure 1).

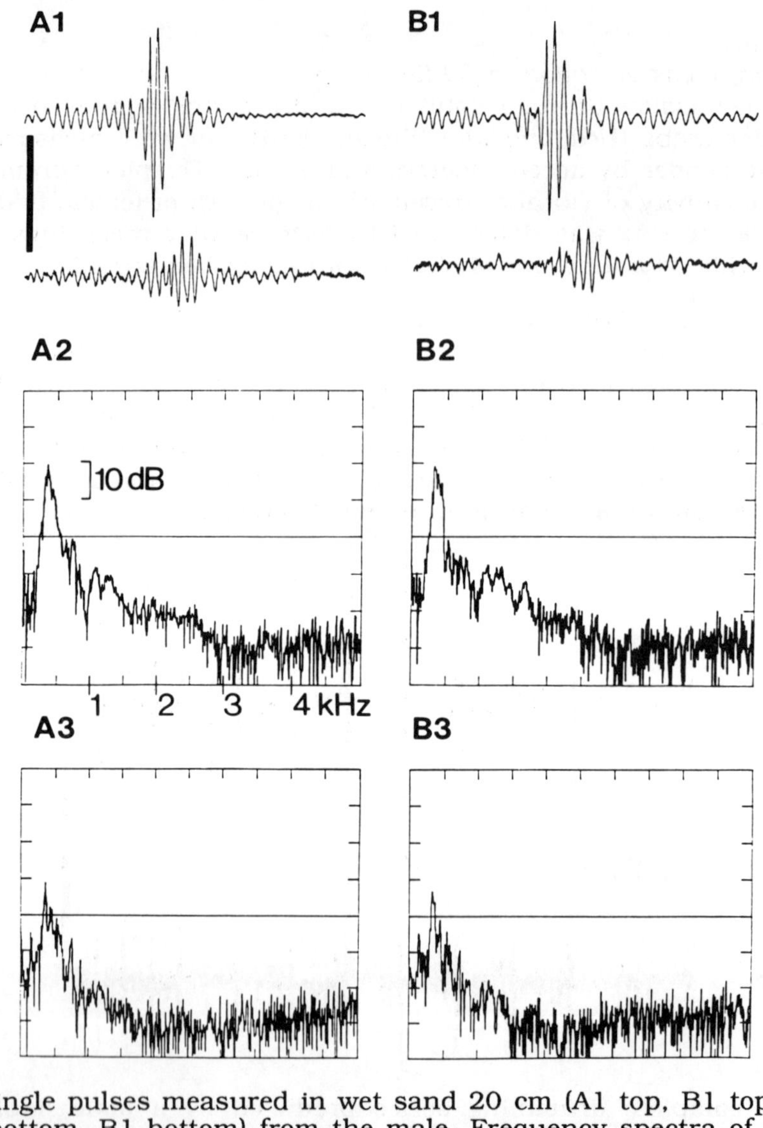

Fig. 2. Single pulses measured in wet sand 20 cm (A1 top, B1 top) and 70 cm (A1 bottom, B1 bottom) from the male. Frequency spectra of the close and the distant acceleration signal are given in A2, B2 and A3, B3, respectively. Calibration: $1 m/sec^2$.

Single pulses from such series were analysed for their spectral energy distribution. The major energy content of a single beat is concentrated to the frequency range 340-370 Hz and is independent of the distance to the signalling male (Figure 2). Drying of the wet sand, as occurs during low tide, does not change this frequency range. If the frequency spectrum of a whole beat series is taken, a smaller but very sharp peak appears at the same frequency as the pulse repetition rate (Figure 3).

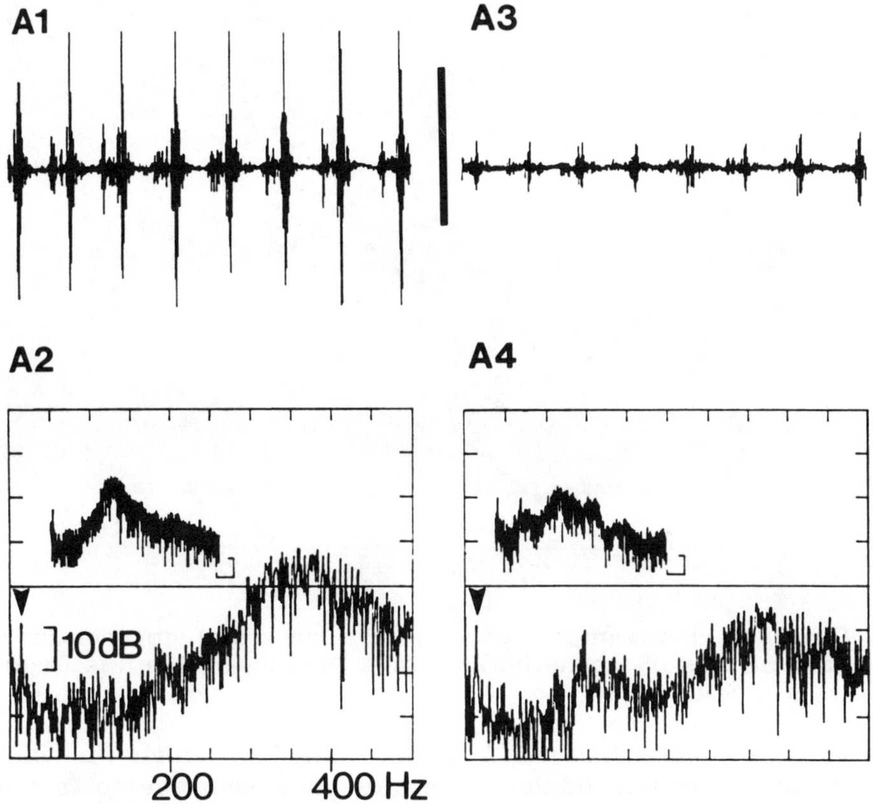

Fig. 3. Pulse series measured in 18 cm (A1) and 68 cm (A3) distance to the male. Calibration: 1 m/sec^2. A2 and A4 show the corresponding frequency spectra. Inset: Full spectrum (DC-5 KHz). Arrows mark the 20 Hz peak.

We thus have the situation that the best transmitted frequency range (340-370 Hz) out of the total *Uca*-produced vibration spectrum is about one decade above the signalling frequency of the male (20-40 Hz). It can be asked which of these two (if any), frequency ranges the sensitivity of the vibration receptors in females is adapted.

Figure 4 shows the spectral sensitivity of three classes of vibration receptors found in the legs of females. The receptors show either one sensitivity peak at 20 Hz (●) or in addition a minor sensitivity peak at about 200 Hz (Δ) or are excited at 20-30 Hz with low threshold values and inhibited by intense stimuli at about 350 Hz (o).

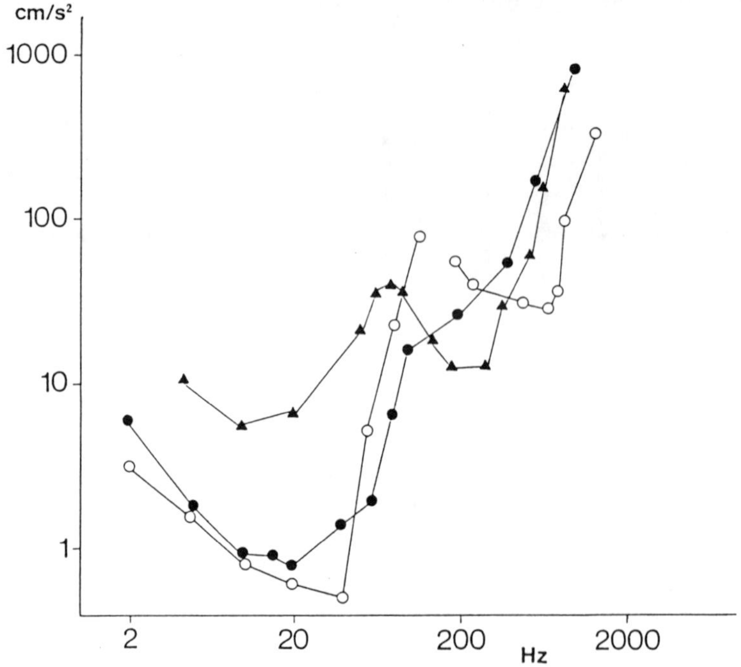

Fig. 4.Threshold curves (means of n=3) for 3 classes of vibration receptors in the walking legs of female fiddler crabs. Abscissa: stimulus frequency. Ordinate: acceleration.

It could be shown that the frequency range to which the vibration receptors of the female fiddler crabs are most sensitive to is not the frequency range transmitted best but the repetition rate of the communicatory signal. If the receptors would be more sensitive to the frequency content of a single pulse, the distance over which the signals reach the females (the active space, Markl 1985) would be greater. However, as any sharp impact onto the sand releases the same kind of vibration spectrum (Aicher & Tautz 1989) any specific information must lie in the repetition rate of the pulses. Thus recognition of the specific signal seems to be of greater importance than does the analysis of sand vibration in general.

*2. Directionality of mechanosensory interneurons in the crayfish**:*

Hair receptors on the tailfan of crayfish can be stimulated by water movements. The sensitivity to stimuli (weak water jets) from different directions was determined for two identified interneurons postsynaptic to the sensory cells that innervate these hairs. The directional sensitivity of the LDS neuron shows a slight asymmetry relative to the symmetry plane of the animal, whereas the directionality of the caudal photoreceptor, postsynaptic to LDS (Reichert et al.1984), shows a marked slope in the plane of symmetry of the crayfish (Figure 5).

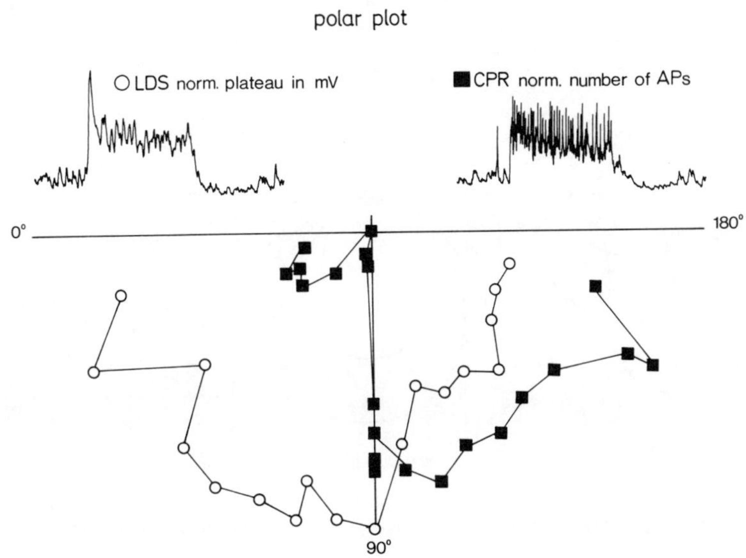

Fig. 5. Directionality of the spiking response of an individual CPR (▪) and the non-spiking response of an LDS-neuron presynaptic to it (o) to water jets from different directions onto the tailfan. Rostral is up, caudal down.

Stimulus fields generated by moving objects in water show directional gradients much less steep than the extreme slope found in CPR neurons and resemble more that of LDS neurons (compare Figs.5 and 6). What is important for behavioral decisions, however, is the message being sent to the brain of the crayfish, the action potentials in CPR. Although the directional characteristics of CPR output does not allow a detailed analysis of the direction of water movements, in a dynamic situation, the "corner" in the directionality of CPR allows determining the moment an animal crosses the midline of the crayfish.

**The experiments were performed during a postdoctoral stay of M.R.Plummer (Boston) in Konstanz in 1984-1986

The special shape of the directional sensitivity of CPR thus generates the space-time-entity, "crossing the midline now". This information is biologically relevant since crayfish catch swimming fish (even at night) by turning so that the prey is directly in front of them and thursting their chelae straight ahead.

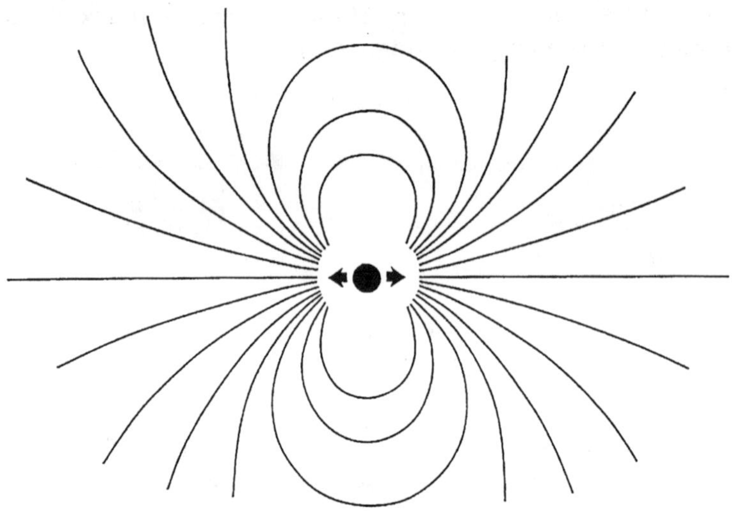

Fig.6. Directionality of the water movements caused by a vibrating sphere. Arrows give vibration direction. Lines show traces along which particles flow.

REFERENCES

Aicher,B. (1987) Vibratorische Kommunikation bei der Winkerkrabbe *Uca pugilator* (Brachyura, Ocypodidae): Vibrationssignale, ihre substratgebundene Fortleitung und neuronale Rezeption. Dissertation Universität Konstanz.

Aicher,B. & J.Tautz (1989) Vibrational communication in the fiddler crab *Uca pugilator* 1.Signal transmission throught the substratum. J.comp.Physiol., in press.

Markl, H. (1985) Manipulation, modulation, information, cognition: some of the riddles of communication. Fortschr.Zool.**31,** 163-194.

Reichert, H., Plummer, M.R. & J.J.Wine (1982) Lateral inhibition mediated by a non-spiking interneuron: circuit properties and consequences for behavior. J.Physiol.Paris **78,** 786-792.

Schleidt, W.M. (1985) Learning and the description of the environment. In: Issues in the ecological study of learning(ed.T.D.Johnston & A.T.Pietrewicz) pp.305-325. Hillsdale: Lawrence Erlbaum Ass.

Frontiers in Crustacean Neurobiology
Advances in Life Sciences

OPERANT CONDITIONING IN THE CRAB

Charles I. Abramson and Richard D. Feinman

Department of Biochemistry, State university of New York Health Science Center at Brooklyn, 450 Clarkson Avenue, Brooklyn, New York 11203, USA.

SUMMARY

Several operant conditioning procedures have been successfully used with the green crab, *Carcinus maenas*. Animals learned to press a bar for food reward and showed high rates of responding on a continuous reinforcement schedule or on a fixed ratio 2 schedule (every other response reinforced). Animals on a variable time schedule showed lower rates of responding. Crabs readily learned a spatial discrimination task in which one bar causes food to be dispensed (S+) and one is inactive (S-). The eye elevation system of the green crab can also be used in a yoked procedure using air puff to the eye as punishment. Master animals reduced the number of eye elevations after reflex withdrawal and showed longer latency compared to yoked controls. A delay introduced between response and punishment reduced the suppressing effect of the punishment.

INTRODUCTION

In defining simple systems as models for learning and memory it has been useful to rely on the traditional conditioning paradigms: classical (Pavlovian) and operant conditioning. One might roughly describe these by saying that classical conditioning describes how animals make associations between stimuli and operant conditioning describes how animals associate stimuli with their own motor actions. Classical conditioning emphasizes sensory integration and operant conditioning, motivation: animals learn new behaviors in order to obtain or avoid some stimulus (reinforcement). Because operant conditioning requires that learning depend on the animals own behavior and because it usually requires a more obviously new behavior, it is generally thought of as more complex than classical conditioning. In the crustacea, three general types of operant approaches can be cited in the literature. First there have been several papers that simply demonstrate that crustaceans are capable of performance for reward (see, e.g. (Schone, 1961); review: (Krasne, 1972)). Second, there have been several extensions of the rather abstract punishment paradigm originally developed by Horridge (1962). Finally, we have recently developed an operant model for the green crab based on lever pressing, a traditional operant procedure for vertebrates (Abramson & Feinman, 1989; Abramson& Feinman, submitted). The lever press system is promising as a learning model because of the extensive study of the physiology of the motor system of crustacea. It also represents learning *per se* and crab performance can be compared to that of other organisms in terms of the operant parameters of schedules, chaining and discrimination. We will discuss the last two aspects of crustacean operant learning beginning with our recent work on lever press.

LEVER PRESS One of the best studied operant procedures in vertebrate species is the "Skinner box" in which presses on a bar or lever or pecks on a key are rewarded with food. A lever box for the crayfish has been reported (Olson & Strandberg, 1979). For the green crab, *Carcinus maenas*, the box is a 9 x 4.5 cm compartment that has a food tube in the middle of the front wall at mouth level. The chamber is suspended in an aquarium which is under continuous filtration. Lever arms descend into the chamber from above. (Figure 1). The levers are attached to micro-switches which are monitored by a computer that controls the contingencies for dispensing of food (pate of squid). Several procedures were used to assess the ability of crabs to control the availability of food food through manipulation of the bar.

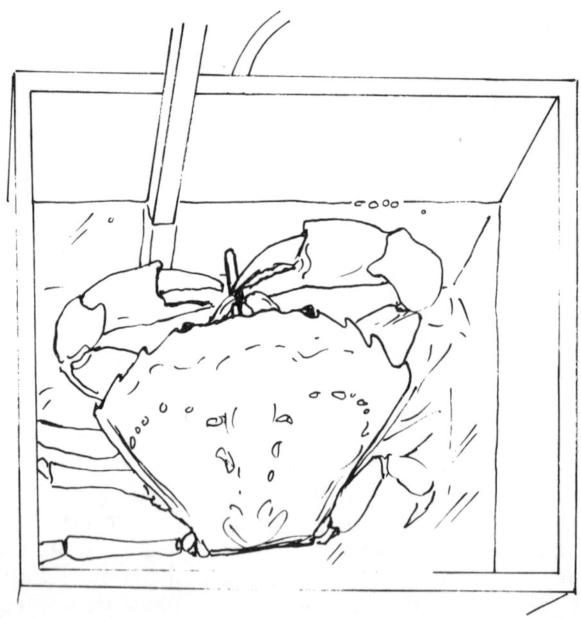

Fig. 1 Operant chamber for lever press conditioning. Typical behavior: an animal presses (or simply bumps into) the bar causing food to appear at the food tube; it puts the tube into its mouth with one claw and presses the bar with the other; extension at the claw-carpopodite joint is the most common strategy. The animal shown is pressing the bar with the left claw and holding the food tube with the right.

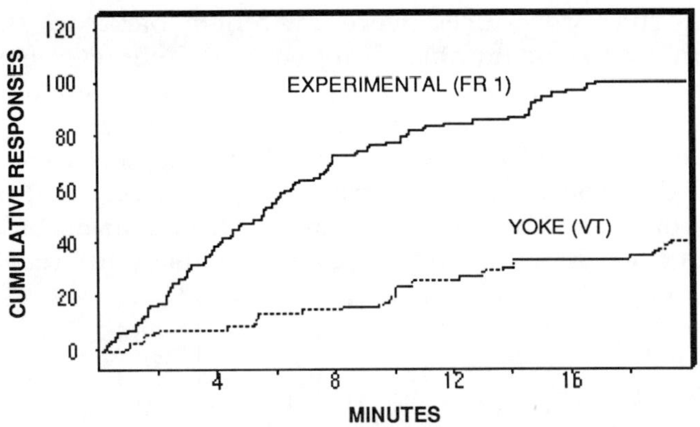

Fig. 2. Cumulative record for crab on FR1 schedule and yoked control (VT schedule).

Fixed Ratio Schedules and Yoked procedure. In the one experiment an animal was subjected to a procedure whereby every press of the bar produced a unit of food. Traditionally, such a regimen is referred to as a continuous reinforcement schedule (CRF) or fixed ratio of 1 (FR 1). The animals tested in this way began pressing the bar at high rates during the first 20 min session; one session was run every day for 5 days with 2 days off and animals were not otherwise fed. To assess the role of the contingencies of reinforcement, a second group of animals was "yoked" to the first. Yoked animals had a similar bar that was inactive. For these animals food was dispensed whenever it was given to the first or "master" group. Thus, these animals received the same amount of food as the master FR animals but any correlation between the pressing behavior and the reinforcement was fortuitous. From the standpoint of the animal, food was dispensed at random time after responding (variable time schedule (VT)). It should be emphasized that this is not a control in the sense that one would expect no learning but rather that the contingencies are less stringent and the exact nature of the difference is a feature of the learning that must be determined. Figure 2 shows the traditional cumulative record, a running total, for the performance of a typical master-yoke pair for one session. The behavior over several days is shown in Figure 3. It is clear that the animal on the VT schedule showed lower rates of responding than the FR animal to which it was yoked. Control for the baseline performance was assessed by giving a third group of animals a 20 min session in the operant chamber with an inactive bar and no food reinforcement. The average behavior of this group (dotted line in Figure 3) indicated that accidental bumping of the bar or spontaneous performance was quite low. After 5 days of training the master and yoke groups were switched. Figure 3 shows that the animals changed their performance in the appropriate direction. After several sessions the procedures were switched back to the original arrangement. Crabs were again able to adjust to the changed contingencies although there is more variation among individual animals (data not shown). Finally, two days of extinction trials (no reinforcement) were run. Retention is above base-line for naive animals but the effect is not a striking effect. We found that continuous reinforcement is not required to maintain high rates of responding. The data in Figure 4 show that crabs are able to press a bar on an FR2 schedule (every other response reinforced).

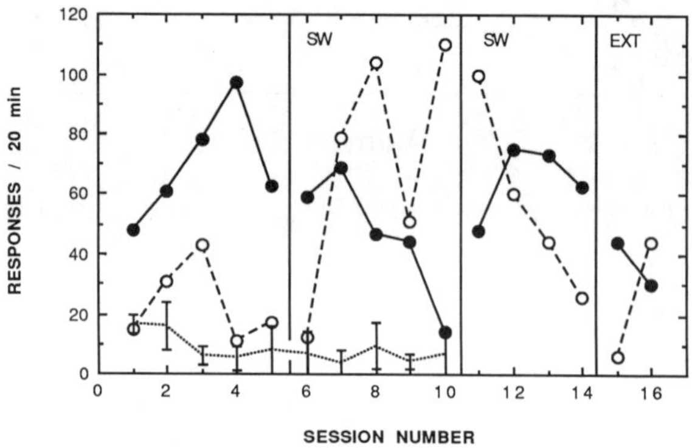

Fig. 3. Lever press responses of master (FR 1; filled symbols) and yoke (VT; open symbols) animals and effect of switching procedures (SW). Sessions were 20 min. In extinction (EX) no responses were reinforced. Dotted line: averages of four control animals placed in apparatus with inactive bar. Error bars indicate the range of experimental points.

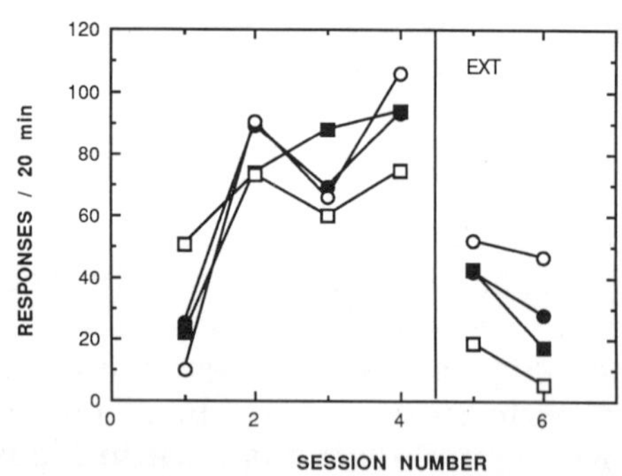

Fig. 4. Lever press responses of crabs on an FR2 schedule. Four crabs that had been trained according to the regimen in Fig. 3 were given one week rest and then tested in the lever box under conditions where every other response produced food reward. After 5 days of training they were given 2 days of unreinforced trials (EX).

Spatial Discrimination in Lever Press. In a second series of experiments, experimental animals were presented with two levers. Pressing one of the levers (S+) was reinforced with food whereas, the other (S-), was not. Fig.

5 shows that by the second day of training, animals were clearly able to discriminate between the two bars. A control group where neither bar was active showed few responses with no obvious preference for one bar or the other. After 6 days of training the bars were switched. Fig. 5 shows that animals were able to learn quickly that the previously inactive bar (S-) could now be used to dispense food. Their ability to "unlearn" bar press on S+ was, however, less impressive. To some extent this was reflected in the typography of the response: after the bars were switched, some animals pressed both simultaneously. Other animals simply persevered in the old method.

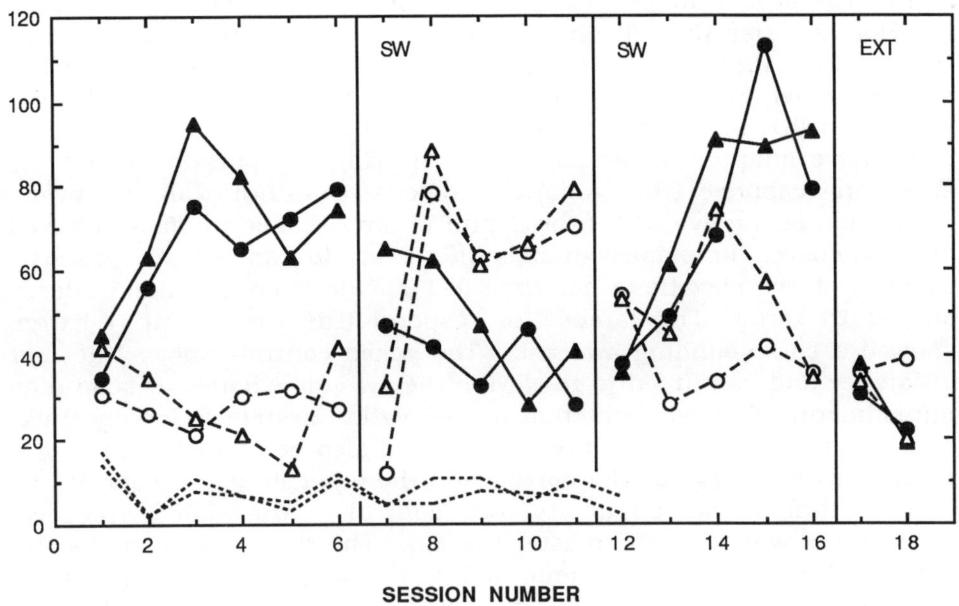

Fig. 5. Discrimination learning in lever press. Two naive crabs were trained in a chamber with one lever that produced reinforcement for every response (S+) and a second that was inactive (S-). Number of presses on S+ bar is shown with filled symbols. The corresponding open symbol shows responses of the same animal on the S- bar. The bars were switched as indicated (SW) so that S- now dispensed food and S+ did not. In the second switch bars were returned to their original mechanism. Symbols refer to the original location of the bar

OPERANT PUNISHMENT IN THE CRAB. The Horridge procedure. Punishment is defined as a procedure in which a specified behavior causes the appearance of an (aversive) environmental stimulus that has the effect of reducing the future occurrence of the response. A simple implementation of this form of operant conditioning is one in which every response of an experimental (master) animal is immediately punished; to control for general (non-contingent) effects of the aversive stimulation, a yoked control receives punishment whenever the master does. In the original paradigm developed by Horridge (1962), a headless cockroach was conditioned to keep its leg out of an electrified solution; controls received shocks whenever the masters did regardless of leg position. Although the original procedure has received a good deal of criticism (see discussion in Abramson & Feinman, 1987) and additional controls are sometimes required, it remains one of the fundamental approaches to conditioning. The procedure has been refined by Hoyle and coworkers (Hoyle, 1980; Tosney & Hoyle, 1977) and Forman (Forman & Zill, 1984; Forman, 1984). Limb position learning in crustacea has been accomplished by variations of the Horridge paradigm (Dunn & Barnes, 1981a; Dunn & Barnes, 1981b; Hoyle, 1976; Punzo 1983; Rafuse 1973; Stafstrom & Gerstein, 1977) and several novel punishment procedures have been described (Becker & Valinski, 1981; Cuadras et al., 1978; Denti et al., 1988).

We have adapted an analog of the Horridge preparation using the eye elevation response (that follows a defensive withdrawal), by punishing extensions of the eye with a brief puff of air . Yoked animals received air-puffs whenever the master animals did. After 30 min of such treatment the number of eye elevations per minute for experimental animals decreased almost to zero. The latency to respond (the time until re-extension) showed a corresponding increase. The yoked controls showed no increase in latency and continued to re-elevate the eye immediately or soon after the punishment. The eye retraction and elevation system is largely unilateral and the yoked punishment procedure could also be carried out using single animals with one eye as the master and the other its yoked control. In this way the animal served as its own control -- the yoked eye receiving punishment whenever the master eye did. The results were similar to that found with pairs of animals, and, in fact, the single animal preparation gave more reliable and reproducible differences between master and yoke than pairs of animals. Retention was tested by subjecting animals to three sessions separated by 12 hr rest. The results indicated some savings but this was not a dramatic effect.

A delayed reinforcement procedure was used in order to evoyd some of the problems of yoked controls. We wanted to demonstrate that the learning was operant in nature, that is, depended on the contingency between the *act* of eye extension and punishment (rather than simply associations between the punishing stimulus and, say, a change in visual field due to retraction). Experiments were performed in which all animals received punishment if they reextended the eye but a delay was introduced between the response and the onset of punishments. The results are shown in Figure 6 where the latencies to extend the eye are shown. A delay of 20 s completely eliminated the suppression of eye extension: animals showed latencies close to zero (immediately re-extended the eye after every punishment) and responded at a consistent high rate throughout the session. Delays of 10, 5 and 2.5 s had decreasing inhibiting affect on acquisition. A delay of 1.25 was indistinguishable from immediate punishment and animals learned rapidly with this minimum delay in reinforcement. The results support an operant interpretation of the punishment procedure and point to a time period of approximately 2 s during which some state or intermediate generated by the motor act must persist for integration with the reinforcer. The delay procedure also controls for the non-contingent effect of punishment; the 10 s delay animals frequently receive more than 150 punishments in the 30 min session, far more than immediately punished animals who typically receive less than 70.

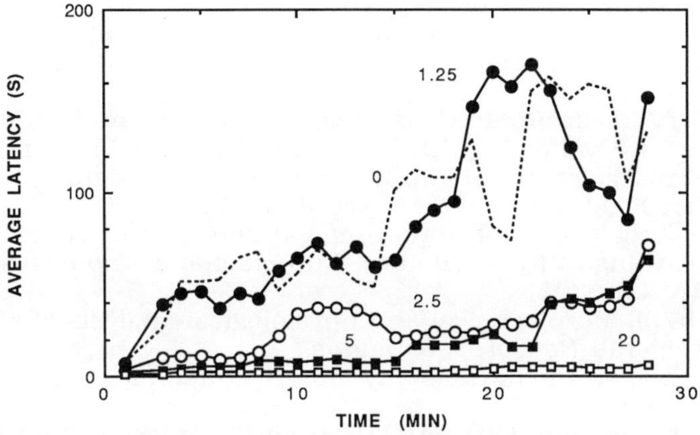

Fig. 6. Average latency for 5 min period for punishment with delay. (N = 8 crabs/group). Each eye elevation was punished with an air-puff following a delay. The delay time in s is shown for each group.

ACKNOWLEDGEMENT

This work was supported, in part, by grant BNS-8819830 form the National Science Foundation of the United States and by funds from the Research Foundation of the State University of New York.

REFERENCES

Abramson, C. I. & Feinman, R. D. (1987). Operant Punishment in the Green Crab, *Carcinus maenas*. Behav. Neural Biol. **48**: 259-277.

Abramson, C. I. & Feinman, R. D. (1989). Lever Press Conditioning in theGreen Crab. Soc. Neurosci. Abst. **15**: 1141.

Becker, A. J., Jr. & Valinski, W. A. (1981). A method for BehaviorModification in Aquatic Crustaceans. Proc. West Virginia Acad. Sci. **53**: 50-56.

Cuadras, J., Vila, E. & Balasch, J. (1978). T-Maze Shock Avoidance in the Hermit Crab *Dardanus arrosor*. Rev. Esp. de Fisiolog. **34**: 273-276.

Denti, A., Dimant, B. & Maldonado, H. (1988). Passive Avoidance Learning in the Crab *Chasmagnathus granulatus*. Phys. & Behav. **43**: 317-320.

Dunn, P. D. C. & Barnes, W. J. P. (1981a). Learning of Leg Position in the Shore Crab, *Carcinus maenas*. Mar. Behav. Physiol. **8**: 67-82.

Dunn, P. D. C. & Barnes, W. J. P. (1981b). Neural Correlates of Leg Learning in the Shore Crab, *Carcinus maenas*. Mar. Behav. Physiol. **8**: 83-97.

Forman, R. R. (1984). Leg position learning by an insect. I. A heat Avoidance Lerning Paradigm. J. Neurobiol. **15**: 127-140.

Forman, R. & Zill, S. (1984). Leg position learning by an insect. II. Motor Strategies Underlying Learned Leg Extension. J. Neurobiol. **15**: 221-237.

Horridge, G. A. (1962). Learning of leg position by headless insects. Nature **193**: 697-698.

Hoyle, G. (1976). Learning of leg position by the ghost crab *Ocypode ceratophthalma*. Behav. Biol.**18**: 147-163.

Hoyle, G. (1980). Learning, using natural reinforcements, in insect preparations that permit cellular neuronal analysis. J. Neurobiol. **11**: 323-354

Krasne, B. F. (1972). Learning in Crustacea. in *Invertebrate Learning.*, 2, (ed. W. Corning, J. Dyal & A. O. D. Willows) pp. 49-130. Plenum Press.

Olson, G. S. & Strandberg, R. (1979). Instrumental Conditioning in crayfish: Lever Pulling for Food. Soc. for Neurosci. Abst., 257.

Punzo, F. (1983). Localization of brain function and neurochemical correlates of learning in the mud crab, *Eurypanopeus depressus* (Decapod). **75A**: 299-305.

Rafuse, D. D. (1973). Morphological and physiological analysis of shock avoidance in the crab *Hemigrapsus nudus*.

Schöne, H. (1961). Learning in the spiny lobster *Panulirus argus*. Biol. Bull. **121**: 354-365.

Stafstrom, C. E. & Gerstein, G. L. (1977). A paradigm for position learning in the crayfish claw. Brain Res. **134**: 185-190.

Tosney, T. & Hoyle, G. (1977). Computer-controlled learning in a simple system. Proc. Royal Soc. London Ser. B. **195**: 365-393.

Frontiers in Crustacean Neurobiology
Advances in Life Sciences

CLASSICAL CONDITIONING IN THE CRAB

Richard D. Feinman, Charles I. Abramson and Robin R. Forman†.

Department of Biochemistry, State University of New York Health Science Center at Brooklyn, 450 Clarkson Avenue, Brooklyn, New York 11203, USA and †Department of Neurology, Medical College of Virginia, Richmond, Virginia 23298 USA.

SUMMARY

The green crab, *Carcinus maenas*, can be trained in a classical (Pavlovian) conditioning procedure. By pairing vibration on the carapace as a conditioned stimulus (CS) with air-puff to one of the eyes as an unconditioned stimulus (US), it is possible to teach the animals to retract the eye during CS presentations. Controls subjected to unpaired stimuli show lower rates of responding. Crabs can also be trained in a signalled avoidance procedure, but the similarity of acquisition curves to those for classical conditioning suggests that the mechanism may be Pavlovian. Electromyograms recorded from the eye muscles can be used to follow conditioning and show that animals can be conditioned with the eye restrained.

INTRODUCTION

To function successfully in a changing environment, animals must not only learn new behaviors but must also learn to call on reflexive responses in new contexts. Experimentally, the latter phenomenon is demonstrated in the classical (Pavlovian) conditioning procedure (Figure 1): an unconditioned stimulus (US) which evokes an unconditioned response (UR) in normal animals is paired temporally with a novel stimulus, the conditioned stimulus (CS), which is normally without effect on the animal; after continued paired presentations, the CS begins to evoke a conditioned response (CR) which has some of the features of, or may be identical to, the UR. In the crab, the defensive eye withdrawal reflex can be conditioned to respond to previously neutral stimuli. Aversive stimuli to the anterior portion of the animal -- in our experiments, a mild air-puff to one of the eyes -- causes retraction of the eye into its socket. By pairing vibration of the carapace (normally without effect) as a CS with air-puff as a US, it is possible to teach the animals to retract their eyes in response to the vibration. (Abramson & Feinman, 1988). The eye withdrawal reflex is of interest as a potential neuronal learning model because of the relatively well-studied physiology of the circuit (Burrows & Horridge, 1968a; Burrows & Horridge, 1968b; Sandeman, 1964; Sandeman, 1969a; Sandeman,

1969b). Two identified motor neurons of the optic tract mediate eye retraction. The largest is the main retractor neuron that innervates three muscles. Retraction of the eye is associated with characteristic spiking activity in the main retractor axon which can be seen in myograms recorded from the main abductor muscle, 19a (Figure 5). The retracted state is associated with tonic activity of a slow motor neuron of the oculomotor nerve which is otherwise silent. The activity of this unit is also frequently seen in myograms (Figure 5). Eye retraction has been found to proceed without proprioceptive feedback. Study of the withdrawal response is also simplified by the fact that it does not interact with, and essentially overrides other responses of the eye: the optokinetic or tracking responses to visual stimuli and the geotactic response (Burrows & Horridge, 1968b).

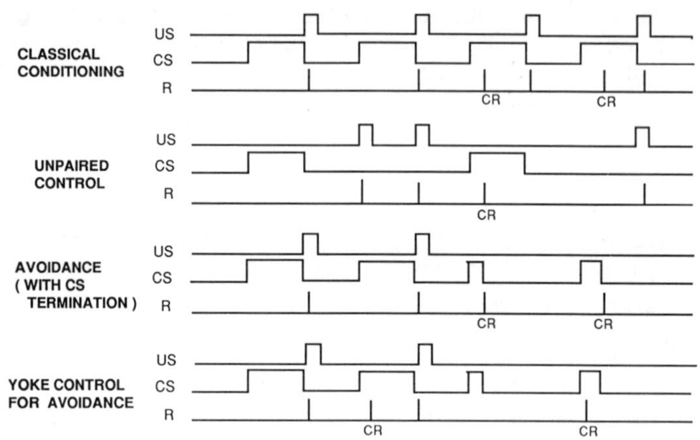

Fig. 1. Formalism of conditioning and control procedures.

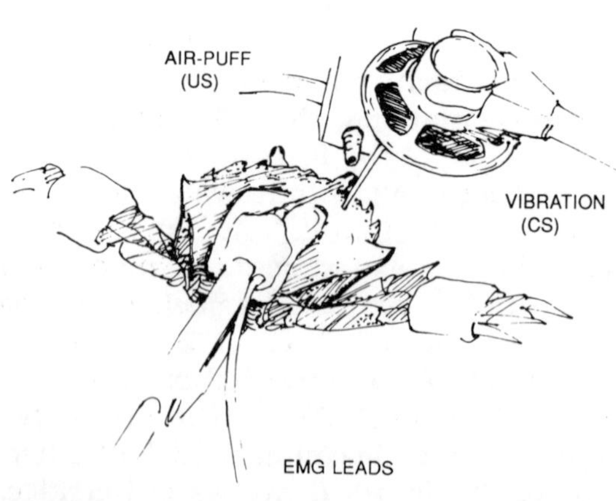

Fig. 2. Experimental set-up for classical conditioning.

METHODS

Animals to be conditioned are subjected to 50 - 100 pairings of the CS followed by the US. A range of stimulus durations is possible. Shorter durations (CS: 1 s, US: 0.1 s) produce the lowest rate of responding in unpaired controls. The CS was a low amplitude 200 Hz vibration administered to the carapace via a needle attached to a loudspeaker (Figure 2). The US was a low intensity puff of air delivered to the eye to be conditioned. Eye retractions can be recorded manually or by using a small flag attached to the eye (detected by an LED/phototransistor pair) or by recording electromyograms (EMGs) from the muscles of the eye. In the last case, two 50 μ silver wires are inserted through a single hole in the cuticle surrounding the eye. This generally does not impair movements of the eye and both physical movement and EMGs can be observed simultaneously. Housing, general handling of animals and additional experimental detail have been described (Abramson & Feinman, 1988; Feinman, et al., 1990).

RESULTS AND DISCUSSION

Classical Conditioning. Figure 3 shows the behavior of a group of crabs subjected to the classical conditioning procedure. It is evident from the figure that acquisition is rapid, reaching about 60 % conditioned responses. Unpaired controls (see Figure 1) showed substantially lower probabilities of responding.

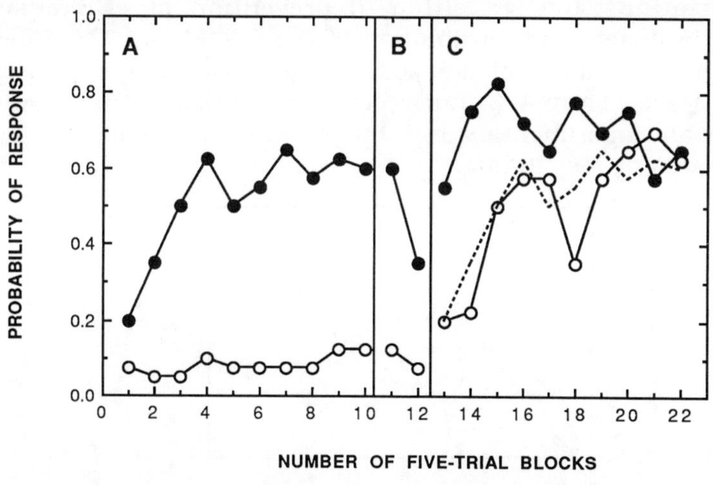

Fig. 3. Classical conditioning of eye withdrawal reflex. Probability of response (number of responses per animal per 5-minute block) for 8 experimental animals and 8 unpaired controls . Animals were given 50 paired (filled symbols) or unpaired (open symbols) presentations of stimuli (**A**). Twenty four hours after acquisition they were given 10 presentations of CS alone (**B**) followed by 50 paired stimuli for both groups (**C**). Dotted line is a duplicate of paired group from **A**, shown for comparison.

There is some retention after 24 hrs as shown by responses to CS alone presentations and , more dramatically, by enhanced re-acquisition. Controls are capable of being conditioned as indicated by their performance when paired stimuli are used after 24 hrs; acquisition in this case looks like the day 1 performance of experimental animals, indicating that there is no obvious inhibition from unpaired presentation of stimuli. Other controls that showed low probabilities of responding included backward conditioning (US presented first), CS only, US only or simply time in the apparatus (Abramson & Feinman, 1988). Generally, the group behavior is reflected in individual animal performance: almost all animals learn, all controls perform at low rates. It is interesting that, although the eye withdrawal reflex is largely unilateral and the contralateral eye did not respond during acquisition, tests of this eye with CS alone showed some transfer of learning (Abramson & Feinman, 1988). This phenomenon is similar to that observed in the nictitating membrane response of the rabbit (Rosenfield & Moore, 1985).

Comparison of signalled avoidance and classical conditioning. In extending our studies of the plasticity of the eye withdrawal mechanism, we tested the ability of crabs to learn a discrete trial signalled avoidance task (Abramson et al., 1988). This conditioning procedure is set up in a manner similar to classical conditioning with the additional feature that responses by the animal can prevent the appearance of the US, that is the animal can avoid an aversive stimulus by responding to the CS as a warning signal. The two major variations involve either *i)* prevention of US onset or *ii)* prevention of US onset and termination of the CS (Figure 1). When either experimental design was implemented, crabs performed well (Figure 4). Yoked controls (see Figure 1), that received presentation of CS and US at the same time as experimentals but independent of their own behavior, showed lower rates of responding.

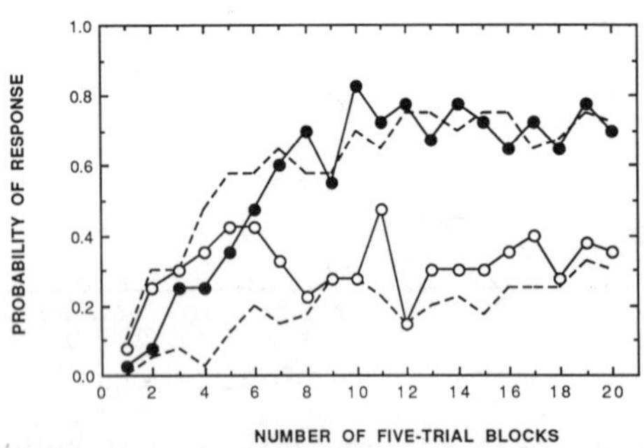

Fig. 4. Signalled avoidance compared to classical conditioning. Probability of response for 8 animals in successive five-trial blocks for avoidance with CS termination (filled circles) and yoked controls (open circles) are compared to probability of response for a different group of 8 animals in classical conditioning (upper dotted line) and unpaired control procedure (lower dotted line).

Signalled avoidance, as designed, is an operant procedure, that is, the animal can control the duration of the CS and the presentation of the US. However, animals that learn in an avoidance procedure may be undergoing a predominantly Pavlovian process, that is, they may associate the signal (CS) with the consequence (US) but may not significantly associate either with their own behavior. We suspect that this might be the case with eye withdrawal; as a defensive reflex, it may be designed for "over-kill," and may not require information about the effects of the action. The absence of proprioceptive feedback would be consistent with this idea. We compared performance in avoidance with classical conditioning and, as shown in Figure 4, the acquisition curves are almost identical. Although the similarity of the curves does not require that they proceed by the same process -- the two learning procedures may share a common rate determining step -- it is suggestive that the crab eye is a classical (Pavlovian) system. In many cases, for rats in a shuttle box, for example, responding is much higher in avoidance than classical conditioning.

The behavior of crabs in avoidance is thus paradoxical. It fulfills one of the predictions of operant avoidance: yoked controls do not perform as well as experimentals. On the other hand, experimental animals do not perform better than those in classical conditioning, that is, do not appear to benefit from being able to avoid the US. Several theories have been proposed to explain these results (see discussion in Woodward & Bitterman, 1973 and Abramson, et al., 1988). One theory suggests yokes and experimentals may be subjected to different (compound) CS presentations and that feedback from the sensory state associated with eyes up or down will be different for the two subjects. Other possibilities are that the observed performance in both classical and avoidance procedures are operant in mechanism, reinforcement being provided by the attenuation of the air-puff when the eye moves. To address these possibilities and as a background to developing a reduced preparation, we measured the role of the eye movement in classical conditioning.

Conditioning of the restrained eye. EMGs can be used to record the development of the conditioned response; in animals with freely moving eyes the characteristic phasic activity recorded from the muscle always correlated with withdrawal whether evoked by CS or US (Feinman et al., 1990) (Figure 5). Two characteristics of the conditioning not evident in gross measurements of the behavior were, first, that CRs were frequently

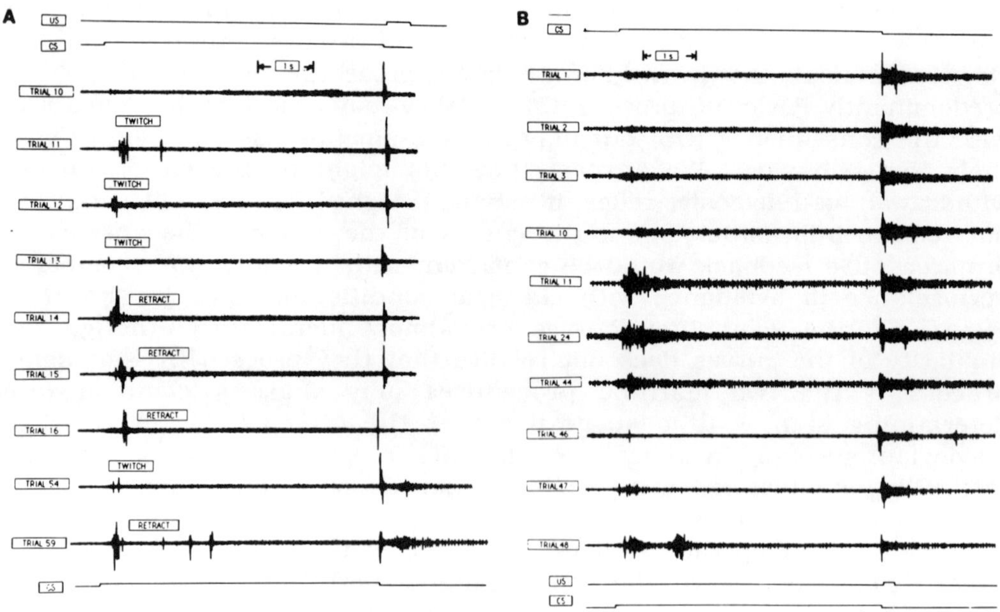

Fig.5 Electromyographic record of classical conditioning. Myograms recorded from muscle 19a of the eye.
A. animal with freely moving eye **B**. animal with immobilized eye.

more intense than the URs and, second, there was habituation of the UR as the experiment proceeded. The latter observation may be of interest in terms of comparison with habituation of defensive reflexes in other crustacea such as the crayfish tail flip response (Krasne & Woodsmall, 1969) or in other invertebrate learning systems (Carew & Sahley, 1986).

To assess the role of eye movement *per se* in classical conditioning, the eye was held down with rubber bands and conditioning was carried out in the usual manner; responses during acquisition were followed by recording the pattern of EMGs. Figure 5, panel B shows typical results for an animal with a restrained eye. Of eight animals tested in this way, five showed a pattern of acquisition that was similar to that for animals with moving eyes. After conditioning, the animals' eyes were freed, the EMG wires were cut and they were tested, behaviorally, for retention, extinction and re-acquisition. All eight animals were indistinguishable from unrestrained or unoperated animals by these tests. Thus, even for those animals that did not show significant numbers of CRs, there was integration of the sensory pairing. The results suggest that attenuation of the air-puff does not reinforce CRs and that visual stimuli are not part of the CS. Thus, eye movement is not required for conditioning. The muscles of the eye are contracting, of course, and it is still to be determined if, in fact, the open loop nature of the reflex is maintained in the learning situation.

ACKNOLEDGEMENTS

This work was supported in part by grant BNS-8819830 from the National Science Foundation and by funds from the Research Foundation of the State University of New York

REFERENCES

Abramson, C. I., Armstrong, P. M., Feinman, R. A. & Feinman, R. D. (1988). Signalled avoidance in the eye withdrawal reflex of the green crab. J. Exp. Anal. Behav. **50**: 483-492.

Abramson, C. I. & Feinman, R. D. (1988). Classical Conditioning of the Eye Withdrawal Reflex in the Green Crab. J. Neurosci. **8**: 2907-2912.

Burrows, M. & Horridge, G. A. (1968a). Eyecup withdrawal in the crab Carcinus, and its interaction with the optokinetic response. J. Exp. Biol. **49**: 285-297.

Burrows, M. & Horridge, G. A. (1968b). Motoneurone discharges to the eyecup muscles of the crab *Carcinus*. J. Exp. Biol. **49**: 251-267.

Carew, T. J. & Sahley, C. (1986). Invertebrate learning and memory: from behavior to molecules. Ann. Rev. Neurosci. **9.**: 435-486.

Feinman, R. D., Llinas, R. H., Abramson, C. I. & Forman, R. R. (1990). Electromyographic Record of Classical Conditioning in the Green Crab. Biol. Bull. **176**: in press.

Krasne, B. & Woodsmall, K. (1969). Waning of the crayfish escape response as a result of repeated stimulation. Anim. Behav. **17**: 416-424.

Rosenfield, M. E. & Moore, J. W. (1985). Red nucleus lesions impair acquisition of the classically conditioned nictitating membrane response but not eye-to-eye savings or unconditioned response amplitude. Behav. Brain. Res. **17**: 77-81.

Sandeman, D. C. (1964). Functional Distinction between Oculomotor and Optic Nerve in *Carcinus*. Science **201**: 302-303.

Sandeman, D. C. (1969a). Integrative properties of a reflex motoneuron in the brain of the crab *Carcinus maenas*. Z. fur Vergleich. Physiol. **64**: 290-464.

Sandeman, D. C. (1969b). The Synaptic Link between the Sensory and Motoneurones in the Eye-withdrawal Reflex of the Crab. J. Exp. Biol. **50**: 87-98.

Woodward, W. & Bitterman, M. E. (1973). Pavlovian analysis of avoidance conditioning in the goldfish (*Carassius auratus*). J. comp. physiol. Psych. **82**: 123-129.

STRUCTURAL AND FUNCTIONAL LEVELS IN THE ORGANIZATION OF DECAPOD CRUSTACEAN BRAINS

David Sandeman

School of Biological Science, University of New South Wales, Kensington, Sydney, Australia

SUMMARY

The decapod crustacean brain is structurally arranged into neuropile areas that are associated with afferent nerve roots. The organization of the brain areas is considered in relation to examples of behaviour ranging from simple (eye withdrawal reflex) to complex (tactile exploration).

INTRODUCTION

A concentration of nervous tissue at the anterior end is a characteristic feature of bilaterally symmetrical animals. Whether this is relatively small and called a "cerebral ganglion" or very large and called a "brain", there is little doubt that this structure plays a dominant role in the behaviour of all animals, if only because it receives the inputs from the guiding sense organs of sight, smell, touch and equilibrium. There is not much evidence to suggest that the brain in arthropods is principally different in its function from any other area of the CNS. The division of the brain into areas of neuropile associated with particular afferents for example, is also a feature of the abdominal ganglia in crustaceans, as is the association of motor systems with the particular neuropile areas relevant to the behavioural activity they generate. The abdominal ganglia, while certainly subject to controls related to the senses incorporated in the head, exhibit considerable functional autonomy (Leise et al 1986). There are some neuropiles, however, that contain large numbers of neurons and are uniquely represented in the brain. They are not directly associated with either primary afferents or motor neurons and in most cases their function is not completely understood.

In the following account I attempt to relate the structural organization of the decapod brain to its function. Real neuronal circuits can be described that are the basis of some behavioural actions, even if we are still naive about the details, degrees of freedom and strategies employed at the subcellular level. A question now before us is whether the type of circuits that have been worked out for the simpler responses are also, in a slightly more elaborate form, the basis for the vastly more complex tasks that we see animals accomplishing. Or is there a very different principle operating in the nervous system that allows it to handle large amounts of information simultaneously in many parallel channels? The traditional method of exploring the nervous system with microelectrodes has revealed a great deal about the lower levels of organization and has "cracked" many of the reflexive systems. But recordings from interneurons that we assume belong to the next level of organization and that pass between the neuropile areas have not always been easy to interpret in either the invertebrate or vertebrate nervous systems.

Although the functional organization within the brain is a continuum from the simple to the complex, for the purpose of this review I consider examples of behaviour at three levels: simple reflexive actions, compensatory actions, and volitional actions (i.e. generated by the animal itself).

STRUCTURAL ORGANIZATION IN THE DECAPOD BRAIN

There are three main divisions in the brain: the protocerebrum, consisting of two lateral protocerebral lobes (=optic lobes) which in the decapod crustaceans are contained in the stalked eyes, and the median protocerebrum which is located centrally. The lateral protocerebral lobes are each divided into five neuropiles: the lamina, external medulla, internal medulla, terminal medulla and hemiellipsoid body. The neurons in the lamina, external medulla and internal medulla are geometrically ordered reflecting the rows of ommatidia in the compound eye. The terminal medulla and hemiellipsoid body are complex non-geometrically ordered neuropiles that can be resolved into 13 distinct areas, 8 of which contain dense knots of neuropile, or glomeruli. The hemiellipsoid body and two of the neuropile areas of the terminal medulla are connected directly to the accessory and olfactory lobes of the deutocerebrum by the olfactory globular tract (Blaustein et al 1988).

The lateral protocerebrum accounts for a significant part of the brain of the decapods but a large part of it (lamina, external medulla and internal medulla) may be devoted entirely to visual processing and can be regarded to be part of the receptor organ. Extensive neuronal computation is required to transform the simple changes in light intensity in the photoreceptors into a measure of the velocity and direction of a moving image, coded as nerve impulses. In many mechanoreceptive systems, velocity and directional information is extracted by the physical organization of the receptor organ and already coded in action potentials in the primary afferent axons. The terminal medulla and hemiellipsoid body are embryologically derived from the median protocerebrum and although they may take part in visual processing they are certainly heavily involved in the integration of olfactory behaviour (Maynard and Sallee 1970, Derby and

Blaustein 1988). Lying close to the medulla terminalis is the X organ-sinus gland system, a neurosecretory structure and the probable source of many of the known neurohormones in the crustacea (Arechiga et al 1985).

The lateral protocerebral lobes are linked to the median protocerebrum by the protocerebral tracts (= optic tracts). The median protocerebrum consists of four lobes, two anterior and two posterior. Situated between the anterior and posterior pair lies the central body, a specialised area of neuropile with no known primary afferent inputs. A feature of all arthropod brains, the function of the central body is still obscure. No electrical recordings have been made of the responses of neurons in the central body of crustaceans. Immunocytochemical studies have shown that 8 relatively large serotonin containing neurons with cell bodies on each side of the brain, cross through the central body, have massed terminals there and then project out and down into the upper layers of the posterior lobes of the median protocerebral neuropile (Sandeman et al 1988). We have evidence from immunocytochemical studies that serotonin, proctolin, substance P, FMRFamide and GAD are all present in the central body. No structure similar to the central body is present in any other ganglion in the CNS and it represents one of the few principal distinctions between the brain and the ventral ganglia.

Behind the protocerebrum is the deutocerebrum, receiving afferent inputs from the antennules. The neuropiles of the deutocerebrum include the olfactory lobes, which receive a purely chemoreceptive input (Sandeman & Denburg 1976, Mellon et al 1989) and the lateral and medial antennular neuropiles that receive inputs from the statocysts and mechanoreceptors of the antennules (Yoshino et al 1983, Blaustein et al 1988) and also contain the motor neurons for the control of the antennules. Motor neurons to the eye muscles have their axons either in the optic tract or oculomotor nerves with synaptic fields shared between the neuropiles of the median protocerebrum, lateral antennular neuropile and tegumentary neuropile (see below). Included in the deutocerebrum are the paired accessory lobes, which are large in crayfish and virtually absent in crabs, and have no primary afferent input. Containing many glomeruli and linked to the lateral protocerebrum by the olfactory globular tract, the accessory lobes have been associated with olfaction, although Hanström (1925, 1929) pointed to the presence of large accessory lobes in crustaceans with poor vision, well developed antennules and long antennae, and their virtual absence in the brachyurans with good vision and short antennae. The olfactory and accessory lobes are unique neuropiles containing large numbers of small neurons and found only in the brain.

The parolfactory lobes are also contained in the deutocerebrum. In the crayfish these are bipartite and consist of fine-fibered and coarse-fibered halves. Axons ending in the parolfactory lobe travel in the deutocerebral commissure that runs across the brain between the accessory lobes. No afferent inputs to the parolfactory lobes are known and no similar structures are found in any other ganglia. In the brachyurans the parolfactory lobes are more difficult to distinguish, being almost entirely incorporated into the deutocerebral commissure. Hanström (1947) referred to all the deutocerebral neuropiles apart from the olfactory and accessory lobes as the parolfactory lobes, thus creating a confusion in the terminology that has been perpetuated by several authors (Maynard 1965, Sandeman and Luff 1973, Yoshino et el 1983) but corrected by Tsvileneva and Titova (1985) who returned to Hanström's original (1925) and more appropriate description where he separated the deutocerebral neuropiles into the parolfactory lobes and the lateral and median antennular neuropiles. The architecture and projections of the neurons in the parolfactory lobes has not been studied with modern physiological and anatomical methods and so we know little about their function.

Two small neuropiles have been identified in the crayfish to lie between the olfactory and accessory lobes and the lateral antennular neuropiles. Figured by Helm (1928) and redescribed by Tsvileneva and Titova (1985) they are associated with 5 large serotonin containing neurons that branch in the olfactory and accessory lobes (Sandeman and Sandeman 1987; Sandeman et al 1988). Although small, this neuropile may represent one of the connections between the olfactory and accessory lobes and higher order neurons in the deutocerebrum that ascend to the optic lobes outside the olfactory globular tract (Tautz et al 1986, Derby and Blaustein 1988) or that descend in the oesophageal connectives (Ache and Sandeman 1980, Hamilton and Ache 1983).

The tegumentary neuropile and antennal lobes are contained in the tritocerebrum. The purely afferent tegumentary nerve from the dorsal carapace terminates in the tegumentary neuropile and the antennal lobe contains the sensory, motor and interneurons that control the antennal movements. The antennal neuropile has some geometric order in it. Whether this has some functional significance, or is only the result of continued growth of the flagellum is not known although the latter is more likely. Segments are added to the antennal flagellum throughout the life of the animal and the motor neurons that move the flagellum have a comb-like architecture with branches extending down into the sensory part of the antennal neuropile (Sandeman et al 1988). As the number of antennal segments increases the antennal neuropile probably lengthens distally. Sequentially added branches of the motorneuron growing down into the new neuropile could result in the geometrically ordered appearance.

Although the astacid crayfish provide us with a simple base plan of the decapod crustacean brain, there are fairly significant differences in the appearance of the neuropiles in different decapod groups (Blaustein et al 1988). The palinurid brains for example are "folded" so that the median protocerebrum lies dorsal to much of the deutocerebrum, making the interpretation of the connectivity between the various neuropiles more difficult. We also find greater areas of deutocerebral neuropile containing glomeruli in *Jasus verrauxi*, a southern hemisphere palinurid, than in the brain of the parastacid *Cherax*.

The application of immunocytochemical labelling techniques to decapod crustacean brain has revealed many neurons containing biogenic amines or neuropeptides and the catalogue of identified cells that can be recognised with this technique will certainly continue to expand (Elofsson 1983, Beltz and Kravitz 1983, Siwicki and Bishop 1986, Dircksen and Keller 1988, Mangerich and Keller 1988, Sandeman et al 1988). Neurones that contain the same neuroactive substance may not belong to the same functional subsystem, but the method provides us with an array of identified neurons to explore that may have neuromodulatory effects on particular afferent inputs or entire behaviour patterns.

FUNCTIONAL ORGANIZATION IN THE DECAPOD BRAIN

Level 1: Level 1 actions are defined as those where a relatively simple stimulus (to mechanoreceptive hairs) results in a response always involving the same muscle groups and with the action always in the same direction. The number of neurons essential for the response is small, latencies are short implying a direct link between the sensory input and the motor output, the movement is in a particular direction and the intensity of the response is the only degree of freedom.

An example of a level 1 action is found in the protective eye withdrawal of the crab. Several very large eye muscles in *Carcinus* and *Scylla* are responsible for the rapid eye withdrawal and only two motor neurons are used to effect the reflex although other motor neurons are recruited to hold the eye in the withdrawn position (Burrows 1967, Sandeman 1971). The latencies between stimulation of the purely sensory tegumentary nerve that innervates the carapace and the discharge of the motor neurons, is short enough to indicate that they are monosynaptically connected. There is physiological evidence for the involvement of other neurons in the response, both inhibitory and excitatory, although the anatomy of these elements has not been described (Sandeman 1967, 1969a). The reflex can also be evoked by stimulating receptors around the eye, antenna and antennule. The description of the central architecture of the motor neurons is incomplete but their branches extend to the tegumentary, antennary and antennular neuropiles (Sandeman 1969b, Sandeman and Mendum 1971).

Interneurons are not inserted between the afferent neuropiles and the motor neurons in this system, perhaps because they all lie in the same ganglion and the integration of the inputs and the generation of the response is within the capabilities of the motor neurons. They do not require an interneuronal subsystem to perform an extraction of complex features not present in the raw afferent signal.

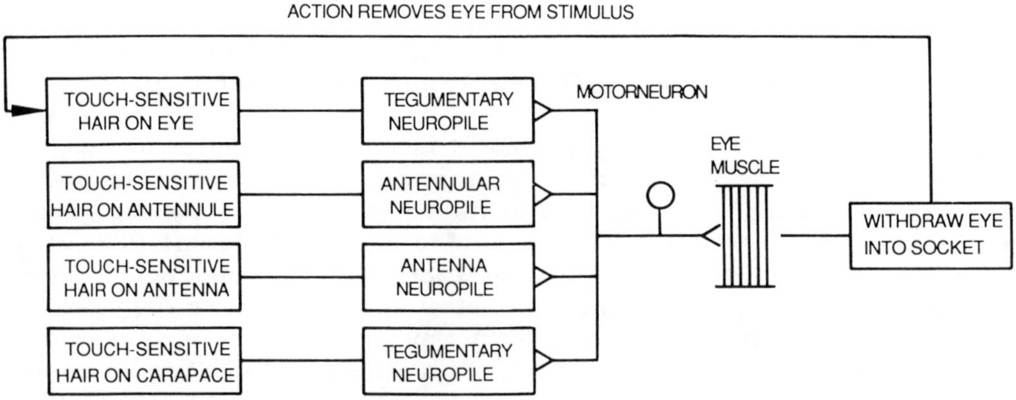

Fig. 1. A summary and circuit diagram of the reflex eye withdrawal of the crab eye. For explanation, see text.

A neuronal circuit that could satisfactorily account for the reflex withdrawal of the eye is shown in Fig. 1 and can be explained as follows: phasic discharges from mechanoreceptors on the eye, antennules, antennae or carapace are conveyed along separate nerve bundles to their respective neuropiles. These neuropiles contain the synaptic fields of the two large motor neurons (only one is shown in Fig. 1) that sum the inputs from the receptors, without needing to distinguish their origin, and respond with a single burst of action potentials. This leads to the contraction of the large muscles in the eye that withdraw it into the eye socket. No controlling or modifying information, correlated with the eye movement, is fed back to the afferent inputs, unless the response was caused by a touch to the eye itself, in which case the stimulus would be removed.

The behaviour is highly predictable, and tightly stimulus coupled. This does not mean to say that we have no more to gain from the study of such a behaviour. A closer look at the reflex reveals that it displays all the quantitative variability of any behavioural action and has become a valuable preparation for the study of operant and classical conditioning (see Abramson et al; Feinman et al, this volume).

Level 2: Level 2 actions can be defined as those in which the stimulus is received by receptors contained in highly selective, complex sensory organs (statocysts, eyes, proprioceptors) which provide a signal that quantitatively and qualitatively determines the nature of the behavioural response. The responses may involve sets of reciprocally acting motor systems, are often controlled by sensory feedbacks and can be influenced by several afferent inputs.

An example of a level 2 action can be found in the compensatory actions of the stalked eyes of crabs. Able to move in all three planes, the eyes are suspended by a system of muscles which allows them complete freedom of movement, i.e. there are no joints articulating about fixed pivots such as are present in most other appendages of the animal's body, that would restrict their movements to a particular plane. No proprioceptive systems extend between the eyestalks and the proximal members of the eyestalk assembly, and eye position is the result of the concerted activity of a number of motor neurons controlled by a velocity-sensitive visual feedback (Sandeman 1977).

The compensatory eye movements are also produced by rotation of the animal about its various axes, or by rotation of the substrate on which the animal stands, in relation to its body (Varju and Sandeman 1982). In every case the movement of the eyes is such to ensure that they remain stationary in relation to the visual world.

Reflecting the multimodal nature of the compensatory behaviour, the synaptic fields of the oculomotor neurons are spread through the neuropiles of the median protocerebrum, deutocerebrum and tritocerebrum (Sandeman and Okajima 1973). Considerable integration and computation of the photoreceptor signals takes place and recordings from the protocerebral tracts of crabs, suggest that the extraction of the parameters of direction and velocity, required to drive the optokinetic response, is achieved within the neuropiles of the lateral protocerebrum before being transmitted along the protocerebral tracts to the median protocerebrum (Sandeman et al 1975).

The input to the oculomotor neurons from the statocyst afferents on the other hand, is direct. Synaptic delay between the statocyst primary afferents and oculomotor neurons is about 2 millisecs (Silvey and Sandeman 1976), excluding the interpolation of an interneuronal subsystem. The statocyst of the crab however, is a highly sophisticated and finely tuned sense organ capable of accurately extracting the direction and amplitude of angular accelerations that are imposed on it (Sandeman and Okajima 1972). Hence the oculomotor neurons that reach into the antennular neuropiles can be directly and appropriately driven by the signals in the primary afferents.

The input to the oculomotor neurons from the leg proprioceptors has not been explored at the physiological or anatomical level. Complex proprioceptive systems are found at the bases of the legs that monitor the direction and velocity of leg joint displacements (Bush and Cannone 1985, Clarac 1985). All that is required is an ascending interneuron to collect these outputs and transfer them to the oculomotor system. Such an interneuron has not yet been identified.

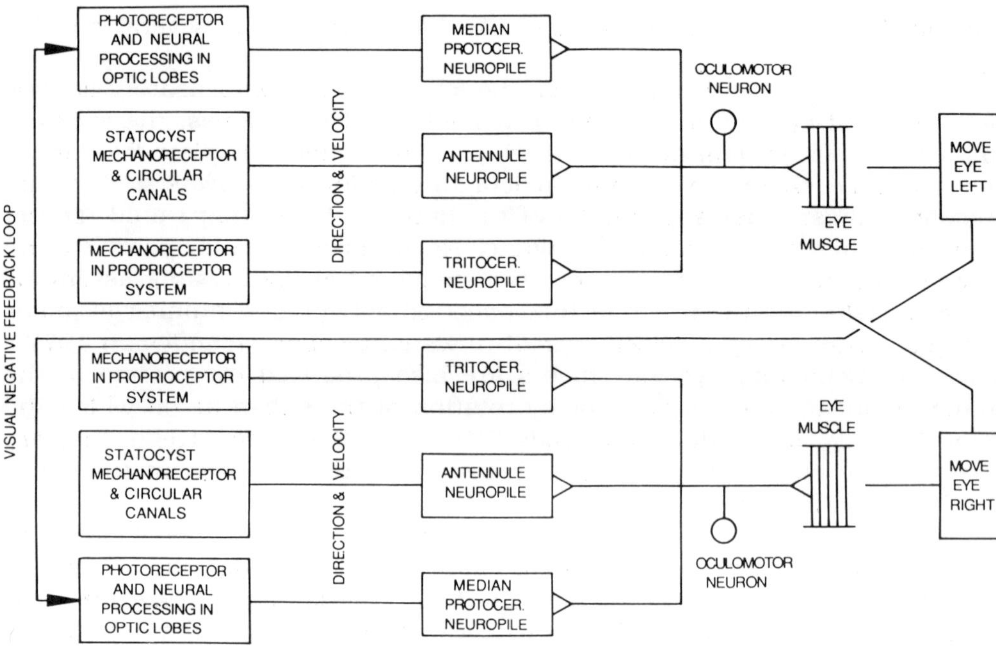

Fig. 2. A summary and circuit diagram of compensatory eye movements in the horizontal plane, brought about by the eyes, statocysts and leg proprioceptors in the crab. For explanation, see text.

A neuronal circuit summarising the inputs, integrative operations and outputs of the eye compensation system is shown in Fig. 2 and can be explained as follows: photoreceptors in the eyes are able only to sense changes in light intensity and so need neural computation in the optic neuropiles to transform this into information about the direction and velocity of the image movement. This information is transferred to the median protocerebrum.

Mechanoreceptors in the statocyst are directionally sensitive to deflection but need to be arranged in a specific order in the canals of the statocyst so that they can extract the magnitude and direction of the angular accelerations imposed on them. The primary afferents from the statocyst end in the lateral antennular neuropiles.

Mechanoreceptors in the bases of the legs of the crab are arranged across the joints and detect the direction and velocity of leg movements. This information is most likely gathered by one or more interneurons and transferred to the brain.

The motor neurons of the eye consist of two populations, those that move the eye to the right and those that move it to the left. The directional and velocity information signalling the movement of the animal, for which compensation must be made, is present in the neuropiles of the protodeuto-and tritocerebrum that also contain branches of the motor neurons. Here it is addressed to, and summed in the appropriate motor neurons which are brought to threshold and discharge. Muscle contraction and eye movement follow. Unlike the eye withdrawal though, the action that is generated by the motor neurons has a direct effect on one of the afferents that drive the response: movement of the eye will induce a secondary, visually driven compensatory effect in the opposite direction. In the circuit in Fig. 2 this is shown by the feedback connection from the eye movement (output), to the visual input of the antagonistic muscle set. Note that the eye movement will not affect the inputs from the statocyst or proprioceptors. The simple summation of the three inputs may be expected to produce a signal that would overcompensate in the absence of the visual feedback and it has been suggested that the role of the visual system under natural conditions is to counteract this (Sandeman 1983).

There are still aspects of the optokinetic system that are not understood or even explored. In optokinetic nystagmus for example, the slow following movement of the eye is alternated with a rapid saccade in the opposite direction. The initiation of these saccadic discharges in the oculomotor neurons can take place in preparations where the eye has been removed, and so does not rely on a peripheral signal. Nothing is known about the neurons that initiate the fast saccades.

Although tightly stimulus coupled, the compensatory responses vary in their intensity with the state of arousal of the animal and provide us with a test-bed to explore the action of neuromodulatory systems in the brain (Erber and Sandeman 1989 and this volume).

Level 3: Third level actions are defined as those that do not require a maintained external stimulus for their continuance. The initiation of the behaviour appears to come from the animal itself although it is possible to set conditions under which the behaviour is more likely to occur. Many afferent and motor systems are involved.

The tactile exploration of an area by an animal provides us with a good example of level 3 activity. Antennae are present in all arthropods and many of the nocturnally active species must depend almost entirely on these organs to guide them. The second antennae of many decapod crustaceans are highly developed and unlike insects do not carry olfactory receptors. Of relevance for this account is that a clear distinction can be made between passive touch where an object is brought against the antenna of a stationary animal, and active touch where the animal extracts information about an object through its own active palpation of it.

The tactile exploratory behaviour of reversibly blinded Australian freshwater crayfish *(Cherax)* in a novel environment was observed when they were released into an aquarium containing a refuge (empty beer can) and a row of cylinders of different sizes arranged around the perimeter and in the center of the aquarium (Varju and Sandeman 1989). An analysis of video recordings of animals in the new environment showed that when first placed in an aquarium they actively explored the entire area available to them. Having come across the refuge they established themselves therein and made explorative sorties from this point. Initial sorties were made at a slow pace with frequent but relatively short stops at objects which were palpated with the antennae and tested with the chelae and walking legs. Subsequent sorties were characterised by longer pauses but more rapid locomotion between stops. Most time was spent in exploring the refuge. Animals needed about 20 minutes to complete an exploration of a tank measuring 50 cm by 50 cm, and would then move around it with increasing velocity. Setting up a feeding station at some distance from the animal's refuge ensured that they made regular sorties and allowed the effect of a change in the nature or position of the objects in the aquarium on the animals behaviour to be tested. Altering the surface texture of an object, or blocking a previously open pathway resulted in an abrupt halt and backing away after contact with the obstruction. This was followed by careful tactile exploration of the novel object. Observation of the animal's attempt to return to its refuge when cut off from it, lead to the conclusion that *Cherax* is able to construct a spatial map of its immediate environment.

An examination of the sensory and central structures that are available to the animal in the context of this behaviour is of interest. The sensory system is relatively simple. The flagella of crayfish have many mechanoreceptors that can signal both contact and distortion of the flagellum (Sandeman 1989). The basal joints of the antenna are constrained to move along two planes but as these are at right angles to one another the flagellum can move in every possible direction. The movements of the basal joints are monitored by stretch sensitive receptors that code predominantly velocity and direction of motion (Sandeman 1985).

The antennae have their own central neuropile containing the sensory endings, motor and local interneurons necessary for the antennal reflexes. These are avoidance and resistance reflexes, and assistance reflexes that may serve to keep the antennal flagellum straight (Sandeman 1989).

The antennular neuropile however, lacks the large numbers of small neurons that are usually associated with learning activities. Associative learning in lobsters for example has been found to use olfactory and visual cues (Fine-Levy et al 1988). The correlated neuropiles are the olfactory lobes, the terminal medulla and perhaps also the accessory lobes, all areas of dense neuropile containing large numbers of neurons. In searching for a neuropile area of this nature that could be involved in tactile learning, the early comments of Hanström (1925,1929) concerning the presence of the large accessory lobes in crustacea with poor vision and long antennae come to mind. While anatomical evidence supports an olfactory function for the accessory lobes, the lobes also receive inputs from the protocerebrum and tritocerebrum (Blaustein et al 1988). A large tract of axons links the medial edges of the antennal neuropiles to the deutocerebral commissure which in turn projects to the accessory lobes (Tsvileneva and Titova 1985). Hanström's intimation of a wider role for the accessory lobes, perhaps including a tactile function, is worth further examination.

The tactile exploratory behaviour of the crayfish is not so easily modelled in terms of serial neuronal circuits as are the reflex eye withdrawal and compensatory eye movements. We are faced with an action that is sustained with no apparent external stimulus and where many of the afferent subsystems are simultaneously or sequentially activated. Information is extracted from the environment by actions of the animal and its response to a novel topography leads us to propose a template matching process between the afferent input and some neural construct of the spatial properties of the environment in the brain of the animal.

We are forced to draw a different sort of flow chart to summarise this behaviour, shown in Fig. 3, which can be explained as follows: there are three modes to the exploration behaviour which could be described as "initial", "confirmatory" and "policing", all self-motivated. In the initial mode, locomotion is slow but steady and the animal could be building up a spatial map using tactile landmarks that it finds in a particular direction and known distance from the refuge, similar to the spatial maps that have been proposed to account for the behaviour of foraging bees (Cartwright and Collett 1987). A neural template of the landmarks, which may not be very detailed, is stored in the nervous system during the first excursion. In the confirmatory mode, movement between the landmarks is more rapid. The positions of the landmarks within the map are confirmed when the actual distance and direction travelled to reach them, matches what is already present in the spatial map. The longer period of time spent at the landmarks increases the detail contained in the neural template of the landmark. In the policing mode, the animal moves quickly between landmarks that continue to fit their templates and are no longer novel. A change in the topography is perceived as a mismatch between the position of the landmarks on the stored spatial map and represents a strong stimulus. This switches the behaviour back to the second, or first mode, depending on how much of the topography is changed and how inappropriate the stored template has become. A change in the nature of the landmark, but not its position, is detected by comparison between the tactile features of the landmark with the stored template.

Fig. 3. (next page) A summary of possible processes that underlie tactile exploration of an aquarium by *Cherax*. For an explanation, see text

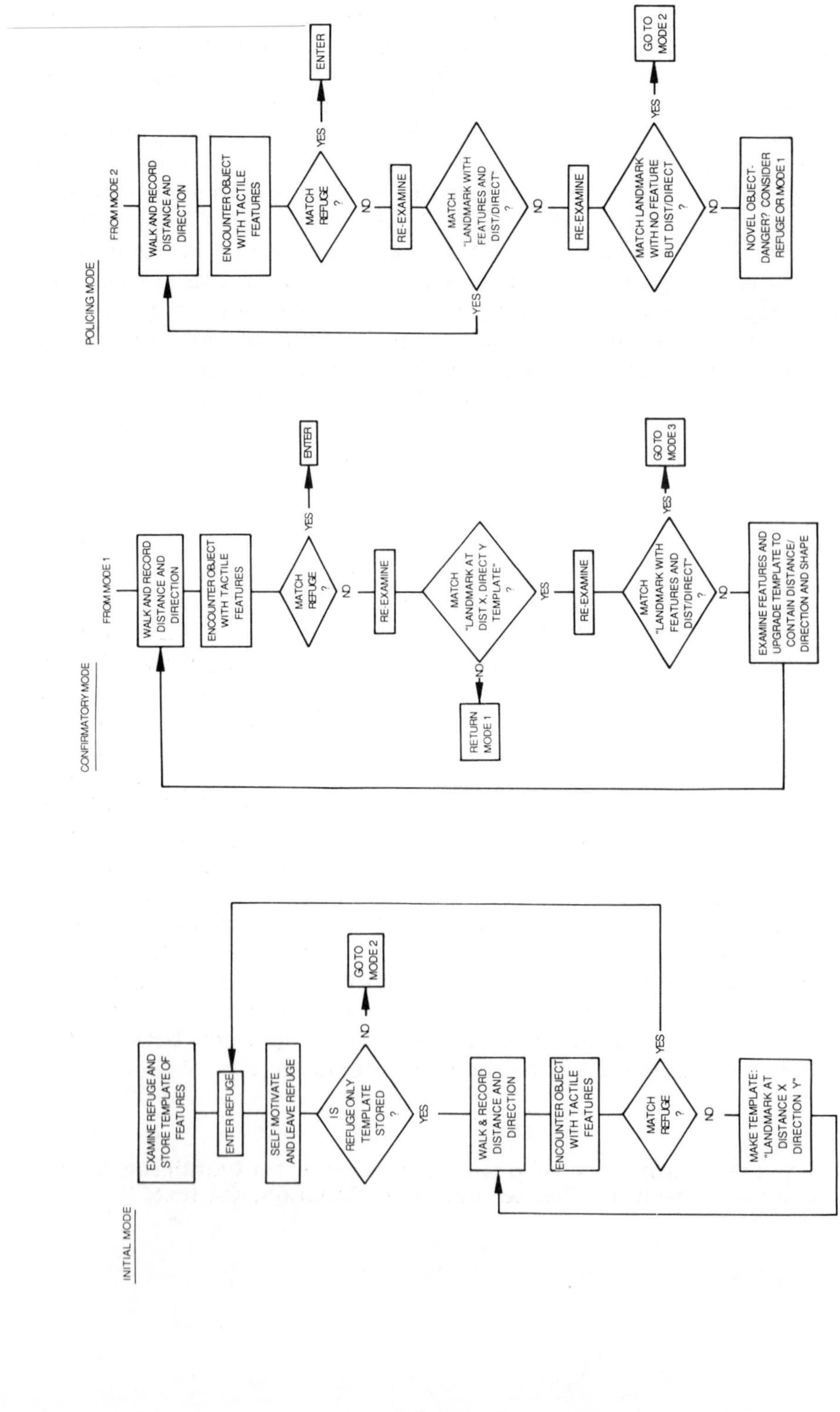
INITIAL MODE
EXAMINE REFUGE AND STORE TEMPLATE OF FEATURES
ENTER REFUGE
SELF MOTIVATE AND LEAVE REFUGE
IS REFUGE ONLY TEMPLATE STORED ?
NO
GOTO MODE 2
YES
WALK & RECORD DISTANCE AND DIRECTION
ENCOUNTER OBJECT WITH TACTILE FEATURES
MATCH REFUGE ?
YES
NO
MAKE TEMPLATE: "LANDMARK AT DISTANCE X DIRECTION Y"
CONFIRMATORY MODE
FROM MODE 1
WALK AND RECORD DISTANCE AND DIRECTION
ENCOUNTER OBJECT WITH TACTILE FEATURES
MATCH REFUGE ?
YES
ENTER
NO
RE-EXAMINE
MATCH "LANDMARK AT DIST X, DIRECT Y TEMPLATE" ?
NO
RETURN MODE 1
YES
RE-EXAMINE
MATCH "LANDMARK WITH FEATURES AND DIST/DIRECT" ?
YES
GOTO MODE 3
NO
EXAMINE FEATURES AND UPGRADE TEMPLATE TO CONTAIN DISTANCE/ DIRECTION AND SHAPE
POLICING MODE
FROM MODE 2
WALK AND RECORD DISTANCE AND DIRECTION
ENCOUNTER OBJECT WITH TACTILE FEATURES
MATCH REFUGE ?
YES
ENTER
NO
RE-EXAMINE
MATCH "LANDMARK WITH FEATURES AND DIST/DIRECT" ?
YES
NO
RE-EXAMINE
MATCH LANDMARK WITH NO FEATURE BUT DIST/DIRECT ?
YES
GO TO MODE 2
NO
NOVEL OBJECT- DANGER? CONSIDER REFUGE OR MODE 1

PARALLELS IN ANIMAL NERVOUS SYSTEMS

The close parallels that are found in the organization of the central nervous systems in many animals follow directly from the tendency to evolve receptor organs that are finely tuned to some modality, and the need to preserve the qualitative properties of these signals by addressing them to particular areas of the brain. That the central nervous systems in both vertebrates and invertebrates are arranged in this way has been confirmed many times.

Within this first level of organization we find another feature common to many animals: hard-wired connections between particular receptors and specific motor systems result in a number of preprogrammed "behaviours". Studies on the invertebrates with their relatively small number of neurons, many of which can be uniquely identified, have extended this principle to include some relatively complex behavioural sequences among those determined by hard-wired circuits, and have shown how an important and adaptive degree of flexibility is brought into such hard-wired systems by the addition of gating and modulation (Hisada and Takahata 1979, Wine 1984, Takahata, this volume).

The hope is that an investigation of the higher levels of behaviour in the more convenient invertebrate preparations will provide us with the insights we need to understand the larger vertebrate brains. This line of reasoning depends not only on establishing an equivalence at the behavioural level between the animals to be compared but in finding ways to explore the higher levels of behaviour in the invertebrates.

The investigation of the lower levels of behaviour in the invertebrates was significantly advanced by borrowing techniques and terminology from systems engineers whose models of servo systems were often designed to perform the same kinds of operations as the level 1 and level 2 actions described here. Intracellular recording and dye marking from individual neurons is an ideal method for the examination of the components in the serially arranged neural circuits that are the basis of such actions, and the identifiability of the single neuronal elements in the invertebrates allows complete descriptions to be achieved. These methods are probably not entirely adequate for the exploration of the higher level systems, and nor are the servo system models appropriate. Multichannel recordings on the other hand that show the interactions between sets of neurons have been immediately successful in revealing some of the hitherto unsuspected neural mechanisms that are operating during behavioural actions (Getting and Dekin 1985, Moore and Larimer 1988, Heinzel 1988).

If it is true that we can only understand something we have already invented, then it is probably a good time for the circuit busting "wet" neurobiologists, working from the bottom upwards, to have a careful look at the musings of those interested in artificial intelligence and working from the top down. There are a number of thoughtful general models available that may help us to design experiments that are a little different from the ones which were adequate to elucidate the circuitry of the reflex systems. Certain minimal requirements for example, have been set down for a system that needs to solve problems and change its behaviour adaptively according to experience. Such systems need to have an inference engine, or some device that will cope with the "if-then" process and a data base that can be altered depending on the correctness of the response of the "if-then" system. We immediately recognise the above properties in each single neuron: the "if-then" process can be seen as the tradeoff between the various inhibitory and excitatory inputs to the neuron which, with its threshold, will eventually make a "decision" and the data base is the molecular makeup of the cell membrane which ultimately controls the cell's response to incoming signals and which can be altered by experience.

While the concept of the central nervous system as a collection of many hundreds of computers arranged both serially and in parallel may not be immediately helpful for us, it could encourage the erection of models of a very different nature to those inspired by the servo system engineers, particularly when we attempt to understand behaviour such as the tactile exploration in crayfish where the "if-then" matching process is not on the scale of single neurons close to the input, but at the level of interneuron sets or matrices that are capable of representing complex spatio-temporal templates. Even such models however, need the confirmation that can only come from the continued study of the behaviour of animals, and of the anatomy, physiology and molecular biology of the nervous system at every level. As a pioneer model system the brain of the decapods may yet provide the top-downers and bottom-uppers with a place to meet.

REFERENCES

Ache, B.W. & Sandeman, D.C. (1980) Olfactory-induced central neural activity in the Murray crayfish, *Euastacus armatus*. J. Comp. Physiol. **140**:295-301

Arechiga, H., Garcia, U. & Rodriguez-Sosa, L. (1985) Neurosecretory role of crustacean eyestalk in the control of neuronal activity. In *Model Neural Networks and Behaviour*. (ed. A.I.Selverston) p.361-379. New York: Plenum Press,.

Beltz, B. & Kravitz, E.A. (1983) Mapping of serotonin-like immunoreactivty in the lobster nervous system. *J. Neurosci.* **3**:585-602

Blaustein, D.N., Derby, C.D., Simmons, R.B. & Beall, A.C. (1988). Structure of the brain and medulla terminalis of the spiny lobster *Panulirus argus* and the crayfish *Procambarus clarkii*, with an emphasis on olfactory centers. *J. Crustacean Biol.* **8**:493-519.

Burrows. M. (1967) Reflex withdrawal of the eyecup in the crab *Carcinus*. *Nature*, Lond. **215**:56-57

Bush, B.M.H. & Cannone, A.J. (1985) How do crabs control their muscle receptors? In *Feedback and Motor Control in Invertebrates and Vertebrates*. (eds. W.J.P. Barnes and M.H. Gladden) pp. 145-166. London: Croom Helm.

Cartwright, B.A. & Collett, T.S. (1987) Landmark maps for honeybees. *Biol. Cybern.* **57**:85-93

Clarac, F. (1985) Stepping reflexes and the sensory control of walking legs in crustacea. In *Feedback and Motor Control in Invertebrates and Vertebrates.* (eds. W.J.P. Barnes and M.H. Gladden) pp. 379-400. London: Croom Helm.

Derby, C.D. & Blaustein, D.N. (1988). Morphological and physiological characterization of individual olfactory interneurons connecting the brain and eyestalk ganglia of the crayfish. *J. Comp. Physiol.* **163**:777-794.

Dircksen, H. & Keller, R. (1988) Immunocytochemical localization of CCAP, a novel crustacean cardioactive peptide, in the nervous system of the shore crab, *Carcinus maenas L. Cell Tissue Res.* **254**:347-360

Elofsson, R. (1983) 5HT-like immunoreactivity in the central nervous system of the crayfish *Pacifastacus leniusculus. Cell Tissue Res.* **232**:221-236

Erber, J. & Sandeman, D.C. (1990) The effect of serotonin and octopamine on the optokinetic response of the crab *Leptograpsus variegatus. J. Neurobiol.* (in press)

Fine-Levy, J.B., Girardot, M-N., Derby, C.D. & Daniel, P.C. (1988) Differential associative conditioning and olfactory discrimination in the spiny lobster *Panulirus argus. Behavioral and Neural Biol.* **49**:315-331

Getting, P.A. & Dekin, M.S. (1985) *Tritonia* swimming. A model system for integration within rythmic motor systems. In *Model Neural Networks and Behaviour.* (ed. A.I. Selverston) pp.3-20. New York: Plenum Press.

Hamilton, K. & Ache, B.W. (1983) Olfactory excitation of interneurons in the brain of the spiny lobster. *J. Comp. Physiol.* **150**:129-143

Hanström, B. (1925) The olfactory centres in crustaceans. *J. Comp. Neurol.* **38**:221-250.

Hanström, B. (1929) Das Deutocerebrum der Crustaceen. *Zool. Jb. Anat.* **51**:535-548.

Hanström, B. (1947) The brain, the sense organs and the incretory organs of the head in the Crustacea Malacostraca. *Acta Univ. Lund. Adv. 2 N.F.* **43**:1-44.

Heinzel, H.G. (1988) Gastric mill activity in the lobster. I. Spontaneous modes of chewing. *J. Neurophysiol.* **59**:528-550.

Helm, F. (1928) Vergleichend-anatomische Untersuchungen über das Gehirn, insbesondere das "Antennalganglion" der Decapoden. *Z. Morphol. Ökol. Tiere* **12**:70-134.

Hisada, M. & Takahata, M. (1979) Control of uropod position by descending statocyst-driven interneurons in the crayfish. In *Integrative Control Functions of the Brain.* (eds. M. Ito, N. Tsukahara, K. Kubota and K. Yagi) pp. 192-193. Amsterdam: Elsevier.

Leise, E.M., Hall, W.M. & Mulloney, B. (1986). Functional organization of crayfish abdominal ganglia: I. The flexor systems. *J. Comp. Neurol.* **253**:25-45.

Mangerich, S. & Keller, R. (1988) Localization of pigment-dispersing hormone (PDH) immunoreactivity in the central nervous system of *Carcinus maenas* and *Orconectes limosus* (Crustacea) with reference to FMRFamide immunoreactivity in *O. limosus. Cell Tissue Res.* **253**:199-208

Maynard D.M. (1965) Integration in crustacean ganglia. *Symp. Soc. exp. Biol.* **20**:111-149.

Maynard, D.M. & Sallee, A. (1970). Disturbance of feeding behaviour in the spiny lobster, *Panulirus argus,* following bilateral ablation of the medulla terminalis. *Zeit. vergl. Physiol.* **66**:123-140.

Mellon, D., Tuten, H.R. & Redick, J. (1989) Distribution of radioactive leucine following uptake by olfactory sensory neurons in normal and heteromorphic crayfish antennules. *J. Com. Physiol.* **280**:645-662.

Moore, D. & Larimer, J.L. (1988) Interactions between the tonic and cyclic postural motor programs in the crayfish abdomen. *J. Comp. Physiol.* **163**:187-199.

Sandeman, D.C. (1969a) Integrative properties of a reflex motoneuron in the brain of the crab *Carcinus.* *Z. vergl. Physiol.* **64**:450-464

Sandeman, D.C. (1969b) The synaptic link between the sensory and motoneurons in the eye-withdrawal reflex of the crab. *J. exp. Biol.* **50**:87-98

Sandeman, D.C. (1971) The excitation and electrical coupling of four identified motoneurons in the brain of the Australian mud crab, *Scylla serrata.* *Z. vergl. Physiol.* **72**:111-130

Sandeman, D.C. (1977) Compensatory eye movements in crabs. In *Identified Neurons and Behavior of Arthropods.* (ed. G.Hoyle) pp.131-147. New York: Plenum Press.

Sandeman, D.C. (1983) The balance and visual systems of the swimming crab: their morphology and interaction. In *Multimoded Convergences in Sensory Systems* (ed. E. Horn) pp.213-229. *Fortschritte der Zoologie,* **28**. Stuttgart: Gustav Fischer Verlag.

Sandeman, D.C. (1985) Crayfish antennae as tactile organs: their mobility and the responses of their proprioceptors to displacement. *J. Comp. Physiol.* **157**:363-373

Sandeman. D.C. (1989) Physical properties, sensory receptors and tactile reflexes of the antenna of the Australian freshwater crayfish *Cherax destructor.* *J. exp. Biol.* **141**:197-217.

Sandeman, D.C. & Denburg, J. (1976) The central projections of chemoreceptor axons in the crayfish revealed by axoplasmic transport. *Brain Res.* 115:492-496.

Sandeman, D.C. & Luff, S.E. (1973) The structural organization of glomerular neuropile in the olfactory and accessory lobes of an Australian freshwater crayfish *Cherax destructor.* *Z. Zellforsch.* **142**:37-61.

Sandeman, D.C. & Mendum, C.M. (1971) The fine structure of the central synaptic contacts on an identified crustacean motoneuron. *Z. Zellforsch.* **119**:515-525

Sandeman, D.C. & Okajima, A. (1972) Statocyst-induced eye movements in the crab *Scylla serrata* I. The sensory input from the statocyst. *J. exp. Biol.* **57**:187-204

Sandeman, D.C. & Okajima, A. (1973) Statocyst-induced eye movements in the crab *Scylla serrata* III. The anatomical projections of sensory and motor neurones and the responses of the motor neurones. *J. exp. Biol.* **59**:17-38

Sandeman, D.C., Kien, J. & Erber, J. (1975) Optokinetic eye movements in the crab, *Carcinus maenas* II. Responses of optokinetic interneurons. *J. Comp. Physiol.* **101**:259-274.

Sandeman, D.C., Sandeman, R.E. & Aitken, A.R. (1988) Atlas of serotonin-containing neurons in the optic lobes and brain of the crayfish *Cherax destructor*. *J. Comp. Neurol.* **269**:465-478.

Sandeman, R.E. & Sandeman, D.C. (1987) Serotonin-like immunoreactivity of giant olfactory interneurons in the crayfish brain. *Brain Research* **403**:371-374.

Silvey, G.E. & Sandeman, D.C. (1976) Integration between statocyst sensory neurons and oculomotor neurons in the crab *Scylla serrata*. III. The sensory to motor synapse. *J. Comp. Physiol.* **108**:53-65.

Siwicki, K.K. & Bishop, C.A. (1986) Mapping of proctolin-like immunoreactivity in the nervous systems of lobster and crayfish. *J. Comp. Neurol.* **243**:435-453

Tautz, J., Erber, J. & Ache, B. (1986) Chemosensitive interneurons ascend the optic nerve in the crayfish. *Naturwissenschaften* **73**:154-156.

Tsvileneva, V.A. & Titova, V.A. (1985) On the brain structures of decapods. *Zool. Jb. Anat.* **113**:217-266.

Varju, D. & Sandeman, D.C. (1982) Eye movements of the crab *Leptograpsus variegatus* elicited by imposed leg movements. *J. exp. Biol.* **98**:151-173.

Varju, D. & Sandeman, D.C. (1989) Tactile learning in a new habitat and spatial memory in the crayfish *Cherax destructor*. In *Dynamics and Plasticity in Neuronal Systems*. (eds. N. Elsner and W. Singer), pp. 21 Stuttgart: Thieme.

Wine, J.J. (1984) The structural basis of an innate behavioural pattern. *J. exp. Biol.* **112**:283-319

Yoshino, M., Kondoh, Y. & Hisada, M. (1983) Projection of statocyst sensory neurons associated with crescent hairs in, the crayfish *Procambarus clarkii* Girard. *Cell Tissue Res.* **230**:37-48.

Frontiers in Crustacean Neurobiology
Advances in Life Sciences

DIRECTIONALITY OF ANTENNAL SWEEPS IN RESPONSE TO WATER VIBRATION STIMULI IN CRAYFISH (*PROCAMBARUS CLARKII*)

Barbara Schmitz

Fakultät für Biologie, Universität Konstanz,
Postfach 5560, 7750 Konstanz 1, Federal Republic of Germany

SUMMARY

The analysis of antennal sweeps in intact crayfish (*Procambarus clarkii*) reveals that the animals are able to lateralize water vibration stimuli as well as to distinguish between different stimulus directions. The magnitude of sweeps of the ipsilateral antenna, which are usually directed backwards, is correlated with the angle between start position of the antenna and stimulus position. This dependence vanishes after obstructing information of tailfan mechanoreceptors by cutting the connective between the fifth and sixth abdominal ganglion.

INTRODUCTION

Unilateral water vibration stimuli elicit active antennal movements in resting, non-tethered crayfish (*Orconectes limosus*, Tautz 1987). While the ipsilateral antenna usually sweeps backwards and thus towards the stimulus, the contralateral one may sweep backwards or forwards with equal probability. Very recently it was shown that stimuli applied merely to the tailfan, and thus to its mechanosensory hairs, are sufficient to elicit antennal responses (Hamm 1989). In the present study the dependence of antennal sweeps on the direction of water vibration stimuli was investigated in detail in tethered crayfish. Experiments were conducted in intact animals as well as after cutting the connectives between the fifth and sixth (last) abdominal ganglion in order to elucidate the contribution of tailfan receptor input to the directionality of the antennal response.

METHODS

35 (test series I) and 14 (test series II) male and female crayfish (*Procambarus clarkii*, body length: 6 to 10 cm) were used in the behavioural tests. The animals were blinded by covering the rostrum including the eyestalks with a strip of tape and then tethered in the center of a 86 cm water basin (cf. Elepfandt and Wiedemer 1987). Sweeps of both the ipsilateral and contralateral antenna in response to unilateral water vibration stimuli (frequency: 100 Hz, vibration amplitude: 0.6 mm, duration:

2.5 s, interstimulus interval: at least 1 min, distance rostrumvibrator: 15 cm, stimulus position (see Fig. 1): 0°, 30°, 60°, 90°, 120°, 150°, 180° (test series I) or 30°, 90°, 150° (test series II) were video-monitored and analyzed by single frame replay analysis. In test series II identical test paradigms were applied to the crayfish both before and after cutting the last abdominal connective.

For each test the following data were evaluated; see Fig. 1:

- stimulus position (R)
- start- and end position of ipsi- and contralateral antenna (SI, SC, EI, EC; positive values: ipsilateral side; negative values: contralateral side),
- start- and end-angle of the ipsilateral antenna relative to the stimulus (RSI, REI; positive values: stimulus in front of antenna; negative values: stimulus behind antenna),
- sweep angle of ipsi- and contralateral antenna (SEI, SEC; positive values: forward sweep, negative values: backward sweep).

FIGURE 1

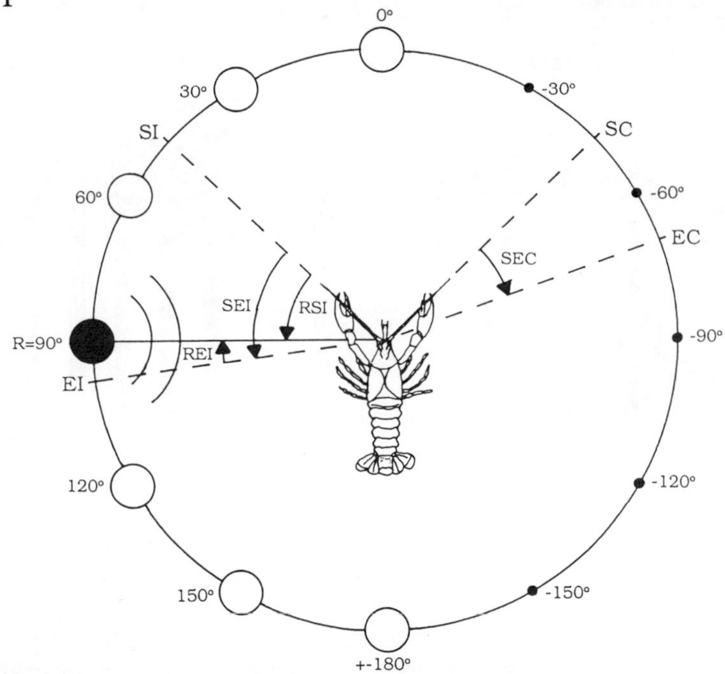

RESULTS

In test series I the crayfish were stimulated 5 to 68 times (n=806) and showed sweeps of the ipsilateral and/or contralateral antenna in response to 67% of stimulations (n=537). The start position of the ipsilateral antenna (SI) on average amounts to 73±34°, that of the contralateral one (SC) to -

78±38°. Irrespective of the stimulus position (R), sweeps of the ipsilateral antenna are usually directed backwards (SEI negative: 68%) rather than forwards (SEI positive: 24%) and on average amount to -20±38°, while the contralateral antenna sweeps backwards (SEC negative: 55%) or forwards (SEC positive: 36%) and on average -10±53° in response to the stimulus (Fig. 2).

FIGURE 2

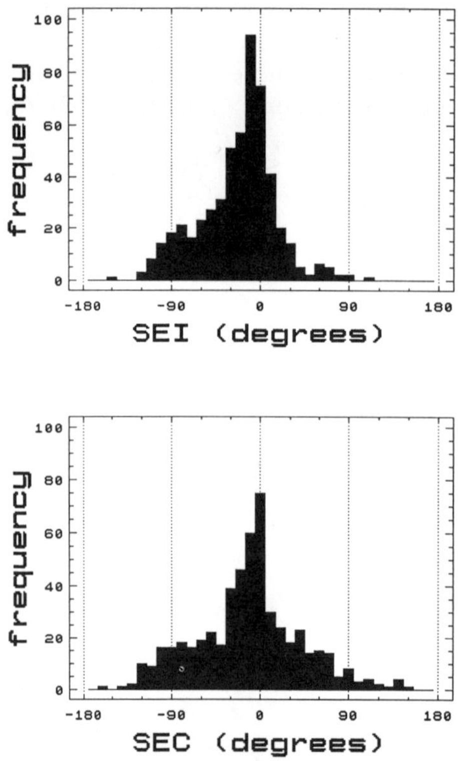

FIGURE 3

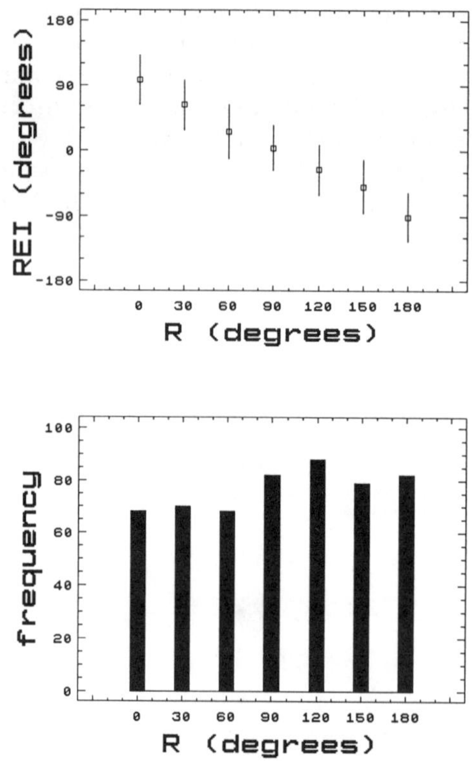

These results are in accordance with previous findings (Tautz 1987, Hamm 1989) and show that the crayfish are able to detect on which side the stimulus is presented.

Do crayfish also distinguish between different unilateral stimulus positions? In a first step it was investigated whether the ipsilateral antenna points towards the stimulus after sweeping. As shown in Figure 3, this is in fact the case for a stimulus position of R=90°: the end-angle relative to the stimulus position (REI) on average merely amounts to 3.1°. However, for more rostral (60° - 0°) or caudal stimulus positions (120° - 180°) the deviation increases progressively.

In a second step the influence of the start angle of the ipsilateral antenna relative to the stimulus (RSI) on the sweep angle of this antenna (SEI) was evaluated seperately for each of the 7 stimulus positions. As shown in Figure 4, there is a linear dependence of the mean sweep angle on the start angle RSI for each case. For R = 90° the data points coincide with the angle bisecting line, i.e. SEI is equal to RSI, the antenna sweeps on average up to the stimulus position. For more rostral or caudal stimulus positions (see above) there is an increasing parallel shift of values away from the angle bisecting line.

FIGURE 4

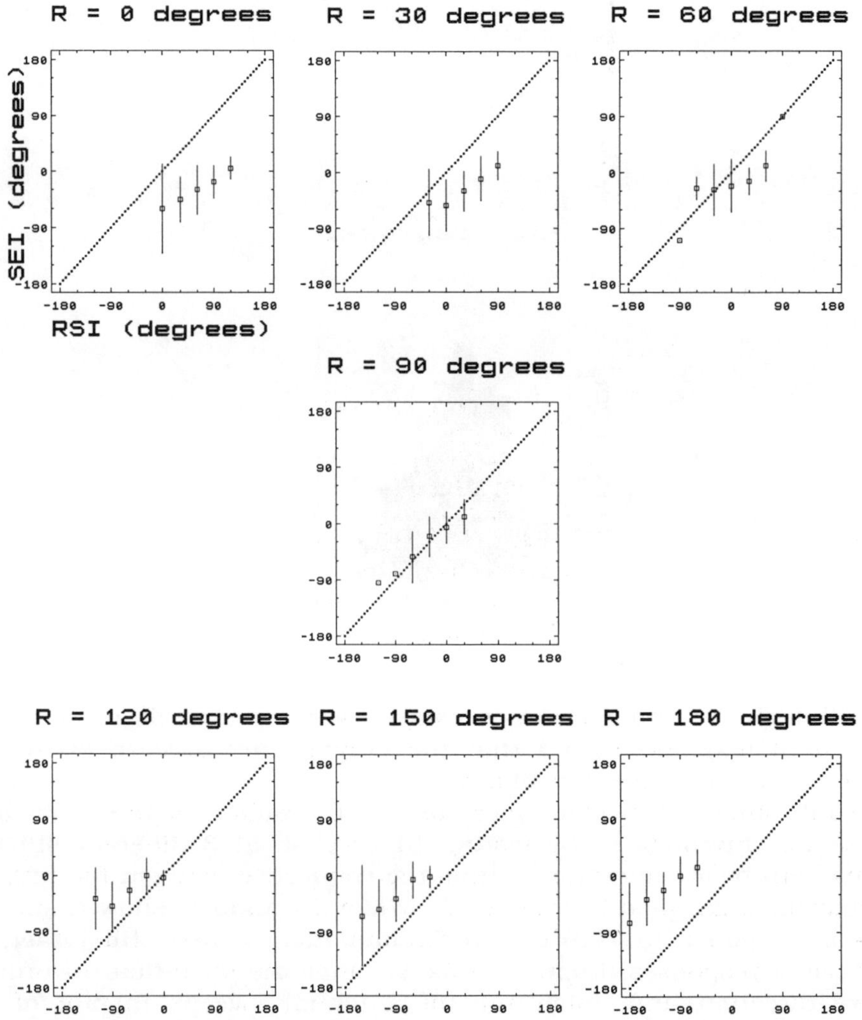

Figure 5 shows the dependence of SEI on RSI for all tests performed. Except for a stimulus position of 120° the sweeps of the ipsilateral antenna are on average directed backwards (SEI negative). The mean magnitude of these sweeps, however, increases for negative RSI-values (stimulus position behind antenna) and decreases for positive RSI-values (stimulus position in front of the antenna).

FIGURE 5

R = 0 - 180 degrees

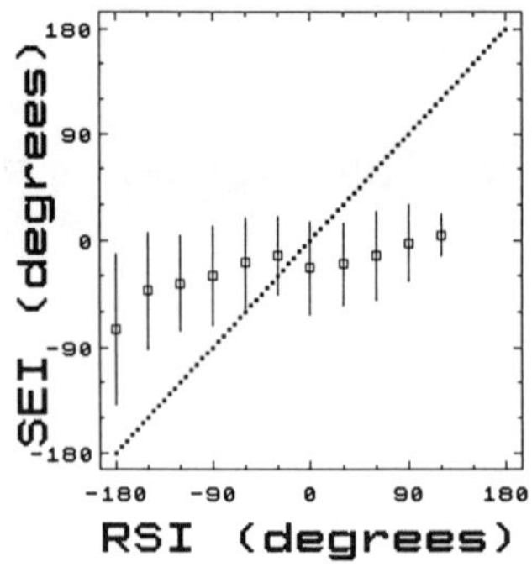

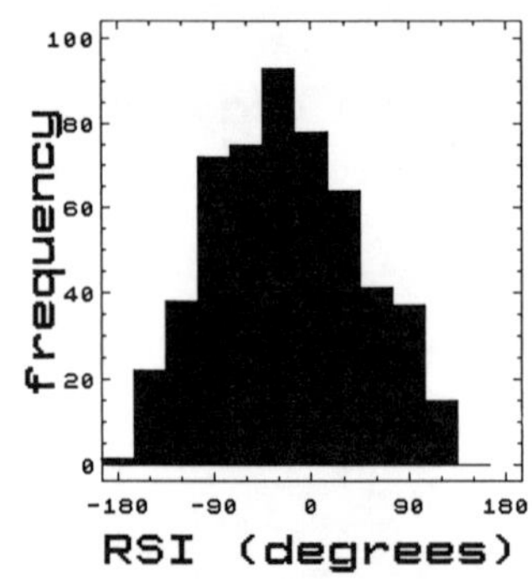

Thus, although the antenna is not always sweeping towards the stimulus, the antennal response shows that the crayfish are able to distinguish different unilateral stimulus positions.

The contribution of mechanoreceptors on the tailfan to the behavioural response was investigated by testing 14 crayfish at 3 different stimulus positions both before and after cutting the connective between the fifth and sixth abdominal ganglion (test series II). While the animals showed antennal sweeps in response to 70.9% of the stimulations when still intact, the percentage of responses dropped to 54.4% after the operation. In order to compare direction and magnitude of antennal sweeps inspite of this difference in responsiveness, the data were selected in such a way as to obtain the same number of responses at a given stimulus position for the individual crayfish both before and after surgery. This procedure resulted in a data base of 123 responses each. The most interesting result of this comparative analysis is shown in Figure 6. While the linear dependence of the ipsilateral sweep angle (SEI) on the start-angle of the antenna relative to the stimulus position (RSI) is reestablished in intact animals, it vanishes after the operation (student's t-test, $P < 0.005$).

FIGURE 6

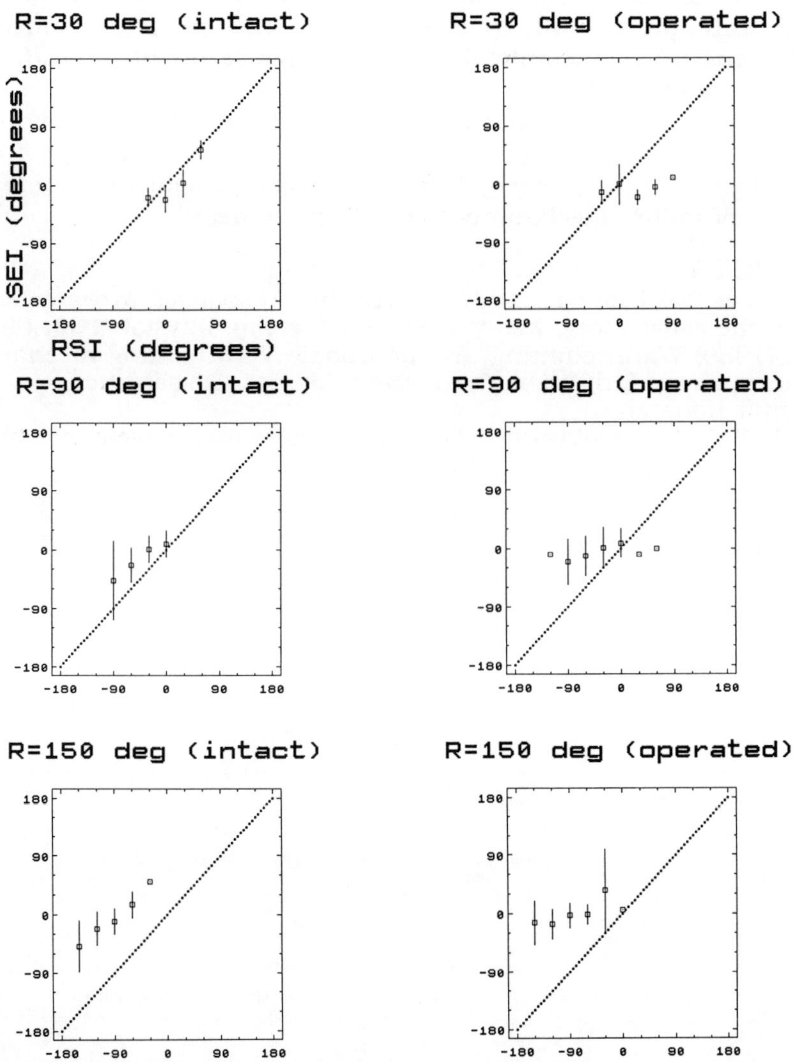

Thus, although the crayfish still show antennal sweeps in response to water vibration stimuli after the operation, the ability to distinguish between different stimulus angles is obviously lost after obstructing information of tailfan mechanoreceptors.

DISCUSSION

In general the ipsilateral crayfish antenna responds with backward sweeps to water vibration stimuli (Fig. 2). In this way the antenna, which is usually kept in a frontal position, in most cases approaches the stimulus.

As shown in Figure 4 and 5, the crayfish are able to distinguish between different stimulus directions. Merely for a stimulus position of 90° the ipsilateral antenna actually points towards the vibration source after sweeping. Thus, in intact animals sweeping per se might be sufficient for exact stimulus localization.

On the other hand as shown in Figure 6, the differential antennal response obviously depends on mechanosensory information from the tailfan. It will be the subject of further investigations to elucidate the contribution of tailfan mechanoreceptors in more detail.

REFERENCES

Elepfandt A. & Wiedemer L. (1987) Lateral-line responses to water surface waves in the clawed frog, *Xenopus laevis*. J. comp. Physiol. **160:** 667-682.

Hamm, I. (1989) Wahrnehmung und neuronale Verarbeitung mechanischer Reize im intakten Flußkrebs *Orconectes limosus*. Dissertation, Universität Konstanz.

Tautz, J. (1987) Water vibration elicits active antennal movements in the crayfish, *Orconectes limosus*. Anim. Behav. *35*: 748-754.

Frontiers in Crustacean Neurobiology
Advances in Life Sciences

CONTRALATERAL LEG COORDINATION: ANALYSIS OF CURVE WALKING IN CRAYFISH

Uwe Müller

Fakultät für Biologie, Universität Bielefeld, Postfach 8640, D-4800 Bielefeld 1, FRG

SUMMARY

A crayfish walked with the legs of each side on two separate motor-driven belts. Although the belts were driven with different speeds, the animal tried to synchronize the leg movements of both sides. The resulting effect can be described as relative coordination. The efficiency of coordination was strongly dependent on the ratio of frequencies between both sides. A model calculation is presented which is sufficient to describe the legs interactions.

INTRODUCTION

Walking can be described as a behaviour in which the legs of an animal perform oscillatory movements, switching between two well defined states: in forward walking, the power stroke is the time interval when the leg has substrate contact, supports the body and moves posteriorly. During the return stroke the leg is lifted, deloaded and moves anteriorly. The position where the leg switches from power to return stroke is called the posterior extreme position (PEP); the switch from return to power stroke occurs at the anterior extreme position (AEP).

The legs have to be synchronized in order to produce a coordinated movement. This is the task of coordinating mechanisms which supervise the leg's interactions. During stable walking their action is normally not observable, but it can be revealed when disturbances are applied experimentally. This method was used in the analysis of ipsilateral leg coordination in crayfish (Cruse & Müller, 1986). In these experiments the period of one leg's movement was prolonged experimentally. After removing the obstruction the phase relations between the manipulated leg and its adjacent legs were different from the undisturbed case. The adjacent legs reacted to this deviation from the normal phase angle within the next step. Two general mechanisms returned the legs to their stable state. Anterior legs showed an increase in period as a result of a reduction in the speed of the return stoke. Posterior legs, in contrast, showed a decrease in period which was caused by an advance of the switch from the return to the power stroke. This occurred before the normal AEP was reached. Both compensations were strongly phase dependent and led to a complete recovery of the normal phase relations for all legs within the following step cycle.

This method is useful when the eigenfrequencies of the oscillators are equal. For the analysis of coordinating influences between contralateral legs a second method was used. It relies on the possibility of inducing walks in which the legs on the two sides of the animal step with slightly different frequencies. With this method all possible phase relations can be generated in order to study the leg's reactions. This form of analysis will be presented here.

METHODS

A crayfish walked with the legs of each side on separate, motor-driven belts. The movements of all eight walking legs were recorded using the position electrodes described in Cruse & Müller (1984). Fig. 1 shows the movement traces of all legs.

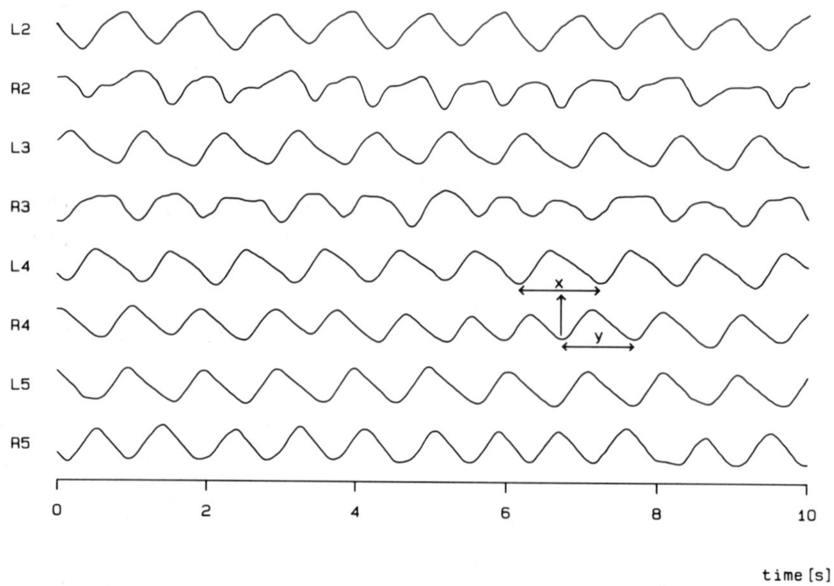

Fig. 1. Stepping pattern of legs 2-5 of the left (L) and right (R) side. The abscissa is time. Upward deflection indicates a return stroke, downward deflection a power stroke. The period (y) is defined as the time interval from the beginning of one return stroke to the next. The phase (x) is defined as the beginning of the return stroke of the measured leg, within the period of the reference leg. The ratio of belt speeds (left to right) is 0.95.

Slightly different belt speeds induced a shift in the phase relations between contralateral legs from one step to the next. Nevertheless, the animal tried to synchronize the leg movements of both sides in order to produce coordinated stepping. This was done by modulating the amplitude and period of the legs. For lack of space only the 4th and 5th leg pair are discussed here. The anterior leg pairs generally showed similar but more variable behaviour.

RESULTS

A standard method for investigating the influences of coupled oscillators is the evaluation of their phase response curves (PRC, Pavlidis 1973, Stein 1976). In a PRC the changes in the period of the measured oscillator are plotted against the phase with respect to a reference oscillator. This is shown for L4 versus R4 and vice versa in Fig. 2A,B. In both measurements all phase values are represented, but a preferred mean angle is apparent, as is visible in the frequency distributions shown in the histograms in Fig. 2C,D.

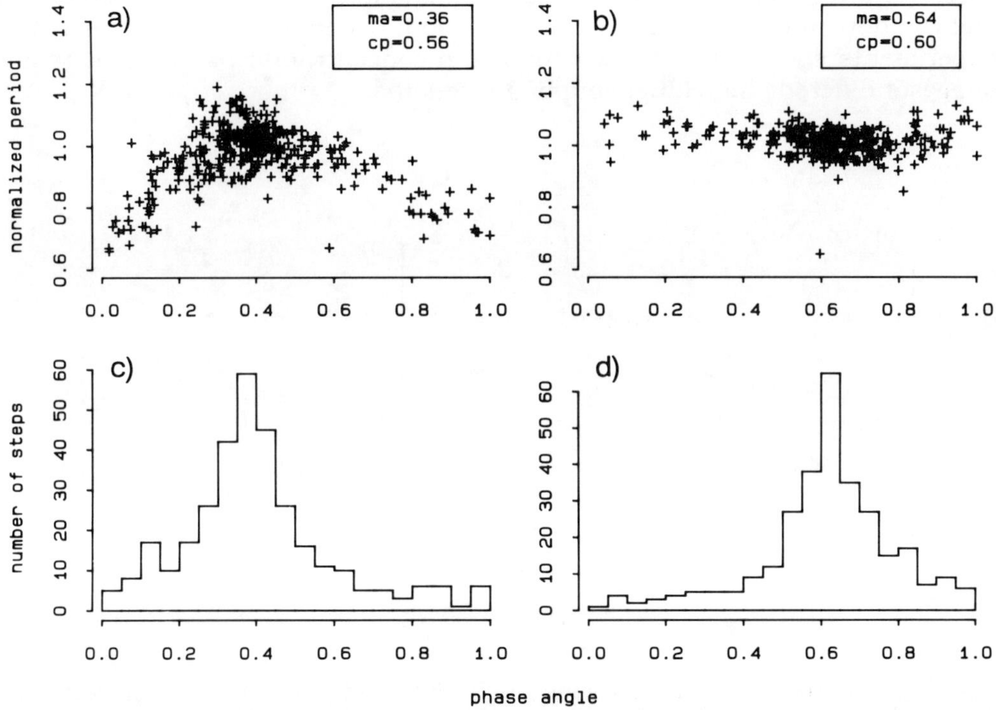

Fig. 2A-D. Phase response curves and phase histograms for contralateral legs (pair 4). The ordinate in (A,B) shows the normalized period of the measured leg as a function of the phase relation between the legs. The ordinate in (C,D) shows the number of steps per bin. Bin width is 0.05. The ratio of belt speeds left to right is 0.95. In (A,C) the right leg is measured and the left leg is the reference leg. In (B,D) the opposite case is drawn.

The values in Fig. 2A indicate that the period of the faster leg was decreased, when the phase was above or below 0.4. When the phase was near 0.4 the period did not differ from the mean period. This change led to a proper coordination, which is expressed by the density of the points (Fig. 2A). The leg of the slower side, in contrast, showed no deviation from the mean period for any phase (Fig. 2B). However this is an example of an extreme unidirectional influence. In most experiments similar influences acted in both directions, but with different strengthes. Qualitatively that side walking with the lower frequency is the more dominant one.

Fig. 3A,B is a comparison for the fifth leg pair of the results of 13 different experiments (circles). The abscissa in both cases is the ratio of the periods of the measured legs, produced by changing the speed ratio of the left and right belt. The ordinate in Fig. 3A shows the mean phase angle of the measured leg in the cycle of the reference leg. In Fig. 3B the corresponding concentration parameter is plotted. Both parameters are clearly dependent on the ratio of period. A comparison between the experiments shows large variations in the concentration parameters, which suggests different individual coupling strengths.

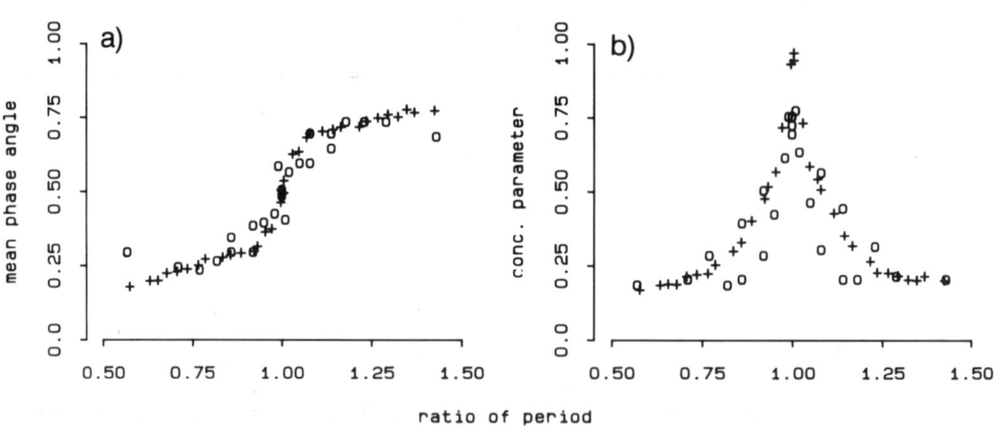

Fig. 3. Dependence of mean phase angles (A) and concentration parameters (B) on the ratio of period. Circles: experiments. Each value is an average of between 125 and 345 single observations. Crosses: model calculations (n = 250). Each speed ratio tested produces a point less than 1 at the given ratio and a second, with the other leg serving as the reference leg, above 1 at the inverse of the ratio. Mean phase angles and concentration parameters were determined using circular statistics (Batchelet 1982). All values were significant different from a random distribution (Rayleigh test, p <0.01).

DISCUSSION

Separate measurements of the durations of return and power stroke showed that the described compensation was produced by a spatial modulation of the AEP. This is illustrated in Fig. 4: the PRC of the reference leg is plotted as a spatial limitation on the AEP of the measured leg. Thus, depending on the phase both the return stroke and the power stroke of the influenced leg will be more or less shortened. Although steps of the measured leg started at very different phase angles within the period of the reference leg (as shown in the first step), they are concentrated at a phase angle around 0.4 within the next two steps. This leads to relative or gliding coordination, first described by von Holst (1943).

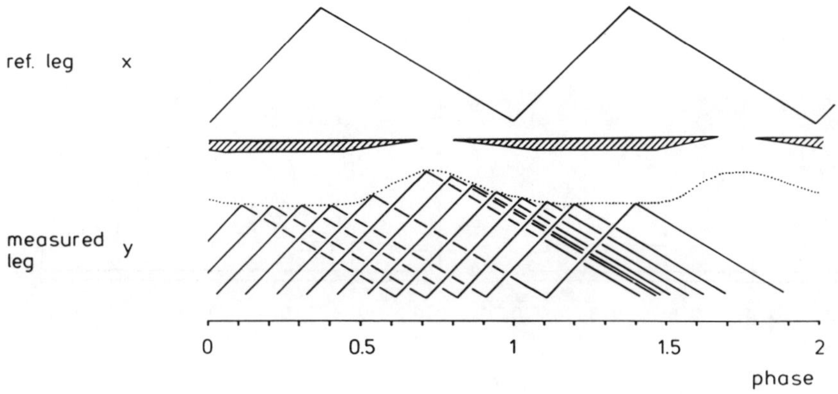

Fig. 4. Influence of a dominant oscillator (x) on a subdominant one (y). The hatched area indicates the time interval and strength of the influence, which can be calculated directly from the measured PRC's.

A model calculation was developed to investigate whether influences like the ones described are sufficient to guarantee a coordination between the contralateral legs. It consists of four coupled relaxation oscillators. The PRC's were generated as a function of the position of an influencing oscillator. They act on the AEP of a connected oscillator (as shown in Fig. 4) and are weighted with a coupling factor which determines the strength of coupling.

A simulation of a single experiment is presented in Fig. 5. The mean phase angles as well as the concentration parameters can be adjusted to the experimental results by varying either the coupling coefficients or the ratio of the eigenfrequencies of the oscillators. This is shown in a simulation of the experiments of Fig. 2A-D. Mean phase angles and concentration parameters were of the same order of magnitude as those of the experimental results.

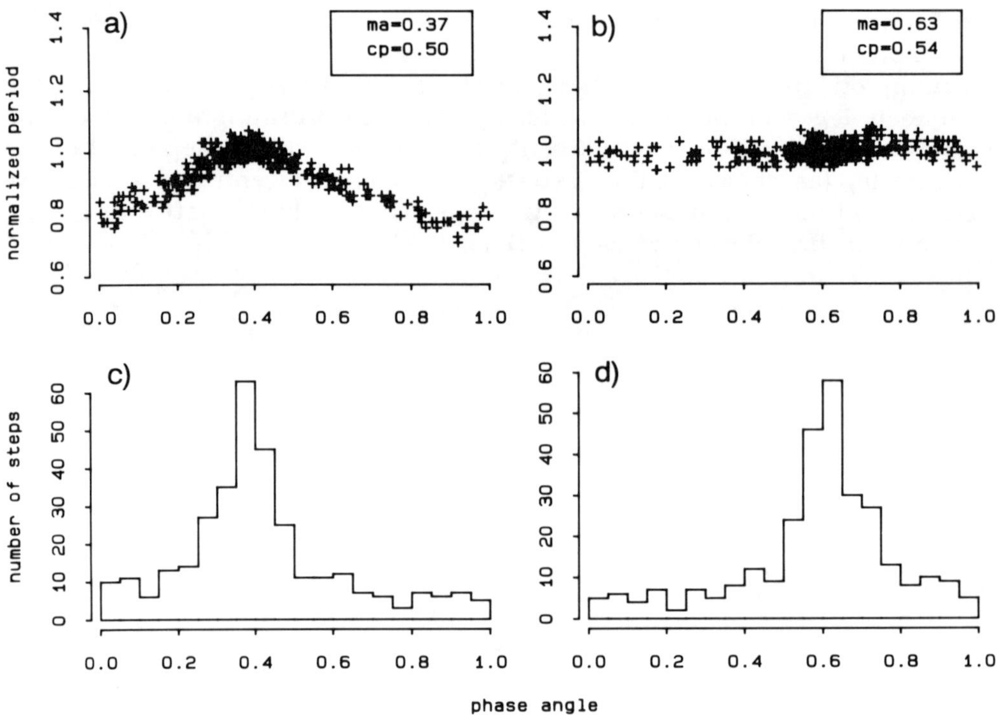

Fig. 5a-d. Phase response curves (a,b) and phase histograms (c,d) for the simulation of the experiment shown in Fig. 2. The ratio of the eigenfrequencies for the oscillators is 0.95. All other parameters correspond to those of Fig. 2.

Varying the ratio of eigenfrequencies of the oscillators in the model calculation led to very similar results than the experiments with different belt speeds, shown in Fig. 3 (squares). The coupling values were the same as used in the simulation shown in Fig. 5. In this case the measurements of the model calculations were of the same order of magnitude as the average experimental results. Experiments with lower concentration parameters can be simulated by diminishing the coupling values.

CONCLUSION

The major features appearing in contralateral leg coordination of crayfish can be explained by a simple, position dependent, mutual influence between adjacent contralateral legs. Further model calculations (Müller 1989), which for lack of space cannot be presented here, showed that the assumption of couplings between diagonal leg pairs is not necessary. The most parsimonious hypothesis is that one coordinating mechanism, very similar to that acting in the posterior direction between ipsilateral legs is sufficient for describing the experimental results.

This work was supported by DFG (CR 58/6-2)

REFERENCES

Cruse H. and Müller U. (1984) A new method measuring leg positionof walking crustaceans shows that motor output during return stroke depends upon load. J.exp.Biol. **110:** 319-322.

Cruse H. and Müller U. (1986) Two coupling mechanisms which determine the coordination of ipsilateral legs in the walking crayfish. J.exp.Biol. **121:** 349-369.

Holst E. von (1943) Über relative Koordination bei Arthropoden. Pflügers Archiv **246:** 874-865.

Müller U. (1989) Coordination of contralateral legs in walking ´crayfish. In Biological Motion, (ed. W. Alt & G. Hoffmann) in press. Berlin: Springer.

Pavlidis T. (1973) Biological Oscillators: Their Mathematical Analysis. New York: Academic Press.

Stein P.S.G. (1976) Mechanisms of interlimb phase control. In Neural Control of Locomotion, (ed. R.M. Herman, S. Grillner, P.S.G. Stein & D.G. Stuart) pp.465-487. New York: Plenum Press.

Frontiers in Crustacean Neurobiology
Advances in Life Sciences

PROPRIOCEPTIVE CONTROL OF CRAYFISH BASAL LEG MOTOR NEURONES: SYNAPTIC CONNECTIONS

Brian Bush and Peter Skorupski

Department of Physiology, University of Bristol, School of Veterinary Science, Park Row, Bristol BS1 5LS, U.K.

SUMMARY

The neural basis of phase-dependent modulation of reflexes mediated by the thoracic-coxal muscle receptor organ (TCMRO) and chordotonal organ (TCChO) of the basal joint of the 4th pereiopod (walking leg) of the crayfish, has been studied in an isolated thoracic nervous system preparation. Intracellular recording and current injection reveal that the T fibre, one of two nonspiking afferents of the stretch-sensitive TCMRO, makes monosynaptic excitatory connections with several motor neurons (MNs) of the leg promotor muscle and with at least one remotor MN (REM1). It also makes inhibitory connections, probably disynaptic, with promotor MNs and other ("type II") remotor MNs. The TCChO, which responds solely to strand release, excites type II remotor MNs and some promotor MNs but not others. Central postsynaptic inhibition is implicated in reflex modulation during spontaneous rhythmic activity.

INTRODUCTION

The single thoracic-coxal muscle receptor organ (TCMRO), which lies in parallel with the coxal promotor muscle at the base of each walking leg in crabs and crayfish, mediates a well defined stretch reflex in the promotor muscle (Bush, 1977, 1981; Bush & Cannone, 1985; Sillar & Skorupski, 1986). This "resistance reflex" tends to resist passive remotion (backward movement) of the leg at its thoracic-coxal joint. Under certain conditions this negative feedback reflex reverses in sign to reveal a positive feedback, "assistance reflex", in which the antagonistic remotor MNs are now excited by TCMRO stretch and promotor MNs are inhibited (DiCaprio & Clarac, 1981; Skorupski & Sillar, 1986).

The isolated thoracic ganglia of the crayfish can generate rhythmic motor activity involving strictly alternating bursts of impulses in promotor and remotor MNs (Sillar & Skorupski, 1986). In the course of this motor output the reflex effect of stretching the TCMRO varies in a phase dependent way (Skorupski & Sillar, 1986). During the remotor phase of the rhythm promotor MNs are inhibited and remotor MNs excited by TCMRO stretch, whilst the reverse occurs during the promotor phase.

The synaptic connections underlying this phase-dependent reversal of reflexes have been studied in the isolated thoracic nervous system. This study has revealed the presence of two distinct functional groups of remotor MNs, and possibly also two different promotor MN groups. The sensori-motor system is further complicated by the presence of a chordotonal organ (TCChO) which lies alongside the TCMRO but responds only to release of the receptor strand, i.e. during promotion at the T-C joint. The reflex effects of the TCChO are also considered here.

METHODS

An isolated thoracic nervous system preparation of the crayfish, *Pacifastacus leniusculus* (Sillar & Skorupski, 1986), was used. This comprised the 3rd, 4th and 5th pereiopod ganglia, together with the TCMRO and TCChO connected to the 4th ganglion by their sensory nerves; the motor innervation of the TCMRO was cut. Both receptor strands, still attached proximally to their common receptor rod, were hooked at their distal ends to a puller device and stimulated mechanically by constant velocity (1-10 mm.s-1) stretch-hold-release length changes (0.5-1.0 mm). Glass micropipettes filled with 2M KAc or Lucifer yellow in 1M LiCl were used to record from and inject current into the selected neurons. Extracellular suction electrodes simultaneously recorded impulse activity in the cut nerve roots of the promotor and remotor muscles. Motor neurons were identified by 1:1 correlation of the intracellularly and extracellularly recorded spikes.

RESULTS

Several promotor MNs and at least one remotor MN ("REM1") show depolarizing responses to stretching the TCMRO/TCChO complex (Figs. 1A,B; 2A). The amplitude of these responses varies directly with the velocity and amplitude of stretch, and also with the prevailing level of excitability of the preparation (as reflected in the motor activity recorded extracellularly), more quiescent states favouring promotor MN responses. More importantly in the present context, the response of each motor neuron varies in a systematic way with the phase of any ongoing rhythmic motor output. During the promotor active phase, when several promotor MNs discharge strongly, the intracellularly recorded promotor MN depolarizes on receptor stretch, but during the reciprocal phase when remotor MNs are active, the promotor MN shows a delayed hyperpolarization following a small transient depolarization (Fig.1A). In contrast, REM1 depolarizes strongly during the active remotor phase of the rhythm, but its response on stretch is greatly reduced - not in this case reversed - during the reciprocal, promotor phase (Fig.1B). A constant current negative pulse injected into REM1 just before each stretch shows that MN conductance is increased in the reciprocal phase

This suggests that some form of chemical synaptic input of central origin during this phase could account for the reduced response.

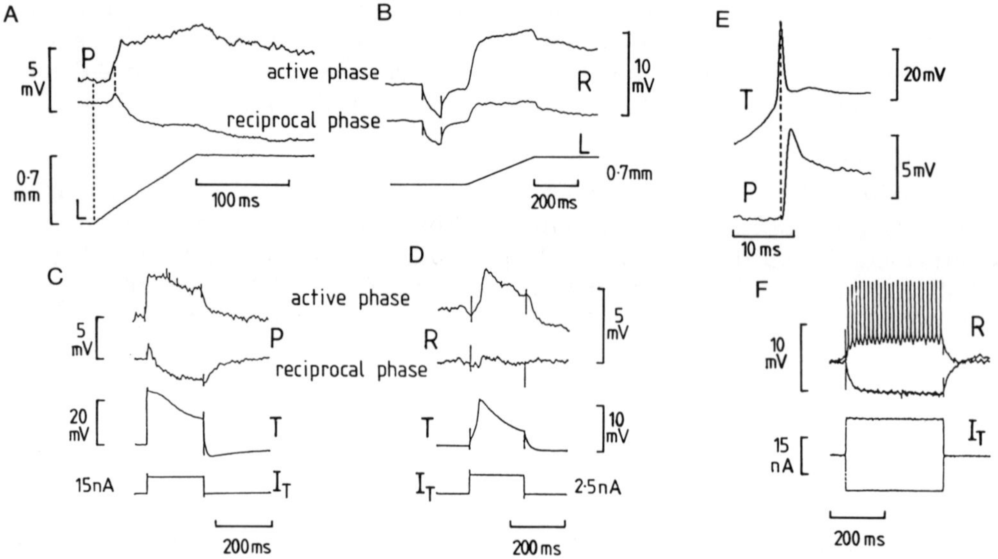

Fig.1. Intracellularly recorded reflex responses of promotor MNs (P in A,C,E) and the remotor MN, REM1 (R in B,D,F) to TCMRO stretch (L in A,B: stretch upwards) and T fibre depolarization (T in C-E) by current injection (IT). A-D, Phase-dependent variation of MN responses during spontaneous rhythmic motor activity: top traces - active phases, 2nd traces - reciprocal phases; initial membrane potential -60 to -65mV in the reciprocal phases, 10-15 mV more depolarized in the active phases; each trace is the average response of 7 to 23 stimulus repetitions; in B, a 1nA negative pulse is injected into REM1 just before the stretch. E, a spike-like transient in the T fibre (elicited by a current pulse, not shown) gives an estimate for the synaptic latency of the promotor MN response of 1.7ms. F, 2mM cadmium in the superfusate does not block synaptic transmission from the T fibre to REM1: both depolarizing and hyperpolarizing pulses evoke postsynaptic responses; the former causes impulse discharge. (Adapted from Skorupski, 1990, and in preparation).

Synaptic connections underlying reflex reversal. Simultaneous intracellular recordings from the T fibre and motor neurons show that the T fibre alone can mediate both the normal and the reversed reflex. If, instead of mechanical stimulation of the TCMRO, the T fibre is stimulated directly with depolarizing current during rhythmic motor output, promotor MNs are excited during their active phase, but mainly inhibited during the reciprocal phase of remotor activity (Fig.1C). Closer examination of the reciprocal phase response shows it to be biphasic: promotor MNs are transiently depolarized at short latency,following T fibre stimulation, before the onset of the hyperpolarizing response. The latency to the initial depolarization in both active and reciprocal phases is the same, and is short enough (1.5 2.0 ms from the onset of the current pulse; see also Fig.1E) to suggest a direct, monosynaptic excitatory connection (allowing for electrotonic delays and the large time constant of the nonspiking T fibre). The inhibition of the reciprocal phase occurs 6 30 ms later (depending on the amplitude of the current pulse). This suggests that the T fibre directly excites promotor MNs, but that during the remotor phase of rhythmic motor activity this excitation is shunted out by a parallel inhibitory reflex pathway, which must be at least disynaptic to allow for the increased delay (see Skorupski, 1990 [and in preparation] for detailed evidence concerning synaptic delays).

At least one remotor MN, REM1, is excited by T fibre depolarization during the active remotor phase, but this excitation is absent or much reduced during the reciprocal (promotor) phase (Fig.1D). The latency of this response suggests that, like promotor MNs, these remotor MNs are also directly excited by the T fibre. These connections are at least partly electrical, since they are not blocked by 2mM cadmium (Fig.1F). The phase dependence of this remotor response could, as implied above, be accounted for by centrally originating postsynaptic inhibition of remotor MNs during the promotor phase of the rhythm, which could shunt out the T fibre input (cf. Fig.1B).

Reflex effect of the TCChO. The TCChO consists of about 30 bipolar neurons with conventional spiking afferents that respond to release of their receptor strand, i.e. in the opposite direction to the TCMRO. In contrast to the remotor MN considered above (REM1), some remotor MNs are excited on release in a classical resistance reflex (Fig.2A). Intracellular recordings from such MNs during rhythmic motor output show that this reflex too is phase dependent, although a reversal does not occur (Fig.2B). The amplitude of the reflex response is again correlated with phase dependent changes in motor neuron conductance during rhythmic activity, further supporting the notion of central postsynaptic inhibition as a mechanism for regulating these reflexes.

Subclasses of remotor MNs. From the foregoing evidence it seems that remotor MNs can be classified into two groups on the basis of their reflex responses to stimulation of the two receptor organs (see Fig. 3). Those that are excited by the T fibre, exemplified by REM1, receive no evident

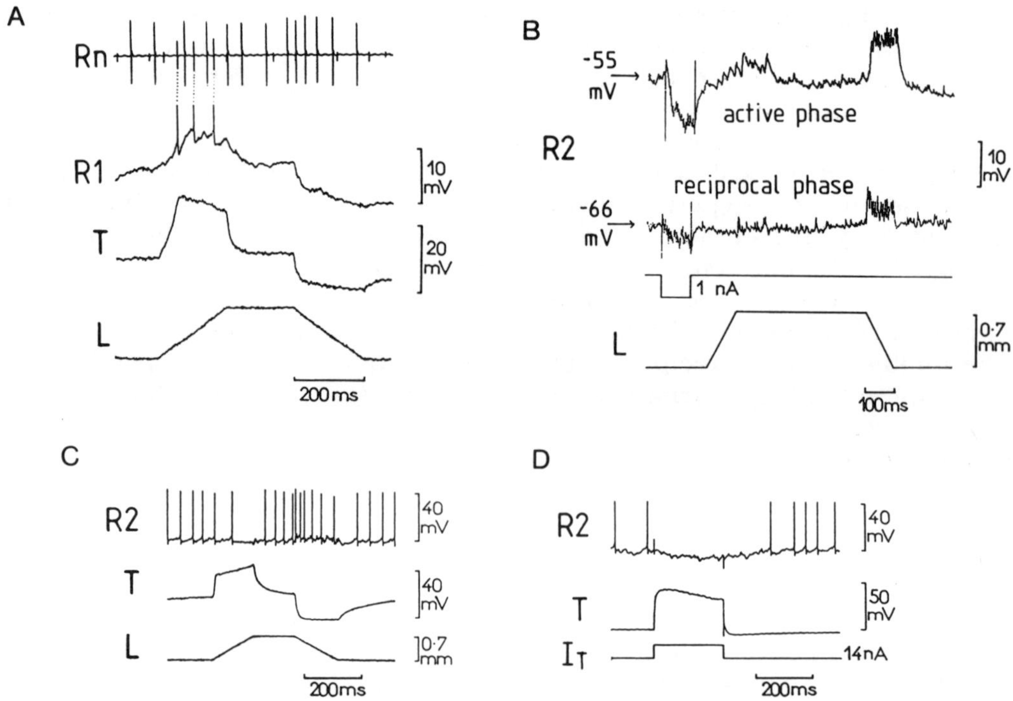

Fig. 2. Two types of remotor MN with different TC afferent inputs. A. Intracellular recording from a REM1 MN (R1) and the T fibre (T), with simultaneous extracellular recording from the remotor nerve (Rn), during a stretch-release stimulus of the TCMRO and TCChO together (L, stretch upwards). REM1 receives excitatory input during stretch only (ie. T fibre mediated), eliciting 3 spikes (Rn and R1), while another, extracellularly recorded remotor MN increases its firing rate during strand release (ie. TCChO mediated). B. A "type II" remotor MN (R2) receives TCChO input on strand release which evokes larger compound EPSPs during the active remotor phase of the spontaneous ongoing motor rhythm than during the reciprocal phase; note the different initial membrane potentials in the two phases. The MN input resistance falls during the reciprocal phase (smaller response to a -1nA current pulse injected via the recording electrode). C, D: Simultaneous intra-cellular recordings from a type II remotor MN (R2) and the T fibre (T) during combined TCMRO and TCChO stimulation (L), and during current induced depolarization of the T fibre (IT), show inhibition mediated by the T fibre in both C and D and excitation by TCChO release in C.

excitation on release of the TCChO strand (Fig.2A). Those excited by the TCChO, on the other hand, are generally not excited on stretch (Fig.2C);

there is in fact some evidence that this class of remotor MN ("type II") is inhibited by the T fibre (Fig.2D). There may also be some remotor MNs excited by both receptors.

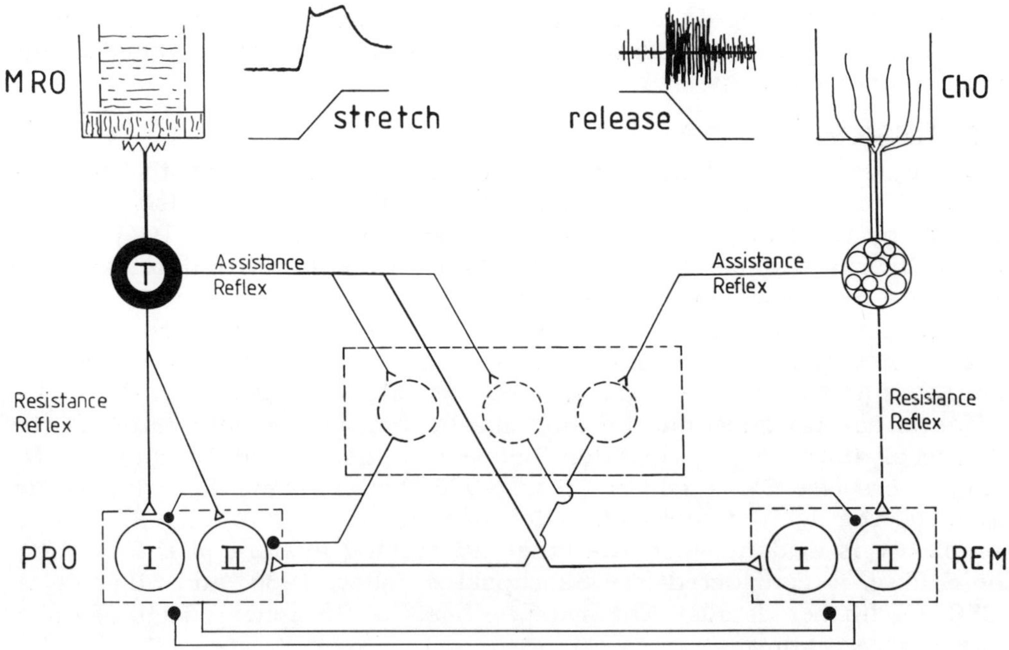

Fig. 3. Provisional representation of the reflex connections from the TC-MRO and TC-ChO to promotor (PRO) and remotor (REM) motor neurons. Solid lines indicate known connections; broken lines indicate neuronal elements for which there is as yet no direct evidence. Open triangles represent excitatory synapses (at least partly electrical in the case of the T fibre outputs); closed circles represent inhibitory synapses. Reciprocal inhibitory connections between the PRO and REM MN pools are indicated, although evidence for these is not considered here. The other non-spiking afferent of the TCMRO, the S fibre, is not shown.

Subclasses of promotor MNs. Reflex input to promotor MNs from the TCMRO is also not homogeneous, but we have not yet worked this out in detail. Some, but not all, promotor MNs are excited on release by the TCChO; this reflex is more labile than the TCChO to remotor MN reflex.

This suggests that promotor MNs may also be classifiable into two functional groups on the basis of different proprioceptive inputs.

However the distinction is not nearly as clearcut as that between the two remotor MN groups, and both promotor MN groups are excited by the TCMRO, to a greater or lesser extent. Furthermore, as with the remotor MNs, all these promotor reflexes vary in a phase-dependent manner during rhythmic motor activity.

DISCUSSION

Our current view of the synaptic connections underlying the reflexes mediated in motor neurons innervating the two basal leg muscles of the crayfish by the two thoracic-coxal proprioceptor organs, the TCMRO and the TCChO, is summarised in Fig. 3. Both the resistance reflexes and the assistance reflexes considered here can be accounted for by quite

simple individual reflex pathways which, when incorporated into one system, provide for the remarkable versatility of what might at first sight be thought of as a more or less "hard-wired" neural mechanism.

One of several questions needing clarification is the importance of the reciprocal inhibitory connection between remotor and promotor MNs shown here (see Skorupski & Sillar, 1988, for experimental evidence) in providing the delayed reflex inhibition of promotor MNs observed. Further complexity is evident when the other nonspiking afferent of the TCMRO, the S fibre, is considered (see Skorupski & Sillar, 1986, and Sillar et al, 1986, for further details). The synaptic basis of the reflex effects of the S fibre is not yet known.

It could be that the operational subdivision of both promotor and remotor MNs described here on the basis of responses recorded in the isolated preparation reflects a functional division of motor neuron task groups. Some MNs may be wired to receive predominantly positive feedback, others so as to receive predominantly negative feedback. Such task groups could be selectively used in different postural and locomotory contexts. A parallel distinction between positive and negative feedback to different motor neurons of the same muscle is seen in the dual motor innervation of the TCMRO in the crab (Bush & Cannone, 1985), a sub-system yet to be investigated in the crayfish.

REFERENCES

Bush, B.M.H. (1977) Nonimpulsive afferent coding and stretch reflexes in crabs. In Identified Neurons and Behavior of Arthropods (ed. G. Hoyle) pp. 439-460. New York: Plenum Press.

Bush, B.M.H. (1981) Non-impulsive stretch receptors in crustaceans. In Neurones without Impulses (ed. A. Roberts & B.M.H.Bush) pp. 147- 176. Cambridge: Cambridge University Press.
Bush, B.M.H. & Cannone, A.J. (1985) How do crabs control their muscle receptors? In Feedback and Motor Control in Invertebrates and Vertebrates (ed. W.J.P. Barnes & M.H. Gladden) pp. 145-166. London: Croom Helm.
DiCaprio, R.A. & Clarac, F. (1981) Reversal of a walking leg reflex elicited by a muscle receptor. J.exp.Biol. **90:** 197-203.
Sillar, K.T. & Skorupski, P. (1986) Central input to primary afferent neurons in crayfish, *Pacifastacus leniusculus,* is correlated with rhythmic motor output of thoracic ganglia. J.Neurophysiol.**55:**678-688
Sillar, K.T., Skorupski, P., Elson, R.C. & Bush, B.M.H. (1986) Two identified afferent neurones entrain a central locomotor rhythm generator. Nature, **323**: 440-443.
Skorupski, P. (1990) Synaptic connections underlying phase-dependent reflexes in crayfish. In Neural and Sensory Mechanisms in Locomotion (ed. D.M.Armstrong & B.M.H.Bush). Manchester University Press.
Skorupski, P. & Sillar, K.T. (1986) Phase-dependent reversal of reflexes mediated by the thoracocoxal muscle receptor organ in the crayfish, Pacificastacus leniusculus. J.Neurophysiol. **55**: 689-695.
Skorupski, P. & Sillar, K.T. (1988) Central synaptic coupling of walking leg motor neurones in the crayfish: implications for sensorimotor integration. J.exp.Biol. **140:** 355-379.

Frontiers in Crustacean Neurobiology
Advances in Life Sciences

PROPRIOCEPTION FROM CHORDOTONAL ORGANS IN CRUSTACEAN LIMBS

François Clarac

Laboratoire de Neurosciences Fonctionnelles - CNRS - 31, chemin Joseph Aiguier - 13402 Marseille Cedex 9 - France.

SUMMARY

Chordotonal organs are leg joint mechanoreceptors. They are composed by a various number of bipolar sensory cells grouped by pairs in scolopidia which are inserted on a moving strand. Their physiological properties are briefly summarized and a new in vitro CB chordotonal preparation is presented.

INTRODUCTION

The first anatomical description of a limb chordotonal organ in the Crustacea was done by Barth (1934). However the Barth' organ is now considered to be a neuromuscular structure the myochordotonal organ. Twenty years later Burke (1954) and Wiersma (1959) ; Wiersma and Boettiger (1959) gave physiological data about chordotonal organs. Following these pioneering works, numerous studies both on their ultrastructures and their functions have been published and summarized in Mill (1976). More recently, isolated nervous preparations have opened a new field of physiological researches, e.g. on the sensory integration of chordotonal activities within the central nervous system during motor activity.

Each chordotonal organ consists of an innervated elastic strand (or sheet) which usually spans a leg joint; the strand is composed of an external layer of amorphous connective tissue whereas the inner layer consists of strand cells, collagen and dendrites of the sensory cells (20-80). The dendrites of the bipolar sensory cells are embedded by pair in a complex sensilla called a scolopidium. Each receptor is labelled according to the joint where it is located: e.g. at the the pro-dactylopodite (P-D) joint, the chordotonal is named the P-D chordotonal organ (Fig. 1A). In this report we would like to demonstrate how a chordotonal organ is a good physiological preparation for students and to give after a survey of the physiological properties of these sense organs, the main lines of the present research (fig. 1A).

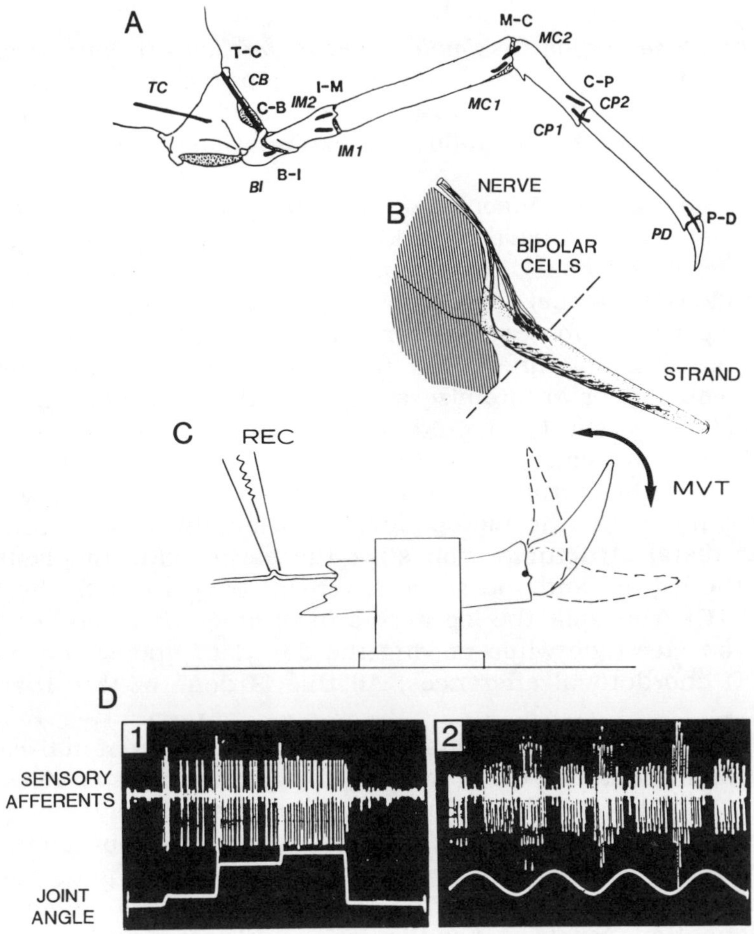

Fig. 1 : Chordotonal organ in Crustacean limb :
A - General organization of a crayfish leg with the different joints and the chordotonal organs : (the thoraco-coxopodite (T-C), the coxo-basipodite (C-B), the basi-ischiopodite (B-I), the ischio-meropodite (I-M), the mero-carpopodite (M-C), the carpo-propodite (C-P) and the pro-dactylopodite (P-D)) and the chordotonal organs for each joint (TC, CB, BI, IM1, IM2, MC1, MC2, CP1, CP2, PD).
B - Drawing of the crayfish PD chordotonal organ stained with methylene blue.
C - Simple dispositive to record the PD sensory afferences (see : sensory recording)
D - Recordings of sensory nerve bundles containing position units (1) and movement units (2).

I -The P-D chordotonal organ, a simple example for sensory basic studies

During student training course held in the Neurobiology Laboratory in Arcachon, the PD chordotonal organ was used for basic sensory neurophysiological studies; the following explanations are given like a simple recipe:

- You need a crab (Carcinus maenas, or any other one !) if you are near the sea, or a crayfish (Procambarus clarkii, or Astacus leptodactylus, or Pascifastacus leniusculus...), a simple electrophysiological set up (preamplifier and oscilloscope), and a dish with sea water or appropriate saline. For the experiment you use only one out of the eight walking legs. To record the PD chordotonal afferences following Wiersma and Boettiger (1959) technic, you cut or autotomize a leg near the C-B joint, then you severe the apodemes of the flexor and the extensor muscles (at the M-C joint) and by lateral movements you break the M-C joint condyles. Very gently you pull apart the meropodite from the distal part of the leg you are left with the leg nerves in the meropodite free from the tissues and still attached to the distal structures. You stick the carpopodite in plasticine, ventral side of the leg up, and you set a movement transducer to the tip of the dactyl (Fig. 1C). You split the leg nerves in bundles that you record in turn by a succion electrode while moving the dactyl to find which bundle contains the PD chordotonal afferences. All this is done in less thant 10 minutes.

The four physiological types of sensory units of the chordotonal can be shown. 1) Movement sensitive units respond to either stretch or release of the strand (Fig. 1D2); Mill (1976) named them respectively elongation sensitive movement cells -ESMCs- and relaxation sensitive movement cells - RSMCs. 2) Position units discharge only around a certain joint position either in aperture or in closure (Fig. 1D1) ; Mill (1976) called them respectively elongation sensitive position cells - ESPCs - and relaxation sensitive position cells - RSPCs. The discharge of these units are not modulated by passive movements and most of them are activated only for the extreme positions of the joint.

Students can also dissect the PD chordotonal organ of another leg and stain it with methylene blue. Two groups of bipolar cells can be visualized (Fig. 1B), the proximal one contains large cells which are movement units whereas the distal group which is composed by small cells are quite exclusively position units.

II- Summary of the physiological properties of the leg chrodotonal organs

All the data known can be summarized as following :

1) Comparison between the different chordotonals: In a leg, each joint has one chordotonal organ except M-C and C-P joints with two. In the four groups of decapods, Astacuran, Palinuran, Anomuran and Brachyuran, sligh

anatomical differences exist. The TC chordotonal organ is present only in Astacuran. The basi-ischio-meropodite region is quite complex. A true B-I joint is present only in Homarus and Astacus and have one chordotonal organs which have disappeared in the other groups as the B-I joint is no more functional. However in this region, two sensory structures, the cuticular stress detectors (CSD1, CSD2)) record the exoskeletton deformations and have scolopidia associated with the cuticle. The I-M joint has a large angular excursion in Homarus and Astacus and have two chordotonal organs whereas in the other animals the anterior IM is linked with the myochordotonal organ which detects the M-C joint movements.

Every chordotonal organ has both movement units (ESMCs and RSMCs) and position units(ESPCs and RSPCs) ; however in the MC2, CP2, IM and BI chordotonal organs when it is present, sensory units respond only to the release of the strand.

2) Transduction: comparing the results obtained in ultrastructure (Whitear, 1962) and in physiology (Mill & Lowe, 1973), Mill (1976) drew the following conclusions :

a) Dendrites in the scolopidia are all sensitive to stretch but their stimulation depends upon their insertion in the strand : the ESMC sclopidia are firmly attached to the inner layer of the strand, and respond to any elongation of the support which stretch the dendrites ; on the other hand the dendrites in the RSMC scolopidia are stretched when the strand is released.

b) The difference between position and movement units seem to be due to a difference in the support composition.

c) Within a scolopidia, dendrites are paired, Hartman & Boettiger (1967) studying the PD chordotonal suggest that both cells of scolopidia respond to the same direction of stretch but with different sensitivity.

3) Are chordotonal organ also tension receptors? This question was really not clear in the literature. Specific tension receptors exist but are very close to the location of the chordotonal receptors.

Indeed, MacMillan & Dando (1972) in the crab, described sensory nerves to muscle apodemes which specificaly record the muscular tension. In the crab callinectes, Hartman (1985) demonstrated that the the PD chordotonal nerve contains a specific afferent nerve to the closer apodeme (closer apodeme sensory nerve CASN) which records exclusively the closer tension. Furthermore this is not a unique case within the legs in which several muscle apodemes have been shown to be innervated. So when the chordotonal is close to an apodeme, it is difficult to clearly distinguish the sensory informations between the chordotonal and the muscular apodeme tension receptors. Thus chordotonal organs seems to be exclusively articular receptor and the muscular tension is recorded by the apodeme receptor and also through the cuticule by either the CSDs and/or by the funnel canal organs which are particularly abundant in the dactyl (see Libersat, Zill & Clarac, 1987).

4) Reflexes: in intact as in dissected preparations, stimulation of a chordotonal organ induce a reflex response in the muscle which has been passively stretch by joint stimulation. Such resistance reflexes (Bush, 1962) can be for each chordotonal organ but it can be also modulated by the apodeme tension receptors (Clarac & Dando, 1973). However a reflex response is simultaneously recorded in all the other leg muscles, e.g. the CB chordotonal organ is able to modulate the muscle responses of the all leg muscles but its action is more powerful on the T-C and the M-C muscles (Clarac et al., 1978).

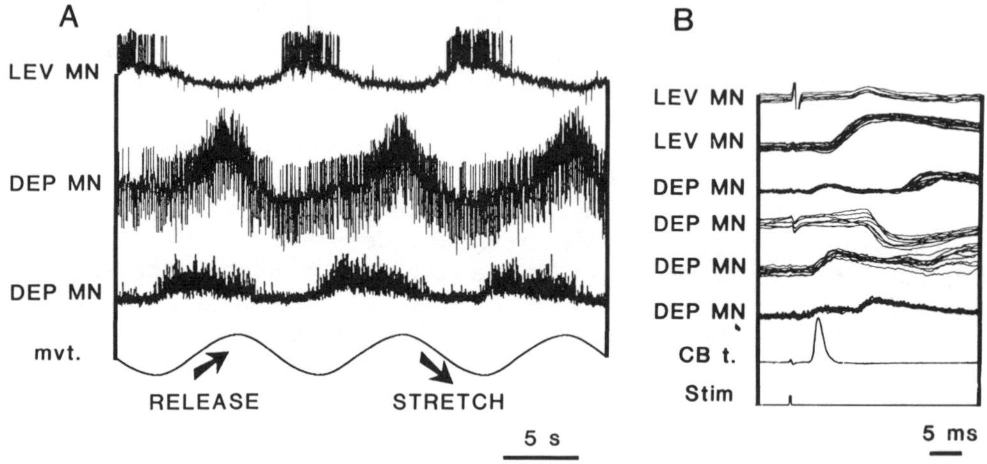

Fig. 2: Reflex responses of levator and depressor MNs to a mechanical CB strand stimulation (A) or to an electrical CB nerve stimulation. A) passive stretching or releasing induces a resistance reflex in the MNs. B) An electrical stimulation of the CB nerve elicits an action potential in a single CB terminal (CBt) and either an EPSP or an IPSP in different levator (LEV) or depressor (DEP) motoneurones (MNs).

A careful study, nevertheless, demonstrate that the reflex response is very variable and depends mostly upon the central "state" of the animal. As it was demonstrated by Bässler (1976), stimulating the femuro-tibial chordotonal organ in the stick insect, the resistance reflex can be switched to an assitant reflex also in the crustacean walking leg.

Most of the data presented here were obtained on fixed animals, partly dissected. To decipher the intracellular nervous organisation, a new in vitro preparation has been performed in which the thoracic ganglia have been isolated along with one given proprioceptor (Sillar & Skorupski, 1986).

III- New findings on the CB chordotonal organ

We have developed an in vitro preparation with the 4th and 5th ganglion desheathed in Procambarus clarkii in which the CB chordotonal organ is intact in such a way it can be stimulated either mechanically by stretching or releasing its strand or electrically at the level of its sensory nerve. Intracellular recordings of the leg nerve motoneurones (MNs) and of the interneurones are done routinely . In these preparations intracellularly recordings of the CB terminals are possible and mechanical stimulations of the CB strand allow to characterize the different sensory units by their physiological responses. However often superimposed EPSP of large duration (20 to 50 msec) and of very variable amplitude (until 10-15 mv) are recorded with the sensory responses (Fig. 3A).

In in vitro preparations, the motoneurone activity can be in 2 states: most of the time, a tonic motor activity is recorded in the different motor nerves but when oxotremorine (10^{-5}M) is added to the bath, a slow rhythmic activity (around 20 sec or 40 sec the period) is elicited in the motor nerves. We have systematically studied the reflex responses of the levator and depressor MNs to both mechanical or electrical stimulations of the CB afferences. In highly active tonic preparations, the reflex elicited always corresponds to a resistance reflex eventhough its intensity can be variable : a release of the strand which mimicks an elevation, facilitates the depressor MNs whereas a stretch of the strand facilitates the levator MNs. The MN response is variable and depends upon the central drive (fig. 2A). Some MN shows spikes while other only displays EPSPs other presents very large EPSP from unknown origin which are modulated by the CB stimulations. The different reflex pathways to the MNs can be analysed by electrical stimulation of the CB nerve (Fig. 2B): several types of responses in the depressor and in the levator MNs are obtained and correspond to simple EPSPs or IPSPs or to a more complex response with several events. When a CB terminal is recorded simultaneously with the motor nerves, response occurs with a delay around 4 ms, which corresponds to the time necessary for conduction from the receptor to the ganglion ; this first EPSP in the MN is a monosynaptic response and this has been demonstrated by classical tests (high Ca^{++} ; O Ca^{++}; high stimulation frequency; Cattaert & El Manira, unpublished). However, in the more complex responses, the first electrical event is followed by late responses which suggest the presence of complementary polysynaptic pathways as they disappear when a high concentration of Ca^{++} and Mg^{++} is applied.

In rhythmic preparations the resistance reflex can reverse to an assistance reflex. But sometimes the CB stimulations seem unuable to change the ongoing motor activites although they can speed up or slow down the central rhythm demonstrating that the CB afferences are able to act directly to the locomotory generator.

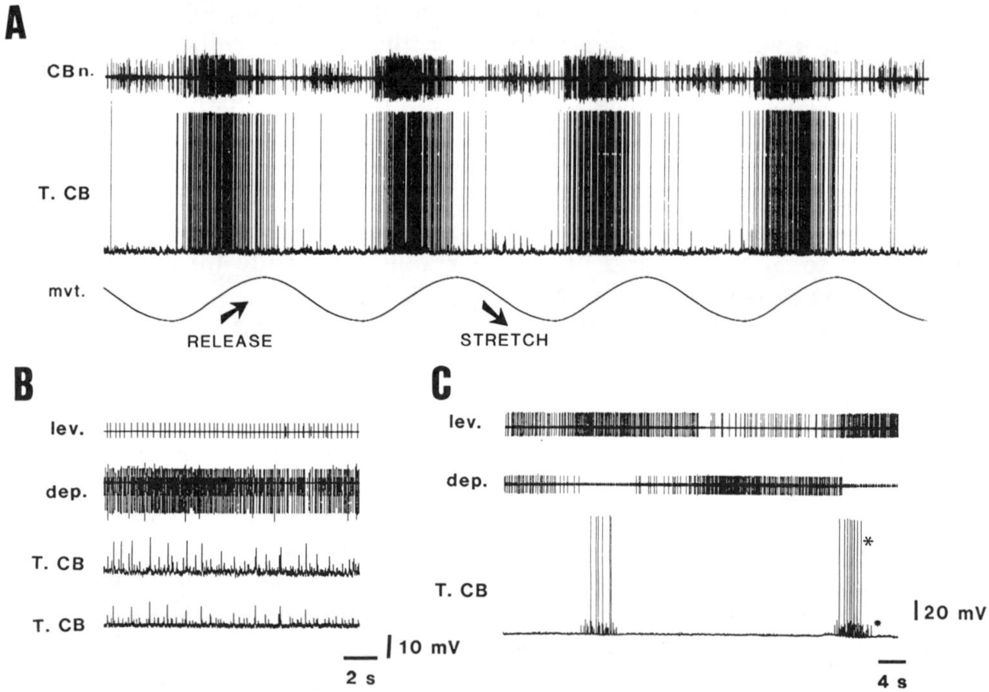

Fig. 3 : PADs in the CB terminals. A) Intracellular recording of a single CB terminal (T.CB) during a CB mechanical stimulation (mvt) and extracellular CB nerve (CB.n) activity. B) In an in vitro preparation characterised by a tonic discharge in the levator and depressor nerve, both CB terminals recorded present continuous and mostly common PADs. C) When the preparation becomes rhythmic, the EPSPs in the terminals occur also rhythmically and even produce antidromic spikes.

The great variability in the CB reflex responses in in vitro preparation confirms that was observed in chronic experiments. These variabilities in the reflex responses have to be searched at the interneuronal level and some may have been described by Chrachri & Clarac (in press). However recently another type of modulation has been demonstrated at the level of the CB terminals themselves (fig. 3). In these terminals the large EPSP recorded can be considered as primary afferent depolarization PAD (Kirk, 1985). They seem to have a common central origin since 2 terminals recorded from different locations in the neuropile could received highly correlated PADs (Fig. 3B). Moreover in rhythmic preparations the PADs discharge in bursts associated with the rhythm (fig. 3C) and in these cases antidromic action potentials induced by the PADs have been recorded in the CB nerve. To demonstrate that the PADs correspond really to a presynaptic inhibition, the CB nerve was stimulated in order to evoke a spike recorded intracellularly in the fibre terminal ; the analyse of the spike variations shows a directly correlation between the reduction of the spike amplitude and the membrane potential of the CB terminal. The reduction in amplitude of the spikes coming from the CB by the PAD are likely to be due to an increase in the membrane conductance of the terminal and should result in an inhibition of the spike transmission (Cattaert et al., in press).

This peripheral modulation of sensory afferences seems to be a very common phenomenon; it has been described in Crustacean (Kirk, 1985 ; Sillar & Skorupski, 1986 ; and Bush in this volume) but it is also present in mammals (see Dubuc et al., 1988) and seems often to be linked to fictive locomotion.

In conclusion the possibility of intracellular studies of the different central components when chordotonal afferences interact with the central motor activities open a wide field for new types of experiments which might answered many questions about the functions of these proprioceptors.

REFERENCES

Barth, G. (1934) Untersuchungen über Myochordotonalorgane bei dekapoden Crustaceen. Zeitsch. wiss. Zool. **145:** 576-624.

Bässler, U. (1976) Reversal of a reflex to a single motoneuron in the stick Insect *Carausius morosus*. Biol. Cybernetics **24:**47-49.

Burke, W. (1954) An organ for proprioception and vibration sense in Carcinus maenas. J. Exp. Biol. **31:**127-137.

Bush, B.M.H. (1962) Proprioceptive reflexes in the legs of *Carcinus maenas* (L.). J. Exp. Biol. **39**:89-105.

Cattaert, D., El Manira, A., Marchand, A. & Clarac, F. Central control of the sensory afferent terminals from a leg chordotonal organ in crayfish in vitro preparation. Neurosc. Let. (in press).

Chrachri, A. & Clarac, F. (1987) Induction of rhythmic activity in motoneurons of crayfish thoracic ganglia by cholinergic agonists. Neurosc. Lett. **77:**49-54.

Chrachri, A. & Clarac, F. Synaptic connections between motor neurons and interneurons. J. Neurophysiol. (in press).

Clarac, F. & Dando, M.R. (1973) Tension receptor reflexes in the walking legs of the crab *Cancer pagurus*. Nature **24**3:94-95.

Clarac, F., Vedel, J.P. & Bush, B.M.H. (1978) Intersegmental reflex coordination by a single joint receptor organ (CB) in rock lobster walking legs. J. Exp. Biol. **73** :29-46.

Dubuc, R., Cabelguen, J.M. & Rossignol, S. (1988) Fluctuations of dorsal root potential and antidromic discharges of primary afferents during fictive locomotion in the cat. J. Neurophysiol. **60:**2014-2036.

Hartman, H.B. (1985) Tension receptors on the closer muscle apoderm in the walking legs of the blue crab, *Callinectes sapidus*. J. Comp. Physiol. **157:**355-362.

Hartman, H.B. & Boettiger, E.G. (1967) The functional organization of the propus-dactylus organ in *Cancer irroratus* say. Comp. Biochem. Physiol., **22**:651-663.

Kirk, M.D. (1985) Presynaptic inhibition in the crayfish CNS : pathways and synaptic mechanisms. J. Neurophysiol. **54**(5):1305-1325.

Libersat, F., Zill, S. & Clarac, F. (1987) Single unit responses and reflex effects of force sensitive mechanoreceptors of the dactyl of the crab. J. Neurophysiol. **57(**5):1601-1617.

MacMillan, D.L. & Dando, M.R. (1972) Tension receptors on the apodemes of muscles in the walking legs of the crab *Cancer magister*. Mar. Behav. Physiol. **1**:185-208.

Mill, P.J. (1976) Chordotonal organs of Crustacean appendages. In Structures and function of proprioceptors in the invertebrates, (ed. P.J. Mill) pp. 243-297. London:Chapman and Hall.

Mill, P.J. & Lowe, D.A. (1973) The fine structure of the PD proprioceptor of Cancer pagurus.I. The receptor strand and the movement sensitive cells. Proc. Roy. Soc., Series B, **184:**179-197.

Sillar, K.T. & Skorupski, P. (1986) Central input to primary afferent neurons in crayfish *Parcifastacus lemisculus* is correlated with rhythmic motor output of thoracic ganglia. J. Neurophysiol. **55(**4):678-688.

Whitear, M. (1962) The fine structure of crustacean proprioceptor. I. The chordotonal organs in the legs of the shore crab, *Carcinus maenas*. Phil. Trans. Roy. Soc. London **B245**:291-325.

Wiersma, C.A.G. (1959) Movement receptors in decapod Crustacea. J. Mar. Biol. Ass. U.K. **38**:143-152.

Wiersma, C.A.G. & Boettiger, E. (1959) Unidirectional movement fibres from a proprioceptive organ of the crab *Carcinus maenas*. J. Exp. Biol. **36:**102-112.

COLORPLATES

LEGENDS TO COLORPLATES I-VII

PLATE I

SEE CRONIN (PAGE 58)

Optical filters distally to the rhabdom of the central band of ommatidia in mantis-shrimps (Hoplocarida, Gonodactylidae):
A: View of mid-band ommatidia of the eye of *Odontodactylus scyllarus*.
B: Longitudinal section through frozen material (hence somewhat crumbled) of mid-band ommatidia in *Gonodactylus chiragra* showing the optical filters (seen in this illumination in blue and red) altering the spectral sensitivity of retinula cells.

PLATE II

SEE YAMAGUCHI & OKADA (PAGE 193)

Differential staining of a SF (left O38) and an NGI (right G3).
A:Dorsal view of whole-mount preparation. The 038 and G3 were staineddifferentially with ethidium bromide and Lucifer Yellow, respectively.**B**: Sagittal section of the preparation through the midline. **C:** Sagittal section at a distance of 80 μm from the midline. The levels of sections in B and C correspond to those marked with b and c in A, respectively. Note that the SF extends its branchelets toward the cluster at the point where they encircle the cluster, and that the unstained processes of other members of the cluster can be seen. Arrow heads in B and C indicate the axon of SF.

PLATE III

SEE KIRK & GOVIND (PAGE 140)

Primary **A**fferent **D**epolarizing **I**nterneuron (**PADI**, Type 1) of the sixth abdominal ganglion in the crayfish .*Procambarus clarkii.* This interneuron is activated indirectly by LG and MG fibers and depolarizes sensory (displacement sensitive, hair type sensilla on telson and uropods) afferent terminals, thereby reducing transmitter release. PADI represents the class of efferent inhibitors modulating sensory pathways at the point of their entry into the CNS. Top is anterior.

PLATE IV

SEE ARECHIGA ET AL.(PAGE 373)

Neuron from the crustacean X-organ injected with Lucifer Yellow, showing the cell body and some of the axon and branchings in the neuropil.

PLATE V

SEE MEIER & REICHERT (PAGE 523)

Frontal section through the developing brain and optic lobes of the lobster, *Homarus gammarus*, stained with a neuron-specific anti-HRP antibody (FITC-conjugated). The developing optic neuropil is most intensely stained. The surface of the neuronal somata is stained as well.

PLATE VI

SEE MEIER AND REICHERT (PAGE 523).

Sagittal section through the developing stomatogastric ganglion and surrounding tissue stained with an anti-HRP antibody (FITC-conjugated) in the lobster, *Homarus gammarus* . Both the neuropil and the surface of the neuronal somata of the stomatogastric ganglion are stained. The stomatogastric nerve can be seen projecting towards the bottom left. The epithelium of the stomach separates the stomatogastric ganglion from the lumen of the stomach at the bottom center..

PLATE VII

SEE MULLONEY ET AL.(PAGE 439)

Wholemounts of crayfish abdominal ganglia (A4) with swimmeret motor neurons that had been backfilled with Co^{++} and later intensified with silver (Leise et al. 1987). Anterior is at the top, and A, B and C_V are ventral, frontal views. **A**: A fill of both N1s, showing the full bilateral complement of motorneurons. **B**: A fill of the anterior branch of the left N1, showing one left swimmeret´s RS motor neurons. **C_V**: A fill of the posterior branch of the left N1, showing one left swimmeret`s PS motor neurons. **C_D**: Dorsal view of the same ganglion, focused on the processes that project to the opposite lateral neuropil.

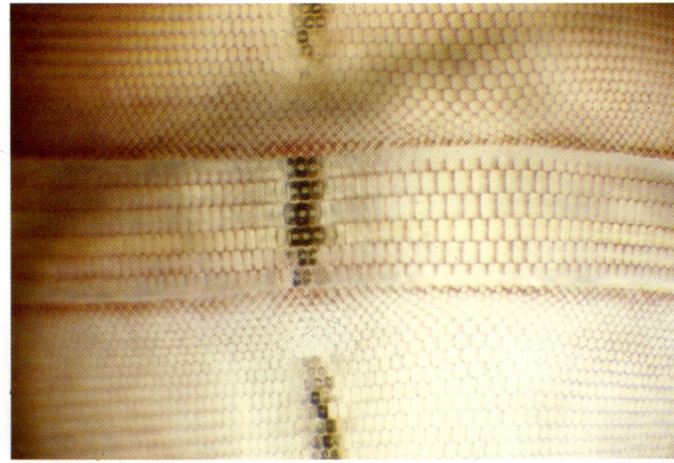

PLATE I **A**

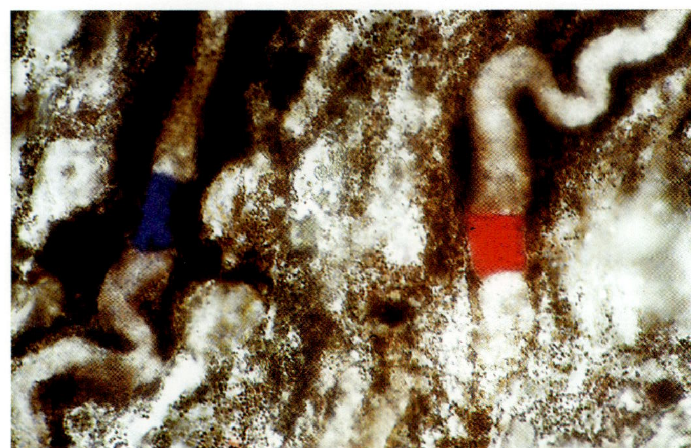

PLATE I **B**

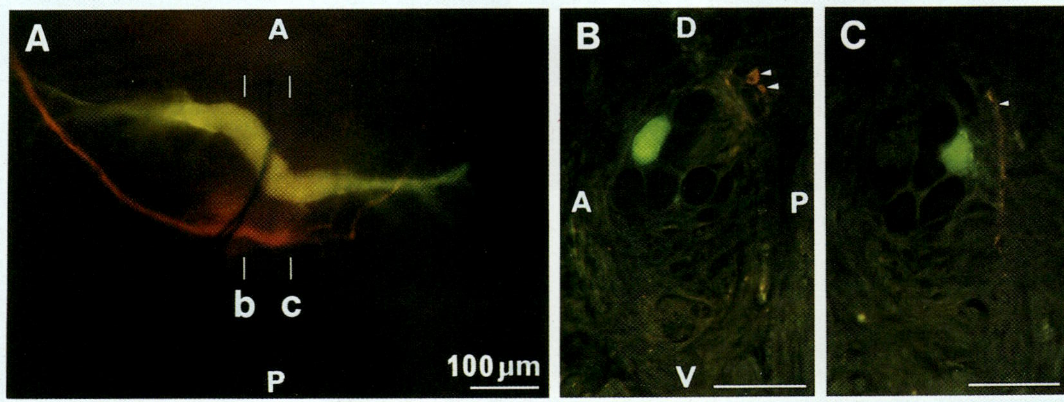

PLATE II

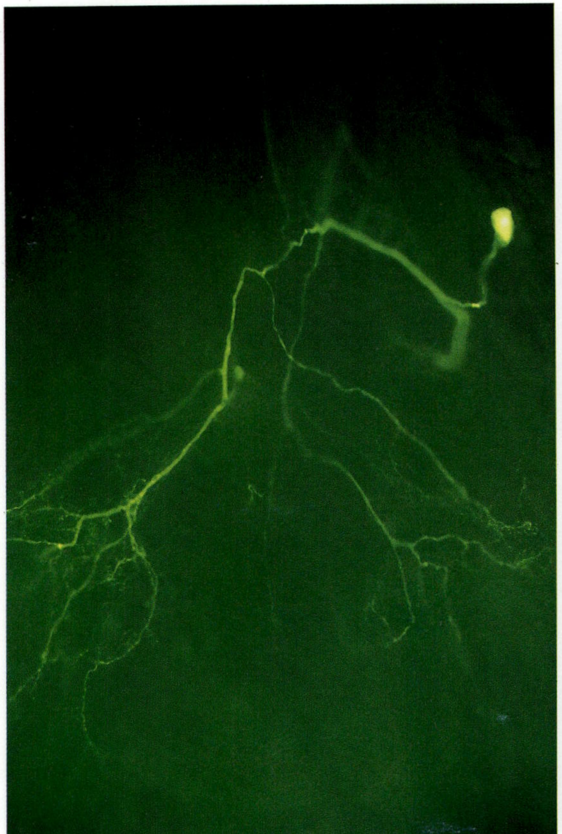

PLATE III

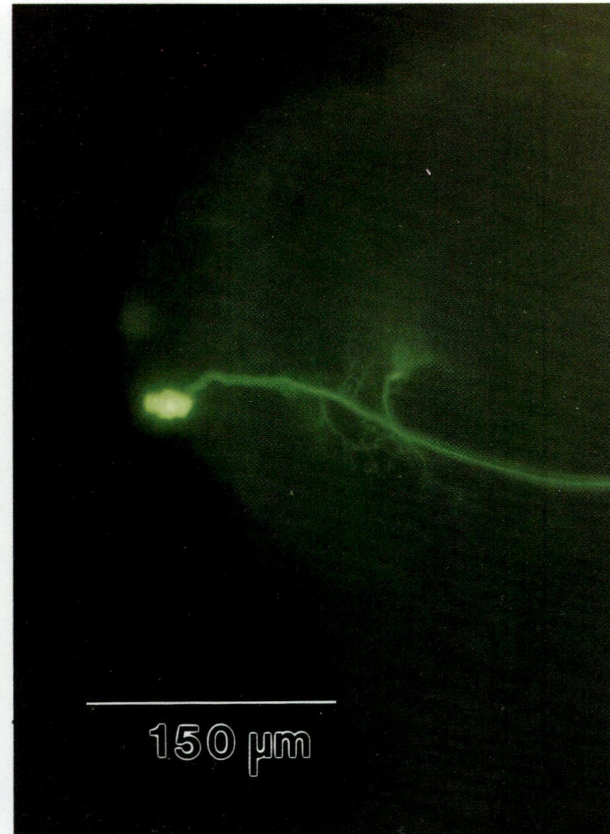

PLATE IV

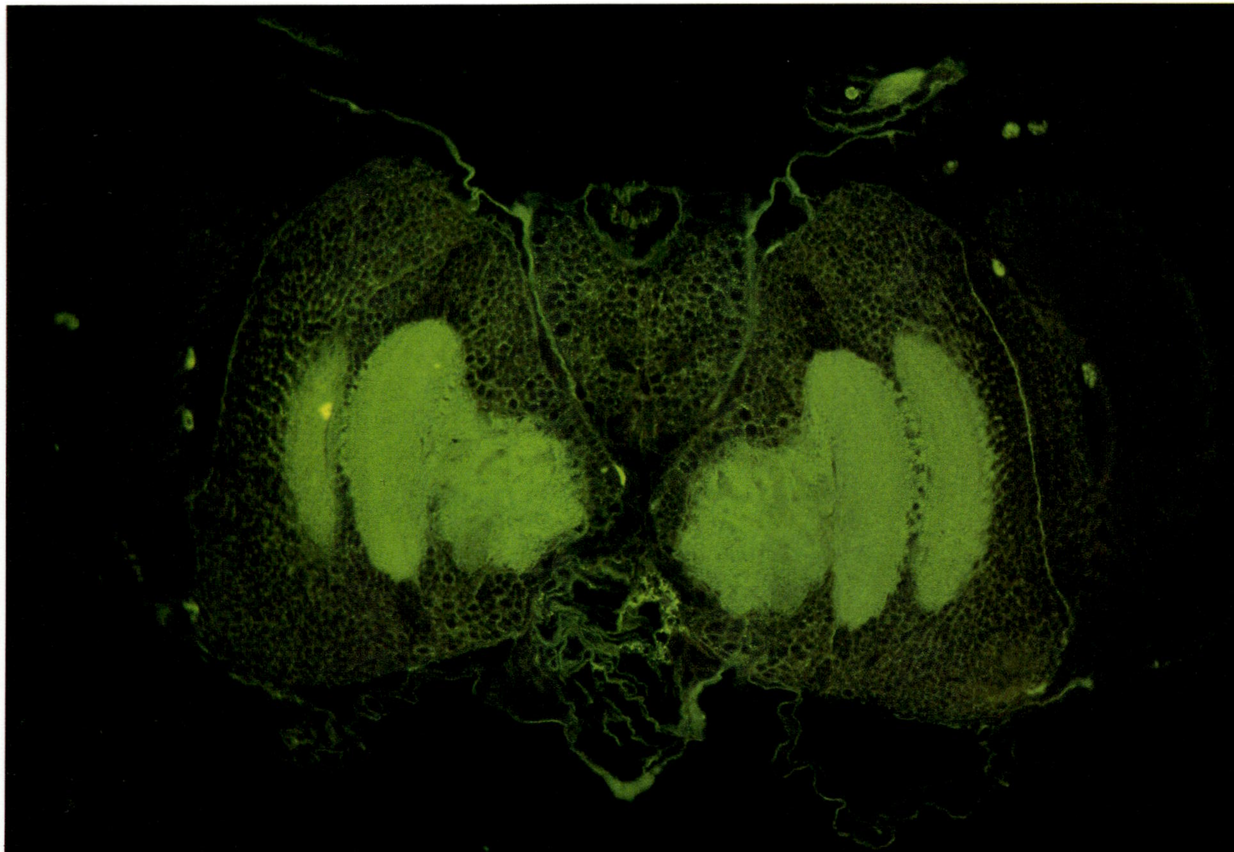

PLATE V

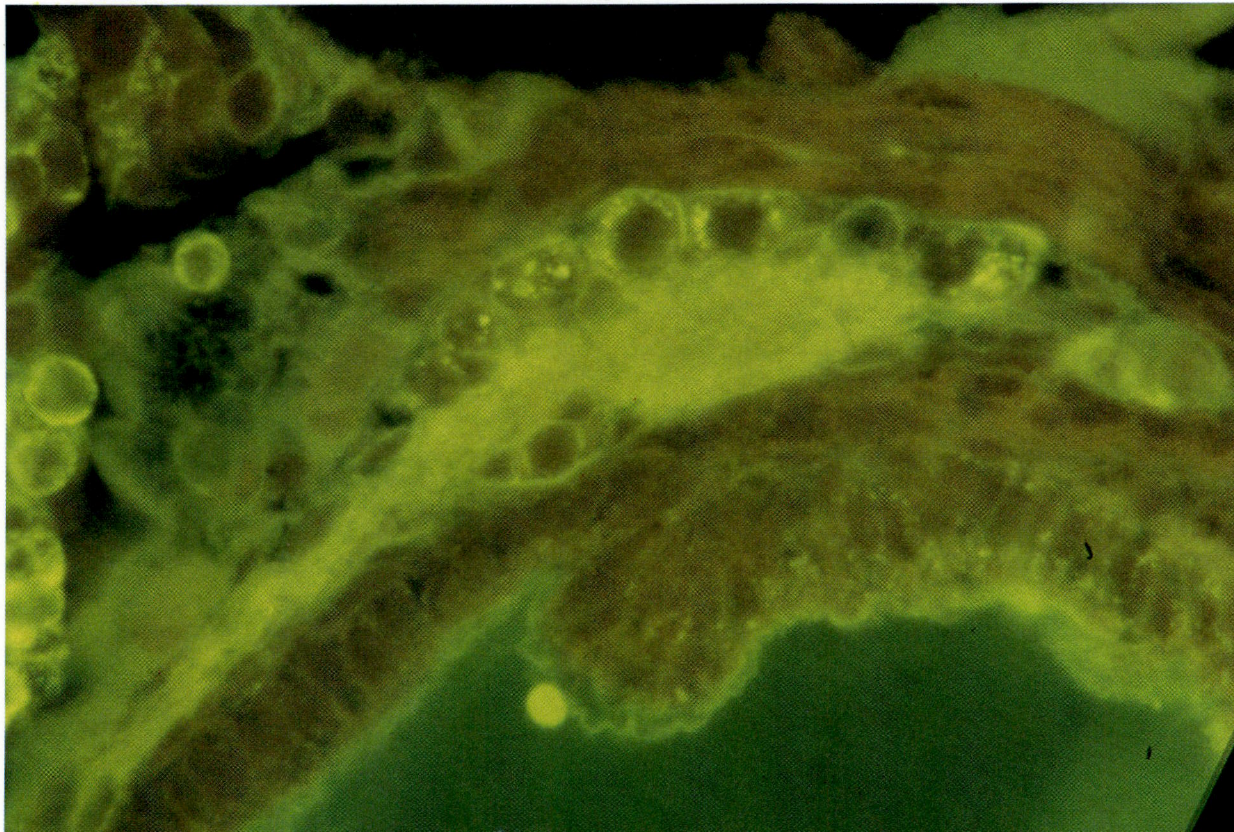

PLATE VI

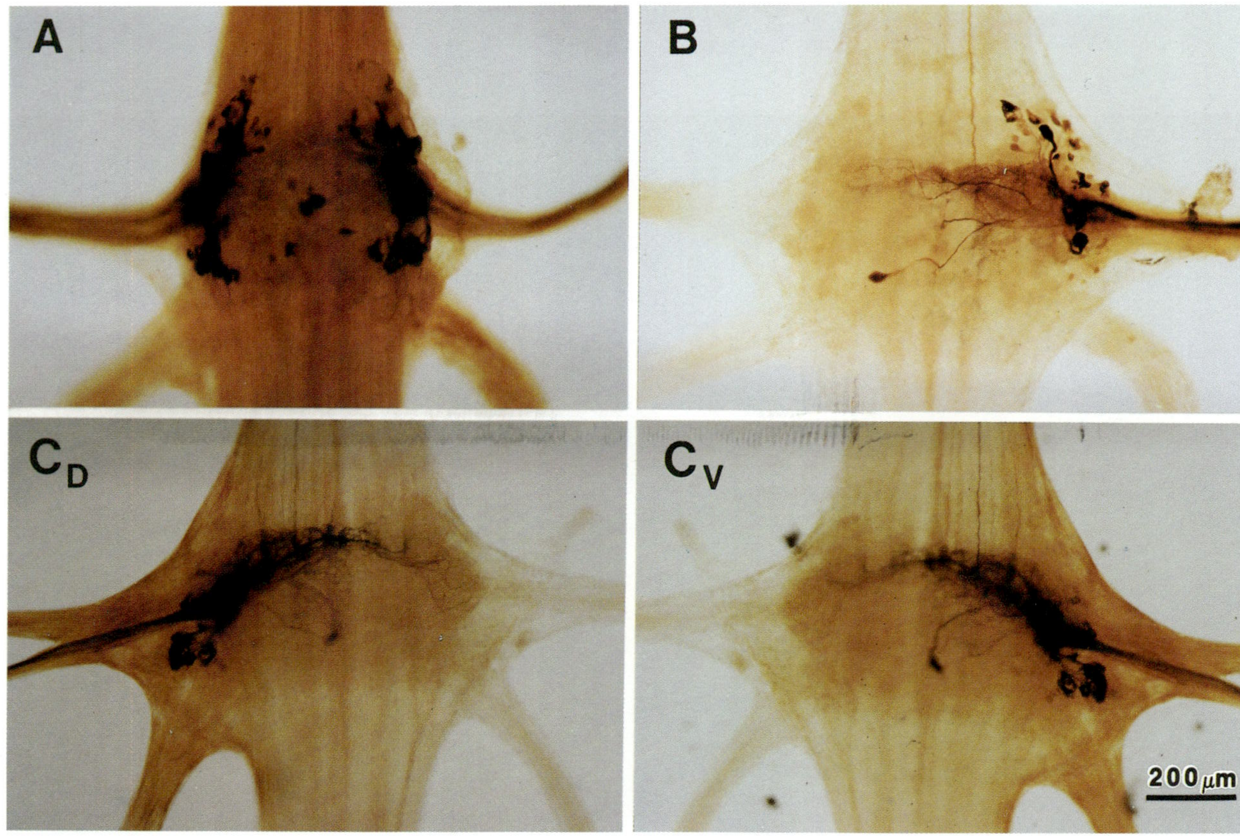

PLATE VII

Frontiers in Crustacean Neurobiology
Advances in Life Sciences

INHIBITION THROUGH NEURONS OF THE COMMON INHIBITORY TYPE (CI-NEURONS) IN CRAB MUSCLES

Werner Rathmayer

Fakultät für Biologie, Universität Konstanz,
Postfach 5560, D-7750 Konstanz, Federal Republic of Germany

SUMMARY

The CI neurons innervating the leg muscles in crabs are mainly tonically active during walking. They suppress synaptic excitation predominantly in the tonic fibers in all leg muscles. This facilitates rapid contraction and relaxation cycles of the limb muscles. Whereas specific inhibitors exert inhibition only when their activity is closely coupled to the discharge of the excitatory neuron, the effects of CI neurons persist over a longer period. This guarantees effective presynaptic inhibition of excitatory transmitter release without tight coupling of CI to excitatory discharges. It explains the effective inhibition exerted by a single CI neuron on a large number of muscles located in different joints of the leg, some of which are coactivated during walking.

INTRODUCTION

With few exceptions, the inhibitory innervation of arthropod muscles is exerted by neurons which innervate several (from two to many) different muscles, therefore being termed common inhibitory neurons (CI-neurons). In crabs, all intrinsic and extrinsic muscles of a walking leg share inhibitory innervation through a single CI-neuron (Rathmayer & Bevengut, 1987). Only the opener and stretcher muscles in the legs receive, in addition to CI, a second, specific inhibitor. This paper deals with the functional significance of CI innervation and the differences between presynaptic inhibition exerted by specific and common inhibitors.

ACTIVITY AND FUNCTIONAL IMPORTANCE OF CI

For the crab *Eriphia spinifrons* it was shown that CI neurons become activated when the animal starts walking. In contrast to the rhythmic discharges of the excitatory neurons, where each burst of impulses is followed by a silent period before the next step, CI neurons are active throughout the locomotory cycle (Ballantyne & Rathmayer, 1981). The discharge of CI occurs in a predominantly tonic way with low, irregular instantaneous discharge frequencies around 20 Hz, with occasional high frequency discharges (Fig. 1). No consistent or significant correlation of the high frequency discharge to that of excitatory neurons was found.

The activity patterns of the slow closer excitor (SCE) and the CI neuron recorded en passant from the proper axons in *Eriphia* crabs during walking on a treadmill (Ballantyne & Rathmayer, 1981) were used to stimulate selectively the axons of these two neurons in isolated recipient leg preparations. Fig. 2 shows the tension responses of a recipient closer muscle to SCE (a) and to combined SCE and CI stimulation (b) with a donor sequence recorded from a crab during 14 consecutive steps. CI increased the speed of relaxation between SCE-evoked contractions with little or no reduction in the amplitude of the individual contractions. The increased speed of relaxation of the closer muscle at the end of each SCE burst enabled the dactylopodite to return to its starting position before the onset of the next step. Activity of CI seems to be essential to promote a phasic pattern of limb muscle performances during rapid walking.

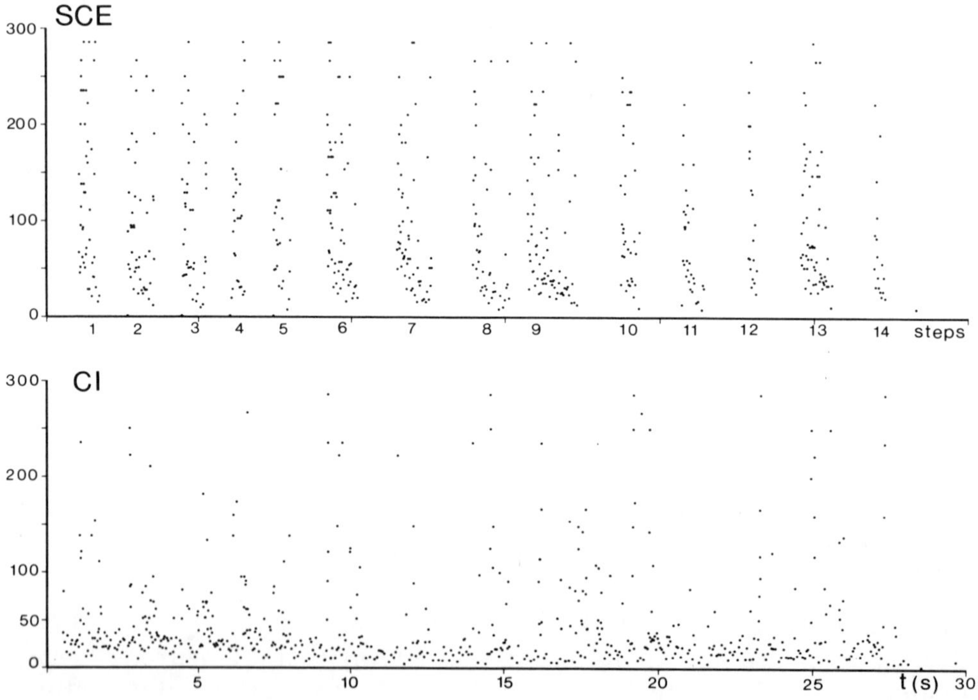

Fig. 1 Instantaneous discharge frequencies of the slow closer excitor (SCE) and the common inhibitor (CI) during 14 consecutive steps of the crab *Eriphia* walking on a treadmill.

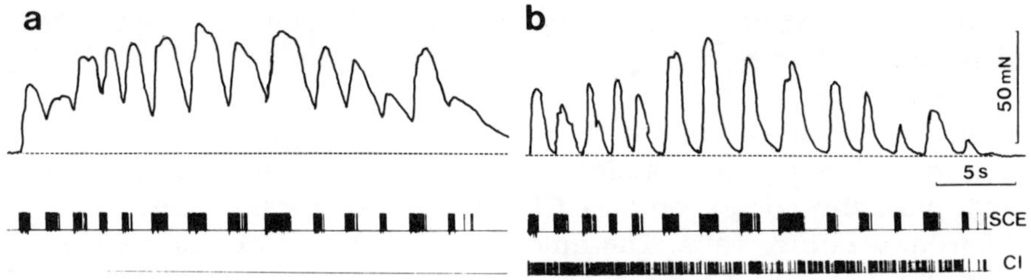

Fig. 2 Contractions of a closer muscle in an isolated *Eriphia* leg (recipient preparation) upon stimulation of SCE and CI, isolated in the meropodite, with patterns produced by a donor crab during 14 consecutive steps (instantaneous discharge frequency shown in Fig. 1). A: Tension response of the recipient closer to the donor sequence of SCE alone. B: Response to the combined SCE and CI donor sequences (shown in lower traces).

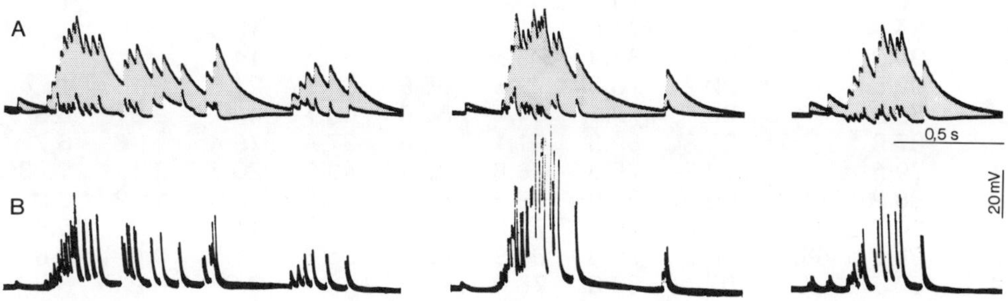

Fig. 3 Simultaneous intracellular recordings from two muscle fibers of different type (A: tonic type I fiber; B: phasic type II fiber) in the closer of *Eriphia* upon stimulation of SCE (upper trace) and SCE combined with CI (lower trace) with sequences obtained from a donor crab. Two traces are superimposed in each record. The amount of inhibition in the tonic fiber is shown by the shaded area. In the phasic fiber, inhibition is barely detectible.

This effect of CI is achieved predominantly by its action on tonic muscle fibers (type I fibers, Rathmayer & Maier, 1987), where CI produces strongest inhibition through post- and mainly presynaptic mechanisms (Rathmayer & Erxleben, 1983). This was confirmed for each of the seven muscles controlling the three distal joints of the walking legs (Wiens et al.,1988). Fig. 3 illustrates the amount of inhibition in a tonic and a phasic fiber of a recipient closer muscle when SCE and CI were stimulated with three donor sequences recorded from a walking crab. The phasic type II fibers, whose innervation is identical to that of the tonic fibers, are little affected through CI.

Table 1 lists the percentage of inhibition in the depolarizations of tonic and phasic closer muscle fibers of *Eriphia* when the muscle was stimulated with excitatory donor patterns alone (Fig. 3A, upper trace) or with the same excitatory plus the corresponding CI-donor patterns (Fig. 3A, lower trace) obtained from walking crabs. The amount of inhibition during each step was measured as the difference in the area between the depolarizations obtained without and with CI-stimulation (stippled area in Fig. 3).

Table 1: Amount of inhibition (%) during stepping in different muscle fiber types

	Tonic type I-fibers							Phasic type II-fibers		
Steps	a	b	c	d	e	f	g	h	i	j
5	87.8	86.7		70.1	60.0					11.8
6	84.8			74.5	61.0			12.8		
7	95.0		90.8	83.4	73.6			14.5		
8	92.5		92.2	78.3	72.5	65.6	54.5	21.5	2.1	11.4
9	89.3		86.1	72.1	64.4	55.6	40.7	4.8	2.9	6.8
10	87.9		93.8	69.5	71.1	63.4	37.4	16.4	11.6	6.7
11	79.5		78.2	75.3	76.8	48.1	40.6	20.7	3.1	15.8
12a	88.2	94.0	86.6	80.9	69.3	69.2	33.5	16.9	14.2	0.0
12b	94.7	90.1	90,0	76.6	72.9	62.7	40.7	14.2	3.7	5.6
13	91.9	88.9	78.6	76.0	67.9	62.9	35.7	16.5	0.0	6.6
14			97.1	80.3	76.0	71.8		9.2	6.2	3.7
MEAN	89.2	89.9	88.2	76.1	69.6	62.4	40.4	14.7	5.5	7.6
S.D.	4.7	3.1	6.5	4.5	5.7	7.5	6.8	5.0	4.9	4.7

a - j: different experiments; a - d: fibers 2; e: fiber 3; f,g: fibers 4; h - j: fibers 5 (according to numbers in Rathmayer and Maier, 1987)

During walking, the amount of depolarizations in tonic fibers was reduced through CI-activity from 90 to 40 % (mean 73.6 ± 18 S.D., n = 7), depending on the individual fiber, in the phasic fibers, however, only from 15 to 5 % (mean 9.3 ± 4.8 S.D., n = 3). The contractions of the limb muscles during the steps therefore are predominantly due to the activity of the phasic muscle fibers, because synaptic excitation in the tonic fibers is greatly suppressed. CI neurons thus play an important role in the division of labor among limb muscles where the fibers receive identical excitatory input.

THE TIMING OF INHIBITORY EFFECTS

For optimal effects of inhibitory neurons on excitatory neuromuscular transmission, precise timing between inhibitory and excitatory neuronal activity is necessary. Only those action potentials in the inhibitory neuron which occur within a small time window will produce effective presynaptic inhibition. Dudel & Kuffler (1961) and Wiens & Atwood (1975), studying the two specific inhibitors of the opener and stretcher muscles in the walking legs of crayfish and different crabs, showed that the interval between stimulation of the I- and the E-axon for maximal inhibition of excitatory junction potentials (ejps) ranged between 2 and 9 ms, depending on the preparation. The amount of inhibition decreased rapidly when I-stimulation occurred a few ms earlier or later than this optimum (fig. 4). 50 percent inhibition was obtained over a small time interval of 5 to 8 ms between I-and E-stimulation. At intervals longer than 15 ms, an inhibitory impulse usually was no longer able to reduce the following ejp.

The close timing of the arrival of inhibitory and excitatory action potentials at the neuromuscular junctions is a characteristic feature of inhibition through specific inhibitors. Such timing is possible because the conduction velocities of the opener/stretcher excitor and of the specific inhibitors are rather similar (4,1 m/s versus 3.9 m/s: Ballantyne & Rathmayer, 1981). A similar timing is difficult to establish for the CI neurons because of the wide distribution of their target muscles and the greater differences in axonal conduction velocities (2.7 m/s for CI compared with 4.3 m/s for SCE and 5.8 m/s for FCE; Ballantyne & Rathmayer, 1981). For an average leg of *Eriphia* (8 cm length), this implies that action potentials generated in the CI neuron need 11 ms longer to arrive at the closer muscle than those of the SCE neuron. In order to occur within a time window similar to that of specific inhibition, the action potential in CI must be generated approx. 13 to 20 ms before that in SCE. The time should become shorter for muscles such as the levator and depressor situated proximally in the leg which are also innervated by CI.

During walking several proximal and distal muscles are coactivated. Fig. 5 shows the activity patterns of the major leg muscles during walking derived from 70 steps of a leg on either the leading or trailing side. The activity of the closer overlaps with that of several other muscles (shaded area). In the legs on the trailing side, the closer is coactivated during the return stroke with the flexor and the levator. On the leading side, the activity of the closer coincides with that of the flexor and partly with that of the levator and depressor muscles during the power stroke. Theoretically, it is difficult to maintain precise timing between the generation of action potentials in CI and in the different excitatory neurons innervating widely separated, but coactivated muscles.

When we began studying the time course of presynaptic inhibition through CI in muscles of *Eriphia* (Rathmayer & Florey, 1974; Rathmayer &

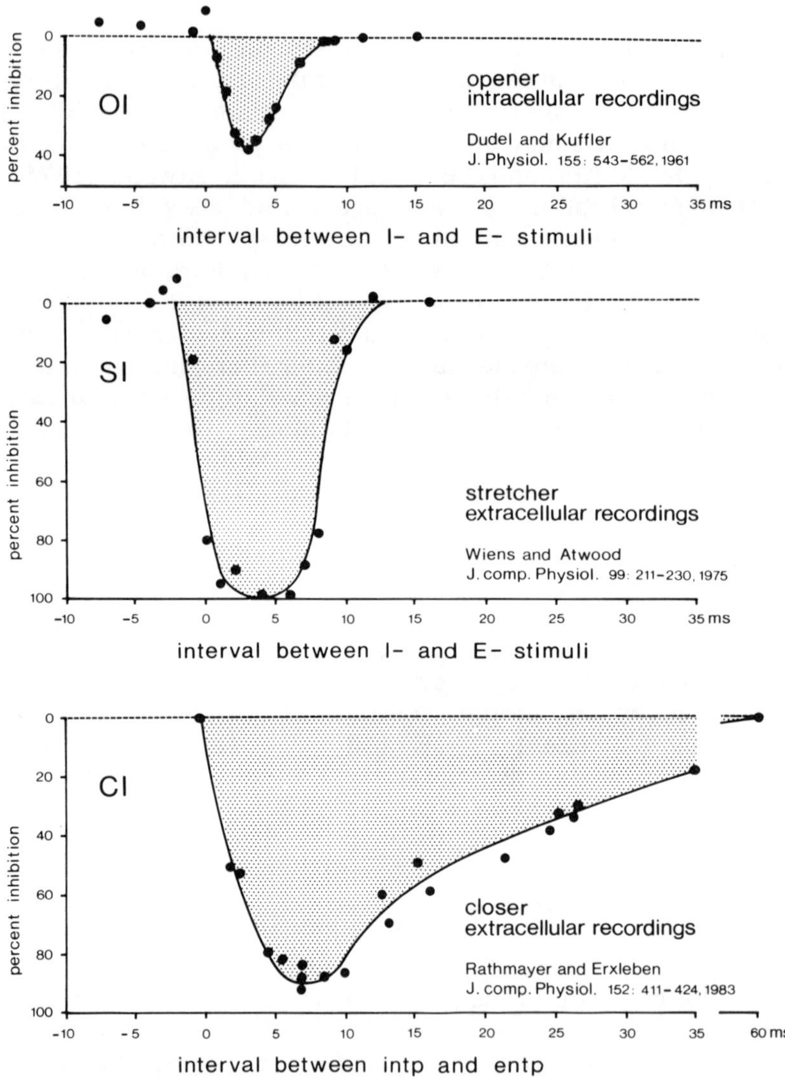

Fig. 4. Time course of presynaptic inhibition through specific (OI and SI) and common inhibitors (CI). The data for OI and SI were rearranged to match with those for CI. The arrival of inhibitory and excitatory action potentials at the neuromuscular junctions were not known for the specific inhibitors. Inhibition begins with a rapid onset in both types, but its decline lasts much longer in CI. OI and SI: stimulation at 1 Hz, CI at 14 Hz.

Erxleben, 1983), we noticed a long-lasting persistence of this type of inhibition. This was most obvious in the mechanical responses elicited by low frequency stimulation of SCE upon a single high frequency burst of CI.

The depression of the contractions could last for several minutes. Focal recording of the arriving action potentials in the inhibitory and excitatory nerve terminals (nerve terminal potentials, intp and entp) in the closer muscle enabled the accurate determination of intervals between inhibitory and excitatory events at particular neuromuscular junctions. As with the specific inhibitors, an optimum in timing was found: presynaptic inhibition through CI was maximal when the intp occurred 5 to 8 ms prior to the entp (fig. 4).

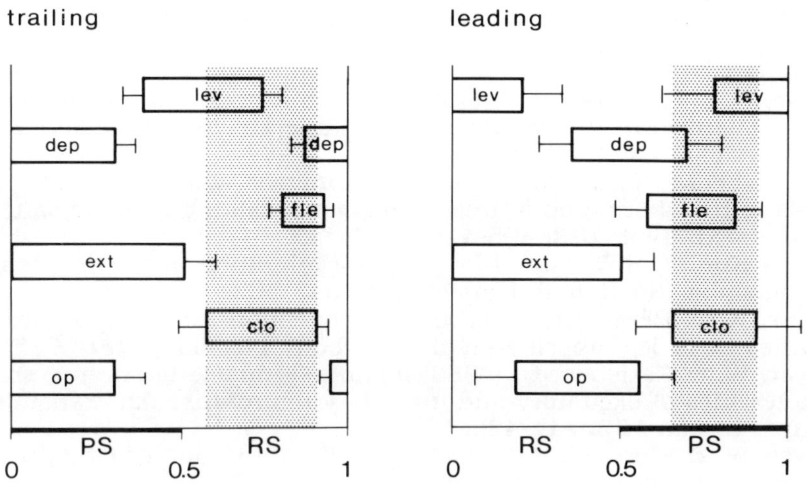

Fig. 5 Burst duration and phase relationships of six leg muscles (levator, depressor, flexor, extensor, closer, opener) in Carcinus walking freely in water. The time from the onset of one extensor muscle burst to the next was taken as a step period. Step periods were normalized for determining phase relationships. Mean values and SD of burst durations are shown. PS power stroke, RS return stroke (modified from Clarac et al., 1987).

At some junctions the ejps were inhibited up to 95 %. In contrast to the narrow time window in which the specific inhibitors were active, inhibition through single action potentials of CI persisted over several tens of ms. Intps preceding entps by 35 ms still produced 20 to 45 % inhibition of the following ejps; in one case an intp caused 10 % inhibition of ejp amplitudes even after 120 ms. Fig. 4 also shows that at an interval of 15 ms, when specific inhibitors usually are no longer effective, there is still 50 % inhibition of the ejp through CI.

The long persistence of presynaptic inhibition through CI can overcome the difficulties which arise in matching the tonic discharge of the CI neuron to the phasic activity of several coactivated excitatory motoneurons supplying a number of muscles in different positions in the leg. The distribution and the underlying mechanisms for this long lasting effect are yet unknown.

ACKNOWLEDGEMENTS:
The work of the author has been supported by grants of the Deutsche Forschungsgemeinschaft (SFB 156). Some of the earlier experiments were conducted together with Drs. D. Ballantyne, C. Erxleben and E. Florey at the Stazione Zoologica, Naples. We thank the director for hospitality and D. Ruhrmann for unfailing technical assistance. Dr. M. Hammelsbeck kindly provided help with computer analysis.

REFERENCES

Ballantyne, D. & Rathmayer, W. (1981) On the function of the common inhibitory neuron in the walking legs of the crab, *Eriphia spinifrons*. J. comp. Physiol. **143**: 111-122.

Clarac, F., Libersat, F., Pflüger, H.-J. & Rathmayer W. (1987) Motor pattern analysis in the shore crab (Carcinus maenas) walking freely in water and on land. J. exp. Biol. **133:** 395-414.

Dudel, J. & Kuffler, S.W. (1961) Presynaptic inhibition at the crayfish neuromuscular junction. J. Physiol. **155**: 543-562.

Rathmayer, W. & Bevengut, M. (1986) The common inhibitory neuron innervates every leg muscle in crabs. J. comp. Physiol. A **158**: 665-668.

Rathmayer, W. & Erxleben, C. (1983) Identified muscle fibers in a crab. I. Characteristics of excitatory and inhibitory neuromuscular transmission. J. comp. Physiol. **152**: 411-420.

Rathmayer, W. & Florey, E. (1974) Presynaptic inhibition of long duration at crab neuromuscular junctions. Pflügers Arch. **347:** 77-81.

Rathmayer W., & Maier, L. (1987) Muscle fiber types in crabs: Studies on single identified muscle fibers. Am. Zool. **27:** 1067-1077.

Wiens, T.J. & Atwood, H.L. (1975) Dual inhibitory control in crab leg muscles. J. comp. Physiol. **99**: 211-230.

Wiens, T.J., Maier, L. & Rathmayer, W. (1988) The distribution of the common inhibitory neuron in brachyuran limb musculature. II. Target fibers. J. comp. Physiol. A **163:** 651-664.

Wiens, T.J. & Rathmayer, W. (1985) The distribution of the common inhibitory neuron in brachyuran limb musculature. I. Target muscles. J. comp. Physiol. A **156**: 305-313.

Frontiers in Crustacean Neurobiology
Advances in Life Sciences

ACTIVATION OF THE SWIMMERET RHYTHM BY STIMULATION OF THE SECOND THORACIC ROOTS

Abdesslam Chrachri

University of California, Davis, Department of Zoology andUniversity of Glasgow, Department of Zoology, Glasgow G12 8QQ, Scotland, U.K.

SUMMARY

In the crayfish, *Pacifastacus leniusculus*, the rhythmical activity of the swimmeret motor pattern is strongly modified by stimulating the second thoracic roots.

Stimulating the second thoracic roots modifies the activity of most swimmeret neurons. It increases the frequency of the rhythm and the frequency of spikes within cell bursts, also it increases the total amplitude of membrane potential oscillations of some swimmeret neurons.

The effects on the swimmeret rhythm by stimulating the second thoracic roots are established slowly and are of long duration.

INTRODUCTION

For several decades, it has been possible to demonstrate that rhythmic behaviour is programmed by central neuronal networks, the endogenous activities of which are determined by the synaptic interactions between neurons in the network and by the cellular properties of neurons in the network (reviewed by Grillner, 1977; Delcomyn, 1980).

A large body of information has been collected concerning the generation of rhythmic motor patterns by isolated invertebrate preparations, notably, leech swimming (Kristan & Calabrese, 1976), *Tritonia* swimming (Getting & Dekin, 1985) and the crustacean stomatogastric system (Selverston & Moulins, 1987). It has been possible to identify many elements of the central pattern generator (CPG) and to describe their properties (Selverston & Moulins, 1985). Nevertheless, the identification of neurons in such networks and the determination of their synaptic relationships is insufficient to explain either the flexibility of behavioral sequences controlled by such networks or the manner in which such sequences are initiated and terminated. In fact, it appears that even those properties determining the endogenous activity of pattern generators can be modulated. For example, the bursting activity of oscillatory neurons can be induced, amplified or eliminated (Parnas et al. 1974). Thus, it is of interest to study the mechanisms controlling central pattern generators.

When isolated from the crayfish *Pacifastacus leniusculus*, the chain ofabdominal ganglia is still able to generate rhythmic motor pattern. Mulloney et al. (1987) demonstrated that the neuropeptide proctolin activated the swimmeret rhythm. Swicki and Bishop (1986) mapped the proctolin-like immunoreactivity in the nervous systems of the lobster and crayfish. They demonstrated that the second thoracic roots contain sheath cells and axons that showed proctolin-like immunoreactivity.

I carried out this study to find out whether the second thoracic roots could affect the swimmeret rhythm or not.

METHODS

Experiments were performed on the nerve cord of the crayfish *Pacifastacus leniusculus*. Animals were obtained from commercial suppliers and held in aquaria that contained temperatederated tap water. The ventral nerve cord (VNC) of both males and females were used in this study. The isolated VNC contains both thoracic ganglia (from TG3 to TG5) and abdominal (A1 to A6) ganglia (Fig. 1A). The preparation was then pinned out in a Sylgard-lined dish and bathed continously with oxygenated saline (Van Harreveld, 1936). Fine electrodes were placed in contact with the posterior branch of the first nerve of each abdominal ganglion which contains axons of the power-stroke motor neurons, and the second thoracic roots. These electrodes were insulated from the bath with Vaseline to record differentially from these nerves or to stimulate them (the position of the extracellular electrodes is illustrated in Fig. 1A; filled circle). The third and the fourth abdominal ganglia were desheated for intracellular recordings. A conventional bridge circuit was used for intracellular recording and passing current pulses with a single microelectrode. Motor neurons were identified by correlating extracellular and intracellular action potentials, and by the occurrence of an antidromic action potential after stimulating the first abdominal nerve. Interneurons were characterized as neurons without one-to-one correlation between their action potentials and any spike recorded extracellularly in the first abdominal nerves. This physiological identification of the swimmeret neurons was usually confirmed by staining these neurons with Lucifer Yellow (Stewart, 1978). Glass microelectrodes were filled with 3% Lucifer Yellow in 3 M lithium chloride (40 to 80 Megohms). Neurons were filled using 0.5 sec duration, 10 nA hyperpolarizing current at 1 Hz for 20 to 40 min. Intracellular recordings were performed within the neuropilar region because it is not possible to record electrical events within the cell body (Reichert and Krenz, 1986).

RESULTS

Most preparations displayed spontaneous rhythmic motor output called swimmeret rhythm. Sometimes, however, the preparations were silent or showed an intermittent rhythm. In this cases, stimulation of the second thoracic roots at 25 Hz for 3 to 6 sec provoked a long-lasting activation of the swimmeret rhythm (Fig. 1B). Intracellular recordings from swimmeret motor neurons and interneurons demonstrated that the second thoracic roots stimulation affected most of the swimmeret neurons.

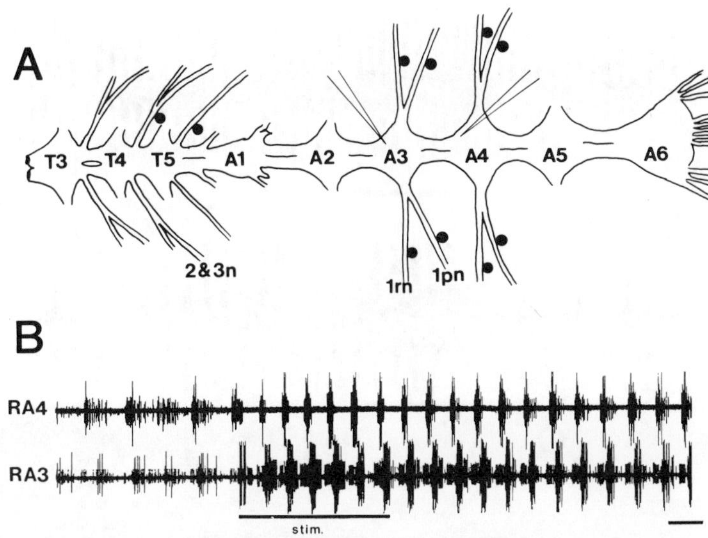

Fig. 1. Drawing of the isolated nerve cord of the crayfish, Pacifastacus leniusculus. (A) The preparation contains the third (TG3), the fourth (TG4) and the fifth (TG5) thoracic ganglia and all abdominal ganglia. Extracellular recordings were performed from the posterior branch of the first abdominal nerves (that contains axons of the power-stroke motor neurons) and from the second thoracic roots. Intracellular recordings were performed from the third and/or the fourth abdominal ganglia. (B) A 4.2 sec stimulation of the second thoracic root causes a long-lasting activation of the swimmeret rhythm.
Black dots show the position of the extracellular electrodes.
1pn: posterior branch of the first abdominal nerve; 1rn: anterior branch of the first abdominal nerve.
Horizontal bar: 1sec.

The second thoracic root stimulation provokes a long-lasting activation of the swimmeret rhythm (Fig.1B). This effect is also represented by the frequency of the power-stroke activity of RA4 (Fig. 2B). The increase of the frequency of the rhythmic activity of RA4 after a 4.6 sec stimulation of the second thoracic root is illustrated graphically by plotting the frequency of the RA4 power-stroke activity (Fig. 2C; filled circle). The maximum frequency is reached 2 sec after the start of the second thoracic root stimulation; the frequency of the RA4 activity then slowly decreased and still greater than the control 16 sec after the end of the stimulation. Fig. 2A shows that, in contrast, when the swimmeret rhythm is rapid stimulation of the second thoracic root does not affect the frequency of the swimmeret rhythm. This is illustrated graphically by plotting the frequency of RA4 power-stroke activity (Fig. 3C; open circle).

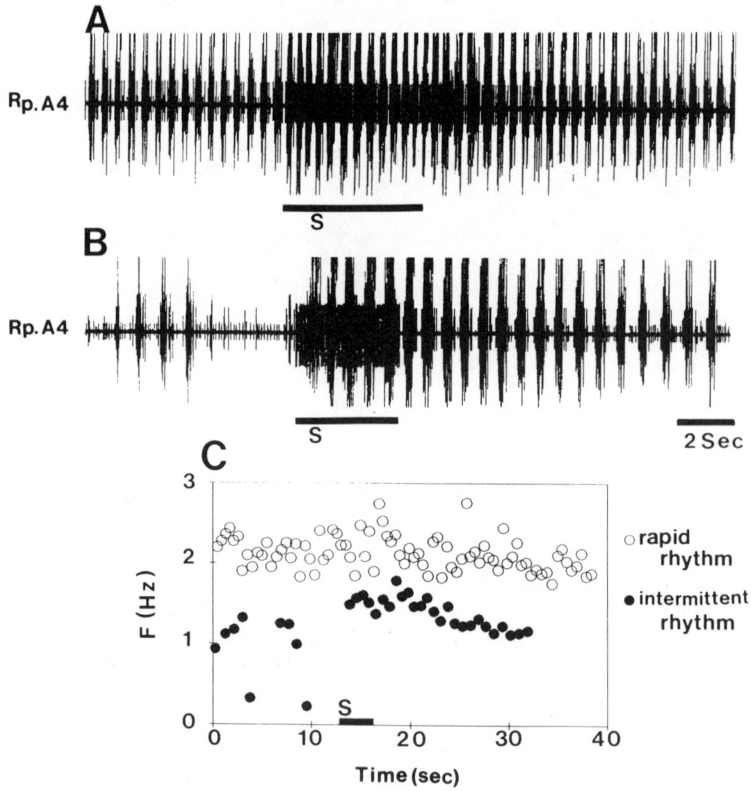

Fig. 2. The stimulation of the second thoracic roots increases the frequency of an intermittent rhythm to that of a spontaneously rapid rhythm. (A) A rapid swimmeret rhythm represented by the extracellular activity of a RA4 power-stroke activity is not accelerated by a stimulation of the second thoracic root. (B) An intermittent swimmeret rhythm represented by a RA4 power-stroke activity is accelerated by the second thoracic root stimulation. (C) Graphic representation of the effects of the second thoracic root stimulation on the frequency of the swimmeret rhythm as a function of time. Filled circles represent an intermittent rhythm, open circles represent a rapid rhythm.

The second effect of the second thoracic roots stimulation is an increase in the spike frequency within bursts. This is illustrated in Fig. 3A and shown graphically in Fig. 3B. A 5.5 sec stimulation of the second thoracic root increases significantly the spikes frequency of one RA4 powerstroke motor neuron than before the start of the stimulation. The maximum increase is reached 2.2 sec after the start of the stimulation and is still greater than the control 17 sec after the end of the stimulation.

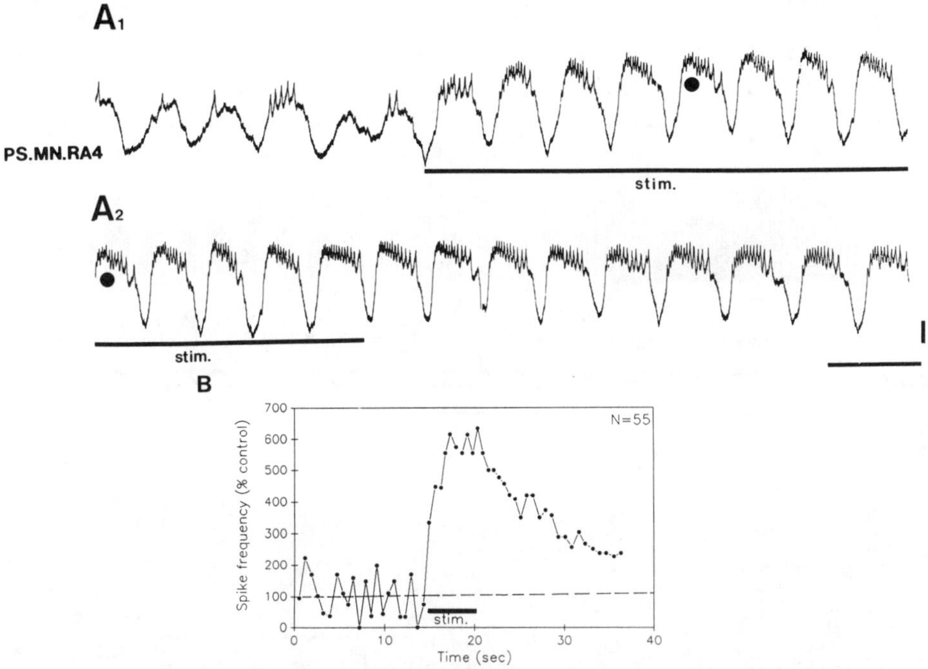

Fig. 3. A second thoracic root stimulation increases the frequency of spikes within bursts of the swimmeret neurons. (A1, A2) Intracellular recording of a power-stroke motor neuron recorded in the RA4 before , during and after the stimulation of the second thoracic root. (B) Spike frequency of this power-stroke motor neuron is expressed as percentage of the control frequency (calculated from bursts before the stimulation).
The black dot shows the same cycle of the RA4 motor neuron.
Horizontal bar: 1 sec.
Vertical bar: 10 mV.

The third effect of the second thoracic roots stimulation is an increase of the total amplitude of membrane potential oscillations of some swimmeret motor neurons (Fig. 4). A 5 sec stimulation of the second thoracic root causes an increase of the total amplitude of membrane potential oscillations of a power-stroke RA3 motor neuron and of an interneuron recorded in RA4 (Fig. 4A). The increase of the total amplitude of membrane potential oscillations of two swimmeret neurons (Figs. 4B1, 4B2) is represented graphically in Figs. 4C1, 4C2. The maximum total amplitude of oscillations is reached 2 to 3 sec after the start of the second thoracic roots stimulation. The amplitude of oscillations of these swimmeret neurons was still greater than in the control 17 to 20 sec after the end of the second thoracic roots stimulation.

DISCUSSION

The study presented in this paper show the general effects of the stimulation of the second thoracic roots on the swimmeret rhythm. The second thoracic roots stimulation seems to affect most of the swimmeret neurons.

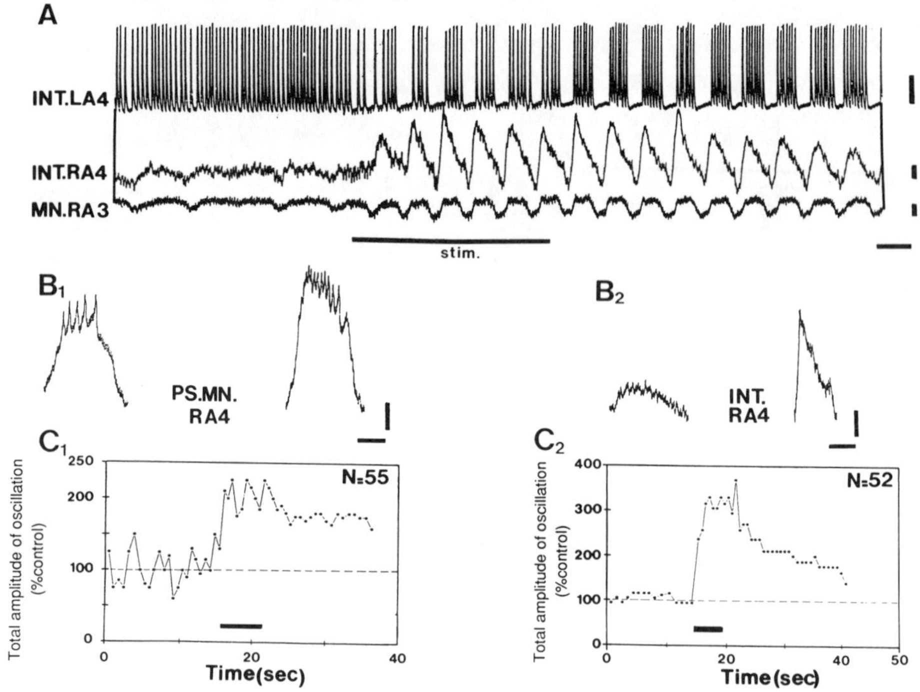

Fig.. 4. A second thoracic root stimulation increases the total amplitude of membrane potential oscillations of certain swimmeret motor neurons and interneurons. (A) illustrates such an effect. (B1,B2) Recording of control bursts (First burst in B1, B2) and bursts after (second burst B1, B2) stimulation of the second thoracic root. (C1, C2) Total amplitude of membrane potential oscillations of a RA4 power-stroke motor neuron (C1) and a RA4 interneuron (C2) is expressed as percentage of the control of the amplitude of membrane potential oscillations of these two neurons (calculated from cycles before stimulation of the second thoracic root).
Horizontal bar: 1 sec (A); 500 msec (B1, B2).
Vertical bar: 5 mV (A); 13 mV (B1); 6 mV (B2).

We do not know whether the stimulation of the second thoracic roots affects directly each individual abdominal ganglion or not. However, using low Ca^{++} saline in the thoracic and/or in different individual abdominal ganglia does not stop the second thoracic effects (Chrachri, 1988). Also in certain motor neurons and interneurons the second thoracic root stimulation provokes one-for-one EPSPs (Chrachri, unpublished data).

These results might suggest that the second thoracic root stimulation affects directly some of the swimmeret neurons.

It seems that the activation of the swimmeret rhythm by stimulating the second thoracic root occurs with a long latency and outlasts the duration of the stimulation. Such a slow onset and long time course are typical of neuromodulation (Kupfermann, 1979). In recent years, these slow modulating systems have been shown to play a role in the control of neuronal excitability (Hartzell, 1981; Adams et al. 1982), in the control of bursting properties in neurons (Barker & Gainer, 1974; Russell & Hartline, 1982; Dickinson & Nagy, 1983; Dickinson et al. 1988) and the control of myogenic activity in muscles (Evans & O'Shea, 1978; Calabrese & Arbas, 1985; Meyrand & Moulins, 1986). Some of these modulatory systems have been associated with neurotransmitters. For example, in the crustacean stomatogastric system, Nagy & Dickinson, 1983 demonstrated that an identified interneuron, APM, modulate the pyloric activity by acetylcholine action on muscarinic receptors, Nusbaum & Marder, 1987 demonstrated that an identified proctolin-containing neuron (MPN) also modulate the pyloric rhythm. Also the serotonergic Retzius cells modulate the swim CPG in leech (Kristan & Nusbaum, 1983).

Mulloney et al. 1987 demonstrated that the neuropeptide proctolin can turn on and modulate the swimmeret rhythm, while other suspected Crustacea neurotransmitters and transmitter analogues did not excite the swimmeret rhythm. Investigations are currently underway in order to determine whether the activation of the swimmeret rhythm by stimulation of the second thoracic roots is associated with the neuropeptide proctolin or not.

For a better understanding of a behavioral significance of the second thoracic roots, further study should involve simultaneous recordings from at least the different abdominal motor systems; the swimmeret, the flexor and the extensor systems.

ACKNOWLEDGMENTS

My thanks to Prof. Brian Mulloney for his kind support and encouragement on this project. This research was supported by NSF Grant BNS 87-19397 to B. Mulloney.

REFERENCES

Adams,P.R., Brown, D.A. & Constanti, A. (1982). M-currents and other potassium currents in bullfrog sympathetic neurones. J. Physiol. Lond. **330**:537-572.

Baker, J.L. & Gainer, H. (1974). Peptide regulation of bursting pacemaker activity in molluscan neurosecretory cell. Science **184:**1371-1373.

Calabrese, R.L. & Arbas, E.A. (1985) Modulation of central and peripheral rhythmicity in the heartbeat system of the leech. In Model Neural Networks and Behavior (ed. A.I. Selverston). pp. 69-85. New York: Plenum Press.

Chrachri, A. (1988). Excitation and inhibition of the swimmeret rhythm by stimulation of the second thoracic nerves. Neurosci. Abstr. **4**:700.

Delcomyn, F. (1980). Neural basis of rhythmic behaviors in animals. Science **210**:492-498.

Dickinson, P.S. & Nagy, F. (1983). Control of a central pattern generator by an identified modulatory interneurone in Crustacea. II. Induction and modification of plateau properties in pyloric neurones. J. Exp. Biol. **105**:59-82.

Dickinson,P.S., Nagy,F. & Moulins, M. (1988). Control of central pattern generators by an identified neurone in Crustacea: Activation of the Gastric mill motor pattern by a neurone known to modulate the pyloric network. J. Exp. Biol. **136**:53-87.

Evans, P.D. & O'Shea, M. (1978). The identification of an octopaminergic neurone and the modulation of a myogenic rhythm in the locust. J. Exp. Biol. **73:**235-260.

Getting, P.A. & Dekin, M.S. (1985). Mechanisms of pattern generation underlying swimming in *Tritonia*. IV. Gating of central pattern generator. J. Neurophysiol. **53:**466-480.

Grillner, S. (1977). On the neural control of movement. A comparison of different basic rhythmic behaviors. In Function and Formation of Neural Systems, (ed. G.S. Stent), pp. 197-224. Berlin: Dahlem Konferenzen.

Hartzell, H.C. (1981). Mechanisms of slow post-synaptic potentials. Nature, Lond. **291:**345-364.

Kupfermann, I. (1979). Modulatory actions of neurotransmitters. A. Rev. Neurosc. **2:**447-465.

Kristan, W.B. & Calabrese, R.L. (1976). Rhythmic swimming activity in neurones of the isolated nerve cord of the leech. Brain Res. **65** (3):643-668.

Kristan, W.B. & Nusbaum, M.P. (1983). The dual role of serotonin in leech swimming. J. Physiol. Paris **78:**743-747.

Meyrand, P. & Moulins, M. (1986). Myogenic oscillatory activity in the pyloric rhythmic motor system of Crustacea. J. Comp. Physiol. A **158:**489-503.

Mulloney, B., Acevedo, L.D. & Bradbury, A.G. (1987). Modulation of the swimmeret rhythm by octopamine and the neuropeptide proctolin. J. Neurophysiol. **58:**584-597.

Nagy, F. & Dickinson, P.S. (1983). Control of a central pattern generator by an identified modulatory interneurone in Crustacea. I. Modulation of the pyloric motor output. J. Exp. Biol. **105:**167-173.

Nusbaum, M.P. & Marder, E. (1987) A newly identified modulatory proctolin- containing neuron (MP neuron) in the stomatogastric nervous system of the crab *Cancer borealis*. Neurosci. Abstr. 13:1257.

Parnas, I., Armstrong, D. & Strumwasser, F. (1974). Prolonged excitatory and inhibitory synaptic modulation of a bursting pacemaker neuron. J. Neurophysiol. **37:**594-608.

Reichert, H. & Krenz, W.D. (1986). In vivo visualization of individual neurons in arthropod ganglia facilitates intracellular neuropil recording. J. Comp. Physiol. **158:**625-637.

Russell, D.F. & Hartline, D.K. (1982). Slow active potentials and bursting motor patterns in pyloric network of the lobster, *Panulirus interruptus*. J. Neurophysiol. **48**:914-937.

Selverston, A.I. & Moulins, M. (1985). Oscillatory neural networks. A. Rev. Physiol. **47**:29-48.

Selverston, A.I. & Moulins, M. (1987). The Crustacean Stomatogastric System. New York: Springer-Verlag.

Stewart, W.W. (1978). Functinal connections between cells as revealed by dye-coupling with a highly fluorescent naphthalimide tracer. Cell. **17:**741-759.

Van Harreveld, A. (1936). A physiological solution for fresh water crustacea. Pro. Soc. Exp. Biol. & Med. **34**:428-432.

Frontiers in Crustacean Neurobiology
Advances in Life Sciences

SWIMMERET EVOKED CONTROL OF ABDOMINAL POSTURE IN LOBSTERS: INHIBITION OF EXTENSION ANTAGONISTS

Charles H. Page and Vibhakar C. Kotak

Department of Biological Sciences and Bureau of Biological Research, Rutgers University, Piscataway, N. J.08855 USA

SUMMARY

Tactile stimulation of an abdominal swimmeret appendage in lobster alters the activity of most intersegmental extension and flexion producing interneurons (EPIs and FPIs) in the abdominal nerve cord. The resulting EPI excitation and FPI inhibition are appropriate for the postural motor program evoked by swimmeret stimulation. This program includes simultaneous extension excitation and flexion inhibition.

Microelectrode recordings from pairs of FPIs and flexor motor neurons, indicate that the sensory evoked IPSPs produced in the FPIs and the flexion efferents are elicited by different GABAergic interneurons.

Since blocking FPI spike discharge reduces the rate of spontaneous flexor motor neuron spiking, and FPIs are inhibited during periods of spontaneous and swimmeret evoked extension, inhibition of the FPIs contributes to the suppression of flexion during the extension motor program.

INTRODUCTION

Mechanosensory stimulation of an abdominal swimmeret in lobster initiates a fictive abdominal extension response (swimmeret evoked postural response or SEPR) by exciting the tonic extension efferents and inhibiting the tonic flexion efferents (Fig. 1) (Kotak & Page, 1987).

The abdominal nerve cord of clawed lobsters and crayfish contains several hundred intersegmental postural interneurons (PIs) hypothesized to control abdominal position (Larimer, 1988). These PIs excite and/or inhibit postural efferents when stimulated by intracellular current injection (Jellies & Larimer, 1985; Jones and Page, 1986).

Although most (80%) are flexion producing interneurons (FPIs) that excite flexion efferents (flexor motor neurons and extensor peripheral inhibitor) and inhibit extension efferents (extensor motor neurons and flexor peripheral inhibitor), a minority evoke postural extension activity (EPIs) by exciting extension efferents and inhibiting flexion efferents.

The long delay for initiation of SEPRs (35ms) suggests that interneurons interposed between afferents and efferents mediate these responses, rather than direct afferent-efferent connections (Kotak & Page, 1987).

Since EPI excitation coupled with FPI suppression should produce a postural extensionmotor program, it is probable that sensory evoked excitation of EPIs and inhibition of FPIs is important for generation of the SEPR.

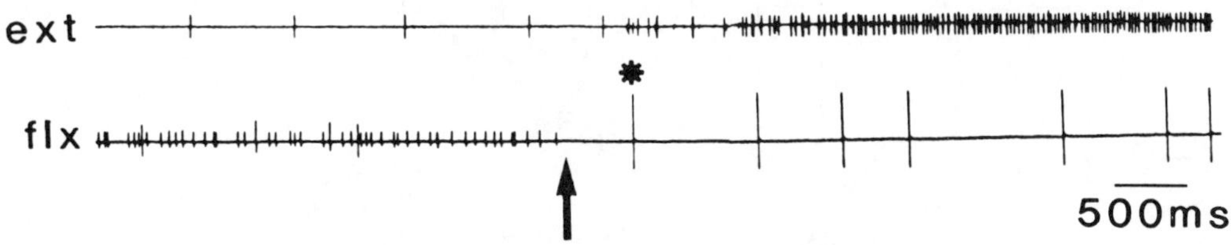

Fig. 1. The swimmeret evoked extension motor program.
Tactile stimulation of the swimmeret (arrow) initiated fictive extension. Excitation of extensor motor neurons (upper trace) is accompanied by suppression of the flexor motor neurons and excitation of the flexor peripheral inhibitor (asterisk) (lower trace).

RESULTS

To test our hypothesis that the SEPR is mediated by PIs, we used intracellular microelectrodes to record simultaneously from PI and motor neuron somata located in the second abdominal ganglion (A2) of a reduced abdominal nerve cord preparation which consisted of A2-A3 with attached left 2nd swimmeret (Fig. 2).

Since several FPI somata are located readily for microelectrode penetration (compared with the infrequently encountered EPIs), our analysis focused on FPI suppression during the SEPR, with special attention to FPIs 303 and 305 (f3FPIs). These FPIs were identified by their vigorous excitation of flexor motor neuron f3, soma location and axon projection Injection of depolarizing current into a f3FPI sufficient to initiate a burst of spikes, evokes strong bilateral excitation of f3. In contrast to many other FPIs, f3FPI spiking does not affect any other postural efferents. Like most PIs that we have recorded from, f3FPIs influence efferent activity through a polysynaptic pathway.

Dual microelectrode recordings from a f3FPI and f3 show little correlation between FPI spikes, and EPSPs or spikes in f3. The absence of one to one coupling between FPI spikes and f3 was confirmed by examining multiple traces of intracellular recordings of f3 activity triggered by f3FPI spikes (Fig. 3).The long delay (about 15ms) for initiation of compound EPSPs in f3 by injecting depolarizing current into a f3FPI also supports the absence of monosynaptic connections between f3FPI and f3.

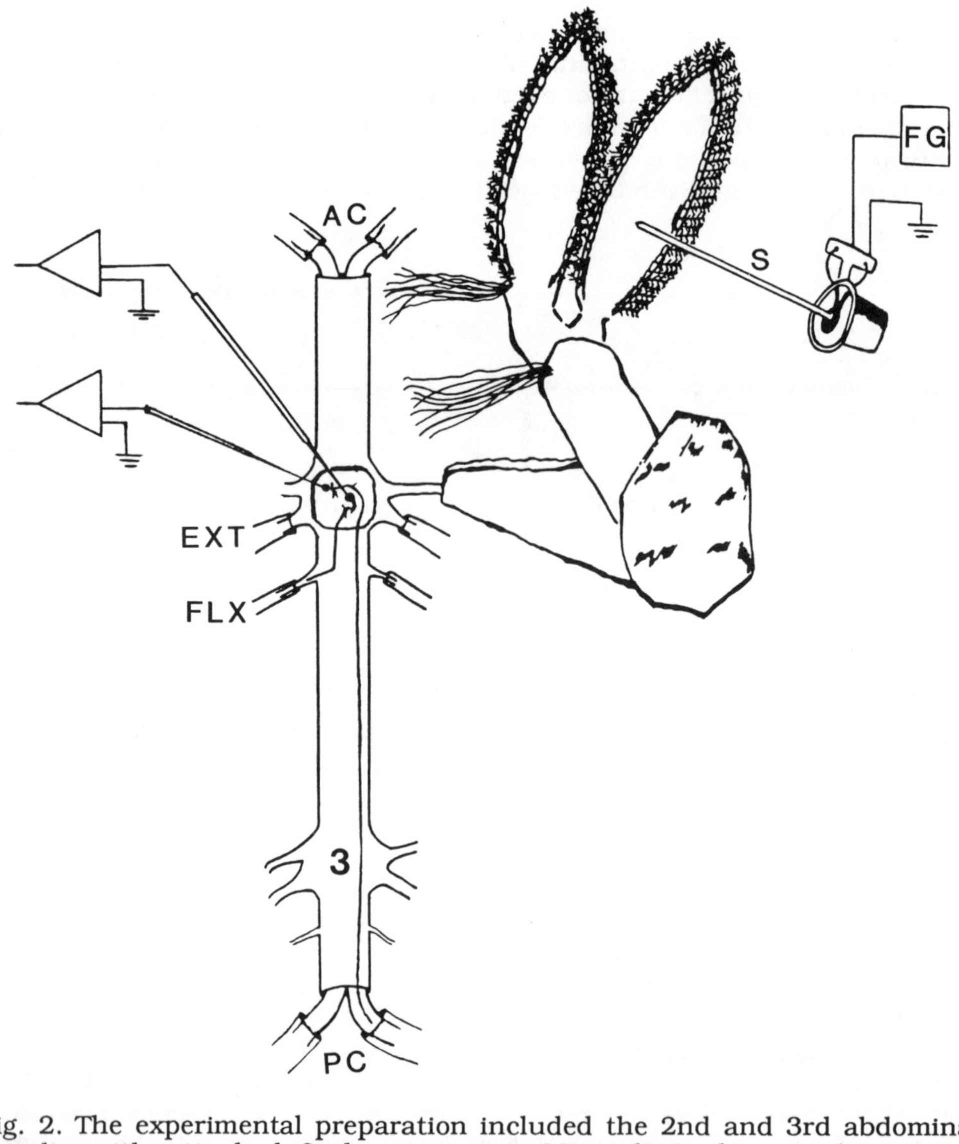

Fig. 2. The experimental preparation included the 2nd and 3rd abdominal ganglia with attached 2nd swimmeret. Microelectrode recordings were obtained from identified postural interneurons and efferents in the 2nd ganglion. Spike activities were monitored with suction electrodes attached to the extensor (EXT) and flexor (FLX) roots and to the ascending (AC) and descending (DC) hemiconnectives. Tapping of the swimmeret surface or deflection of sensilla was produced by a stimulus probe (S) attached to a speaker driven by a function generator (FG).Stronger responses were initiated by stroking the swimmeret with a fine brush.

Tactile stimulation of the swimmeret was provided by a mechanical tapper attached to a speaker cone (Fig. 2) or manual stroking with a brush. Swimmeret stimulation initiated compound synaptic potentials (cPSPs) in every PI we examined. These responses were usually appropriate for the SEPR motor program; extension antagonists (FPIs) were inhibited, while extension synergists (EPIs) were excited. They included cIPSPs in 35 of 36 FPIs (one produced EPSPs) and cEPSPs in all 5 EPIs examined. For example excitation of swimmeret afferents inhibited FPIs 201, 202, 302, 303 and 305,

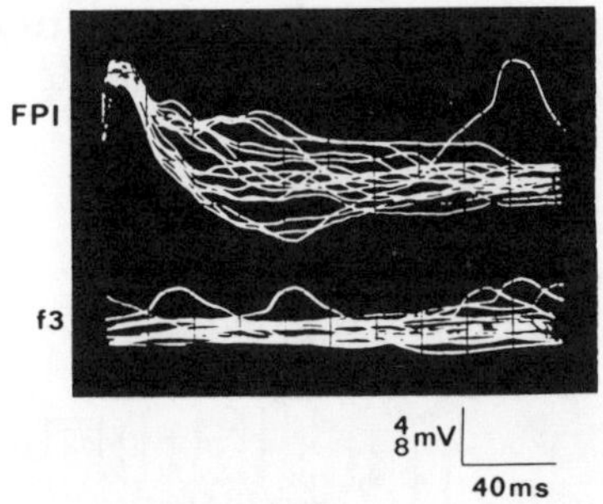

Fig. 3. f3FPI and f3 are not monosynaptically coupled.
When f3FPI spikes trigger the oscilloscope trace, f3 potentials time locked to the f3FPI spikes are not observed. Fifteen consecutive sweeps.

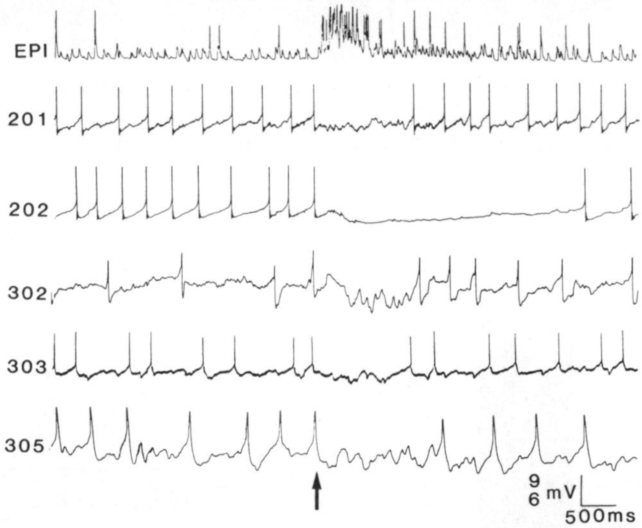

Fig. 4. Tactile stimulation of swimmeret (arrow) initiates compound synaptic potentials in postural interneurons.EPSPs elicited in EPI increase spiking (upper trace) while IPSPs evoked in 5 identified FPIs inhibit FPI spike discharge (lower 5 traces).and excited an unidentified EPI that evoked a strong extension response in the postural efferents (Fig. 4).

The receptive fields of the cIPSPs recorded from FPIs during a SEPR (and cEPSPs from the few EPIs examined) included the entire swimmeret (we did not examine other regions of the abdomen). Similar cIPSPs were recorded from FPIs regardless of the type of mechanoreceptor that was stimulated (feathered hairs, female specific smooth hairs, and hypodermal receptors). Stimulation of a single swimmeret evoked responses in ipsilateral and contralateral f3FPI somata. The wide range of receptor types that affect an individual PI, the large receptive field, the long delay for sensory initiation of a cPSP in a PI (about 25ms), and the bilateral nature of these responses all suggest that sensory interneurons are interposed between the mechanosensory afferents and most PIs.

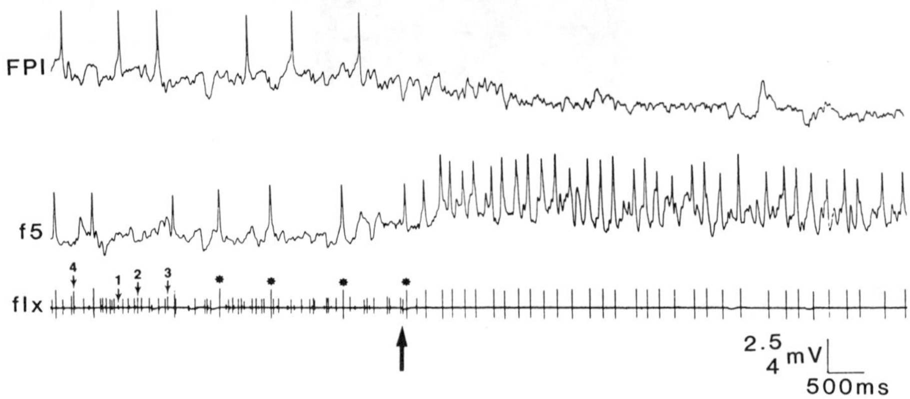

Fig. 5. Spontaneous shift (arrow) from flexion to extension motor program is correlated with f3FPI inhibition.
Note inhibition of flexor excitors 1, 2, 3, 4 and activation of the f5 inhibitor (asterisk).

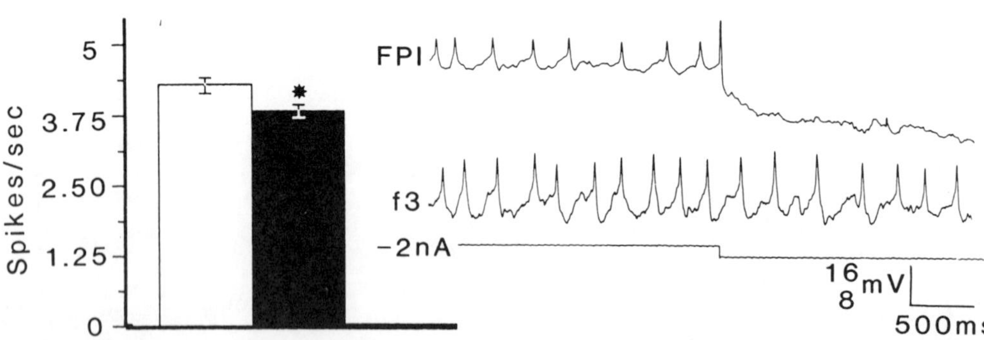

Fig. 6. Injection of hyperpolarizing current into a f3FPI reduces spontaneous f3 discharge. Bar graphs for 1 sec periods before (open) and during (solid) current injection. Reduction of f3 spiking is significant. (P<0.015 t test). 22 trials.

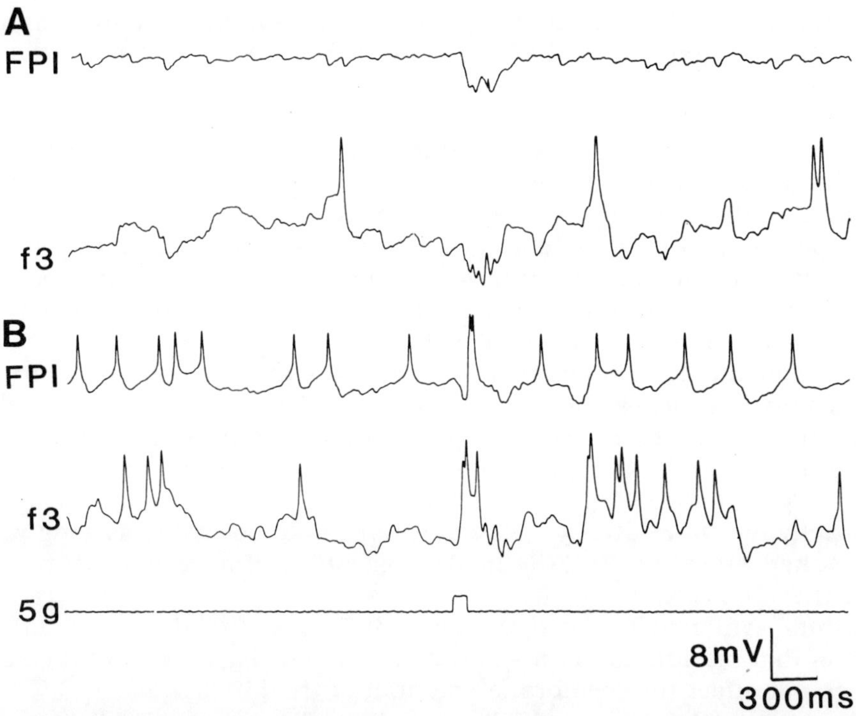

Fig. 7. 50μM picrotoxin in bath blocks IPSPs generated in f3FPI and f3 in response to 5g tap of swimmeret. A. before and B. after addition of picrotoxin. Note shift to excitatory response.

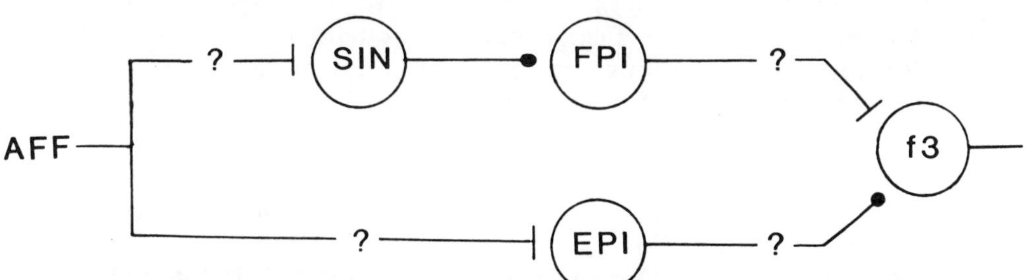

Fig. 8. Summary diagram for neural circuit that suppresses flexion activity during a swimmeret evoked extension response. "T" terminals are excitatory, solid terminals are inhibitory.? indicates that additional interneurons may be interposed in the pathway. AFF = tactile sensitive swimmeret receptors; SIN = inhibitory sensory interneurons; EPI and FPI = extension and flexion producing interneurons; f3 = flexor motor neuron f3.

The cIPSPs evoked in FPIs must be mediated by inhibitory interneurons since mechanosensory afferents are not known to be inhibitory.

Inhibition of the FPIs contributes to the flexion inhibition component that is characteristic of both SEPRs and centrally generated extension motor programs. For example, whenever ongoing efferent activity switched spontaneously from a flexion to an extension motor program, the f3FPIs were inhibited (Fig. 5). Similarly, spontaneous bouts of flexion activity which include large (5 fold) increases in f3 spike discharge, are accompanied by moderate (2 fold) increases in spiking of f3FPIs.

The importance of f3FPI inhibition for flexion suppression during a SEPR or other extension motor program is indicated by the significant reduction in ongoing f3 spike discharge observed when f3FPI spiking is blocked by hyperpolarizing current injection (Fig. 6).

The flexion inhibition component of the SEPR includes the generation of cIPSPs in FPIs and flexor efferents.

Although preliminary pharmacological studies indicate that both cIPSPs are GABAergic since they are blocked by the non-competitive GABA antagonist picrotoxin (Fig. 7), the cIPSP generated in f3 by swimmeret afferent activity has a latency (54+2ms) that is almost twice as long as the cIPSP evoked in a f3FPI (28+2ms) suggesting that different neurons produce these cIPSPs.

Additional evidence for mediation of f3FPI and f3 cIPSPs by different neurons is that stimulation of a small group of sensilla which produce IPSPs in f3 does not affect the membrane potential of the f3FPI soma.

As summarized in the circuit diagram (Fig. 8), our results demonstrate that suppression of flexion activity during a SEPR involves multiple neural pathways. There are at least two populations of GABAergic interneurons; one evokes cIPSPs in FPIs while the other inhibits the flexion efferents. The two levels at which flexion activity can be suppressed provide differential control of FPI vs. flexion efferent activities, and thereby permit greater flexibility in fine tuning the motor program in response to changes in the behavioral condition of the animal.

REFERENCES

Jellies, J. & Larimer, J. L. (1985) Synaptic interactions between neurons involved in the production of abdominal posture in crayfish. J. comp. Physiol. **156:**861-873.

Jones, K. A. & Page, C. H. (1986) Postural interneurons in the abdominal nervous system of lobster: I. Organization, morphologies and motor programs for flexion, extension and inhibition. J. comp. Physiol. **158**:259-272.

Kotak, V. C. & Page, C. H. (1987) Synaptic responses produced in lobster postural motor neurons by mechanical stimulation of the swimmeret. J. comp. Physiol. **161**:695-703.

Larimer, J. L. (1988) The command hypothesis: a new view using an old example. Trends Neurosci. **11:**506-510.

Frontiers in Crustacean Neurobiology
Advances in Life Sciences

NUMERICAL AND SERIAL ASPECTS OF THE INTERNEURONS CONTROLLING ABDOMINAL POSITIONING IN CRUSTACEANS

James L. Larimer

Department of Zoology, The University of Texas, Austin, TX 78712

SUMMARY

The interneuronsthat underlie abdominal positioning movements in crustaceans, known also as command elements, have certain characteristics which we believe strongly influence their form and function. Key among them are: a) their large numbers, b) the prevalence of synaptic interactions with other command elements, c) the presence of axons that can project into distant parts of the nervous system (projection cells, instead of local cells), d) the presence of a stronger motor effect (bias) in either the rostral or caudal direction away from the site of stimulation and finally, e) a loss of similarity ("serial homology") among abdominal positioning interneurons in different ganglia. Evidence is presented which suggests that these morphological, synaptic and metameric characteristics may be both causally and functionally interrelated.

INTRODUCTION

The interneurons involved in abdominal positioning behaviors in crustaceans (Wiersma and Ikeda, 1964; Kennedy et al., 1967) are characterized by microelectrode stimulation and dye-filling utilizing evoked motor outputs and cell morphologies. The interneurons can be divided into flexion-producing and extension-producing as well as several classes of inhibitory cells (Jones and Page, 1986a,b,c; Larimer, 1988).

Early estimates indicated that large numbers of these interneurons are involved in abdominal positioning behaviors and that they are predominantly axon bearing cells (Kennedy, et al., 1967). Recent studies have not only revised these numbers upward but determined some significant aspects of their axonal projections (Larimer and Pease, 1988). Attention has also been given to the possible causes and meaning of bias in abdominal motor programs. Other studies compared the intersegmental similarity of key effectors of abdominal positioning behaviors such as the tonic abdominal positioning motor neurons, tonic muscles etc., with the intersegmental similarity of the interneurons that control the motor neurons and muscles (Larimer and Pease, 1989). This paper focuses primarily on these numerical and metameric aspects of the abdominal positioning nervous system.

METHODS

Adult crayfish, *Procambarus clarkii*, of both sexes were used, ranging in rostrum-telson length from 8 to 10 cm. In most experiments the abdominal nerve cords were removed under cold anesthesia, pinned in sylgard-lined dishes and bathed with van Harreveld's (1936) saline. Single premotor interneurons were impaled with Lucifer Yellow-filled microelectrodes (Stewart,1978) and stimulated by current injections. Swimmeret motor neurons from root one, extensor motor neurons from root two and flexor motor neurons from root three were recorded in various ganglia from A_1 through A_5. In this way, each motor program was recorded as well as any bias it might exhibit. In some experiments two interneurons were impaled simultaneously to determine their synaptic interactions. Finally, studies on the firing of the premotor interneurons in behaving animals involved minimally dissected preparations capable of exhibiting either spontaneous or evoked abdominal positioning behaviors (Jellies and Larimer, 1986; Murphy et al., 1989).

RESULTS

A catalog of several hundred abdominal positioning interneurons has been assembled consisting of both morphologies and evoked motor programs. Although many of these cells have been seen more than once, new ones, not in the catalog, are encountered on occasion. The total number of abdominal positioning interneurons, both seen and unseen, has been estimated using two mathematical methods (Larimer and Pease, 1988). It was assumed that the samples were gathered at random, that each cell is identifiable and that once identified, each cell is equivalent to a tagged individual in a population. Catalog samples used for calculating the totals were taken from abdominal ganglia A_3, A_4, A_5 and A_6 and consisted of 29, 30, 20 and 35 cells (N=114). Using a modification of the Maximum Likelihood method we estimated the total number of abdominal positioning interneurons in these ganglia to be 34 (27-49), 60 (42-108), 86 (53-186), and 98 (69-180) respectively with 95% confidence intervals (in parentheses) except for A_5 where a 90% confidence interval is given. The Lincoln Index method yielded similar results (Larimer and Pease, 1988). Kondoh and Hisada (1986), using nickel backfilling techniques, have recently counted a total of 198 projection neurons in A_3 and 136 in A_6. Since the abdominal positioning interneurons are virtually all projection cells, many of the total projection cells present must be associated with abdominal positioning behaviors.

In another study, 39% of the flexion cells (N=82) and 7% of the extension-evoking cells (N=29) tested were shown to project their axons from the abdominal cord to the brain (Larimer and Moore, 1984). These widely distributed cell processes could facilitate synaptic interactions with neurons in many parts of the nervous system.

When a unipolar command element (projection cell with one axon) is stimulated, the resulting motor output typically spreads both caudally and rostrally away from the site of stimulation and is often stronger (biased) in one direction. A correlation has been made between the direction of axonal projections of 37 unipolar command elements with somata in A3, A4 and A5 and the direction of bias in their evoked motor outputs (Larimer and Pease, 1988). Of 13 interneurons projecting in the rostral direction, 7 showed outputs biased rostrally, 5 were not biased and only 1 showed a bias in the direction opposite the axonal projection. Among the 24 unipolar cells with caudally projecting axons, 18 released a stronger motor output in the caudal direction, 3 had no bias and 3 exhibited a motor output bias in the direction opposite the axonal projection. Unipolar command elements from A6 necessarily project their axons rostrally. Twenty (20) of these were examined and 11 were biased caudally, 8 showed no bias, while one had a rostral bias. These data will be considered again in the discussion.

An intersegmental comparison has been made between abdominal metameric structures and the premotor interneurons responsible for abdominal movements (Larimer and Pease, 1989). Specifically, we examined identified sensory neurons, the segmental giant neurons, certain segmental axonless (local) neurons, the immunohistochemical maps of serotonin- and proctolin-like neurons, identified motor neurons, the structure and number of fibers in the tonic abdominal flexion and extension muscles, the anatomy of ganglia, skeletal structures and limbs (compiled from the literature, Larimer and Pease, 1989). It was concluded that the intersegmental similarity among these diverse cells and structures has been largely conserved in evolution.

Seventy nine abdominal positioning command elements from the catalogs of abdominal ganglia A3, A4 and A5 were used for the serial comparison of these cells. An elaborate set of criteria was applied to determine whether these cells were serially similar or different in different ganglia (Larimer and Pease,1989). Only 25% of the command elements for abdominal positioning behaviors were found to be "similar" in different ganglia. Since we do not know their embryonic origins, we cannot in the strictest sense consider such cells as *serial homologs* , but assuming them to be serial homologs in the ancestral forms, the data suggest that a major evolutionary divergence has occurred within this group of cells.

DISCUSSION

How are the large numbers of abdominal positioning interneurons used effectively? How do synaptic interactions among these command elements and their projection cell morphologies affect their function? How might a biased output be generated and what could it accomplish? What does it mean to depart from basic metamerism in a group of interneurons?

It is well known that crustaceans such as crayfish or lobsters can assume numerous abdominal geometries that could require large numbers of underlying neurons. Evidence suggests that abdominal positioning interneurons do not work alone, but in sizable groups. In addition, abdominal positioning interneurons are sometimes involved in the control of more than one behavior such as swimmeret movements (Evoy and Kennedy, 1967; Williams and Larimer, 1981; Murchison and Larimer, 1986), swimmeret beating and walking (Cattaert and Clarac, 1983) and steering behaviors (Takahata and Hisada, 1985), all of which might increase the overall number of required neurons.

Command elements with projecting axons could provide numerous opportunities for synaptic interactions with other cells and even among themselves. Indeed, studies using pairs of command elements have shown that two flexion-producing interneurons are often interconnected by excitatory synapses. In contrast, a flexion-producing and an extension-producing interneuron are often interconnected by inhibitory synapses. Furthermore, the same synapses appear to exist between the same pairs of cells in all individuals. However, not all command elements synaptically interact with all other command elements (Jellies and Larimer, 1985). It can be argued that *output bias* as well as the *divergence from serial homology* may have emerged as a consequence of *synaptic interactions* among selected abdominal positioning command elements. The presence as well as the direction of motor output bias can be explained in a number of ways. One might expect that the command element that is stimulated directly could dominate its group because its axon could fire at the highest frequency and thereby convey the strongest signal. More inclusive mechanisms are needed, however, since the direction of bias can be the opposite as well as the same as the axonal projection of the driving cell. For example, net bias might occur because the majority of cells in the functional group have their individual biases in the same direction, or alternatively, those command elements within a functional group with axons projecting in one direction could be excited to a higher frequency than their companions whose axons project in the other direction. It seems likely, therefore, that *bias*, like the *motor program* itself, is a property of the functional group of abdominal positioning interneurons. When the same interneuron is impaled and stimulated in different individuals it is believed to synaptically recruit the same set of interneurons. When the *same* set is recruited it could evoke the *same* motor program and thus the *same* behavior as well as the *same* direction of bias. Whatever the explanation for bias, each biased output could provide the motor program for one of the many abdominal geometries that exists in the animals' repertory.

Published data suggest that the segmental effectors for abdominal and swimmeret movements have largely retained their serial homology. It is therefore surprising to find that the interneurons controlling many of these segmental structures tend to be different in the various abdominal ganglia (Larimer and Pease, 1989). This finding may reflect the differences in evolutionary pressures that bear upon the two sets of structures. For example, a basic plan of morphology among the effectors might serve a limited set of functions in each segment. In contrast, the controlling interneurons not only affect the behaviors locally but project their axons to other parts of the nervous systems for coordinating behaviors at distant sites. Thus the interneurons may have evolved segmentally divergent forms that reflect their complex roles.

ACKNOWLEDGEMENTS

I thank Drs. W. Thompson, H. Zakon, B. Murphy, Ms. B. Kruszewska and Mr. L. Brewer for reading a version of the manuscript. I am particularly grateful to Drs. C. Miall, J. Jellies, D. Moore, B Murphy, C. Pease, L. McAnelly and Mr. D. Murchison for participating in the original experiments. This work was supported by NIH grant NS 05423.

REFERENCES

Cattaert, D. & Clarac, F. (1983) Influence of walking on swimmeret beating in the lobster, *Homarus gammarus*. *J. Neurobiol.*, **14**: 421-439.

Evoy, W. H. & Kennedy, D. (1967) Central nervous organization underlying control of antagonistic muscles in the crayfish. I. Types of command fibers. *J. Exp. Zool.*, **165**: 223-238.

Jellies, J. & Larimer, J. L. (1985) Synaptic interactions between neurons involved in the production of abdominal posture in the crayfish. *J. Comp. Physiol.* A., **156**: 861-873.

Jellies, J. & Larimer, J. L. (1986) Activity of crayfish abdominal-positioning interneurons during spontaneous and sensory-evoked movements. *J. Exp. Biol.* , **120**: 173-188.

Jones, K. A. & Page, C. H. (1986a) Postural interneurons in the abdominal nervous system of lobsters. I. Organization, morphologies and motor programs for flexion, extension and inhibition. *J. Comp. Physiol.* A, **158**: 259-271.

Jones, K. A. & Page, C. H. (1986b) Postural interneurons in the abdominal nervous system of lobsters. II. Evidence for neurons having both command and driver role. *J. Comp. Physiol.* A,**158**: 273-280.

Jones, K. A. & Page, C. H. (1986c) Postural interneurons in the abdominal nervous system of lobsters. III. Pathways mediating intersegmental spread of excitation. *J. Comp. Physiol.* A., **158**: 281-290.

Kennedy, D., Evoy, W. H., Dane, B. & Hanawalt, J. T. (1967) The central nervous organization underlying control of antagonistic muscles in the crayfish. II. Coding of position by command fibers. *J. Exp. Zool.*, **165**: 239-248.

Kondoh, Y. & Hisada, M. (1986) Neuroanatomy of the terminal (sixth abdominal) ganglion of the crayfish, *Procambarus clarkii* (Girard). *Cell Tissue Res.*, **243**: 273-288.

Larimer, J. L. & Moore, D. (1984) Abdominal positioning interneurons in crayfish: Projections to and synaptic activation by higher CNS centers. *J. Exp. Zool.*, **230**: 1-10.

Larimer, J. L. (1988). The command hypothesis: A new view using an old example. *TINS* , **11**: 506-510.
Larimer, J. L. & Pease, C. M. (1988) A quantitative study of command elements for abdominal positioning behavior in the crayfish, *Procambarus clarkii. J. Exp. Zool.* , **247**: 45-55.
Larimer, J. L. & Pease, C. M. (1989) Unexpected divergence among identified interneurons in different abdominal segments of the crayfish, *Procambarus clarkii. J. Exp. Zool.* , (in press).
Murchison, D. & Larimer, J. L. (1986) Dual motor output interneurons. *Soc. Neurosci. Abst.* , **12** : 1299.
Murphy, B. F., McAnelly, M. L. and Larimer, J. L. (1989) Abdominal positioning interneurons in crayfish: participation in behavioral acts. *J. Comp. Physiol.*, **165** : (in press).
Stewart, W. W. (1978). Functional connections between cells as revealed by dye-coupling with a highly fluorescent napthalimide tracer. *Cell*, **14**: 741-759.
Takahata, M & Hisada, M. (1985) Interactions between the motor systems controlling uropod steering and abdominal posture in crayfish. *J. Comp. Physiol.* ,**157**: 547-554.
van Harreveld, A. (1936) A physiological solution for fresh water crustaceans. *Proc. Soc. Exp. Biol. Med.*, **34**: 428-432.
Wiersma, C. A. G. & Ikeda, K. (1964) Interneurons commanding swimmeret movements in the crayfish, *Procambarus clarkii* (Girard). *Comp. Biochem. Physiol.*, **12**: 509-525.
Williams, B. J. & Larimer, J. L. (1981) Neural pathways of reflex-evoked behaviors and command systems in the abdomen of the crayfish. *J. Comp. Physiol.*, **143**: 27-42.

Frontiers in Crustacean Neurobiology
Advances in Life Sciences

THE CRAYFISH POSTURE CONTROL SYSTEM AS A MODEL FOR STUDYING MECHANISMS UNDERLYING BEHAVIORAL VARIABILITY

Masakazu Takahata

Research Institute of Applied Electricity, Hokkaido University, Sapporo 060, Japan

SUMMARY

Crayfish postural reflexes including the uropod steering reflex currently studied show a wide variation in their occurrence probability depending on the animal's behavioral context. Behavioral analysis using EMGs showed that the equilibrium response of uropods was most likely to be elicited by body tilting when the stimulus was given while the animal was performing the abdominal posture movement. Synaptic mechanisms underlying this postural facilitation of the uropod reflex has been investigated by intracellular recording and staining techniques applied to the whole-animal preparation. The uropod motoneurons were found to receive 1) subthreshold EPSPs from the descending statocyst interneurons and 2) sustained depolarization during the abdominal posture movement. Consequently, the uropod reflex would occur as the result of synaptic summation of these two different kinds of synaptic inputs. The sustained depolarization of uropod motoneurons during the abdominal posture movement was shown to be mediated at least partly by local premotor nonspiking interneurons.

INTRODUCTION

Each of individual actions in an animal's behavioral repertoire are in incessant interaction with one another: there are, among them, facilitation, mutual inhibition, preferred transition from one specific action to another, and dominance of a specific action over all others. Classical ethology based on observational studies has revealed that a variety of actions in an animal are organized hierarchically so that individual action can be elicited in response to certain stimuli only under appropriate external and internal conditions (Baerends, 1976). Although neurophysiological mechanisms subserving each individual action have been extensively studied in many animal species, however, no serious effort has been made to clarify the physiological basis of the interaction among behavioral acts except a series of intensive studies on *Pleurobranchaea* behavior by Davis and his colleagues (Davis, 1979; Kovac & Davis, 1980).

The posture control mechanisms of crustaceans have long been studied both at the behavioral and the neuronal levels since Kühn (1914) and von Buddenbrock (1914). The major finding has been that, although crustacean animals have developed a specific equilibrium sense organ called statocyst, the posture reflexes are controlled by several sensory inputs which interact with each other: statocyst, visual and leg proprioceptive inputs (Schöne et al., 1983). However, behavioral analysis showed that the reflexes were controlled not only by the interactive inputs but also by the behavioral context of the animal when the body tilt stimulus was given. For example, the equilibrium response of crayfish uropods was elicited by body tilting with the highest probability when the stimulus was given while the animal was performing the abdominal posture movement. The equilibrium reflex of uropods is thus incorporated into the hierarchical organization of behavioral hierarchyactions in crayfish. In this study, the cellular mechanisms underlying the postural facilitation of uropod reflex in response to body tilting have been investigated with the intracellular recording and staining techniques.

MATERIALS AND METHODS

Adult crayfish, *Procambarus clarkii* Girard, of either sex measuring 7-10cm in body length were obtained commercially and kept in laboratory tanks before experimental use. Methods of behavioral analysis using electromyograms (EMGs) are described elsewhere (Takahata et al., 1984). In order to record the synaptic response of uropod motoneurons to statocyst stimulation, the experimental animal was fixed with its dorsal side up in a chamber filled with crayfish saline in which the abdominal part including the terminal ganglion was submerged. The statocyst receptors were stimulated by bending the crescent hairs with a saline jet directed into the statocyst lumen. To record the motoneuron activity intracellularly during the fictive abdominal posture movement, another type of whole-animal preparation was developed as shown elsewhere (Takahata & Hisada, 1986a). Details of recording and staining procedures are also given in the previous paper.

RESULTS

Summary of EMG study. Behavioral analysis using EMGs of the uropod movement in an animal which was freely walking on a tilted substratum revealed that the body tilt alone was not sufficient for eliciting the steering reflex of uropods (Takahata et al., 1984). Although the direction and magnitude of the uropod reflex were strictly controlled by those of body tilt stimulus (Yoshino et al., 1980), it was found that the elicitation of uropod reflex depended on the behavioral context of the animal as well as the presence of body tilting as the specific stimulus for the reflex. The interaction of steering reflex system with other locomotion-related acts is summarized in Fig.1 which shows that both facilitatory and suppressive effects are exerted on the steering system. In the current study, the neurophysiological mechanisms underlying the facilitatory interaction between the steering and the abdominal posture system was investigated.

Subthreshold EPSPs evoked by descending statocyst interneurons. When the statocyst was stimulated while the animal was at rest, the uropod motoneurons usually showed no discernible responses. However, subthreshold excitatory postsynaptic potentials (EPSPs) were observed in some

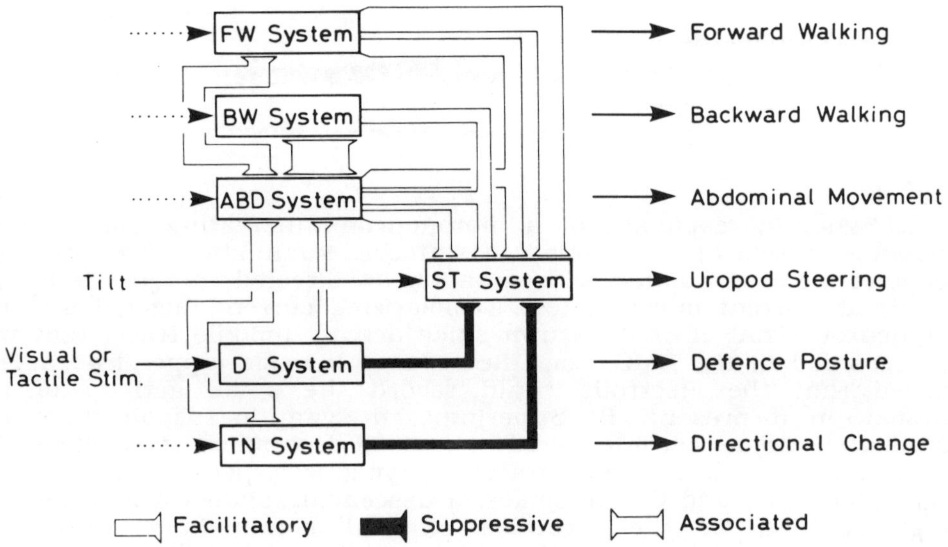

Fig.1 Interaction of uropod steering reflex with locomotion-related acts. Thickness of arrows indicates the degree of interaction. FW, forward walking; BW, backward walking; ABD, abdominal posture movement; ST, steering reflex; D, defence posture; TN, turning movement. (from Takahata et al., 1984)

cases to follow the descending spike activities recorded in the circumesophageal connective (Fig.2). The peak amplitude of these EPSPs was less than 1mV. Since they followed the descending spikes with 1:1 relationship, they seemed to have been evoked monosynaptically, although more rigorous examination is needed to establish the synaptic connection between descending statocyst interneurons and uropod motoneurons.

The reason why the motoneuron response is absent in many cases in spite of similar stimulating conditions is not known. A possibility would be that the input synapses from the descending statocyst interneurons were located electrotonically distant from the major dendritic branches where the microelectrode usually penetrated the motoneurons.

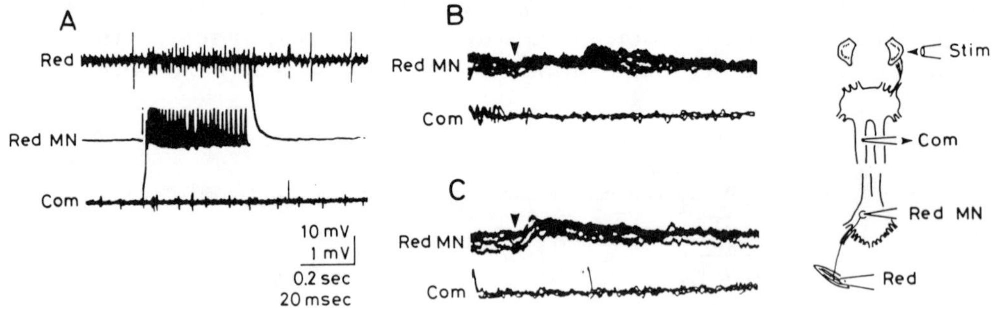

Fig.2. Synaptic responses of a motoneuron innervating the reductor exopodite muscle of the uropod to statocyst stimulation. The statocyst receptors were stimulated with a saline jet directed into the statocyst lumen. A: Current injection test. Depolarizing current injected into the motoneuron (1nA) elicited its own spike activity (middle trace) that was also recorded in the EMG from the reductor muscle (upper trace). This showed that the electrode could record the spike activity of the motoneuron if present. B: Superimposed synaptic responses of the motoneuron (upper trace) triggered by a small descending spike elicited by the statocyst stimulation (lower trace). C: Synaptic responses triggered by a large spike. In B and C, the spikes of descending statocyst interneurons were recorded in the circumesophageal commissure while the experimental animal was in the rest condition. No spike activity was observed in uropod motoneurons in response to statocyst stimulation. A, B and C were obtained from the same animal.

Synaptic activity of uropod motoneurons during the fictive abdominal movement. Uropod motoneurons showed sustained depolarization during the fictive abdominal posture movement. The depolarization was subthreshold in fast motoneurons whereas in slow motoneurons it was often suprathreshold, with action potentials superimposed on the sustained depolarization (Fig.3). The magnitude of this depolarization was typically 5-10mV. The depolarization lasted as long as the abdominal posture system continued to be active. Injection of constant current into the motoneuron through the recording electrode revealed that the membrane resistance showed a decrease during the sustained depolarization (Takahata & Hisada,

1986a). This observation indicated that the depolarization was due to excitation rather than disinhibition.

Role of local nonspiking interneurons in postural facilitation of uropod steering. The results shown above suggested that the uropod motoneuron activity during the steering reflex would be the result of synaptic summation of the subthreshold EPSPs from the descending statocyst pathway with the sustained depolarization during the abdominal posture movement, although the actual summation of these two synaptic inputs could not be confirmed because of technical difficulties in such an experiment. However, the observation that the spike activities of descending statocyst interneurons remains almost the same independent of whether the abdominal posture system is active or not (Takahata & Hisada, 1985) indicates that the sustained depolarization would be causal for the motoneuron spike activity to be elicited by the statocyst interneurons.

Intracellular recording and current injection test revealed that local premotor nonspiking interneurons were at least partly responsible for producing the sustained depolarization in motoneurons (Takahata & Hisada, 1986b). Some of them received depolarizing input while others hyperpolarizing input when the abdominal posture system was in action.

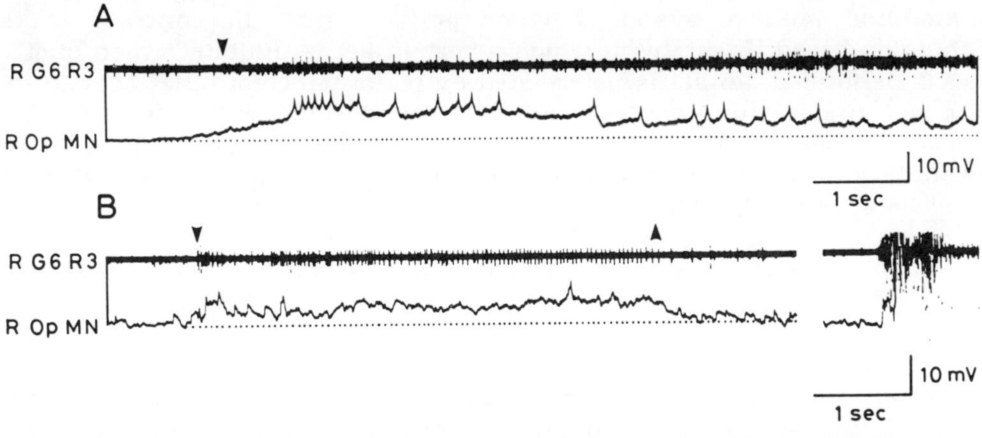

Fig.3. Sustained depolarization of uropod motoneurons during the fictive abdominal posture movement. A: Suprathreshold depolarization recorded in a slow motoneuron (lower trace) innervating one of the opener muscles of uropod. Overall spike activity in opener motoneurons (upper trace) showed an increase when the abdominal movement occurred (indicated by an arrowhead). B: Subthreshold depolarization in another slow opener motoneuron. The first and second arrowheads on the upper trace indicate the beginning and ending of posture movement respectively. The depolarization lasted as long as the posture movement continued. (modified from Takahata & Hisada, 1986a)

In either type of interneurons, artificial membrane potential change by current injection in the observed direction caused an increase in the uropod motoneuron activity just as in the abdominal posture movement.

DISCUSSION

Excitatory synaptic interaction as the basis of behavioral variability . The variation in an animal's response to an identical external stimulus can be accounted for in certain cases by the functional organization of individual behavioral acts (Baerends, 1976): in order for a certain response to be elicited by a specific stimulus, the animal must be in the appropriate behavioral context for the response. Neurophysiological mechanisms underlying such behavioral organization have been thought to be based on synaptic inhibition (Rowell, 1964; Kovac & Davis, 1980). Bentley (1969) observed that leg motoneurons of cricket at rest received continuous inhibitory input and that they were disinhibited by sensory stimulation to the cercus to generate action potentials for evoking the evasive behavior.

Hierarchical organization of behavior, however, can also be based on excitatory synaptic interaction as in the crayfish posture control system. Present study showed that 1) uropod motoneurons at rest received no inhibitory input and 2) they received depolarizing excitatory input when the abdominal posture system became active. Thus, in contrast to the inhibition-based hierarchy in which a certain act is inhibited when another act is performed, an act is potentiated by performance of other acts so that the act under their control can be elicited only while the animal is performing one of those acts. Under natural conditions, both inhibitory and excitatory synaptic interactions seem to be working in organizing the behavioral hierarchy (Fig.1).

Nonspiking interneurons as the modulator of neuronal circuit operation. The excitatory interaction between the abdominal posture and the descending statocyst system was shown to be mediated at least in part by nonspiking interneurons. Since the first report in cockroach (Pearson & Fourtner, 1975), they have been found in many invertebrate motor control systems (Siegler, 1985). Although their physiological properties have been intensively analysed (Burrows & Siegler, 1978; Burrows, 1979), however, their behavioral role is still to be investigated. Several possible advantages of nonspiking neural communication in the behavioral control have been generically discussed (Pearson, 1976) to seek for their embodiment in the nonspiking interneurons.

In this study, nonspiking interneurons were shown to participate in gating the descending statocyst-motor pathway by providing motoneurons during the abdominal posture movement with sustained excitation that would sum up with the otherwise subthreshold EPSPs from the statocyst to elicit spike activity. They seem to work as the integrator based on their membrane electrotonus to convert discrete synaptic potentials into continuous output to motoneurons as observed in their sustained depolarization (Fig.3). Functional advantages of an integrating element in the neuronal circuit for controlling behavior have been pointed out by Pearson (1976). Further study is needed to test in other systems the possibility that nonspiking interneurons might function as the modulatory element in the behavioral control by taking advantage of their integrative property.

Supported in part by Grants-in-Aid from MESC Japan (63304005, 01540585).

REFERENCES

Baerends, G.P. (1976) The functional organization of behaviour (The Niko Tinbergen Lecture). Anim. Behav. **24:** 726-738.

Bentley, D.R. (1969) Intracellular activity in cricket neurons during the generation of behavior patterns. J. Insect. Physiol. **15**: 677-699.

Burrows, M. (1979) Synaptic potentials effect the release of transmitter from locust non-spiking interneurons. Science **204**: 81-83.

Burrows, M. & Siegler, M.V.S. (1978) Graded synaptic transmission between local interneurones and motoneurones in the metathoracic ganglion of the locust. J. Physiol. **285**: 231-255.

Davis, W.J. (1979) Behavioral hierarchies. Trends in Neurosci. **2** 5-7.

Kovac, M.P. & Davis, W.J. (1980) Neural mechanism underlying behavioral choice in Pleurobranchaea. J. Neurophysiol. **43**: 469-487.

Kühn, A. (1914) Die reflektorische Erhaltung des Gleichgewichtes bei Krebsen. Verh. Dtsch. Zool. Ges. **24**: 262-277.

Pearson, K.G. & Fourtner, C. (1975) Nonspiking interneurons in walking system of the cockroach. J. Neurophysiol. **38:** 33-52.

Pearson, K.G. (1976) Nerve cells without action potentials. In Simpler Networks and Behavior (ed. J. C. Fentress) pp.99-110. Sunderland, MA: Sinauer.

Rowell, C.H.F. (1964) Central control of an insect segmental reflex. I. Inhibition by different parts of the central nervous system. J. Exp. Biol. **41**: 559-572.

Schöne, H., Neil, D., Scapini, F. & Dreissmann, G. (1983) Interaction of substrate, gravity and visual cues in the control of compensatory eye responses in the spiny lobster, Palinurus vulgaris. J. Comp. Physiol. **150:** 23-30.

Siegler, M.V.S. (1985) Nonspiking interneurons and motor control in insects. Adv. Insect Physiol. **18**: 249-304.

Takahata, M., Komatsu, H. & Hisada, M. (1984) Positional orientation determined by the behavioural context in Procambarus clarkii Girard (Decapoda: Macrura). Behaviour **88:** 240-265.

Takahata, M. & Hisada, M. (1985) Interactions between motor systems controlling uropod steering and abdominal posture in crayfish. J. Comp. Physiol. **157**: 547-554.

Takahata, M. & Hisada, M. (1986a) Sustained membrane potential change of uropod motor neurons during the fictive abdominal posture movement in crayfish. J. Neurophysiol. **56:** 702-717.

Takahata, M. & Hisada, M. (1986b) Local nonspiking interneurons involved in gating of the descending motor pathway in crayfish. J. Neurophysiol. **56**: 718-731.

von Buddenbrock, W. (1914) Über die Orientierung der Krebse im Raum. Zool. Jb. (Zool.) **34**: 479-514.

Yoshino, M., Takahata, M. & Hisada, M. (1980) Statocyst control of the uropod movement in response to body rolling in crayfish. J. Comp. Physiol. **139:** 243-250.

Frontiers in Crustacean Neurobiology
Advances in Life Sciences

TONIC MOTONEURONES IN THE THIRD ABDOMINAL GANGLION OF THE SHRIMP, *CRANGON CRANGON*

Gerald Bothe

Zoologisches Institut und Museum, Universität Hamburg, Martin-Luther-King-Platz 3, 2000 Hamburg 13, Federal Republic of Germany*

SUMMARY

Efferent neurones in the third abdominal ganglion of the shrimp, *Crangon crangon*, were studied using cobalt staining techniques. They are involved in extension and tonic flexion. In each half segment, one pair of neurones and two groups of five neurones each are involved in extension. Six motoneurones (F1-F6) per half segment are involved in tonic flexion. Three have an ipsilateral soma, three a contralateral soma. The smallest neurone (F1) sends its axon through the next rostral superficial third root. F1 through F5 are tonically active. F6 shows a spontaneous burst-like discharge pattern. A comparison with published data on crayfish shows a high degree of similarity concerning both neuroanatomy and physiology. In *Callianassa* and *Pagurus*, physiological parameters differ, but the number of motoneurones is the same as in *Crangon*. Patterns of neurones change apparently slowly during evolution.

INTRODUCTION

Form and function of systems undergo changes during evolution. Animals studied in physiology, however, are members of only a few taxa. For better understanding of the function of neural assemblies, one should know which structural or functional parameters changed or were conserved during evolution. In Crustacea, the postural system is well known in lobsters and crayfish, which belong to the infraorder Astacidea of Decapoda. Its parts have been characterized at the cellular level (see Page, 1982 for review and Wine & Hagiwara, 1977, Wine et al., 1974, Thompson & Page, 1982, Kirk & Glantz, 1981). Additional work was done on *Callianassa* and *Upogebia* (infraorder Thalassinidea) (Kahan, 1971) and on *Pagurus* (infraorder Anomura) (Chapple, 1969, 1977). In this study, the abdominal postural system was studied in the infraorder Caridea, which is thought to have retained many plesiomorphic characters. Data of the shrimp, *Crangon crangon*, neuroanatomy and some physiological parameters are compared to those of other Decapoda.

*present address: Fakultät für Biologie, Universität Konstanz, 7750 Konstanz, Federal Republic of Germany

MATERIAL AND METHODS

Brown shrimp, *Crangon crangon*, with a body length 40 - 60 mm were captured in the littoral near Helgoland and Sylt. They were kept in artificial sea water with 2.8% salinity at 10°C. Experiments were done at 20°C.

For anatomy and electrophysiology, shrimp were dissected in cold (8°C) saline (380mM Na^+, 7.5mM K^+, 10.25mM Ca^{2+}, 6.9mM Mg^{2+},, 377.5mM Cl^-, 2mM SO_4^{2-}, 5mM Tris (Sigma), pH 7.4).

Nerve activity was recorded with suction electrodes. Preparations were stable for 3 - 5 h. Neurones were backfilled via cut nerve ends using a cobalt-proline complex. This complex was produced by adding drops of a concentrated solution (60% w/v) of l-proline to 10% $CoCl_2$ (w/v) until all cobalt ion was complexed. This point was determined by adding a drop of this solution to 0.01N NaOH. If the cobalt is not completely bound, a blue precipitate forms. The cobalt-proline solution was diluted with 1 - 2 parts of distilled water for backfilling. Parts of the ventral nerve cord containing the third abdominal ganglion and its nerve roots were dissected and backfilled. Preparations were kept at 4°C for 12 to 36 h. Ganglia were silver-intensified (Bacon & Altman, 1977). The pH of the reducing solution was adjusted to 3.2 to speed the reaction.

RESULTS

Anatomy of nerves and postural muscles. The organization of the postural muscles and the muscle receptor organs in the shrimp, *Crangon crangon* is shown in Fig. 1. To facilitate comparison, the anatomical organization in the crayfish, *Procambarus*, is is depicted below (Fig. 1A, from Page, 1982). In both species, the overall organization of the postural system is similar.

In *Crangon*, the abdomen is slightly compressed laterally. The posterior insertion point of the superficial flexor muscles is on the posterior side of the hard cuticular "bridge". The second root of the abdominal ganglia is split into a rostral and a caudal branch. The latter innervates the extensor muscles, the muscle receptor organs and a small part of the cuticle. The organization of the third root in shrimp and crayfish is identical.

Abdominal motoneurones. Cobalt fills of the dorsal part of the caudal branch of the second root revealed twelve neurones in three groups (Fig. 2; see Fig. 2A for comparison with *Procambarus*). Two groups, containing five neurones each, are located ipsilaterally. Two neurones are contralateral. In addition, five axons are stained which do not possess a soma within this ganglion. Comparing the neurones in *Crangon* with those of *Procambarus* (Wine & Hagiwara, 1974), the neurones might be identified as follows: the ipsilateral-rostral small neurones are the tonic extensor motoneurones, the ipsilateral-caudal large neurones are the phasic extensor motoneurones, the two contralateral neurones are the peripheral inhibitors, the large axons are those of the muscle receptor organs.

Cobalt-proline backfills of the superficial third root of the third abdominal ganglion revealed six neurones, three ipsilateral and three contralateral (Fig. 3; see Fig. 3A for comparison with *Procambarus*). The neurones have been named F1 - F6 according to size with F6 being the largest. The smallest contralateral neurone sends its axon through the next rostral superficial third root. One large neurone has an ipsilateral soma. Another large cell, F5, lies contralaterally. It is the peripheral inhibitor of the tonic flexor muscles. Shrimp and crayfish show similar number and distribution of superficial flexor motoneurones.

Physiology. Recordings from the superficial third root of *Crangon* show tonic activity of four units. Assuming that the largest neurones have the largest axons and impulses, the impulses with the greatest amplitude can be related to neurone F6, the unit with the lowest tonic activity. In isolated, unstimulated preparations, the impulse frequency is below 1 Hz. F5 has smaller impulses and an impulse frequency of 20 Hz. The remaining two classes of impulses are apparently composed of F1/F2 and F3/F4, respectively. Class F3/F4 has a discharge rate of about 25 Hz. Class F1/F2 fires with 25Hz. The discharge rate of F1-F6 varied from 30 Hz to 100 Hz.

Some isolated ventral nerve cord preparations showed cyclic bursting. In such phases of high activity, discharge rates were 10 Hz (F6), 45 Hz (F5), 75 Hz (F3/F4) and 25 Hz (F1/F2). In bursts, the activity recorded from the superficial third root varied from 120 to 200 Hz.

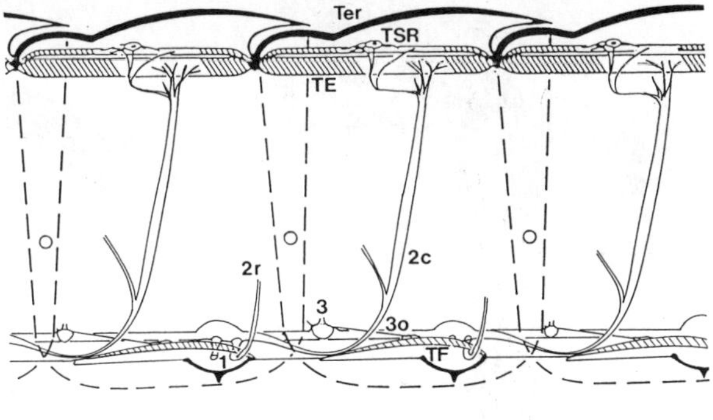

Fig. 1: Organization of postural muscles and muscle receptor organ in the shrimp abdomen. TE: tonic (=superficial) extensor muscle; Ter: tergite; TF: tonic flexor muscle; TSR: tonic stretch receptor; 1: 1st root; 2r: rostral branch of 2nd root; 2c: caudal branch of 2nd root; 3: 3rd root; 3o: superficial branch of 3rd root; circles mark pivot points between abdominal segments.

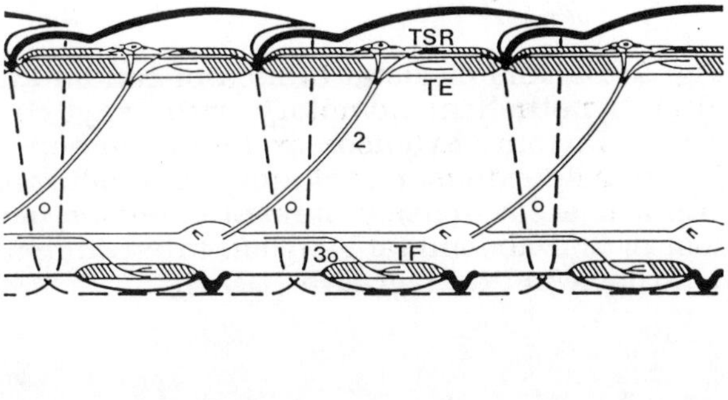

Fig.1A: Organization of postural muscles and muscle receptor organ in the crayfish abdomen. 2: 2nd root; other abbreviations: see legend of Fig. 1. (from Page, 1982)

DISCUSSION

The abdominal postural system of decapod Crustacea has been investigated in Astacidea (*Procambarus*: Wine & Hagiwara, 1977, Wine et al., 1974, Homarus: Thompson & Page, 1982), Thalassinidea (*Callianassa*, *Upogebia*: Kahan, 1971) and Anomura (*Pagurus*: Chapple, 1969, 1977). As shown in this study, the postural system of the shrimp, *Crangon crangon* (Caridea), shows a high degree of similarity with that of Astacidea.

Procambarus (Fig. 3A), *Homarus* and *Crangon* (Fig. 3) have six neurones which innervate exclusively the superficial flexor muscle. Furthermore, in all three species, three of these neurones have a contralateral soma and the smallest of them sends its axon through the next rostral superficial third root. In *Homarus*, however, three neurones innervating phasic flexor muscles each send a branch into the superficial third root. The extensor motor system shows an equally high degree of similarity between Astacidea and Caridea (Fig. 3, 3A).

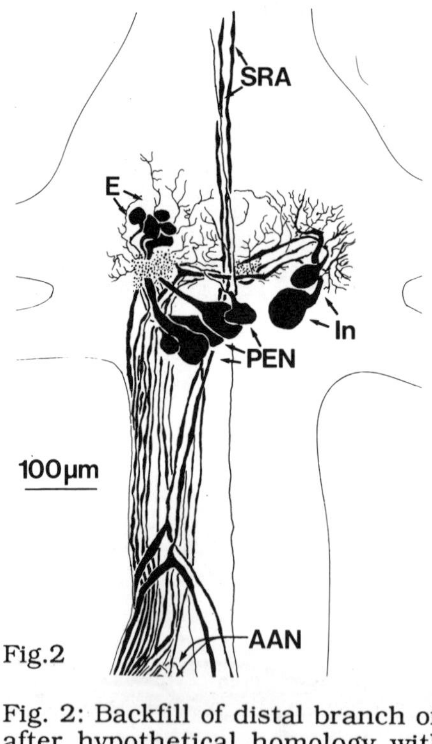

Fig.2

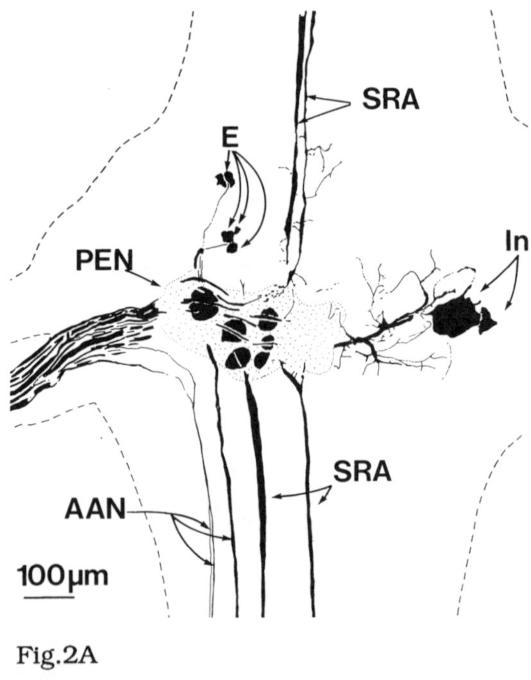

Fig.2A

Fig. 2: Backfill of distal branch of caudal 2nd root in *Crangon*. Units named after hypothetical homology with crayfish: AAN: axons of accessory neurones; E: tonic extensor excitatory motoneurones; In: inhibitory neurones; PE: phasic extensor excitatory motoneurones; SRA: strech receptor axons; stippled area: densely stained extensor neuropil. Fig. 2A : Backfill of 2nd root of 2nd abdominal ganglion in *Procambarus*. Other Abbreviations see Fig. 1 (From Wine & Hagiwara, 1974).

Considering the electrophysiological properties, F1-F5 show sustained tonic activity, whereas F6 has little or no spontaneous activity. In *Crangon* (this study) and *Procambarus* (Kirk & Glantz, 1981), F6 shows a patterned discharge in the form of repetitive bursting.

In spite of the different behaviour of crayfish, lobsters and shrimp, no essential differences were detected in the postural system. Only the spontaneous discharge frequency of the postural neurones differs: 30-200 Hz in *Crangon* versus 50 Hz in *Procambarus* (calculated from Wine et al., 1974). The high discharge frequency in *Crangon* could be due to the necessity of stiffening the abdomen during swimming and digging. The high degree of similarity between *Crangon* and *Procambarus* supports the hypothesis that the organization of the postural system in *Procambarus* represents the plesiomorphic state.

In Thalassinidea and Anomura, on the other hand, the abdominal postural system and the neuronal assemblies are modified. The superficial flexor muscles of Calianassa and *Upogebia* (Thalassinidea) are divided into two layers, the ventral layer consisting of extremely slow fibers (Kahan, 1971).

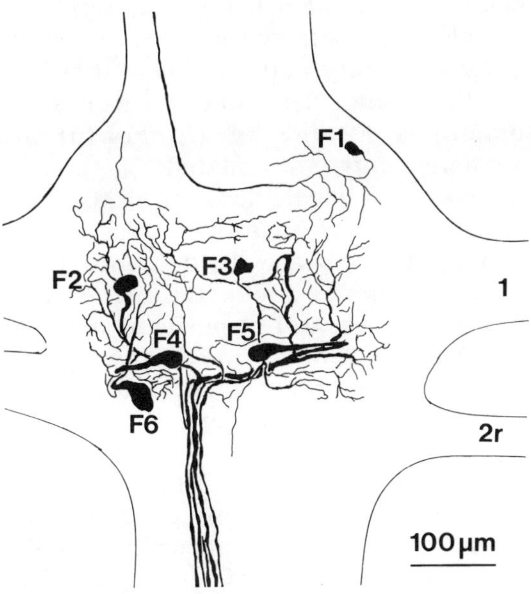

Fig.3

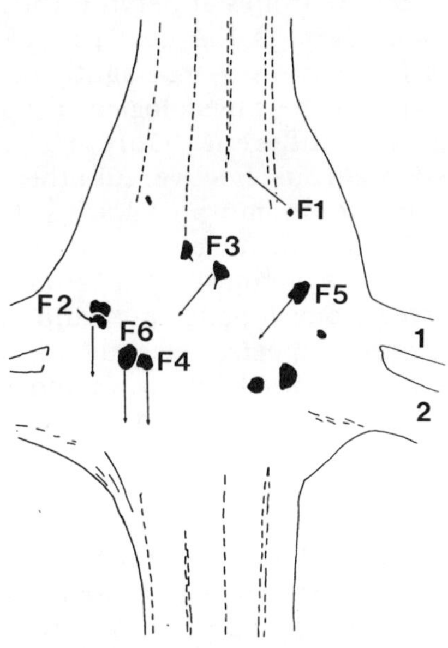

Fig.3A

Fig. 3: *Crangon*, backfill of superficial root of 2nd and 3rd abdominal ganglion. F1-F6: tonic flexor motoneurones, labeled according to size of soma. Fig. 3A: Soma map of 2nd abdominal ganglion in *Procambarus*. Efferents of both superficial 3rd roots are shown; neurones with axons in the right 3rd root are labeled F1-F6. Other abbreviations see Fig. 1. (From Wine et al., 1974)

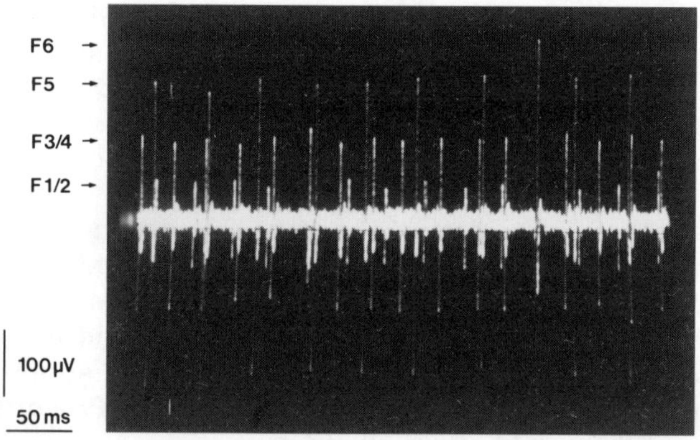

Fig. 4: Extracellular recording from superficial 3rd root of 3rd abdominal ganglion in *Crangon*. 4 classes of impulses can be distinguished, they are labeled F1/2, F3/4, F5 and F6 according to size and physiological properties (see text).

Six neurones innervate these muscles, one of them (F1 or F2) sends its axon through the next rostral superficial third root. The size relationships of the neurones are slightly different, the inhibitory neurone being the third largest. The physiological properties of the "tonic" flexor motoneurones are clearly different. Only F1 and sometimes F2 (F3 in *Upogebia*) are spontaneously active. All other cells are active only if stimulated.

In the Anomuran *Pagurus*, the abdomen has a decalcified, soft cuticle and is hidden in an empty snail shell. It has lost its function in steering and escape swimming. The superficial flexor muscles are divided into three layers, one longitudinal and two circular (Chapple, 1969). As in the other decapod species investigated (see above), the ventral superficial muscles are innervated by six motoneurones per half segment, one of them being inhibitory. The superficial extensor muscles receive one additional inhibitory neurone: i. e. there are seven motoneurones innervating these muscles (Chapple, 1977).

In conclusion, the set of six motoneurones which innervate the superficial flexor muscles was retained through evolution of Decapoda. Their physiological properties, however, have changed according to the behavioural performance neccessary for the survival of the species. In contrast to the stability of the position of neurones in the ganglion, the branching patterns of nerves and axons are highly variable: the superficial third root of Homarus contains additional axons; the second root of *Crangon* is split into two branches. These differences might lead to the conclusion that characters of the nervous system are variable and not useful for phylogenetic studies. This study leads to the contrary conclusion: sets of neurones are very conservative. Their anatomy might be useful for the study of the phylogenic relationships of large groups of arthropoda.

REFERENCES

Bacon, J. P. & Altman, J. S. (1977) A silver intensification method for cobalt-filled neurons in wholemount preparations. Brain Res. 138: 359-363.

Chapple, W. D. (1969) Postural control of shell position by the abdomen of the hermit crab, *Pagurus pollicarus*. I. Morphology of the superficial muscles and their nerves. J. Exp. Zool. 171: 397-408.

Chapple, W. D. (1977) Motoneurons innervating the dorsal superficial muscles of the hermit crab, *Pagurus pollicarus*, and their reflex asymmetry. J. Comp. Physiol. 121: 413-431.

Evoy, W. E. & Kennedy, D. (1967) The central nervous organisation underlying control of antogonistic muscles in the crayfish. I. Types of command fibers. J. Exp. Zool. 165: 223-238.

Kahan, L.B. (1971) Neural control of postural Muscles in *Callianassa californiensis* and three other species of decapod crustaceans. Comp. Biochem. Physiol. 40A: 1-18.

Kirk, M. D. & Glantz, R. M. (1981): Impulse pattern generation in a crayfish abdominal postural motoneuron. J. Comp. Physiol. 141: 183-196.

Page, C.H. (1982) Control of posture. In Biology of Crustacea, Vol. 4: Neural Integration and Behaviour (ed.Sandeman, D.C. & H.L. Atwood), pp. 33-59. New York: Academic Press.

Thompson, C.S. & C.H. Page (1982) Command fiber activation of superficial flexor motoneurons in the lobster abdomen. J. Comp. Physiol. 148: 515-527.

Wine, J.J. & G. Hagiwara (1977) Crayfish escape Behaviour. I. The structure of efferent and afferent neurons involved in abdominal extension. J. Comp. Physiol. 121: 145-172.

Wine, J.J., J.E. Mittenthal & D. Kennedy (1974) The structure of tonic flexor motoneurons in crayfish abdominal ganglia. J. Comp. Physiol. 93: 315-335.

Frontiers in Crustacean Neurobiology
Advances in Life Sciences

THE EXCITABILITY OF THE CRAYFISH LATERAL GIANT ESCAPE REACTION: INHIBITORY CONTROL OF THE LATERAL GIANT DENDRITES

Franklin B. Krasne, Eric T. Vu and Sunhee C. Lee

Department of Psychology and Brain Research Institute,
University of California, Los Angeles, California, 90024, USA.

SUMMARY

Circumstances that increase and decrease the excitability of lateral giant (LG) escape are reviewed. Three types of inhibition (recurrent, post-excitatory, and tonic) that affect direct input to the LG are compared and found to utilize different pathways. Reasons for multiple inhibitory systems are discussed.

INTRODUCTION

Sudden stimulation of the abdomen causes crayfish to rapidly flex their abdomens, which thrust them in a backward/upward direction away from the point of disturbance. This lateral giant (LG) escape reaction, named for the large dorso-lateral nerve cord axons of the response's command neurons, is one of a very few behavior patterns for which we know most of the basic neural circuit all the way from stimulus to response (see Krasne & Wine, 1987 and Wine & Krasne, 1982 for background references). Such knowledge provides great leverage for investigating factors that control whether, on a particular occasion, an animal will or will not respond to an adequate stimulus. To us, understanding this kind of control is the most alluring goal in the study of behavior.

We found a number of years ago that the excitability of LG escape was subject to habituation, and over the years a rather substantial list of factors that can lower excitability has accumulated. Recently several means of increasing it have also been discovered (see Fig. 1 for citations).

A number of factors that suppress excitability affect monosynaptic transmission from primary afferents and sensory interneurons to the LGs themselves (Fig. 1A). Here we summarize recent work comparing the modes of action on the LGs of several of these types of suppression: (1) <u>Recurrent inhibition</u> is a GABA-mediated inhibition that occurs during the operation of the tailflip motor circuitry and helps prevent a new tailflip from starting before one already started is complete. (2) <u>Post-excitatory inhibition (PEI)</u> is a reduction of excitability that develops about 5 ms after the start of a stimulus that excites the LGs even if they do not fire.

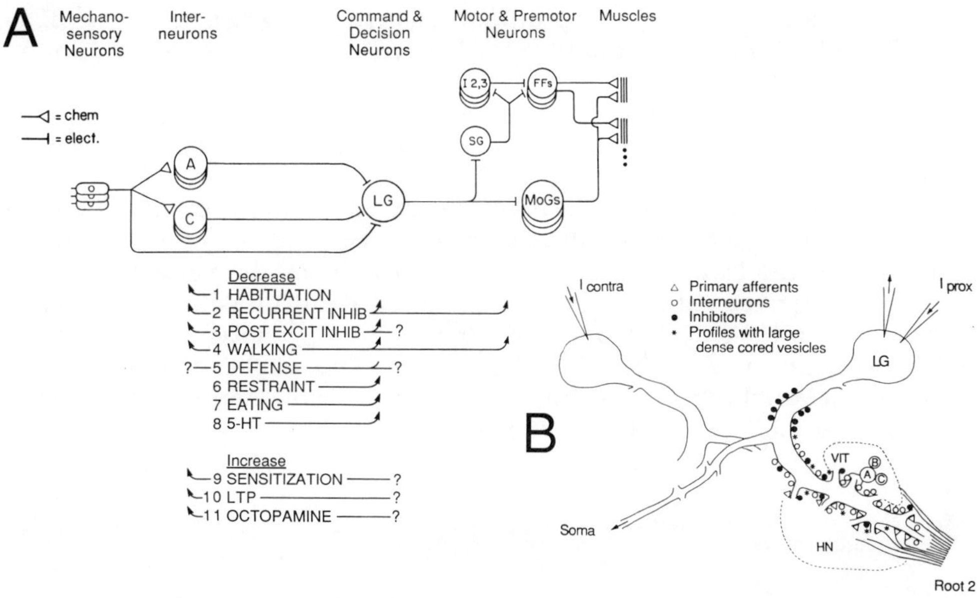

Fig. 1. A. Factors that affect the excitability of LG escape. Arrows indicate points in circuit where transmission is altered. Refs: 1, 2, 5, 6: see Wine & Krasne, 1982; 3: Krasne & Wine, 1987; 4, 5: Fricke et al, 1982; Edwards et al, 1989; 5: Edwards, personal communication; 7: Krasne & Lee, 1988; 8, 11: Glanzman & Krasne, 1983; 9: Krasne & Glanzman, 1986; 10: Miller et al, 1987. B. Cartoon of LG dendrites based on EM analysis.

It is in part because of it that LG reactions only occur to stimuli of abrupt onset. (3) Tonic inhibition is the name we have given to sustained reduction of LG reaction excitability that occurs during feeding and when animals are restrained so that they cannot escape effectively. Suppression during both restraint and feeding are abolished when the connections between abdominal escape circuitry and the rostral half of the nervous system are severed, and both seem to affect transmission to the LGs without altering transmission in sensory or motor circuitry. We will assume that suppression during both feeding and restraint are produced by the same "tonic inhibitory" system, but we note that this assumption might ultimately have to be revised. We believe that tonic inhibition is in many cases the primary determinant of whether an animal will respond to a stimulus.

RESULTS

Fig. 1B indicates the location of input to LG dendrites (Lee and Krasne, in prep.). Primary afferents and interneurons synapse on distal (relative to the axon) dendrites where they produce electrical EPSPs. Input from terminals with elongated synaptic vesicles typical of GABAergic inhibitors are intermixed with excitors distally and also occur by themselves proximally. Finally, intermixed with other distal inputs, one finds processes that contain large, dense cored vesicles that we suspect contain serotonin.

As first shown by Roberts (1968), recurrent inhibition is picrotoxin sensitive, reduces monosynaptic electrical EPSPs to LG recorded at the dendrite/axon juncture by some 30-50%, and reduces the voltage produced by a current injected into the axon or proximal dendrite (V-prox) by almost the same amount. This is illustrated for the monosynaptic EPSP produced in LG by interneuron A (EPSP-A) in Fig. 2B, C. The similarity of attenuation of V-prox and orthodromic EPSPs implies that GABAergic inhibition is occurring proximally, close to the the recording site, and it thus seems

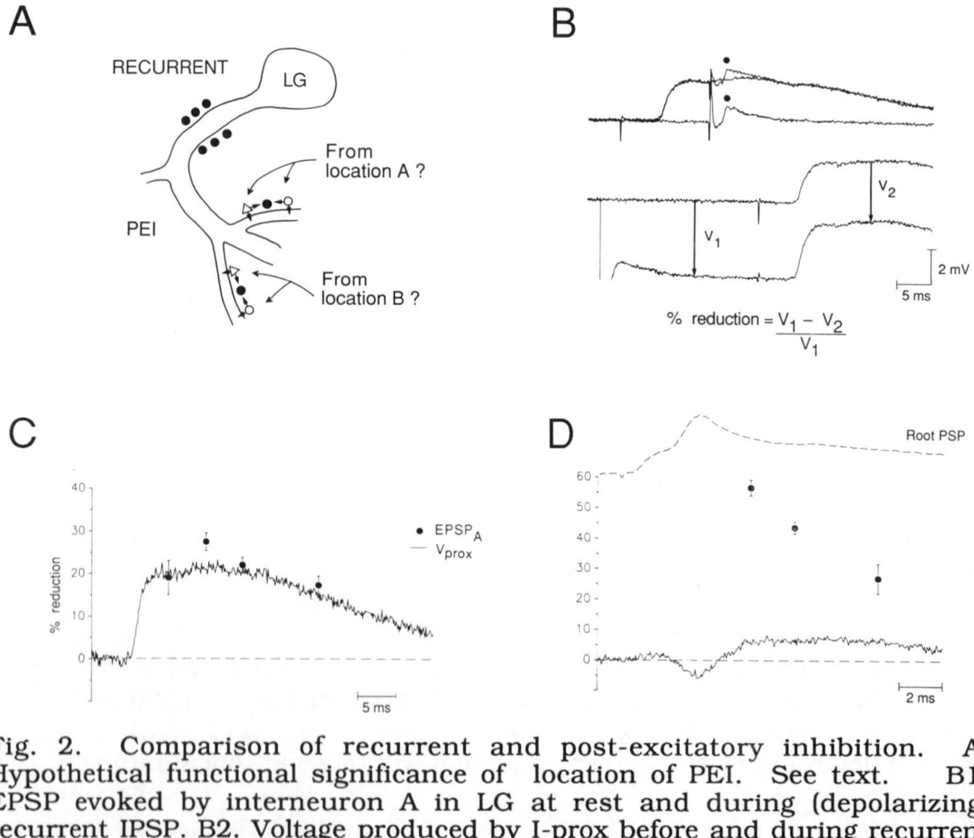

Fig. 2. Comparison of recurrent and post-excitatory inhibition. A. Hypothetical functional significance of location of PEI. See text. B1. EPSP evoked by interneuron A in LG at rest and during (depolarizing) recurrent IPSP. B2. Voltage produced by I-prox before and during recurrent IPSP. Formula indicates how % reduction of V-prox was calculated. C. Reductions of EPSP and V-prox during recurrent inhibition. D. Reductions in EPSP and V-prox during PEI; LG EPSP is shown for reference.

likely that the proximal group of GABA-like terminals portrayed in Fig. 1B is involved in its production.

Similar terminals are also found distally intermixed with excitatory inputs. In examining these distal terminals we noticed an unexpected feature. Both primary afferents and interneurons en route to their LG dendrite targets often form synapses on the presumed inhibitors. This local pathway would be expected to cause inhibition after excitation and could be the pathway underlying the LG portion of post-excitatory inhibition. If this were correct, we should expect that PEI would be GABAergic and relatively remote. Thus, unlike recurrent inhibition, it should produce relatively little reduction of V-prox compared to reduction of orthodromic EPSPs. PEI, shown as the attenuation of EPSP-A, is illustrated in Fig. 2D. V-prox is reduced much less than is EPSP-A, and 7 μM picrotoxin diminishes the reduction by 50% (the same amount it diminishes recurrent inhibition); PEI is also bicuculline sensitive. Edwards (this volume) has shown that depolarization per se can diminish electrical EPSPs. The LG is of course strongly depolarized during PEI, and we believe that the phenomena he describes do play some role in PEI. However, even taking into account the possibility of GABA-independent effects, we are fairly certain that we are correct in concluding that the picrotoxin sensitive component of PEI is due to synapses more remote than those that cause recurrent inhibition*.

Previous work had suggested by a process of elimination that tonic inhibition occurs directly at synapses on the LG dendrites. To evaluate this directly, we examined the effect of restraint-produced inhibition on responses produced in the LGs by monosynaptic input from primary afferents (EPSP-pa), from interneuron A (EPSP-A), and from a commissural synapse input produced by passing a current pulse into the contralateral LG (V-contra) (see Fig. 1B). Animals that are restrained for intracellular recording tonically inhibit if they are in good condition, but the LG can be released from this inhibition if the cord is cut between thorax and abdomen. When we cut the cord, responses of all three varieties rose approximately 12% (Fig. 3A; V-contra not shown); thus in the semi-acute, restrained preparation tonic inhibition appears to cause a 12% reduction in direct inputs regardless of source, which suggests a process of postsynaptic inhibition. EPSPs produced via the disynaptic linkage from primary afferents to interneurons to LG (EPSP-beta) are also inhibited by the same amount, which is consistent with the belief that tonic inhibition does not affect primary afferent to interneuron synapses.

*Picrotoxin at concentrations which produce submaximal block of GABA effects (higher concentrations cause deterioration of EPSPs) cause a 50 % loss of PEI at its peak. Even if one assumed that this loss were the full GABA-produced effect, the ratio of EPSP attenuation to V-prox attenuation would be almost double that for recurrent inhibition.

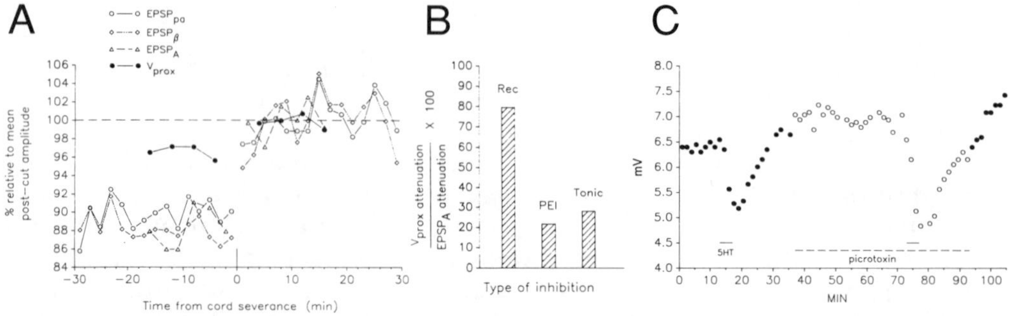

Fig. 3. Tonic inhibition. A. Effect of cutting cord on EPSPs and V-prox. B. Comparison of amount of attenuation of V-prox and of EPSP-A during three types of inhibition. C. Effect of pulse of 1 mM 5-HT on root evoked disynaptic EPSP amplitude before and during perfusion of 10 μM picrotoxin.

The most parsimonious interpretation of these results would be that tonic inhibition involves tonic activity of some of the same GABAergic inhibitory neurons that produce recurrent inhibition and PEI. The reduction of V-prox during tonic inhibition (Fig. 3A, B) is slight, which would suggest that the more distal PEI-producing terminals are involved. Technical problems have delayed our attempts to see whether tonic inhibition is picrotoxin sensitive. However, a different line of experimentation has suggested a quite different possibility.

Kravitz and collaborators have identified serotonin (5-HT) and octopamine as neuromodulators of opposite sign in crustacea (Kravitz, 1986 and this volume). Stimulated by these findings, we several years ago examined their effect on LG escape and found that octopamine increases excitability by up-regulating transmission at primary afferent to interneuron synapses while 5-HT diminishes excitability by affecting transmission to the LGs (Glanzman & Krasne, 1983). Like tonic inhibition, 5-HT also reduces orthodromic EPSPs and V-contra without producing substantial reduction of V-prox. Furthermore, the selective 5-HT-1A agonist 8-OH-DPAT produces the same effects as 5-HT, but at much lower doses.

We would like to find a 5-HT-1A receptor antagonist whose effect on tonic inhibition we could evaluate. But so far we have not found anything that will abolish the 5-HT effects themselves. We have, however, examined the effect of the presumptive 5-HT neuron toxin 5, 7-DHT on tonic inhibition. It had a number of side effects, but it did largely abolish the restraint-produced tonic inhibition without having any effect on the basic, uninhibited excitability of the reflex (Glanzman & Krasne, 1986). This is consistent with the hypothesis that 5-HT mediates tonic inhibition.

Recently Mintz et al (1989) found that glycinergic recurrent and commissural inhibition of the Mauthner cell, which seems analogous to GABAergic recurrent inhibition in crayfish, is up-regulated by serotonin. Since we had found an unidentified type of dense cored vesicle-containing process that could contain 5-HT near distal presumptive inhibitory terminals (immunohistochemistry is needed), it seemed possible that here too 5-HT might work by up-regulating release of inhibitory transmitter. Thus, we examined the effect of picrotoxin on 5-HT produced inhibition. At the doses used, picrotoxin almost entirely obliterated recurrent inhibiton, but it had no visible effect on the serotonin-caused inhibition (Fig. 3C). Thus, it does not look like serotonin-caused inhibition works via modulation of distal GABAergic synapses.

DISCUSSION

The inhibitory control of LG excitability has surprising complexity. There appear to be at least three modes of inhibition: (1) recurrent, which utilizes proximal GABA synapses, (2) post-excitatory, which uses distal GABA synapses as well as other mechanisms, and (3) tonic, which operates distally and may use 5-HT and be independent of GABA.

The preferential involvement of proximal inhibitory synapses in recurrent as compared to post-excitatory inhibition may make sense in terms of the degree of sensory specificity needed for each. Proximal inhibition should lower probability of LG firing for all stimuli indiscriminately, which makes sense for recurrent inhibition. But if there is any somatotopic organization of input to LG dendrites and if PEI really involves local circuits from LG excitors to inhibitors, PEI will preferentially attenuate late arriving input originating from the same channels that initiated the inhibition; input from other stimulus fields would be less attenuated. Thus, PEI would function as a temporal filter to enhance the LG's selectivity to stimuli of abrupt onset, but late arriving stimuli from a different bodily location might be treated as new and not suppressed (Fig. 2A). Experimental tests for such selectivity are obviously called for.

Why tonic inhibition might use yet a third pathway, we cannot yet guess. It could be related to special requirements of a system that operates tonically. Whatever the reason, perhaps it will be related to and ultimately illuminate the reasons for use of 5-HT as a modulator in higher nervous systems.

REFERENCES

Edwards, D.H., Fricke, R.A., & Simon, T.W. (1989) Inhibition of crayfish tail flip circuitry by interneurons that evoke backward walking. *J. Comp. Physiol. A.* in Prep.

Fricke, R.A., Block, G.D. & Kennedy, D. (1982) Inhibition of mechanosensory interneurons in the crayfish. II. Inhibition of interneurons associated with proprioceptive feedback from locomotion. *J. Comp. Physiol.* **153**:443-453.

Glanzman, D.L. & Krasne, F.B. (1983) Serotonin and octopamine have opposite modulatory effects on the crayfish's lateral giant escape reaction. *J. Neurosci.* **3**:2263-9.

Glanzman, D.L. & Krasne, F.B. (1986) 5, 7-Dihydroxytryptamine lesions of crayfish serotonin-containing neurons: Effect on the lateral giant escape reaction. *J. Neurosci.* **6**:1560-9.

Krasne, F.B. & Glanzman, D.L. (1986). Sensitization of the crayfish lateral giant escape reaction. *J. Neurosci.* **6**:1013-20.

Krasne, F.B. & Lee, S.C. (1988) Response-dedicated trigger neurons as control points for behabioral actions: Selective inhibition of lateral giant command neurons during feeding in crayfish. *J. Neurosci.* **8**: 3703-12.

Krasne, F.B. & Wine, J.J. (1987) Evasion responses of the crayfish. In *Aims and Methods in Neuroethology*, (ed. D.M. Guthrie) pp.10-45. Manchester: Manchester University Press.

Kravitz, E.A. (1986). Serotonin, octopamine, and proctolin: Two amines and a peptide, and aspects of lobster behaviour. In *Fast and Slow Chemical Signalling in the Nervous System* (eds. L.L. Iversen & E. Goodman) pp. 244-59. Oxford: Oxford Science.

Miller, M.W., Lee, S.C. & Krasne, F.B. (1987). Cooperativity-dependent long lasting potentiation in the crayfish lateral giant escape reaction circuit. *J. Neurosci.* **7**:1081-92.

Mintz, I., Gotow, T, Triller, A., & Korn, H. (1989). Effect of serotonergic afferents on quantal release at central inhibitory synapses. *Science*, **245**:190-192.

Roberts, A.M. (1968). Recurrent inhibition in the giant fibre system of the crayfish and its effect on the excitability of the escape response. *J. Exp. Biol.* **48**: 545-67.

Wine, J.J. & Krasne, F.B. (1982) The cellular organization of crayfish escape behavior. In *The Biology of Crustacea*, **vol.4**: *Neural Integration and Behavior* (eds. D.C. Sandeman & H.L. Atwood) pp. 241-92. New York: Academic Press.

Frontiers in Crustacean Neurobiology
Advances in Life Sciences

NOVEL MECHANISMS OF DEPOLARIZING INHIBITION IN THE ESCAPE CIRCUIT OF CRAYFISH

Donald H. Edwards and Esther M. Leise

Laboratory of Behavior and Neurobiology, Department of Biology, Georgia State University, Atlanta, Georgia 30303, United States

SUMMARY

Tonic depolarization has an inhibitory effect on excitatory synaptic responses of the lateral giant (LG) command neuron and the motor giant (MoG) motoneuron in the tailflip escape circuit of crayfish. In both cells, tonic depolarization reduces excitatory postsynaptic potentials (EPSPs) and currents (EPSCs). While the mechanism underlying these effects in LG is not yet clear, it appears to be similar to a novel inhibitory process in MoG. In that cell, slow depolarization reverse biases the rectifying electrical synapses from LG and MG and so decreases their transsynaptic conductances.

INTRODUCTION

Depolarizing inhibition is found at only a few sites in the vertebrate CNS. The best known are the terminals of primary afferents in the spinal cord that display primary afferent depolarization (PAD) (Eccles et al. 1962). Depolarizing inhibition is ubiquitous in the crayfish escape system where it affects abdominal primary mechanosensory afferents (Kennedy et al. 1980), the LG command neuron (Roberts 1968), the segmental giant (SG) (Heitler & Fraser, 1988), the MoG motoneuron (Furshpan & Potter, 1959b) and the muscle receptor organ (Kuffler & Eyzaguirre, 1955). In general, depolarizing IPSPs (dIPSPs) are produced by release of GABA which increases the postsynaptic conductance to chloride (Kennedy et al., 1980; Ochi, 1969; Furshpan & Potter, 1959b; Kuffler & Edwards, 1958; Kuffler and Eyzaguirre, 1955; Kravitz et al., 1963).

We have found that the slow depolarization produced in LG and MoG during dIPSPs has an inhibitory effect on these cells that is independent of the increased membrane conductance pro- duced by GABA. In both cells, tonic depolarization reduces EPSPs and associated EPSCs. In MoG, this inhibition is produced in part by "reverse-bias" of the electrically rectifying giant motor synapse (GMS) between the giant fibers (GFs) and MoG (Edwards, 1989a, b). Synapses from mechanosensory afferents and interneu- rons onto LG are also electrical, but have not yet been tested for rectification.

RESULTS

MoG EPSPs are reduced by tonic depolarization . To investigate the effect of depolarization on the EPSPs in MoG, the cell in the third or fourth abdominal ganglion was penetrated with two microelectrodes at the GMS to inject current and record the cell's voltage response. The separation of the electrode tips was less than 50 um; a grounded aluminum foil shield was placed between the microelectrodes to isolate them electrically. Focal suction pipets were used to stimulated selected GFs in a rostral connective of the isolated ventral nerve cord. Qualitatively similar results were obtained from the 12 animals studied.

MoG EPSPs evoked by a GF impulse were increased if they occurred when MoG was hyperpolarized by current injection, and decreased if they occurred when MoG was depolarized (Fig. 1A). Depolarization equal to the peak dIPSP amplitude caused a 30% reduction in EPSP amplitude. dIPSPs evoked by MoGIs in response to the GF impulse also increased during hyperpolarization, but reversed when MoG was depolarized by more than 12 mV.

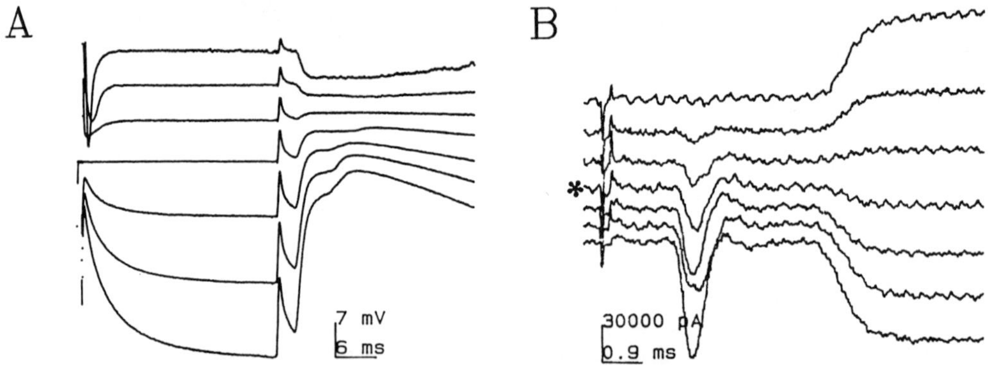

Fig. 1. MoG EPSPs and EPSCs under current and voltage clamp. A. MoG EPSPs and IPSPs triggered by LG impulse during responses to hyperpolarizing and depolarizing current steps (90 nA, 60 nA, 30 nA, 0 nA, -30 nA, -60 nA, -90 nA, not shown). B. MoG EPSCs (top) recorded under two-electrode voltage clamp (bottom) at 30 mV, 20 mV, 10 mV, 0 mV (asterisk), -10 mV,-20 mV and -30 mV from rest potential.

Part of the EPSP reduction can be attributed to a decrease in the input resistance of MoG produced by tonic depolarization. MoG's responses to current clamp indicate that input resistance at the GMS decreased by 25% when the cell was depolarized by 8 mV, which is the amplitude of many dIPSPs. Input resistance decreased by 35% when MoG was depolarized to the IPSP reversal potential. Synaptic current entering MoG from a GF should create a smaller EPSP as it encounters the reduced input resistance.

MoG EPSCs are also reduced during tonic depolarization A smaller EPSP should occur during postsynaptic depolarization if the excitatory current through the GMS is reduced. EPSCs pro- duced by GF stimulation were measured when MoG was held at dif- ferent membrane potentials by a two-electrode voltage clamp applied to the postsynaptic region (Fig. 1B). The EPSCs were quite sensitive to the MoG holding potential: at 10.4 mV depolar- ized from rest, the peak current was reduced by 60% from its value at rest potential, while at depolarizations greater than 20 mV the synaptic current was eliminated. Hyperpolarization of the postsynaptic region produced substantial increases in the GMS current.

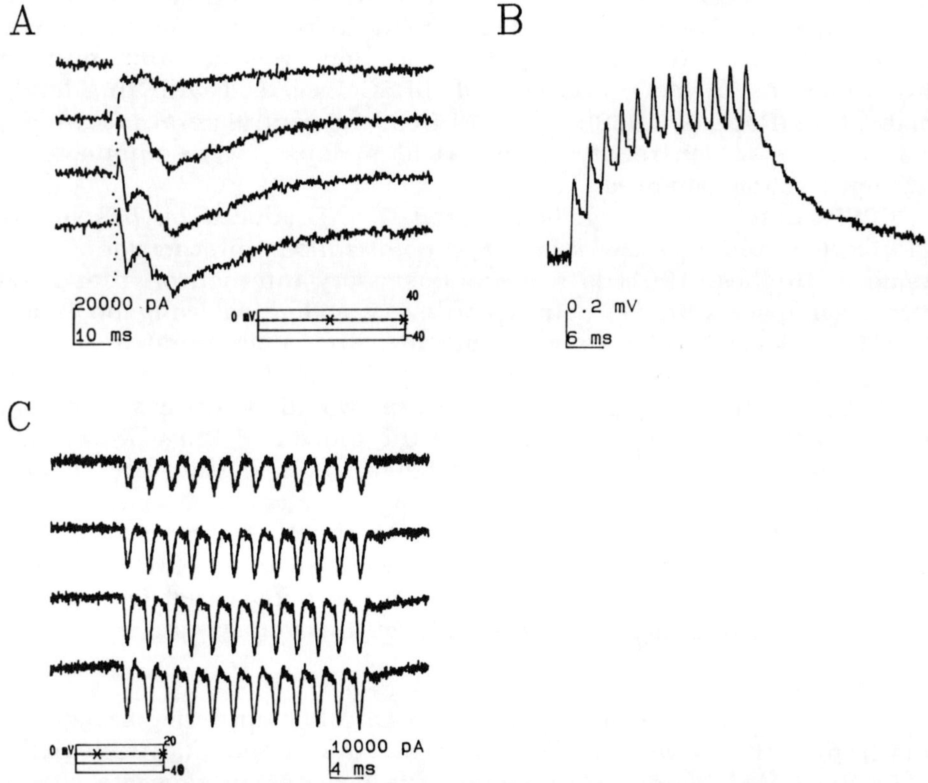

Fig. 2. LG EPSCs and EPSPs during postsynaptic depolarization and hyperpolarization. A. EPSCs recorded in response to shock of ipsilateral ganglionic nerve 2 while LG is held under voltage clamp at 20 mV, 0 mV, -20 mV and -40 mV from rest potential. B. EPSPs evoked by train of interneuron C impulses. C. EPSCs evoked by interneuron C impulses under voltage clamp at 20 mV, 0 mV, -20 mV and -40 mV from rest potential.

Finally, changes in the steady-state clamp current with the holding potential reflected the changes in input resistance observed under current clamp.

LG EPSCs evoked by sensory nerve shock are reduced by depolariza- tion and increased by hyperpolarization. LG neurons in mid- abdominal ganglia receive monosynaptic electrical inputs from primary mechanosensory afferents and polysynaptic electrical inputs from interneurons (Zucker, 1972). Shock of ipsilateral ganglionic nerve 2 excites both primary afferents and interneu- rons, and their currents can be recorded in LG when a two-elec- trode voltage clamp is applied to the initial axon segment of the cell. We found that when the LG membrane potential was held at increasingly hyperpolarized levels (0 to -40 mV) the synaptic current increased, whereas when the neuron was depolarized (0 to +20 mV) the current decreased (Fig. 2A). The LG's input resist- ance was constant over this voltage range. As in MoG, dIPSPs and dIPSCs reversed with this level of depolarization (Roberts, 1968). Currents from the contralateral LG, which is linked through a non-rectifying electrical synapse, were unaffected by postsynaptic voltage changes.

LG EPSPs and EPSCs from interneuron C are reduced by postsynaptic depolarization and increased by hyperpolarization. Interneuron C (A64, Wiersma & Hughes, 1961) is a mechanosensory interneuron that makes electrical synapses with LG neurons in every abdominal ganglion (Zucker 1972). The cell produces a long-lasting, high frequency burst of impulses following a sensory nerve shock. Each impulse produces a sharply rising EPSP in LG, so that a high-frequency burst would produce a temporally summed depolari- zation. We found that the individual PSPs decreased in peak-to- peak amplitude during this depolarization, despite the electrical nature of the synapse (Fig. 2B). Part of this decrease can be accounted for by the depolarization. As with the responses to shock of the sensory nerve, EPSCs evoked in LG under voltage clamp increased in amplitude when LG was hyperpolarized and decreased when it was depolarized (Fig. 2C). As before, LG's input resistance was constant over this voltage range.

DISCUSSION

The reduction in EPSP amplitude seen in MoG upon depolariza- tion results from both delayed rectification and reduced synaptic transmission through the GMS. Voltage clamp makes it possible to separate the two effects by capturing synaptic currents directly. Our results indicate that postsynaptic depolarization reduces transmission through the GMS, whereas hyperpolarization increases it.

Transmission through the GMS is known to be highly dependent on transsynaptic potential: increases in the difference between pre- and postsynaptic potentials increase transsynaptic conduct- ance, while decreases reduce it (Furshpan & Potter, 1959a; Giaume & Korn, 1983). The rest potentials of the two cells differ by 15 mV (LG is the more negative) and the threshold for increasing GMS conductance is reached when LG is 20 mV depolarized relative to MoG. Consequently, the GMS is reverse-biased by 35 mV when both cells are at their normal membrane potentials. Presynaptic impulses must reach 35 mV depolarization before transsynaptic conductance increases; it remains high until the difference between the presynaptic impulse and the rising postsynaptic response falls below 20 mV. When MoG receives a 10 mV dIPSP, this period of high conductance is reduced on both the rising and falling phases of the presynaptic impulse.

The postsynaptic potential cannot develop when MoG is volt- age clamped to a constant holding potential, and so the inhibito- ry effect of the dIPSP on GMS transmission cannot be measured directly. Despite this limitation, the decrease in GMS current observed when MoG was held at the level of the dIPSP demonstrates that reverse bias of the GMS by the dIPSP has a significant inhibitory effect on MoG's response to LG or MG.

We have obtained preliminary evidence which suggests that the electrical synapses made by primary mechanosensory afferents and interneurons on LG are rectifying. If so, then like MoG, the decrease in synaptic currents seen in LG during depolarization is likely to have been produced by reverse-bias of the rectifying electrical synapses. Although this point remains in doubt until the I/V properties of the electrical synapses have been determined, it is still clear that depolarization reduces electrical synaptic inputs to LG. Since LG becomes strongly depolarized for up to 100 ms following an impulse or a below-threshold EPSP, this depolarization can be seen to be self-limiting: each increment of depolarization decreases the EPSCs that would increase it.

The self-limiting character of afferent inputs to LG would allow the cell to be fully responsive to novel inputs when the LG is at rest potential, but less responsive to late or repeated inputs when the cell is already depolarized. This suggestion puts the response properties of one class of mechanosensory interneuron (MSI), typified by interneuron C, in a new light. These cells, called type II by Sigvardt & Wine (1982), respond to a sharp mechanosensory stimulus to the abdomen with a brief high-frequency burst of impulses followed by a sustained lower fre- quency (less than 300 Hz) train of impulses that can last more than 100 ms. The initial burst, like the similar burst in the phasic MSIs (e.g., interneuron A), rapidly depolarizes LG and may evoke an impulse. The subsequent impulse train in C always occurs after the LG impulse in a suprathreshold response and contributes to the sustained depolarization of LG in a subthresh- old response. Since this depolarization acts to reduce subse- quent inputs to LG, the sustained response of C that contributes to it would be inhibitory to

LG. As a result, C's initial re- sponse to sensory input is excitatory to LG and the late response is inhibitory, even though both are mediated by the same electri- cal synapses.

Reverse-bias of rectifying electrical synapses is a novel form of depolarizing postsynaptic inhibition that may exist at most such synapses. In addition to the GMS, rectifying synapses are also found in crayfish between LG and SG, between SG and the fast flexor motoneurons, between SG and a leg promoter motoneu- ron, and possibly between MSIs and LG (Leise, unpublished; Hei- tler & Fraser, 1988). They also exist at similar locations in the hermit crab (Fraser & Heitler, 1988). The postsynaptic elements at these sites are all known to receive depolarizing inhibition that may act to reverse-bias the rectifying electrical synapse.

REFERENCES

Eccles, J.C., Magni, F. & Willis, W.D. (1962) Depolarization of projections of group I afferent fibres from muscle. J. Physiol. **159:** 147-166.

Edwards, D.H. (1989a) Mechanisms of depolarizing inhibition at the crayfish giant motor synapse. I. Electrophysiology. J. Neurophysiol. (submitted). Edwards, D.H. (1989b) Mechanisms of depolarizing inhibition at the crayfish giant motor synapse. II. Quantitative recon- struction. J. Neurophysiol. (submitted).

Furshpan, E.J. & Potter, D.D. (1959a) Transmission at the giant motor synapses of crayfish. J. Physiol. **145**: 289-325. Furshpan, E.J. & Potter, D.D. (1959b) Slow post-synaptic poten- tials recorded from the giant motor fibre of crayfish. J. Physiol. **145:** 326-335.

Heitler, W.J. & Fraser, K. (1988) Thoracic output of crayfish giant command neurones. Soc. Neurosci. Abstr. **14**: 999,
400.9.

Kennedy, D., McVittie, J., Calabrese, R., Fricke, R.A., Craelius, W. & Chiapella, P. (1980) Inhibition of mechanosensory interneurons in the crayfish. I. Presynaptic inhibition from giant fibers. J. Neurophysiol. **43:** 1495-1509.

Kuffler, S.W. & Edwards, C. (1958) Mechanism of gamma aminobutyr- ic acid (GABA) action and its relation to synaptic inhibi- tion. J. Neurophysiol. **21**: 589-610.

Kuffler, S.W. & Eyzaguirre, C. (1955) Synaptic inhibition in an isolated nerve cell. J. Gen. Physiol **39: 1**55-184.

Kravitz, E.A., Kuffler, S.W. & Potter, D.D. (1963) Gamma- aminobutyric acid and other blocking compounds in crustacea. III. Their relative concentrations in separated motor and inhibitory axons. J. Neurophysiol. **26:** 739-751.

Ochi, R. (1969) Ionic mechanism of the inhibitory postsynaptic potential of crayfish giant motor fiber. Pflugers Arch. **311**: 131-143.

Roberts, A.M. (1968) Recurrent inhibition in the giant-fibre system of the crayfish and its effect on the excitability of the escape response. J. Exp. Biol. **48**: 545-567.

Sigvardt, K.A., Hagiwara, G. & Wine, J.J. (1982) Mechanosensory integration in the crayfish abdominal nervous system: Struc- tural and physiological differences between interneurons with single and multiple spike initiating sites. J. Comp. Physiol. A. **148:** 143-157.

Wiersma, C.A.G. & Hughes, G.M. (1961) On the functional anatomy of neuronal units in the abdominal cord of the crayfish, *Procambarus clarkii* Girard. J. Comp. Physiol.**116:** 209-228.

Zucker, R.S. (1972) Crayfish escape behavior and central syn- apses. I. Neural circuit exciting lateral giant fiber. J. Neurophysiol. **35:** 599-620.

Frontiers in Crustacean Neurobiology
Advances in Life Sciences

FACILITATION AND POTENTIATION OF TRANSMITTER RELEASE AT NEUROMUSCULAR SYNAPSES IN THE HEART OF *SQUILLA MANTIS*: FUNCTIONAL AND THEORETICAL IMPLICATIONS

Ernst Florey and Martina Rathmayer

Fakultät für Biologie, Universität Konstanz, D-7750 Konstanz, F.R.G.

SUMMARY

In the stomatopod, *Squilla mantis*, the heartbeat is initiated by periodic bursts of action potentials generated by the heart ganglion. The resulting trains of EPSPs exhibit facilitation, depression and marked post-tetanic potentiation (PTP). Stimulation of single motor axons and intracellular recording of EPSPs revealed that PTP reaches a maximum more than 1 sec after the end of a train of stimuli: the EPSP amplitude may be more than ten times larger than fully facilitated EPSPs.

INTRODUCTION

The striated heart muscle of malacostracan crustaceans is driven by motoneurons of the cardiac ganglion. The electrocardiogram represents summed EPSPs. As a rule, there are no regenerative spikes (Anderson & Cooke, 1971). Intracellular recording reveals that each heartbeat is initiated by a burst of EPSPs of which the first is far larger than the following ones. Indeed, the entire complex of summed EPSPs often looks like a mammalian cardiac action potential, as already pointed out by van der Kloot (1970): a large EPSP is followed by a series of small EPSPs which ride on the descending phase of the first one and result in a typical shoulder (see Fig. 1).

As was shown by Anderson and Cooke (1971) for the heart of *Homarus*, repetitive stimulation of one of the motor axons results in a characteristic pattern of facilitation and anti-facilitation (depression): in a two-pulse experiment, facilitation is observed when the pulse interval is larger than about 0.5 sec. At shorter intervals, the second EPSP is depressed. When longer series of stimuli are employed, there is continued facilitation at frequencies up to 2/sec, but at higher frequencies, facilitation is preceeded by depression. Curiously, post-tetanic potentiation has not been described. As we now show, this potentiation is the essential feature of the normal activation of the heart muscle by patterned bursts generated by the motoneurons of the heart ganglion. The results presented here are part of an investigation of facilitation patterns and of the influence of the cardioregulator innervation and various neurohormones on the discharge pattern of the motoneurons of the heart ganglion. Our study was also concerned with the effect of temperature on the facilitation and potentiation of transmitter release at the neuromuscular synapses, but this aspect will not be covered here.

methods

Our experiments were conducted at the Stazione Zoologica at Naples/Italy on isolated hearts of the stomatopod *Squilla mantis*. The innervation of the Squilla heart has been described in detail by Alexandrowicz (1934). On its dorsal surface, the tubular heart of Squilla bears a ganglion which extends over the entire length of the heart and consists of 13 to 14 neurons whose somata are spaced up to 1 cm apart. Each ganglion cell sends a branched motor axon over the heart muscle. Part of the freshly dissected heart was stretched over a glass tube filled with india ink to enhance visibility of muscle and ganglion cells in dark field illumination (Watanabe et al., 1967). The preparation was submerged in a thermostated plexiglass bath filled with saline (NaCl 490, KCl 8, $CaCl_2$ 10, $MgCl_2$ 12 mM). The temperature was kept at 20°C. After destruction of the ganglion cells, a suction electrode was applied to one of the axons. Various patterns of stimulation were produced with the aid of a programmable electronic stimulator (internal clock). Glass microelectrodes filled with 3 M KCl (10-20 MOhm resistance) were inserted into one of the muscle fibers. Recording equipment was conventional. The records were displayed on a Tektronix 5103 N/D13 oscilloscope and on a Brush-Gould 2400 4-channel chart recorder.

In some experiments, the ganglionic trunk was left intact. This made it possible to record EPSPs resulting from the natural motor pattern generated by the ganglion. Microelectrodes were inserted into a ganglion cell and into a corresponding muscle fiber. In addition, a mechano-electric transducer was attached to the end of the heart tube to record the contractions of the heart muscle.

Results

When the ganglionic trunk was intact, the bursts of EPSPs followed each other at regular intervals similar to those of the heartbeats in the intact animal. Amplitudes and intervals of the EPSPs of a given burst exhibited the characteristic patterns shown in Fig. 1. Depending on the preparation, interburst intervals ranged from 1.0 to 5.8 seconds. In a given burst, EPSP intervals varied between 20 and 160 msec. Burst durations, generally, were less than 0.5 sec. Stimulation of the cardio-accelerator nerves or application of various transmitter substances, e.g. acetylcholine (10^{-6} M) or proctolin (10^{-6} M), prolonged the duration of the burst and/or shortened the interburst interval. In all cases, the first EPSP of a given burst was very much larger than the following ones. In many cases, the intervals between EPSPs of a burst varied. The amplitudes of the EPSPs were then inversely proportional to the length of the interval (see Fig. 1a, b). In some preparations the EPSPs showed more or less regular intervals. In these cases, the second EPSP was the smallest and the following ones increased in amplitude in a pattern typical of facilitation (see Fig. 1c, d). The discharge

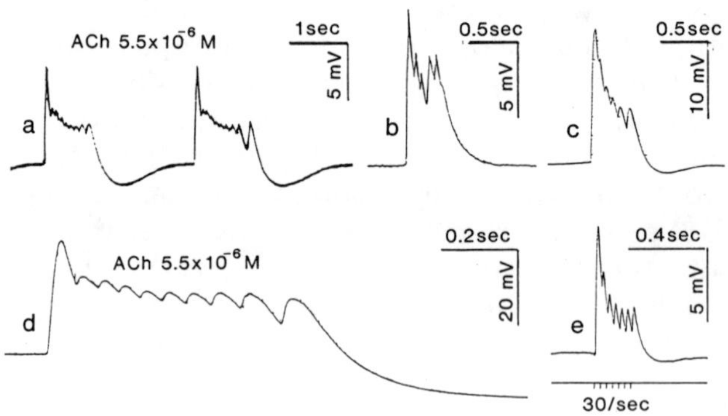

Fig. 1.

pattern of a motoneuron (all ganglion cells of the ganglion fire in the same temporal pattern), the resulting EPSP amplitudes, and the strength of the heart contractions are demonstrated in Fig. 2, which shows a rare case in which a motoneuron alternately fired 1, 2 or 3 spikes per burst. Clearly, each contraction is proportional to the number and amplitudes of the EPSPs

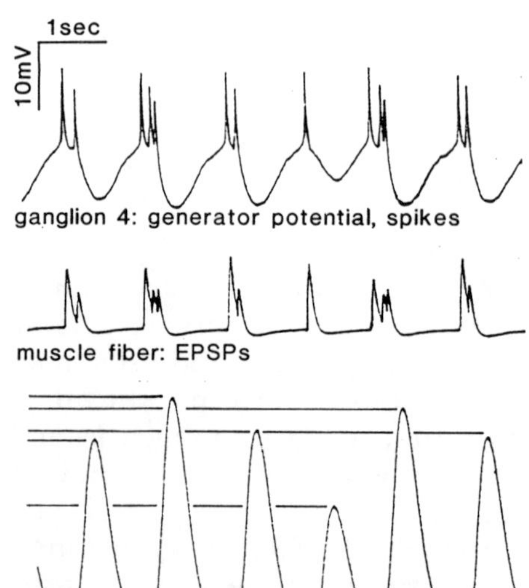

Fig. 2. Simultaneous 3-channel recording of electrical events in the soma of a motoneuron of the heart ganglion,in one of the innervated heart muscle fibers, and of the contractions of part of the entire heart muscle (noncalibrated). The horizontal lines facilitate the distinction of the different amplitudes which, evidently, are proportional to the number of EPSPs in the particular burst but also to the amplitude of the first EPSP of this burst. Note the difference between 2nd and 5th contraction).

in a given burst. It is also evident that the amplitude of the first (or only) EPSP of a burst is proportional to the number of EPSPs in the preceeding burst.

After destruction of the ganglion cells, stimulation of one of the axons with an impulse sequence resembling the natural pattern resulted in EPSPs with an amplitude distribution very similar to that seen in the intact heart (Fig. 1e). In a first series of expriments, we used repetitive trains of stimuli, each train lasting 0.2 to 1.0 second with intertrain intervals of 1 to 5 seconds. Within each train the stimulation frequency was varied over a range of 10/sec to 50/sec. As shown in Fig. 3, the EPSP pattern resulting from the first train in a given series is remarkably different from that produced by subsequent trains: the first EPSP of the first train is quite small, that of successive trains grows enormously. The second EPSP of each train is always the smallest and the subsequent EPSPs show typical facilitation but never reach the amplitude of the first. In successive trains, these EPSPs grow somewhat but to a lesser degree than the first one of each train. Within the range of stimulation parameters used, the growth rate of the first EPSP of successive trains is proportional to the duration and frequency of each train, and (not shown in the figure) inversely proportional to the intertrain interval.

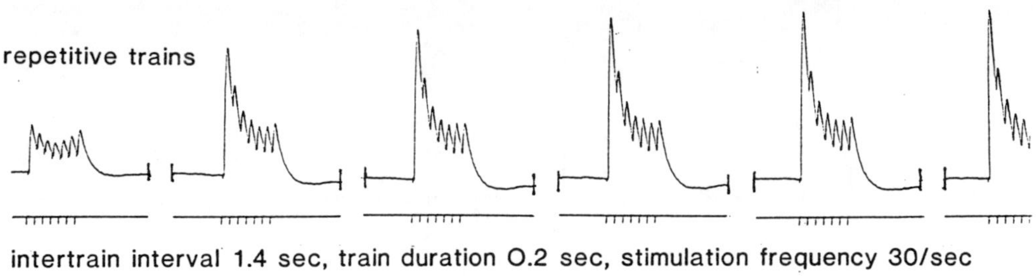

Fig. 3.

To analyze this behavior further, we resorted to a stimulation regime in which a single train (conditioning train) was followed by a single stimulus after an interval of 50 msec to 30 seconds. The procedure was repeated after sufficient time had elapsed to allow the EPSP amplitude to return to a value equal to that of the first (unfacilitated) EPSP of the test series.

The results of these experiments show that the EPSPs within a train show facilitation as long as the stimulation frequency does not exceed 4/sec, in some cases 6/sec. Facilitation occurs at frequencies as low as 1 pulse every ten seconds! At frequencies above 4 - 6/sec, the second EPSP is smaller than the first; this depression increases with increasing frequency.

Later EPSPs again show facilitation and reach amplitudes greater than that of the first (Fig. 4). A test stimulus applied after the end of the train (e.g. 1 sec) results in an EPSP ('test EPSP') whose amplitude is a complex function of the stimulation frequency of the preceeding train but is very much greater than any of the fully facilitated EPSPs observed during the preceeding train. Further experiments have shown that once the train length is greater than the time required for facilitation to reach its maximum, the amplitude of the test EPSP is independent of train length and is proportional only to the stimulus frequency of the preceeding train.

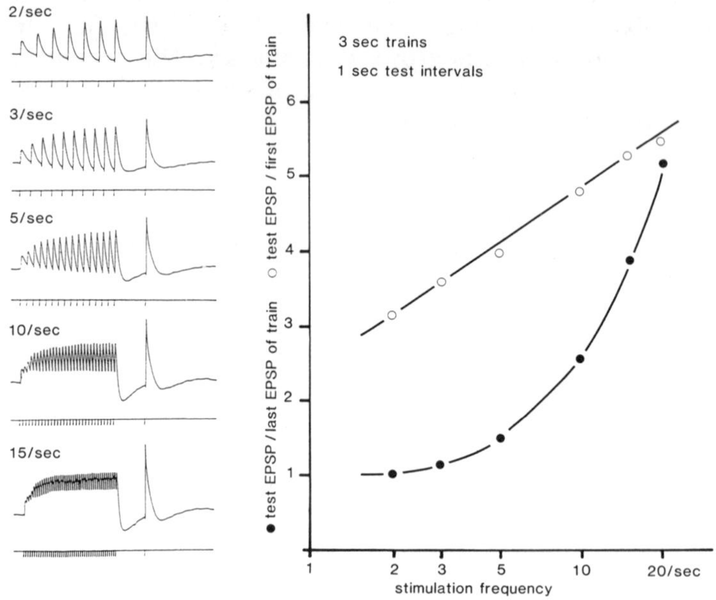

Fig. 4.

When the interval between conditioning train and test stimulus was varied (leaving train length and frequency constant), the amplitude of the test EPSP was found to reach a maximum 0.8 to 1.5 seconds after the last stimulus of the conditioning train. This amplitude exceeded that of the largest EPSP seen during conditioning trains of any frequency. Fig. 5 gives an example; the frequency chosen in this case was rather low, yet the test EPSP reached a maximal amplitude 1.7 times larger than that of the fully facilitated EPSP of the conditioning train. The period of time needed to reach the maximal amplitude of the test EPSP was nearly independent of the train frequency. With stimulation frequencies above 20/sec, test EPSPs reached maximal amplitudes up to 10 times that of the unfacilitated EPSP of the conditioning train. This is symptomatic for post-tetanic potentiation

(PTP). The EPSP pattern seen when trains are repeated at intervals of, say, 1.4 second (Fig. 3) are the result of the combined effects of facilitation and PTP. The time course of the decay of PTP is very much slower that that of the rise to maximum as is shown in Fig. 6 where half rise time is 0.3 sec and half decay time is 2.8 sec.

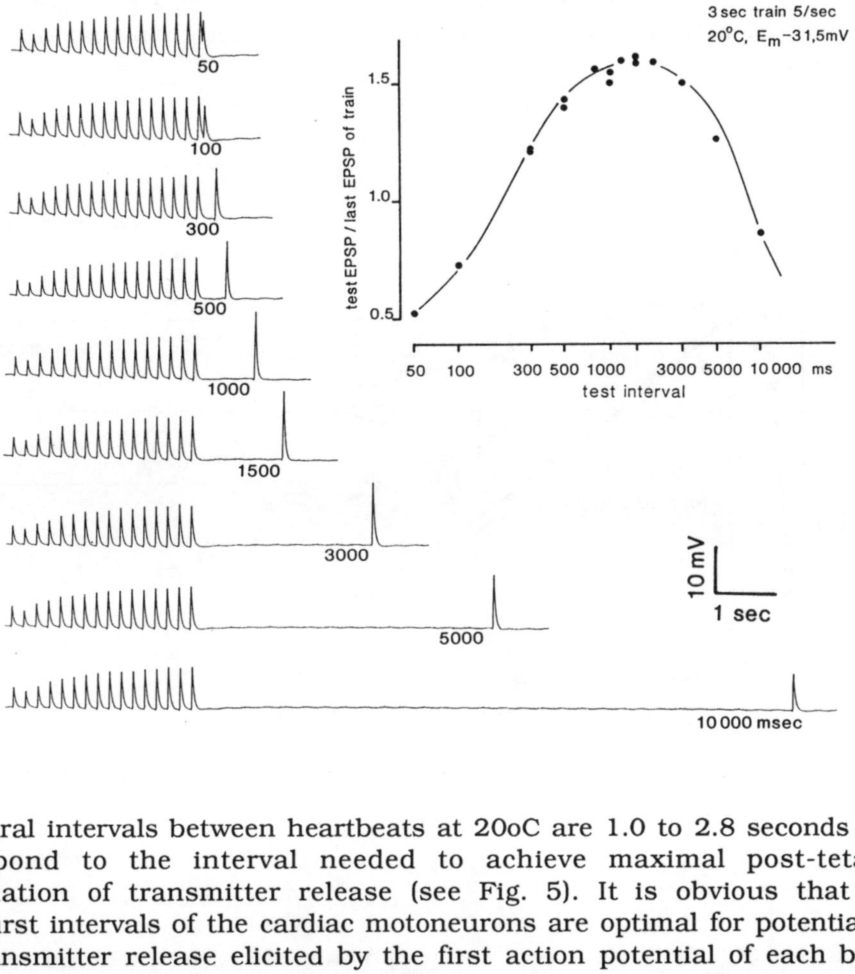

Fig. 5.

Natural intervals between heartbeats at 20oC are 1.0 to 2.8 seconds and correspond to the interval needed to achieve maximal post-tetanic potentiation of transmitter release (see Fig. 5). It is obvious that the interburst intervals of the cardiac motoneurons are optimal for potentiating the transmitter release elicited by the first action potential of each burst reaching the neuromuscular synapses.If the motor axon would generate only one EPSP per second, the fully facilitated EPSP would be only about 1/10 the size of the EPSP following 1 second after a brief burst containing several EPSPs.

The increase of frequency and number of spikes in a given burst of motor impulses which is caused by neurohormones (pericardial organs) and neurotransmitters (cardio-accelerator neurons) not only prolongs each contraction. The main effect will be achieved by the potentiation of the first EPSP of successive bursts.

During natural motor activation of the heart muscle, EPSP frequencies during bursts range, on the average, from 25 to 50/sec. It is striking that at these natural frequencies, facilitation of the EPSPs following the first one of a burst does not reach the amplitude of the first, unfacilitated EPSP, yet PTP elicits a transmitter release many times greater than that of unfacilitated EPSPs, and proportionally even greater than that of the fully facilitated

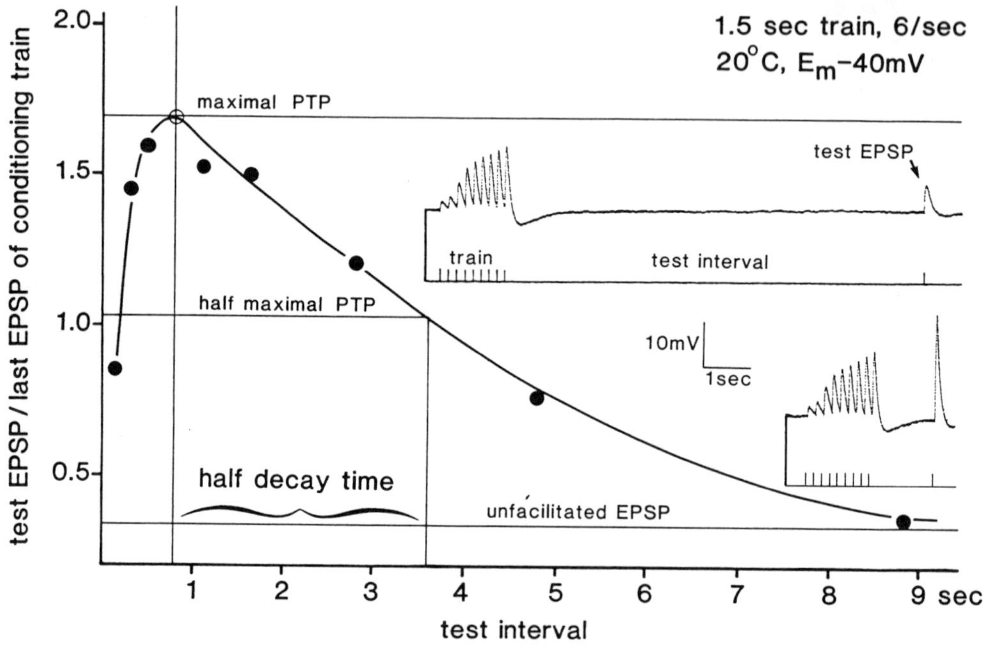

Fig. 6.

EPSPs (see Fig. 4). If we accept the proposition that the fractional release of transmitter from the release store is constant, it follows that the decline of the release seen at higher EPSP frequencies must be due to an exhaustion of the store of releasable transmitter. If, on the other hand, repetitive stimulation is the cause of PTP (provided there is a sufficient interval of time after the repetitive release), it also follows that during that interval, the store of releasable transmitter is not only replenished but increased beyond 'resting' conditions.

ACKNOWLEDGEMENTS:

This investigation has been supported by SFB 138 and SFB 156 of the Deutsche Forschungsgemeinschaft. We thank the Director and staff of the Stazione Zoologica, Naples, for courteous help. Ms. M.A. Cahill deserves credit for her help with figures and manuscript.

REFERENCES

Alexandrowicz, J.S. (1934) The innervation of the heart of crustacea. II. Stomatopoda. Quart.J.microscop.Sci. **76:** 511-548.

Anderson, M. & Cooke, I.M. (1971) Neural activation of the heart of the lobster *Homarus americanus*. J.exp.Biol. **55:** 449-468.

Van der Kloot, W. (1970) The electrophysiology of muscle fibers in the hearts of decapod crustaceans. J.exp.Zool **174**: 367-380.

Watanabe, A., Obara, S. & Akiyama, T. (1967) Pacemaker potentials for the periodic burst discharge in the heart ganglion of a stomatopod. *Squilla oratoria.* J.gen.Physiol. **50:** 839-862.

Frontiers in Crustacean Neurobiology
Advances in Life Sciences

THE CAUDAL PHOTORECEPTOR: A MULTIFUNCTIONAL SENSORY NEURON MAY SELECT ITS OUTPUTS BY SPIKE FREQUENCY

Ted W. Simon and Donald H. Edwards

Laboratory of Neurobiology and Behavior, Georgia State University, Atlanta, GA 30303, U.S.A.

INTRODUCTION

Single neurons are capable of many different firing patterns, and yet few neurons are known that have greatly different responses to different patterns of input, and none are known that influence different populations of postsynaptic cells with different patterns of activity (Kennedy, 1976). The idea of the polymorphic network (Getting & Dekin, 1985) provides a clear scheme of how neurons interact to form different networks serving different but related functions. However, the swim interneurons of Tritonia are know to affect only motoneurons involved in withdrawal or escape swimming. The caudal photoreceptor neurons (CPRs) of crayfish respond very differently to different sensory stimuli and indeed have different populations of postsynaptic targets. Hence, they are true multifunctional neurons. Prosser (1934) identified this well known neuron and recorded its response to abdominal illumination at a number of locations in the nervous system. In a companion study, J.H. Welsh (1934) demonstrated the connection between caudal illumination and locomotor behavior. In addition, the CPRs are sensitive to the laterality of near field water movements (Wilkens & Larimer, 1972; Reichert et al., 1983; Wilkens, 1988) and can have several circadian effects (Fuentes-Pardo & Inclan-Rubio, 1987; Inclan-Rubio & Fuentes-Pardo, 1987).

In this chapter, we will attempt to answer four questions: 1) what are the responses of the CPRs to several types of sensory stimuli with regard to spike frequency and pattern; 2) what are the behavioral or motor effects resulting from CPR activation by these several stimuli; 3) can these effects be selected by the spike frequency of the CPRs; and 4) do these various spike frequencies occur in response to naturally occurring stimuli?

SENSORY PROPERTIES OF THE CAUDAL PHOTORECEPTORS

Photoreceptive properties of the CPRs. The caudal photoreceptors respond to a step increase in illumination of the 6th abdominal ganglion with a short burst of up to 150 Hz followed by a brief hiatus and then a sustained lower frequency train of impulses (Kennedy, 1958a,b, 1963; Wilkens & Larimer, 1972). The peak spike frequency of the response increases with the intensity of illumination, and the latency decreases.

The light response can be thought of as two components: 1) the initial high frequency peak and 2) the sustained train. The peak response adapts very quickly and is over in less than a second. The sustained train of spikes or tonic response continues without decrement for the duration of illumination and, hence, is a measure of the ambient light.

Mechanoreceptive properties of the CPRs. In addition to their photoreceptive properties, the CPRs also function as mechanosensory interneurons. They receive afferent input only in A6 ipsilateral to their dendrites there. The response of one CPR to water movement is a short burst (ca. 300 ms) followed by inhibition (Kennedy, 1963; Wilkens & Larimer, 1972; Flood & Wilkens, 1978). The response of both CPRs to lateralized low frequency water movements is excitation of one neuron of the pair and concurrent inhibition of the contralateral neuron. Inhibition of the contralateral CPR is mediated by the nonspiking Local Directionally Sensitive (LDS) interneuron (Reichert et al,. 1983). LDS receives excitatory input from ipsilateral tactile afferents and inhibits the contralateral CPR. As a result, the response pattern of both neurons is highly dependent on the direction of water movement and may code for low frequency directional water movements (Wilkens, 1988).

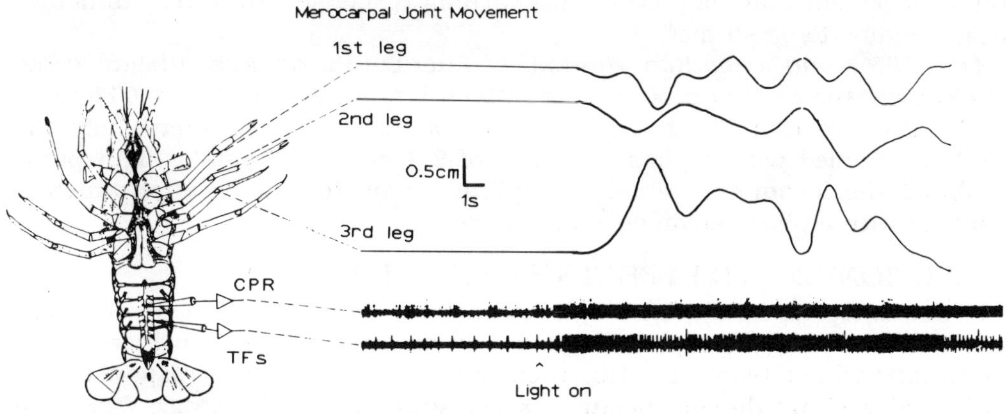

Figure 1. Movements of the merocarpal joints of the first three walking legs, response of a CPR and the TF motoneurons to illumination of A6 with 3500 lux. On the left is a schematic diagram showing the placement of the electrodes and the joints monitored. The left CPR was recorded in the A3/A4 connective, and the TFs were recorded from the left side of A4. The three upper traces are cubic spline fits to m-c joint positions measured in a rostro-caudal axis from a video recording. The two lower traces are the CPR and TF responses. The initial burst of the CPR recorded preceded the locomotor and TF responses by less than a second.

BEHAVIOR AND MOTOR RESPONSES TO CPR ACTIVATION

Locomotion is elicited by the light response. Recently, we found that the CPRs serve as trigger neurons for backward walking (Simon & Edwards, 1989). After a variable latency following the onset of ventral illumination, freely moving crayfish will walk backward and cyclically flex and extend their abdomens. In response to illumination of the caudal ganglion or intracellular stimulation of a CPR, a restrained crayfish will move its legs, and a cyclic pattern of output characteristic of backward walking (Kovac, 1974a,b; Moore & Larimer, 1987) can be recorded from abdominal tonic flexor motoneurons (Fig. 1).

The site of at least one postsynaptic target of CPR-evoked locomotor behavior is in the subesophageal ganglion or more caudal. Both Hermann (1964) and we (1989) have shown that the CPR can elicit walking behavior when the circumesophageal connectives (CECs) are cut.

Effects of CPR mechanoreception. The CPRs and several pairs of headward- sensitive mechanosensory interneurons (MSIs) (Reichert et al., 1983; Wilkens, 1988) serve as directional water movement indicators. The identity of the neural targets for the responses to water movements remains unknown. Behaviorally, one effect of lateralized water movement or touch is a turning response which moves the abdomen away from the stimulus source. The response of the CPRs and other MSIs to lateralized water movement may help evoke this turning response. However, its neural basis remains to be studied.

The CPRs and circadian rhythms. Fuentes-Pardo and Inclan-Rubio (1987) have shown that a 10 minute 2000 lux pulse of light to the CPRs can inhibit the circadian rhythm of the ERG for about 4 days after which the rhythm resumed with a phase advance of 8.4 hours. A similar light pulse inhibited the locomotor circadian rhythm for up to 5 days after which it resumed with a phase advance of 5.8 hours.

SELECTION OF CPR EFFECTS BY SPIKE FREQUENCY

A frequency threshold exists for locomotion. Edwards (1984) observed that if the initial peak spike frequency of the CPRs to a step increase in illumination was below 80 Hz, then the cyclic TF motor response and backward walking did not occur. Direct stimulation of a single CPR at a range of frequencies revealed a spike frequency threshold for the cyclic TF motor response of 60 Hz above dark-adapted firing levels (Simon & Edwards, 1989). This result suggests that neural elements that initiate walking and are postsynaptic to the CPRs require considerable temporal summation to reach threshold. Even above the frequency threshold, the locomotor response occurs less than half the time. The mechanisms of the frequency threshold and the probabilistic response remain unknown.

A lower frequency of spikes will reset circadian rhythms. The tonic firing rates of the CPRs in response to a 10 minute light stimulus that altered circadian rhythms was 30 - 40 Hz. 10 minutes of increased CPR activity at this rate was sufficient to reset ERG and locomotor rhythms (Inclan-Rubio & Fuentes- Pardo, 1987).

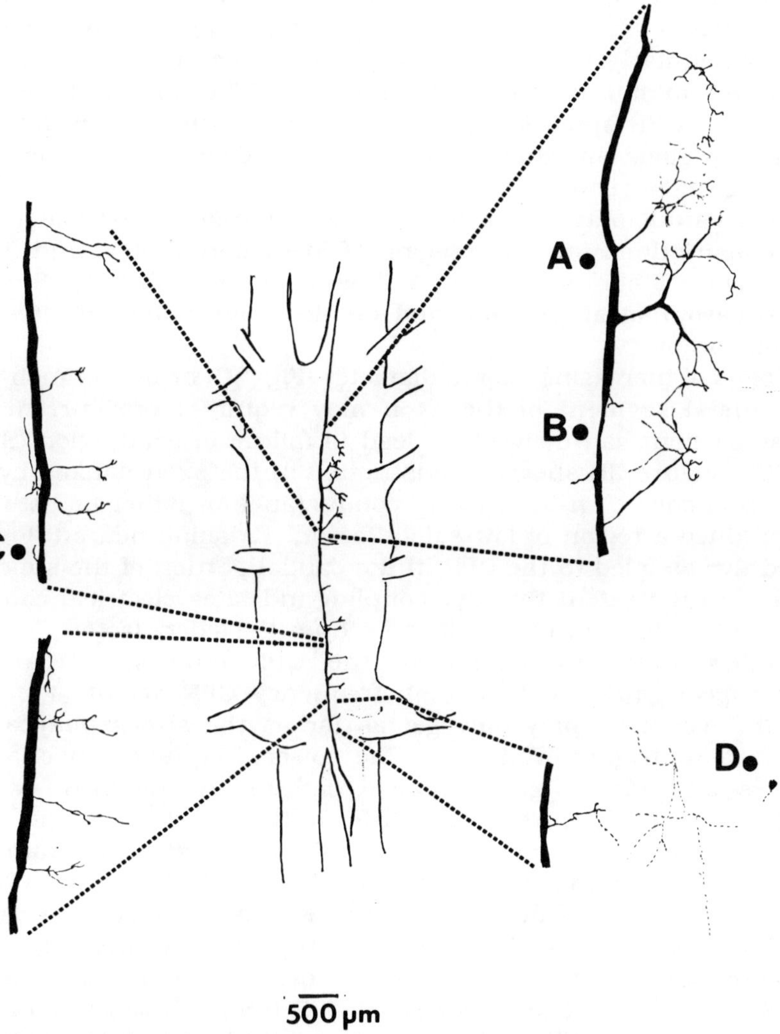

Figure 2. Structure of the CPR in the subesophageal ganglion showing regions at which spike gating may occur. The bullets and accompanying letters indicate relevant morphological details. A. A constriction near a branch point. B,C. Constrictions at which small branches occur may be synaptic gating sites. D. An electrically coupled neuron may act as a current sink.

GATING MAY SEPARATE SPIKE FREQUENCY EFFECTS .

Possible gating of the CPR action potential in the subesophageal ganglion. We have observed gating of the passage of the CPR spike through the subesophageal ganglion in an isolated nervous system. About 50% of the spikes recorded caudal to the ganglion were observed in the CECs.

In an isolated crayfish nervous system, we were able to record the CPR spike extracellularly in the CECs only three times in over thirty attempts. In the intact animal, however, both Prosser (1934) and ourselves were able to record the CPR spike in the CECs. These various data are consistent with the suggestion that gating of the CPR spike occurs in the subesophageal ganglion.

Impulse gating may occur by: 1) accumulation of extracellular K+; 2) axonal constrictions forming regions of low safety factor; and 3) synaptic gating. Figure 2 shows a Lucifer Yellow dye fill (Stewart, 1978) of the CPR in the subesophageal ganglion and details some potential sites at which gating may occur.

At a locus of increasing axonal diameter (Fig. 2C) or at a branch point (Fig. 2A) the distal segment of the axon may require more current than the proximal segment can deliver and lead to failure of conduction (Swadlow et al., 1980). Figure 2B shows a constriction in the axon flanked by two non-varicose branches. An increase in conductance in either or both branches would produce a region of low safety factor. A small neuron (Fig. 2D) was observed dye-coupled to the CPR in the caudal portion of the subesophageal ganglion. To the extent that dye-coupling indicates electrical coupling, this neuron may act as a current sink and reduce the safety factor.

If, under some circumstances, the CPR impulse is gated in the subesophageal ganglion, then high frequency CPR activity i.e. the initial peak light response, may only get as far as the subesophageal ganglion where it may trigger walking. The lower frequency mechanosensory responses and tonic light response can reach the brain where they communicate mechanoreceptive information and produce effects on circadian rhythms. The more caudal CPR terminals in the brain appear to project to or near the antennal lobe (Simon & Edwards, 1989). The antennal lobe is considered a center for mechanosensory integration (Kinnamon, 1979), and water movements have recently been shown to affect antennal movements, in part by directional information from the tailfan (Tautz, 1987). The more rostral CPR terminals are in an appropriate position to affect circadian rhythms. They appear to project to the caudal margin of the optic lobe and the parolfactory lobe. Page and Larimer (1976) have demonstrated the existence of a circadian photoreceptor in the optic lobe and a circadian oscillator somewhere in the brain.

CONCLUSIONS

The walking response is one of the frequency-coded effects of the CPRs. The circadian and mechanosensory effects of the CPR occur at lower frequencies. The question remains: exactly what neural mechanisms do the CPRs utilize to select their targets by spike frequency. As a model of a multifunctional neuron in the animal which is an ideal model system for neurobiology, the caudal photoreceptor continues to invite our curiosity and investigation.

REFERENCES

Edwards, D.H. (1984) Crayfish Extraretinal Photoreception. I. Behavioural and motoneuronal responses to abdominal illumination. J. Exp. Biol. **109:** 291-306

Flood, P.L. & Wilkens, L.A. (1978) Directional sensitivity in a crayfish mechanoreceptive interneurone: analysis by root ablation. J. Exp. Biol. **77:** 89-106

Fuentes-Pardo, B. & Inclan-Rubio, V. (1987) Caudal Photoreceptors synchronize the circadian rhythms in crayfish - I. Synchronization of ERG and locomotor circadian rhythms. Comp Biochem. Physiol. **86A**: 523-527

Hermann, H.T. (1964) Stochastic properties in the negative phototropic behavior of the crayfish. J. Exp. Zool. **155**: 381-402

Inclan-Rubio, V. & Fuentes-Pardo, B. (1987) Caudal photoreceptors synchronize the circadian rhythms of crayfish - II. Functional relationships between caudal and visual photoreceptors. Comp. Biochem. Physiol. **86A**: 529-536

Kennedy, D. (1958a) Electrical Activity of a "primitive photoreceptor" Ann. N.Y. Acad. Sci. **74:** 329-336

Kennedy, D. (1958b) Responses of the crayfish caudal photoreceptor. Am. J. Opthal. **46:** 19-26

Kennedy, D. (1963) Physiology of photoreceptor neurons in the abdominal nerve cord of the crayfish. J. Gen. Physiol. **46**: 551-572

Kennedy, D. (1976) Neural elements in relation to network function. In: Simpler Networks and Behavior, Fentress, J.C., ed. Sinauer Assoc., Sunderland, Mass. pp. 65-81

Kinnamon, J.C. (1979) Tactile input to the crayfish tegumentary neuropile. Comp. Biochem. Physiol. **63A:** 41-50

Kovac, M. (1974a) Abdominal movements during backward walking in crayfish. I. Properties of the motor program. J. Comp. Physiol. **95:** 61-78

Kovac, M. (1974b) Abdominal movements during backward walking in crayfish. II. The neuronal basis. J. Comp. Physiol. **95:** 79-94

Moore, D. & Larimer, J.L. (1987) Neural control of a cyclic postural behavior in the crayfish *Procambarus clarkii*: the pattern-initiating interneurons. J. Comp. Physiol. (A) **160:** 169-179

Page, T.L. & Larimer, J.L. (1976) Extraretinal photoreception in entrainment of crustacean circadian rhythms. Photochem. Photobiol. **23:** 245-251

Prosser, C.L. (1934) Action potentials in the nervous system of the crayfish. II. Responses to illumination of the eye and caudal ganglion. J. Cell. Comp. Physiol. **4:** 363-377

Reichert, H., Plummer, M.R. & Wine, (1983) Identified Nonspiking Local Interneurons Mediate Nonrecurrent Lateral Inhibition of Crayfish Mechanosensory Interneurons. J. Comp. Physiol. **151:** 261-276

Simon, T.W. & Edwards, D.H. (1989) Light-evoked walking in crayfish. Behavioral and motoneuronal responses are triggered by the caudal photoreceptor in the rostral CNS. J. Comp. Physiol. (in review)

Stewart, W.W. (1978) Functional connections between cells as revealed by dye-coupling with a highly fluorescent naphthalimide tracer. Cell **14**: 741- 759

Swadlow, H.A., Kocsis, J.D. & Waxman, S.G. (1980) Modulation of impulse conduction along the axonal tree. Ann. Rev. Biophys. Bioeng. **9:** 143-179

Tautz, J. (1987) Water vibration elicits active antennal movements in the crayfish, Orconectes limosus. Anim. Behav. **35:** 748-754

Welsh, J.H. (1934) The caudal photoreceptor and responses of the crayfish to light. J. Cell. Comp. Physiol. **4:** 379-388

Wilkens, L.A. & Larimer, L. (1972) The CNS Photoreceptor of Crayfish: Morphology and Synaptic Activity. J. Comp. Physiol. **80:** 389-407

Wilkens, L.A. (1988) The crayfish caudal photoreceptor: advances and questions after the first half century. Comp. Biochem. Physiol. **91C:** 61-68

Frontiers in Crustacean Neurobiology
Advances in Life Sciences

PHYSIOLOGICAL PROPERTIES OF CRUSTACEAN MOTOR NEURONS AND THE ALTERATION OF THESE PROPERTIES

Harold L. Atwood and Peter V. Nguyen

Department of Physiology, University of Toronto, Toronto, Ontario, Canada M5S 1A8

SUMMARY

Crustacean phasic motor neurons, recruited for rapid movements, are generally silent, release relatively large amounts of transmitter onto their target muscle fibers and exhibit rapid synaptic depression with repeated activation. Tonic motor neurons, recruited for postural activities or slow movements, are more continuously active, generally produce small, facilitating synaptic potentials in target muscle fibers, and resist synaptic depression. In adult crustaceans, imposition of a tonic pattern of activity on phasic neurons in vivo leads to adaptive alterations of their synaptic physiology and morphology; such neurons assume a more tonic phenotype. Short-lasting inhibition of protein synthesis by cycloheximide, when timed to occur before a period of imposed tonic activity, effectively prevents the activity-dependent adaptive modification of synaptic transmission.

INTRODUCTION

Among the first "uniquely identifiable" neurons to be recognized were the 'fast' and 'slow' axons innervating the claw closer muscle in crayfish. These two neurons are the sole excitatory elements of this large muscle, and they produce very different reactions. The 'fast' axon causes rapid development of tension with relatively few impulses, while the 'slow' axon produces slow, weak movements at low frequencies of activity, and appreciable tension only at much higher frequencies. The 'fast' axon's response is characteristically labile, while that of the 'slow' axon is very stable (Wiersma, 1961).

In part, these different responses are attributable to selective connection of the 'fast' and 'slow' axons to rapidly contracting and slowly- contracting muscle fibers, respectively (Atwood, 1976). However, equal functional importance must be assigned to characteristics of neuromuscular transmission. The 'fast' axon generates larger excitatory synaptic potentials (EPSP's) than the 'slow' axon, and they rapidly decline with maintained activity (Hoyle and Wiersma, 1958). Most 'slow' axon EPSPs actually continue to grow with maintained stimulation ('long-term facilitation': reviewed in Atwood and Wojtowicz, 1986).

'Fast' and 'slow' responses were subsequently described in abdominal and other muscles (Kennedy and Takeda, 1965; Parnas and Atwood, 1986). In general, neurons producing 'fast' responses fire in phasic bursts and rather infrequently, and thus can be termed 'phasic', while those producing 'slow' responses are more continuously active and can be termed 'tonic'.

Undoubtedly, some of the differences between phasic and tonic neurons are genetically determined. However, there is now evidence that neuronal activity plays a role in determining neuronal properties, both in developing and mature motor systems. For example, alterations of muscle activity or sensory input during a critical early stage of development can determine whether the claw of the American lobster assumes a phasic or tonic phenotype (Govind et al, 1987). In adult crustaceans, little was known until recently about the role of neuronal activity in determining neuromuscular properties.

In contrast, activity-dependent alterations are well documented in mammalian muscles (Robbins and Fischbach, 1971; Vrbova et al., 1985). We have undertaken physiological and morphological studies of motor neurons subjected to altered activity in vivo, and have found that adaptive responses occur with altered neural activity (Lnenicka and Atwood, 1985 a,b). Recently, we have shown that such changes can be prevented by interfering with protein synthesis (Nguyen, 1988; Nguyen and Atwood, 1989). Thus, a general picture is developing in which changes in neuronal activity provide a signal for alterations of neuronal properties through addition or modification of neuronal proteins.

RESULTS

Physiological changes. The 'fast' axon of the crayfish (Procambarus clarkii) claw closer muscle, and abdominal phasic axons of both crayfish and American lobster (Homarus americanus), were activated selectively by implanted wire electrodes (Lnenicka and Atwood, 1985a; Mercier and Atwood, 1989; Bradacs, Mercier and Atwood, unpublished observations). Periods of stimulation lasting for 1-2 hrs., at frequencies of 2-5 Hz, were imposed for 1-7 days. Myographic recording was employed to ensure that the axons were activated by the stimulation. In all experiments of this type, the target neuron on one side of the animal was stimulated ('Experimental' neuron), while the contralateral homologous neuron was not stimulated ('Control' neuron). After the final day of stimulation, acute preparations were made to study the neuromuscular responses of the two neurons.

Briefly, the physiological effects noted in these experiments are as follows:

a) In both claw and abdominal muscles, EPSPs produced by single impulses in phasic neurons are markedly reduced in amplitude after chronic stimulation (Figure 1A; Lnenicka and Atwood, 1985 a,b; Mercier and Atwood, 1989; Nguyen and Atwood, 1989).

b) EPSPs produced by repetitive stimulation of 'Control' neurons show typical marked depression, while EPSPs of 'Experimental' neurons resist depression, and sometimes are facilitated (Figure 1A).

c) Records of quantal release from representative synaptic terminals of 'Experimental' neurons show reduced quantal content of initial EPSPs (Mercier and Atwood, 1989), but enhanced quantal content after repetitive stimulation (Lnenicka and Atwood, 1985a). No changes in muscle fiber resistance are apparent. Thus, changes in EPSP amplitude are attributable to presynaptic events related to release of transmitter.

d) The changes in EPSP amplitude caused by chronic stimulation can be induced by stimulation of sensory inputs to the motor neurons, even though few motor action potentials are evoked (Lnenicka and Atwood, 1989). Reversible block of action potentials part-way along the motor axon during direct chronic stimulation of its central (ganglionic) processes does not prevent the adaptive changes (Lnenicka and Atwood, 1989). It is clear that synaptic activity and muscle contraction do not play an inductive role in this long-term neuronal adaptation. Depolarization of the neuron appears to be the primary signal for adaptive events.

e) In the blocked axon, direct chronic situmlation of the distal end also leads (after a delay of 1-2 days) to an adaptive response of the neuron (Lnenicka and Atwood, 1989). This result implies that depolarization of the neuronal membrane at any region provides a signal for adaptive change.

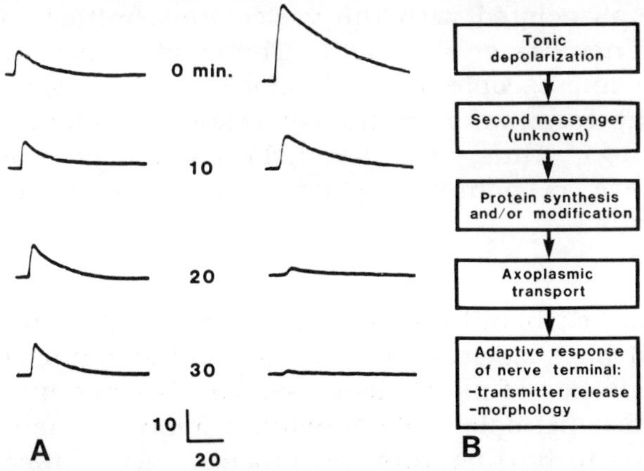

Fig. 1 A. An example of adaptive changes in EPSPs of the crayfish 'fast' closer excitor after 3 days of periodic tonic stimulation. Records were made during 5 Hz stimulation at the times shown. Matched claws from a single animal were used; left-hand records are 'Experimental', right-hand records, 'Control'. The records were made 2 days after the last period of conditioning stimulation. Calibration: 10mV, 20 ms. (Taken from Nguyen, 1988, and Nguyen and Atwood, 1989).

B. Hypothetical scheme for neuronal adaptation.

Inhibition of protein synthesis. In recent experiments, it has been established that injection of cycloheximide (5 g/gm body weight) inhibits protein synthesis in the crayfish central nervous system by 80-90% for a period of about 2 hrs, after which the degree of inhibition gradually declines (Nguyen, 1988; Nguyen and Atwood, 1989). When cycloheximide is injected each day at the time of chronic stimulation, or shortly after stimulation, little or no effect on neuronal adaptation is apparent. However, when cycloheximide is injected 2-6 hours in advance of the stimulation, the adaptive response is markedly attenuated. This result suggests that long-term adaptation depends upon the neuron's ability to synthesize proteins, some of which may be spatially or temporally transient.

Morphological changes. Crustacean tonic and phasic motor neurons differ in their terminal morphology. Synaptic terminals of tonic neurons are markedly varicose, with synapses and mitochondria associated with the varicosities. In contrast, phasic neurons have slender, more uniform terminals, with mitochondria and synapses spaced more uniformly. The size of individual mitochondria, and their relative volume, are greater for tonic terminals.

After several days of periodic chronic stimulation, phasic neurons undergo marked morphological changes and acquire a more tonic phenotype. Varicosities appear along the terminal processes; synapses and mitochondria are associated with the varicosities; mitochondrial size and volume increase (Lnenicka et al., 1986). The changes are apparent at both light and electron microscopic levels (Lnenicka and LePage, 1988). These studies show that terminal morphology responds adaptively to altered activity of the neuron. Thus, both morphological and physiological features of the neuron are responsive to its activity, and phasic or tonic characteristics result.

DISCUSSION

The studies reviewed here illustrate the influence of neuronal activity on morphological and physiological characteristics of synaptic terminals. It is clear that the properties of phasic synapses can become more like those of tonic synapses when periodic tonic activity is imposed. However, there are inherent limitations to how far this can proceed. Even after many days of periodic stimulation, the phasic neuron does not come to resemble its tonic counterpart in all respects. Limitations set during development seem to circumscribe the extent of the transformation.

In addition, some phasic neurons (e.g. the claw's 'fast' closer excitor) appear to lose their ability to adapt as the animal gets older (Lnenicka and Atwood, 1985a), while others (e.g. phasic abdominal neurons) retain adaptive ability with age (Mercier and Atwood, 1989).

Some aspects of physiological adaptation find a ready hypothetical explanation in the linked morphological changes. For example, the increase in fatigue resistance of adapted phasic synapses is logically linked to enlargement of terminal mitochondria, since larger mitochondria presumably generate more ATP to meet the energy demands of ion pumping and transmitter turnover imposed by repetitive nerve impulse activity. A parallel situation has been found in the mammalian central nervous system, where neurons thought to be depolarized by excitatory synaptic inputs have higher levels of cytochrome oxidase activity in their mitochondria than those receiving predominantly inhibitory input (and presumably less strongly depolarized) (Mjaatvedt and Wong-Riley, 1988).

The mechanisms underlying down-regulation of initial transmitter release remain uncertain, but may be linked to changes in terminal excitability or calcium homeostasis.

A key question to be answered is the nature of the link between depolarization and regulation of protein synthesis or protein modification (Figure 1B). One or more second messenger systems may be involved. They could be linked in some way to membrane depolarization or trans-membrane ionic fluxes, the most likely candidates for the initial triggering event in neuronal adaptation.

The adaptive changes described here appear to be similar to ones found elsewhere in both vertebrate and invertebrate nervous systems (Lnenicka and Atwood, 1989; Lnenicka and Murphey, 1989). The crayfish phasic motor neuron thus seems to be an appropriate model system in which to investigate general mechanisms of long-term adaptation.

Supported by Grants from NSERC and MRC, Canada

REFERENCES

Atwood, H.L. (1976) Organization and synaptic physiology of crustacean neuromuscular system. Progr. Neurobiol. **7:** 291-391.

Atwood, H.L. and Wojtowicz, J.M. (1986) Short-term and long-term plasticity and physiological differentiation of crustacean motor synapses. Int. Rev. Neurobiol. **28**: 275-362.

Govind, C.K., Mellon, D.F., and Quigley, M.M. (1987) Muscle and muscle fiber type transformation in clawed crustaceans. Amer. Zool. **27**:1079-1098.

Hoyle, G., and Wiersma, C.A.G. (1958) Excitation of neuromuscular junctions in crustacea. J. Physiol. (Lond.) **143**: 403-425.

Kennedy, D. and Takeda, K. (1965). Reflex control of abdominal flexor muscles in the crayfish. I. The twitch system. J. Exp. Biol. **43**: 211-227.

Lnenicka, G.A., and Atwood, H.L. (1985a) Age-dependent long-term adaptation of crayfish phasic motor axon synapses to altered activity. J. Neurosci. **5:** 459-467.

Lnenicka, G.A. and Atwood, H.L. (1985b) Long-term facilitation and long-term adaptation at synapses of a crayfish motoneuron. J. Neurobiol. **16:** 97-110.
Lnenicka, G.A., and Atwood, H.L. (1988) Long-term changes in neuromuscular synapses with altered sensory input to a crayfish motor neuron. Exp. Neurol. **100**: 437-447.
Lnenicka, G.H. and Atwood, H.L. (1989) Impulse activity of a crayfish motoneuron regulates its neuromuscular synaptic properties. J. Neurophysiol. **61**: 91-96.
Lnenicka, G.A., and LePage, S. (1988) Activity-dependent differences in the number of synaptic varicosities at crayfish motor terminals revealed by light microscopy. Soc. Neurosci. Abstr. **14**: 1208.
Lnenicka, G.A. and Murphey, R.K. (1989) The refinement of invertebrate synapses during development. J. Neurobiol. **20**:339-355
Lnenicka, G.A., Atwood, H.L. and Marin, L. (1986) Morphological transformation of synaptic terminals of a phasic motoneuron by long-term stimulation. J. Neurosci. **6**: 2252-2258.
Mercier, A.J., and Atwood, H.L. (1989) Long-term adaptation of a phasic extensor motoneurone in crayfish. J. Exp. Biol. (in press).
Mjaatveld, A.E. and Wong-Riley, M.T.T. (1988). Relationship between synaptogenesis and cytochrome oxidase activity in Purkinje cells of the developing rat cerebellum. J. Comp. Neurol. **277**: 155-182.
Nguyen, P.V. (1988) Protein synthesis and the expression of long-term adaptation of transmission at a crayfish phasic neuromuscular junction. M.Sc. Thesis, University of Toronto.
Nguyen, P.V. and Atwood, H.L. (1989) Expression of long-term adaptation of synaptic transmission requires a critical period of protein synthesis. J. Neurosci. (in press).
Parnas, I. and Atwood, H.L. (1966). Phasic and tonic neuromuscular systems in the abdominal extensor muscles of the crayfish and rock lobster. Comp. Biochem. Physiol. **18**: 701-723.
Robbins, N., and Fischbach, G.D. (1971) Effect of chronic disuse of rat soleus neuromuscular junctions on presynaptic function. J. Neurophysiol. **34:** 570-578.
Vrbova, G., Navarette, R. and Lowrie, M. (1985) Matching of muscle properties and motoneurone firing patterns during early stages of development. J. Exp. Biol. **115**: 113-123.
Wiersma, C.A.G. (1961) The neuromuscular system. In The Physiology of Crustacea, Vol. II (ed. T.H. Waterman) pp. 191-240. New York: Academic Press.

Frontiers in Crustacean Neurobiology
Advances in Life Sciences

SYNAPTIC CHANNELS ACTIVATED BY GLUTAMATE WITH KINETICS LIKE THE FAST SODIUM CHANNELS

J. Dudel, Ch. Franke and H. Hatt

Physiologisches Institut der Technischen Universität München, Biedersteiner Straße 29, 8000 München 40, F.R.G.

SUMMARY

A completely desensitizing ,glutamatergic, cationic channel type of crayfish muscle was exposed to pulses of glutamate (glu). For low glu concentrations, the maximal response increased with the fifth power of concentration. With 10 mM glu, channel open probability reached its maximum within 0.4 ms, and declined with a time constant of 2 ms in presence of glu. This time constant of desensitization decreased on lowering glu concentration. Channels could be fully desensitized without opening by slowly rising glu concentrations. On removal of glu, channels remained desensitized for about 1 ms, but recovered largely within 2 ms and completely within 5 ms.

INTRODUCTION

Ligand activated membrane channels have been studied usually in equilibrium with the ligand. Among the transmitter activated synaptic channels, most work has been done on the nicotinic receptors/channels of the vertebrate endplate (Neher et al., 1978; Hamill et al., 1981; Colquhoun & Sakmann 1985; Colquhoun & Ogden 1988) and on the glutamatergic, cationic receptors/channels of locusts (Patlak et al., 1979; Cull-Candy et al., 1981; Kerry et al., 1988) and crayfish (Franke et al., 1983; Franke et al. 1986; Hatt et al., 1988a,b). These studies yield openings of channels at relatively low rates, which were organized in 'bursts' of a few ms duration, and during these bursts channels opened and closed repeatedly with average open and closed times in the 100 μs range. The population of channels activated in the steady state appeared to be rather uniform in the different preparations. During natural transmission, receptors at neuromuscular junctions are exposed to a sharp rise in the concentration of transmitter which remains present for at most a few ms. We have developed a 'liquid filament switch' which allows to change solutions at an outside-out patch of membrane within 0.3 ms (Franke et al, 1987). L-glutamate (glu) applied in short pulses to patches from crayfish and locusts elicited rapid channel openings, but also rapid desensitization, i.e. decline of activation in the maintained presence of glu (Franke et al., 1987; Dudel et al., 1988,

1990 a,b,c,). In both preparations a number of kinetically different channel types could be defined. The present report is restricted to the kinetics of the completely desensitizing glutamatergic, cationic channel of crayfish muscle, which is an example of an extremely rapidly transmitting chemical receptor/channel system.

RESULTS AND DISCUSSION

Activations of 3 such channels contained in a patch and exposed to 50 ms pulses of glu with a concentration of 10 mM and 0.5 mM, respectively, are shown in Fig. 1A and B. Each 10 mM glu pulse elicited opening of 1 to 3 channels, but only during the first 5 ms after the beginning of the pulse. The openings are grouped in bursts of an average about 1.5 ms duration. With 0.5 mM glu in the pulse (Fig. 1B) the rate of openings was much lower, and the 'bursts' consisted mostly of only one opening with an average duration of about 0.3 ms. Average responses from the same patch show that with 10 mM glu the open probability rose to a peak of 0.6 within 0.4 ms, and with 1 mM glu to 0.2 also within 0.4 ms (Fig. 1C). With lower glu concentrations the response maxima were reached more slowly, and the maximal open probabilities declined steeply, being approximately proportional to [glu]5 for [glu] ≤ 0.5 mM (Dudel et al., 1990a, Fig.6A). In this concentration range the response to glu exhibits sharp threshold behavior.

The most striking characteristic of the channels in Fig.1 is their rapid and complete desensitization in presence of glu. The time constants of desensitization were 2 ms with 10 mM, 1.3 ms with 1 mM and approximately 0.9 ms with 0.5 mM glu. This is a paradoxical kinetic behavior; desensitization which supposedly involves binding of glu should proceed more rapidly on increasing glu concentration. The paradox is resolved, if one considers also the dependence of burst length on glu concentration. As seen in Fig. 1A and B (also Dudel and Franke 1987), burst length increases when [glu] is raised. This increase in burst length overcompensates the more rapid desensitization process at higher [glu]. If instead of open probability (Fig. 1C) the rate of beginnings of bursts was evaluated (Fig. 1D), desensitization became more rapid, the rate of bursts decaying with an approximate time constant of 0.23 ms with 10 mM glu. At lower [glu], desensitization determined in this manner decreased in rate, in agreement with kinetic predictions.

Fig. 1A and B. Openings of 3 channels contained in an outside-out patch due to pulses of 10 mM (A) and 0.5 mM (B) L- glutamate. The pulses start with the biphasic artefact at the beginning of the traces (end of pulses not shown). Single channel current amplitude was -8 pA, clamp potential -80 mV. In B zero responses are underrepresented. C and D Evaluation of average responses from traces like shown in A and B from same patch. C time course of open probability (probability of one channel to be open), D time course of rate of bursts (rate of beginnings of bursts for one channel), starting with the beginning of the glu pulses. From Dudel et al. (1990a).

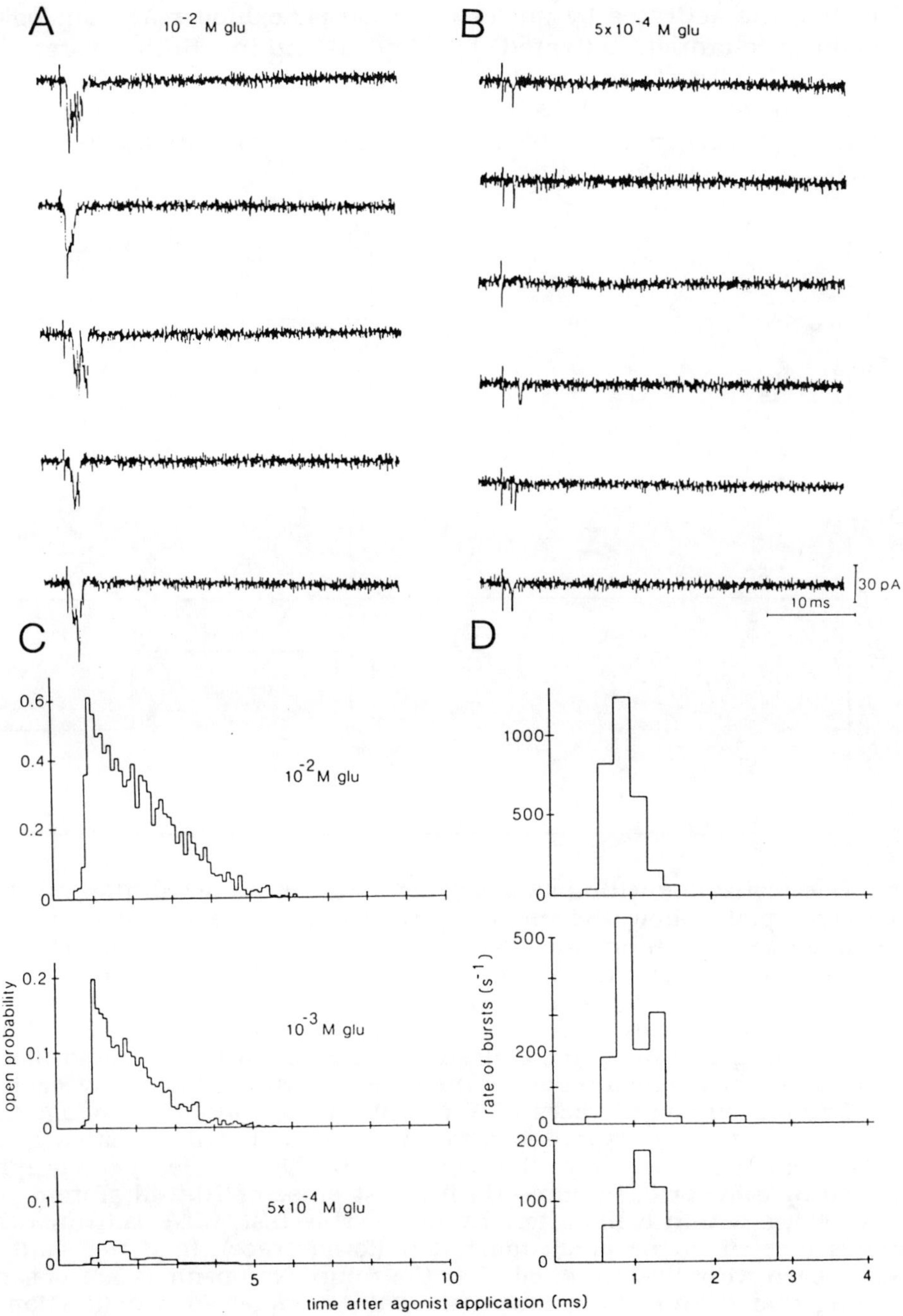
A
10^{-2} M glu
B
5×10^{-4} M glu
30 pA
10 ms
C
D
0.6
0.4
0.2
0
10^{-2}M glu
1000
500
0
open probability
0.2
0.1
0
10^{-3} M glu
rate of bursts (s^{-1})
500
200
0
0.1
0
5×10^{-4} M glu
200
100
0
5
10
1
2
3
4
time after agonist application (ms)

Fig.1

The channels activated by pulses of glu so far exhibit many analogies to the sodium channel activated by depolarization. Both systems are characterised by a sharp threshold in reacting to their specific stimulus, both are fully activated by large stimuli within less than 1 ms, and both are inactivated in presence of the stimulus almost as rapidly as they are activated.

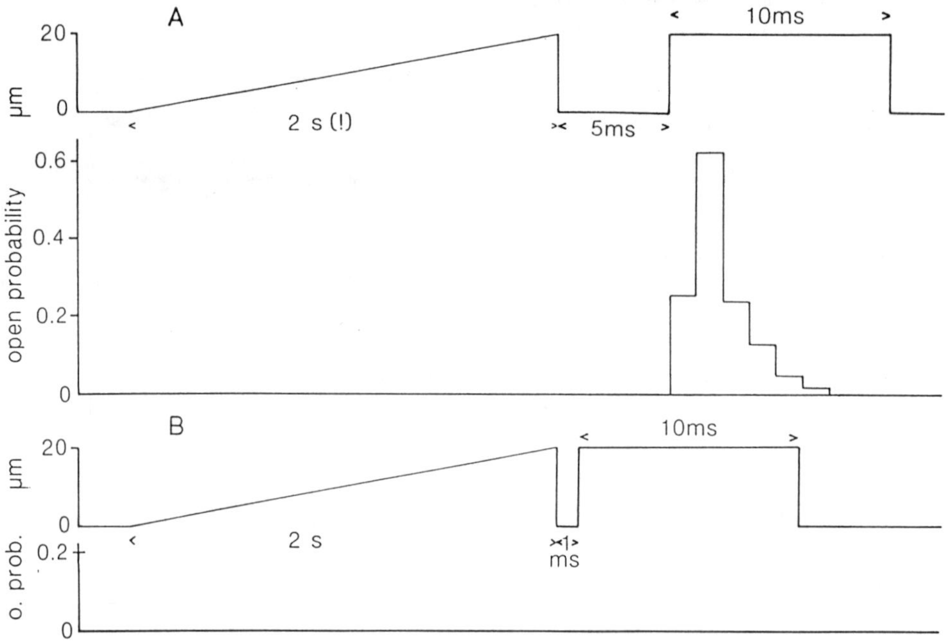

Fig. 2. Desensitization with a slowly rising glutamate concentration. In A and B the uper plots show the displacement of the tube ejecting the liquid filament. At zero position, the filament passes below the patch, the patch being washed by 0 glutamate solution in the bulk superfusion. Then the liquid filament which contains 10-2 M glutamate is moved upward with a ramp voltage which causes the full 20 µm excursion of the piezo within 2 seconds. During this ramp the concentration gradient in the liquid filament from 0 to 10 mM glutamate passes the patch slowly, but does not elicit any channel activation (lower traces in A and B). At the end of the voltage ramp, the voltage at the piezo is switched to zero and the patch is shifted back to zero glutamate solution. From this point on, the time scale in the graphs is expanded by a factor of hundred. In A a test pulse of 10-2 M glutamate for 10 ms follows within 5 ms after the ramp. This test pulse activates the 3 channels present in the patch maximally (lower trace). In B the same test pulse is given with 1 ms interval after the ramp. No openings are observed, indicating that during the 1 ms interval the complete desensitization during the ramp had not been removed. The averages of 'open channels' contain the result of 70 glutamate pulses in A, and of 60 glutamate pulses in B. From Dudel et al. (1990a).

An important characteristic of inactivation in Na^+ channels is the 'independence' from activation (Hodgkin & Huxley 1952). Na^+ channels can be inactivated by low or very slow depolarization without ever opening. The experiment of Fig. 2 tests whether also desensitization by glu can proceed without channel opening. In this experiment the liquid filament containing 10 mM glu was not shifted rapidly to produce a concentration step, but ramplike, moving by 20 µm within 2 seconds. This exposed the patch to a slow rise in glu concentration from 0 to 10 mM. During the ramp no channels opened (Fig. 2A and B). To control whether the channels were really desensitized at the end of the ramp, a 10 ms glu pulse was applied with short intervals after switching off the ramp. When the interval was 1 ms, also the glu pulse did not elicit channel openings (Fig. 2B). When however the interval was increased to 5 ms, the full response to the glu pulse reappeared (Fig. 2A). Thus the slowly rising glu concentration fully desensitized the channels in the patch without opening any of them, and desensitization could be relieved within 5 ms when glu was removed. Desensitization is independent of channel opening in the present system.

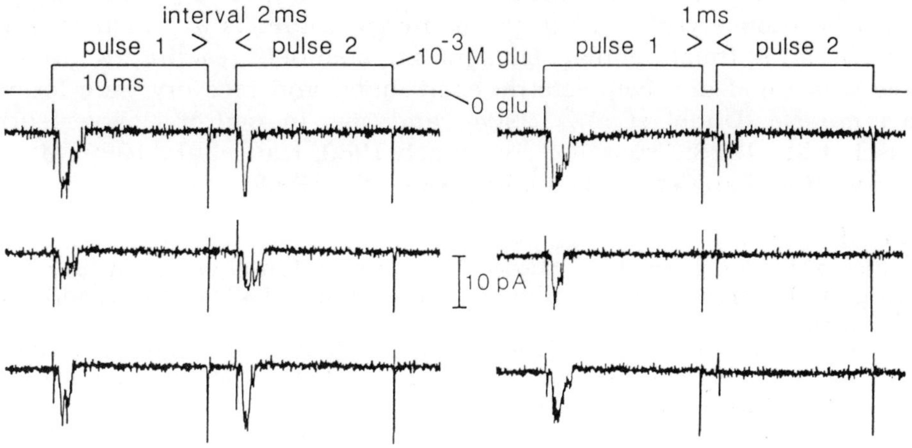

Fig. 3. Time course of resensitization. Pairs of test pulses containing 10-3 M glutamate, each lasting 10 ms, were given with intervals of 2 ms (left column) and of 1 ms (right column) to one patch. The pulses elicited openings of maximally 3 channels and after a few ms complete desensitization. In each pair pulse I is the control, and the response in pulse II indicates the extent of removal of desensitization, i.e. resensitization, during the pulse interval. With 2 ms pulse interval the response during pulse II had almost control amplitude. With 1 ms pulse interval, the responses to pulse II were strongly depressed, no channels opening during most of the trials. Patch potential -80 mV, filter at 5 kHz. From Dudel et al. (1990a).

Another feature which the glutamatergic channels studied here share with the voltage gated Na^+ channels is the rapid recovery from inactivation/desensitization when the gating stimulus is removed. In Na^+ channels inactivation is reversed within a few ms if the membrane is repolarised, and the time course of the returning availability for activation is equivalent to the refractory period of the action potential. We have seen analogous reactions of the glutamatergic channels in Fig. 2. Recovery from desensitization was studied also by applying twin pulses of glu with varying intervals (Fig. 3). When the pulse interval was 1 ms, the channels responded rarely to pulse 2 (about 5 % of the response to pulse 1). When however the pulse interval was lengthened to 2 ms, the response had recovered to 90 % of control, and recovery was complete with 5 ms pulse interval. An S-shaped time course of switching from inactivation to full availability for reactivation is seem also in Na^+ channels when tested by twin depolarization pulses.

The completely desensitizing glutamatergic, cationic channels of crayfish seem to match the characteristics of the action potential excellently and thus are optimally adapted for rapid transmission of information carried by action potentials. These channel characteristics first found in crayfish have recently been observed in other glutamatergic channels in which also quisqualate is an optimal agonist. Quisqualate channels reacting to glutamate pulses with rapid and complete desensitization and recovery were found in locust muscle (Dudel et al., 1990c), and also in neurons of vertebrates (Trussel et al., 1988; Trussell & Fischbach 1989; Hatt et al., 1989; Mayer & Vyklicky 1989; Tang et al., 1989; Franke et al., 1990).

REFERENCES

Colquhoun, D. & Ogden, D.C. (1988) Activation of ion channels in the frog end-plate by high concentrations of acetylcholine.J. Physiol. (Lond.) **395**: 131-159.

Colquhoun, D. & Sakmann B. (1985) Fast events in single-channel currents activated by acetylcholine and its analogues at the frog muscle end-plate. J. Physiol. (Lond.) **369:** 501-557.

Cull-Candy S. G., Miledi, R. & Parker, I. (1981) Single glutamate-activated channels recorded from locust muscle fibres with perfused patch-clamp electrodes. J. Physiol. (Lond.) **321**: 195-210.

Dudel, J., Franke, Ch. & Hatt, H. (1990a) Rapid activation, de- and resensitization of synaptic channels of crayfish after glutamate pulses. Sent in for publication.

Dudel, J., Franke, Ch. & Hatt, H. (1990b) A family of glutamatergic, excitatory channel types at the crayfish neuromuscular junction. Sent in for publication.

Dudel, J., Franke, Ch., Hatt, H., Ramsey, R.L. & Usherwood P.N.R. (1988) Rapid activation and desensitization by glutamate of excitatory, cation-selective channels in locust muscle. Neurosci. Lett. **88**: 33-38.

Dudel, J., Franke, Ch., Hatt, H., Ramsey, R.L. & Usherwood, P.N.R. (1990c) Concentration jump application of agonist to a quisqualate-sensitive glutamate receptor can cause desensitization without channel opening. Sent in for publication.

Franke, Ch., Dudel, J. & Finger W. (1983) Single synaptic channels recorded at glutamate sensitive patches on a crayfish muscle. Neurosci. Lett. **42**: 7-12.

Franke, Ch., Hatt, H. & Dudel, J. (1986) The excitatory glutamate-activated channel recorded in cell-attached and excised patches from the membranes of tail, leg and stomach muscles of crayfish. J. Comp. Physiol. A. **159:** 579-589.

Franke, Ch., Hatt, H. & Dudel, J. (1987) Liquid filament switch for ultra-fast exchanges of solutions at excised patches of synaptic membrane of crayfish muscle. Neurosci. Lett. **77**: 199-204.

Hatt, H., Franke, Ch., Smith, D.O., Rosenheimer, J.L. & Zufall, F. (1989) Rapid desensitization of glutamate channels in -motoneuron enriched cell fraction from embryonic chick spinal cord. In preparation.

Hamill, O.P., Marty, A., Neher, E., Sakmann, B. & Sigworth, F.J.(1981) Improved patch-clamp techniques for high-resolution current recording from cells and cell-free membrane patches.Pflügers Arch. 391: 85-100.

Hatt, H., Franke, Ch. & Dudel, J. (1988a) Ionic permeabilities of L-glutamate activated, excitatory synaptic channel incrayfish muscle. Pflügers Arch. **411**: 8-16.

Hatt, H., Franke, Ch. & Dudel, J. (1988b) Calcium dependentgating of the L-glutamate activated, excitatory synapticchannel on crayfish muscle. Pflügers Arch. **411**: 17-26.

Hatt, H., Zufall, F., Smith, D.O., Rosenheimer, J.L. & Franke, Ch. (1989) Glutamate and quisqualate rapidly activate and desensitize channels in vertebrate central neurons. Dynamics and Plasticity in Neuronal Systems. Proc. of the 17th Göttingen Neurobiology Conference. Ed. N. Elsner and W. Singer. Georg Thieme Verlag Stuttgart, Nr. 34.

Hodgkin, A.L. & Huxley, A.F. (1952) The dual effect of membranepotential on sodium conductance in the giant axon of Loligo.J. Physiol. **116**: 497-506.

Kerry, C. J., Ramsey, R.L., Sansom, M.S.P. & Usherwood, P.N.R.(1988) Glutamate receptor channel kinetics. The effect of glutamate concentration. Biophys. J. **53**: 39-52.

Mayer, M. L. & Vyklicky, L. (1989) Concanavalin A selectivelyreduces desensitization of mammalian neuronal quisqualatereceptors. Proc. Natl. Acad. Sci. USA **86**: 1411-1415.

Neher, E., Sakmann, B. & Steinbach J.H. (1978) The extracellular patch clamp: A method for resolving currents through individual open channels in biological membranes. PflügersArch. **375**: 219-228.

Patlak, J. B., Gration, K.A.F. & Usherwood, P.N.R. (1979) Single glutamate-activated channels in locust muscle. Nature **278**: 643-645.

Tang, Ch., Dichter M. & Morad, M. (1989) Quisqualate activates a rapidly inactivating high conductance ionic channel in hippo-campal neurons. Science **243**: 1474-1477.

Trussell, L.O. & Fischbach, G.D. (1989) Glutamate receptor desensitization and its role in synaptic transmission. Neuron 3: 209-218.

Trussell, L. O., Thio, L.L., Zorumski, Ch.F. & Fischbach, G.D. (1988) Rapid desensitization of glutamate receptors in vertebrate central neurons. Proc. Natl. Acad. Sci. USA. **85**:2834-2838.

Frontiers in Crustacean Neurobiology
Advances in Life Sciences

HISTOCHEMICAL AND BIOCHEMICAL HETEROGENEITY IN A CRUSTACEAN POSTURAL MUSCLE

D.M. Neil and W.S. Fowler

Neurobiology Laboratory, Department of Zoology, University of Glasgow, Glasgow G12 8QQ, Scotland, U.K.

SUMMARY

Histochemical staining methods for SDH activity, total myofibrillar ATPase and the pH lability of myosin ATPase isoforms is in accord with biochemical analyses of contractile and regulatory protein assemblages in demonstrating that two slow fibre subtypes exist in the abdominal superficial muscles of the Norway lobster. Furthermore, there is a correlation between these fibre subtypes and the pattern of their motor innervation. This conjunction of experimental results from three distinct approaches identifies the lobster superficial flexor muscle as a 'pioneer system' in which to examine the development and plasticity of muscle fibre types at the level of identified motor neurones and individual muscle fibres, and in terms of the expression of genes for particular muscle proteins.

INTRODUCTION

Crustacean muscle fibres can be divided into two main categories, fast and slow, on the basis of a number of morphological, physiological and histochemical criteria (Govind & Atwood, 1982; Silverman et al., 1987). A great variation occurs from muscle to muscle in the proportion of each fibre type found. Many leg muscles contain a mixture of fast and slow fibres, thus conferring the ability to produce a wide spectrum of contractile effects (Tse et. al., 1981; Parsons & Mosse, 1982; Maier et. al., 1984). A greater segregation occurs in the dimorphic claws, which comprise muscles of a more homogeneous composition: slow fibres in the crusher closer, and mainly (though not entirely) fast fibres in the cutter closer (Ogonowski et al., 1980). An even more extreme division of labour occurs in the abdominal extensor and flexor muscles of macrurous decapods: the thin sheets of superficial muscles contain slow fibres, while the large masses of deep muscles are composed of fast fibres (Kennedy & Takeda, 1965). As a functional corollary, these two muscle groups are adapted to produce abdominal movements with different characteristics: slow postural adjustments by the superficials and rapid tail flipping by the deep muscles.

The most extensively used histochemical methods for disciminating fast and slow crustacean muscle fibres involve tests both for oxidative capacity, indicative of fatigue resistance, and total myofibrillar ATPase activity, indicative of contractile speed. These two properties tend to vary inversely, slow fibres having a higher oxidative capacity and lower ATPase activity than fast fibres. Another histochemical test for myosin ATPase which is performed in the presence of calcium and involves a preincubation stage in acid or alkali solutions, reliably distinguishes two populations of fibres which contain either a labile or stable myosin ATPase isoform. In some cases this test apparently confirms the simple fast/slow dichotomy of fibre types (Silverman & Charlton, 1980). However, in certain muscles which were previously considered to comprise a homogeneous population of slow fibres, a heterogeneous mix of fibres containing either the labile or stable myosin ATPase isoform can be revealed (Kent & Govind, 1981; Costello & Govind, 1983; Fowler & Neil, 1987). In combination with the other methods, this pH-sensitive test can act as a convenient discriminator of fibre types, and here we report the use of this approach to the study of muscle fibre heterogeneity in the abdominal superficial flexor muscle (SF) of a lobster.

A more rigorous method for fibre typing relies on the electrophoretic separation of myofibrillar protein assemblages (Lehman & Szent-Gyorgyi, 1975; Mykles, 1985a). This technique has demonstrated that multiple isoforms of certain contactile and regulatory proteins are expressed in single fibres, and that the occurrence of these can be used as reliable indicators of fibre type. Thus fast fibres can be distinguished from slow fibres on the basis of the presence of both a particular isoform of paramyosin (P1, Mr = 110,000) and a 75kD protein. This technique also reveals that there are in fact two subtypes of slow fibres. These are distinguishable in terms of the T1 subunit of troponin, which is absent in some slow fibres, designated S1, but present in others, designated S2. Differences have been found in the distribution of these fibre subtypes in the cutter claw closer muscles of crabs and lobsters (Mykles, 1985b), although no extensive survey has yet been made of the abdominal SF muscle.

Crustacean muscles display characteristic patterns of polyneuroronal innervation from restricted motoneurone pools (Atwood, 1976), and in mixed muscles this can involve a high degree of matching between particular motoneurones and fibres of a given type (Costello & Govind, 1983). In the abdominal SF muscle systematic differences in the axonal supply have been reported, each of the five excitatory axons projecting onto a restricted subset of fibres with a spatially graded strength of innervation (Ely & Velez, 1982). We have re-examined the innervation of this muscle in conjunction with the histochemical and biochemical analyses.

METHODS

Histochemistry. Whole abdomens, or dissected SF muscles of adult *Nephrops norvegicus* were cryosectioned, and stained for one of the following: 1. Succinic dehydrogenase (SDH) by incubation with succinate. 2. Total myofibrillar ATPase activity using a method adapted from Mabuchi & Sreter (1980). 3. pH-sensitive mATPase isoforms, as distinguished by pre-incubation in the presence of calcium at high or low pH, followed by incubation with ATP (Silverman & Charlton, 1980).

Biochemistry. The contractile and regulatory proteins of SF (and, for comparison, from the deep flexor muscles) were analysed using discontinuous SDS-PAGE. After glycineration, fibres were separated individually from the muscle and dissolved in SDS buffer overnight. Proteins were separated on 10% polyacrylamide gels, together with low molecular weight standards, and stained with Coomassie blue or silver.

Innervation. The number of axons in the abdominal third superficial root (SR3), which supplies SF, was established from cross sections of fixed material. The location of their cell bodies in the ganglia was determined by conventional methods of retrograde filling with cobalt salts. Using an isolated abdominal preparation, the innervation pattern of SF was determined by correlating the spontaneous activity of different motor axons, identified by their spike size in extracellular recordings from SR3, with epsp's and ipsp's recorded intracellularly in the individual muscle fibres. In some cases the penetrated fibre was filled with dye (Fast Green, Lucifer Yellow) by pressure injection or iontophoresis from the electrode tip, and was subsequently processed histochemically.

RESULTS

Histochemistry. The SF muscle is a thin muscle sheet of approximately 80 fibres, comprising medial and lateral bundles and a central region one fibre thick (Fig. 1). Compared with fibres of the deep flexor muscles, t he SF fibres have lower total myofibrillar ATPase activity and higher SDH activity. However, within SF itself there are systematic differences in staining. All central fibres and most, but not all medial fibres have very low myofibrillar ATPase activity and stain intensively for SDH, while most, but not all lateral fibres have a higher level of myofibrillar ATPase activity and a distinctly lower level of SDH activity.

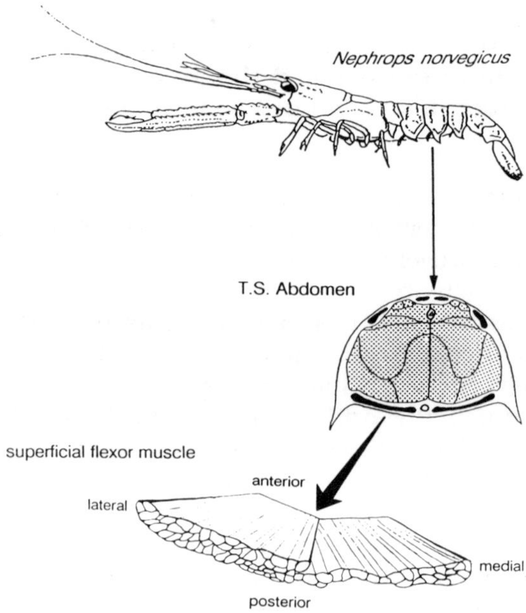

Fig. 1. Morphology of superficial flexor muscle in *Nephrops norvegicus*.

This heterogeneity is also revealed by the tests for the pH sensitivity of the myosin ATPase: in fibres of SF with the higher level of myofibrillar ATPase the myosin ATPase isoform is labile, while in fibres with the lower myofibrillar ATPase level the myosin ATPase isoform is stable (Fig. 2A). Examination of SF muscles from different preparations (Fig. 2B) shows that this heterogeneous distribution of fibre types with two distinct histochemical profiles is similar but not identical from segment to segment in one animal, and from muscle to muscle in different animals.

Biochemistry. Our results obtained using SDS-PAGE are consistent with those of Mykles (1988) in showing that fast fibres of the deep flexor muscles can be distinguished from SF fibres by the presence of the P1 variant of paramyosin (Mr = 110,000) and a 75kD protein (Fig. 3A). This suggests that all SF fibres are indeed of the slow type. However, the distribution of other key variants, most notably those of troponin T, indicate that two fibre subtypes exist in SF, corresponding to those designated S1 and S2 by Mykles (1985b). The troponin T1 variant (Mr = 55,000) is absent in some fibres, identifying them as S1 (Fig. 3A, lane b), but is present in others, identifying them as S2 (Fig. 3A, lane c).

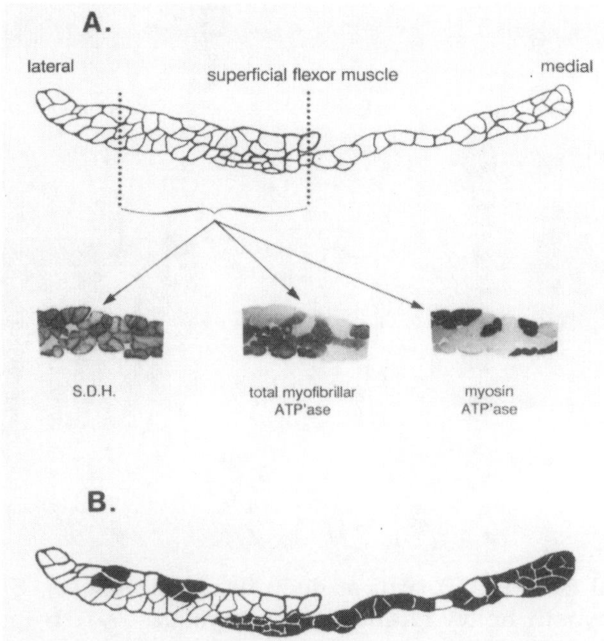

Fig. 2. Histochemical staining of superficial flexor muscle. A. Serial sections stained for succinic dehydrogenase, total myofibrillar ATPase and myosin ATPase. B. Camera lucida drawing of myosin ATPase staining of a superficial muscle from the same segment of a different animal.

By systematically dissecting out fibres from one edge of the muscle to the other it has been possible to use biochemical analysis to determine the distribution of fibre subtypes across SF (Fig. 3B). The fibres of the medial bundle and central region are almost exclusively of the S2 type. In the lateral bundle, however, there is a majority of S1 fibres, but with a certain number of S2 fibres interspersed. This distribution corresponds exactly with the pattern of histochemical staining for myosin ATPase, allowing us to equate labile fibres with the S1 type, and stable fibres with the S2 type.

Innervation. The SF muscle of *Nephrops* is innervated by six motor axons, one of which is, on the basis a positive immunocytochemical reaction for GABA (Neil & Cournil, unpublished observations), a peripheral inhibitor. All muscle fibres receive synaptic input from a number of axons, but there is a tendency for preferential innervation of medial fibres by the smaller, more spontaneously active axons f2 and f3, and of lateral fibres by a larger unit (f4). However exceptions to these general trends occur in all preparations. Particular fibres can be encountered in both medial and lateral locations which display a pattern of synaptic input different from that of neighbouring fibres, but resembling that of fibres from the opposite border (Fig. 4).

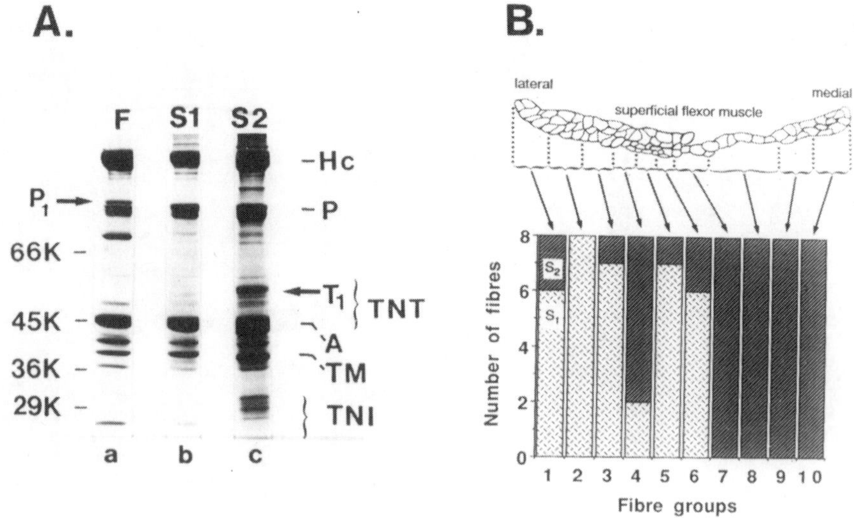

Fig. 3. A.Typical SDS-PAGE run. a, deep flexor muscle; b, SF S_1 fibre; c, SF S_2 fibre; HC, myosin heavy chain; P, paramyosin; TNT, troponin-T; A, actin; TM, tropomyosin; TNI, troponin-I. B. Distribution of fibre types across the superficial flexor muscle.

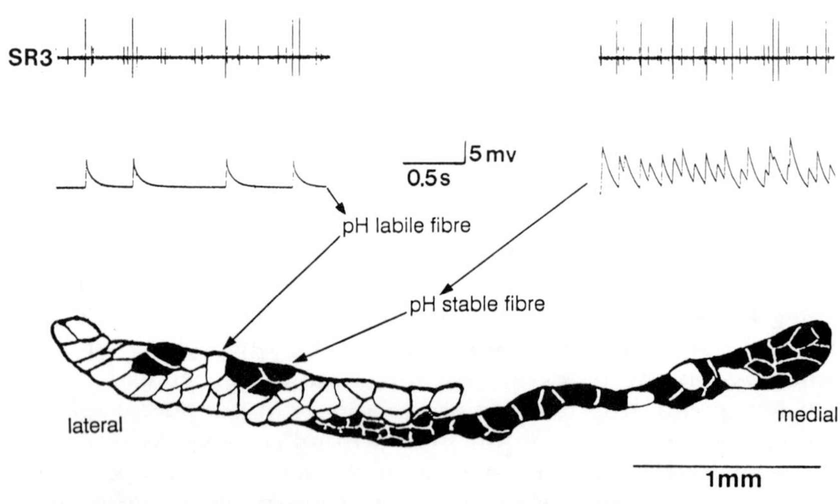

Fig. 4. Innervation of superficial flexor muscle. Upper trace: recording of spontaneous activity in superficial root 3. Lower trace: intracellular muscle recording from the fibres indicated on the section, below, stained for myosin ATPase.

Critical tests of the relationships between the location of a fibre across SF, its innervation pattern and its histochemical staining properties have been performed by dye-marking fibres after intracellular recording. The marked fibres can subsequently be recognised in unstained sections of the muscle prepared for the histochemical tests. In this way it has been possible to ascertain that, whatever their location across SF, fibres which receive preferential innervation from f2 and f3 always contain the pH-stable myosin ATPase isoform, while those innervated most prominently by f4 contain the pH-labile mATPase isoform.

DISCUSSION

Using a number of histochemical and biochemical techniques we have found a widespread heterogeneity in the fibre composition of the lobster SF muscle. While such a finding would not be unexpected for a thoracic limb muscle, it has been a common assumption that the superficial muscles of the abdomen represent a homogeneous set, adapted for postural movements and separate from the deep muscles which contribute to the phasic movements of the tail flip (Kennedy & Takeda, 1965). This assumption is indeed implicit in the studies of Mykles (1985a, 1988) who has used a sample from the SF of crayfish as a tonic muscle 'standard'. It now remains to be determined if the the S1 and S2 fibre subtypes of SF differ in their mechanical properties, as do those of the equivalent fibre types in claw muscles, which have been named 'slow twitch' and 'tonic' respectively, in accordance with their differing contractile performances (Costello & Govind 1983).

In terms of the techniques employed, the biochemical analysis of myofibrillar proteins provides the most unambiguous discrimination between fast and slow fibres, based on the P1 variant of paramyosin, and between the two subtypes of slow fibres, based on the troponin T1 variant. The histochemical methods, taken together, provide results which are consistent with the biochemistry, although individual tests are themselves not always disciminatory. For example, both fast fibres and S1 slow fibres contain pH-labile isoforms of the myosin ATPase. Also, although in SF the level of SDH activity does correlate with slow fibre subtypes, this is not a consistent finding in other postural muscles (Neil et al.,1987).

The pattern of innervation of the lobster SF by its six motor axons appears to be more complex than the graded distribution reported by Ely & Velez (1982). Because of this it has been possible to demonstrate that the observed heterogeneity in this muscle shows an exact correlation with the pattern of synaptic input onto individual fibres. These results imply that a mechanism exists during development for matching the innervating axon with a muscle fibre which expresses particular myofibrillar protein assemblages. This could occur either through a neural induction process, or by a selective acceptance of innervation by predetermined fibre types (Quigley & Mellon, 1984; Pette & Vrbova, 1985). On the basis of the results presented here, we suggest that the lobster SF muscle is a most convenient model system in which to study the mechanisms of neuromuscular differentiation at the level of single muscle fibres and identified motor axons. Furthermore, the fact that the two fibre subtypes in SF differ from each other in terms of only a small number of muscle protein phenotypes will make it feasible to apply the techniques of molecular biology to elucidate the genetic processes involved in the expression of these differences.

ACKNOWLEDGEMENTS

This work was supported, in part, by a Twinning contract from the Commission for the European Communities (ST2J-0249) to DMN, and a grant from the British Council to WSF.

REFERENCES

Atwood, H.L. (1976). Organisation and synaptic physiology of crustacean neuromuscular systems. Prog. Neurobiol. **7:** 291-391.

Costello, W.J. & Govind, C.K. (1983). Contractile responses of single fibres in lobster claw closer muscles: correlation with structure, histochemistry and innervation. J. Exp. Biol. **227**: 381-393.

Ely & Velez (1982). Regeneration of specific neuromuscular connections in the crayfish. I. Pattern of connections and synaptic strength. J. Neurophysiol. **47**: 656-665.

Fowler, W.S. , Higuchi, T. & Neil, D.M. (1987). Different fibre types revealed in a crustacean muscle using histochemical and electrophysiological techniques. J. Physiol. (Lond.) 391: 86P.

Fowler, W.S. & Neil, D.M. (1989). Histochemical heterogeneity correlated with fibre innervation in a lobster postural muscle. J. Physiol. (Lond.) **409:** 72P.

Govind, C.K. & Atwood, H.L. (1982). Organisation of neuromuscular systems. In The Biology of Crustacea, Vol 3, Neurobiology: Structure and Function (eds. H.L. Atwood & D.C. Sandeman) pp. 63-103. New York: Academic Press.

Lehman, W. & Szent-Gyorgyi, (1975). Regulation of muscular contraction. Distribution of actin control and myosin control in the animal kingdom. J. Gen. Physiol. **66:** 1-30.

Kennedy, D. & Takeda, K. (1965). Relex control of abdominal flexor muscles in the crayfish. II. The tonic system. J. Exp. Biol. **43:** 229-246.

Kent, K.S. & Govind, C.K. (1981). Two types of tonic fibres in lobster muscle based on enzyme histochemistry. J. Exp. Zool. **25**: 113-116.

Mabuchi, K. & Sreter, F.A. (1980). Actomyosin ATPase. II. Fiber typing by histochemical ATPase reaction. Muscle and Nerve 3: 233-239.

Maier, L., Rathmayer, W. & Pette, D. (1986). pH lability of myosin ATPase activity permits discrimination of different muscle fibre types in crustaceans. Histochemistry **81**: 75-77.

Mykles, D.L. (1985a). Heterogeneity of myofibrillar proteins in lobster fast and slow muscles: variants of troponin, paramyosin, and myosin light chains comprise four distinct protein assemblages. J. Exp. Zool. **234:** 23-32.

Mykles, D.L. (1985b). Multiple variants of myofibrillar proteins in single fibres of lobster claw muscles: Evidence for two types of slow fibers in the cutter claw muscle. Biol. Bull. **169:** 476-483.

Mykles, D.L. (1988). Histochemical and biochemical characterisation of two slow fiber types in decapod crustacean muscles. J. Exp. Zool. 245: 232-243.

Ogonowski, M.M., Lang, F. & Govind, C.K. (1980). Histochemistry of lobster claw-closer muscles during development. J. Exp. Zool. **213**: 359-367.

Parsons, D.W. & Mosse, P.R.L. (1982). The leg flexor muscle of Carcinus. II. Distribution of muscle fiber types. J. Exp. Zool. **224**: 169-175.

Pette, D. & Vrbova G. (1985). Neural control of phenotypic expression in mammalian muscle fibres. Muscle and Nerve **8**: 676-689.

Frontiers in Crustacean Neurobiology
Advances in Life Sciences

CLONING AND SEQUENCING OF THE CRUSTACEAN HYPERGLYCEMIC HORMONE FROM *CARCINUS MAENAS*

Jörg Gromoll and Wolfgang Weidemann

Institut für Zoophysiologie, Universität Bonn,
Endenicher Allee 11-13, 5300 Bonn, Federal Republic of Germany

SUMMARY

The Crustacean hyperglycemic hormone (CHH) is one of the best known crustacean neuropeptides, with a potent hyperglycemic action. CHH originates in the neurosecretory perikarya of the eyestalk ganglia. Here we describe the cDNA cloning approach for the complete coding region of a prepro CHH. A cDNA library of X- organ tissue of *Carcinus maenas* was established and screening of this library with an oligonucleotide probe yielded one positive clone. Sequencing data of the clone revealed a precursor structure consisting of a putative 26 amino acid signal peptide, a 38 amino acid peptide of unknown function (peptide C) and the 72 amino acid CHH.

INTRODUCTION

The neurosecretory structures in the crustacean eyestalk play an important role in producing various neuropeptides with multiple physiological functions. These structures, especially the medulla terminalis ganglionic X-organ sinus gland (MTGXO- SG) system, have a great potential as a model system for the study of neurosecretory pathways and mechanism in general. This system consists of easily discernible and accessible perikarya (XO) linked by a well defined tract of secretory axons to a classical discrete neurohemal organ, the sinus gland. One of the best known neuropeptides is the crustacean hyperglycemic hormone (CHH). CHH has a potent hyperglycemic action and, possibly, other metabolic effects. The hormone is stored in large amounts in the sinus gland and released into the hemolymph by several stimuli, where it is responsible for the regulation of the glucose level (Keller & Sedlmeier, 1988). Although the number of invertebrate neuropeptides with known amino acid sequences is growing rapidly, our knowledge concerning prohormone structures is still very limited and there has not been shown any such information for a crustacean neuropeptide (Thorndyke & Goldsworthy, 1988). The cDNA cloning approach used for the CHH of *Carcinus maenas* offered the possibility to elucidate the precursor of CHH.

MATERIALS AND METHODS

Clusters of neurosecretory X-organ perikaya were dissected from eyestalk ganglia of 500 *Carcinus maenas* and stored at -70° C. Total RNA was prepared by the guanidinium thiocyanate/CsCl procedure (Chirgwin et al., 1979) and poly A RNA was isolated by chromatography on oligo dT cellulose (Aviv & Leder, 1972). A cDNA library was constructed according to the method of Okayama and Berg (Okayama & Berg, 1982) from 1µg of poly A RNA. The cDNA clones were screened by colony hybridization (Hanahan & Meselson, 1983) with a mixture of 32P- endlabelled oligonucleotide probes that were constructed as shown in Fig.1. Oligonucleotides were synthesized on a Cyclone TM DNA synthesizer (Biosearch) and purified by reversed phase HPLC (Pingoud, 1988) as shown in Fig.2.

Protein	Met	Met	Asp	Glu	Phe	Asp	Gln	Tyr	Ala
m-RNA	5`AUG	AUG	GAU	GAA	UUU	GAU	CAA	UAU	GC 3`
			C	G	C	C	G	C	
DNA	3`TAC	TAC	CTA	CTT	AAA	CTA	GTT	ATA	CG
			G	C	G	G	C	G	

Fig.1.Partial sequence of CHH, the corresponding segment of the mRNA and the synthetic 26-mer oligonucleotide (64-fold degenerated) used in this study.

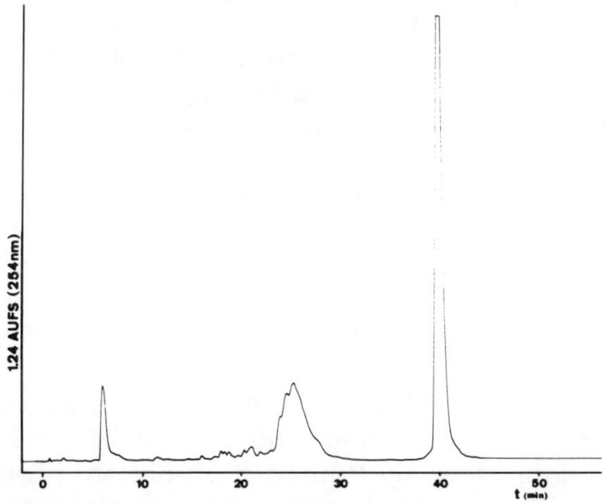

Fig.2.Purification of the 26-mer oligonucleotide containing a hydrophobic, protecting DMT group with reversed phase HPLC. Sample 40µg oligonucleotide, Column Baker C-18, Flow rate 1ml/min, Detection 254 nm, Eluent A 0.1 M TEAB pH 7, Eluent B A/50% CH3CN, Gradient 10%-70%, 60 min.

Hybridizations were carried out at 60° C and filters were washed several times with 6x SET, 0,1% SDS at 65°C. Plasmid DNA of the positive clone was analyzed by restriction mapping. Fragments were subcloned into the pUC 18 vector and nucleotide sequences were determined by the dideoxy sequencing method (Sanger, 1977).

RESULTS

Screening of the cDNA library with the 5` endlabelled oligonucleotide probe yielded one positive clone with an insert length of approximately 2000 bp. Fig.3 shows the part of the cDNA and deduced amino acid sequence which contains the complete coding region for the precursor of CHH. Preceded by a 5` flanking sequence, there is a putative signal peptide followed by peptide C and CHH. The open reading frame consists of 142 amino acids. The remaining part of the cDNA following the stop codon is a large 3' untranslated region, approximately 1500 bp, with a poly A tail at its end. The complete sequence of the untranslated region is not yet fully sequenced and therefore not shown.

DISCUSSION

The open reading frame, consisting of 426 nucleotides, contains the complete coding region for prepro CHH. Preceded by a 5' untranslated region, there is a putative hydrophobic signal peptide , followed by a peptide of unknown function, called peptide C, and CHH. The sequence following the stop codon is a long 3' untranslated region of about 1500 bp with a poly A tail at its end. The coding sequence consists of a putative signal peptide with 26 amino acids and exhibits the common features of signal peptides (Stryer, 1988). It contains one basic amino acid in the amino terminal part and has a long hydrophobic center region, shown in Fig.4. Also the cleavage site, after Ala in position -1 is typically for a signal peptide. Peptide C, 38 amino acids in length, has Mr of 4100 Dalton and shows a significant homology to peptide H of Cardiosoma carnifex described by Newcomb (1987). This homology was also revealed by a search at GENBANK (The Los Alamos National Laboratory), whereas no significant homology between the CHH coding region and other sequences was found. So far neither for peptide C nor for peptide H a biological function has been demonstrated.

Between peptide C and CHH is a Lys-Arg processing site, marked by a box in Fig.3.. CHH consists of 72 amino acids with an Mr of 8500 Dalton and the protein sequence data, done by Edman degradation in our lab (Kegel et al. 1989) are in full agreement with the nucleotide sequence data (Weidemann et al., 1989). The residue Gln in the first position of the CHH is consistent with pyroGlu in the mature neuropeptide, and Gly in front of the three basic residues at the C-terminal is the expected amide group donor for the terminal Val.

```
                            -153
                            -5'CAGTTCGACCAGGAATTCGCAGAAGGAAGACGT

-120  ACACCTCCTCCTATAGTGAACCTTCTAGAATTGTACCCTACCATGTATAGCAAAACTATT
                                                  -26  MetTyrSerLysThrIle

 -60  CCCGCCATGCTAGCAATCATCACCGTAGCCTACCTATGCGCACTCCCGCACGCACACGCA -1
 -20  ProAlaMetLeuAlaIleIleThrValAlaTyrLeuCysAlaLeuProHisAlaHisAla -1

   1  CGCTCCACGCAAGGCTACGGACGCATGGATAGGATTCTGGCGGCCTTGAAAACCTCGCCA
   1  ArgSerThrGlnGlyTyrGlyArgMetAspArgIleLeuAlaAlaLeuLysThrSerPro
      PEPTIDE C -->
  61  ATGGAGCCCAGCGCAGCCCTAGCGGTGGAGAATGGAACTACACACCCGTTGGAAAAGAGG
  21  MetGluProSerAlaAlaLeuAlaValGluAsnGlyThrThrHisProLeuGlu[LysArg]

 121  CAAATTTACGACACGTCCTGCAAGGGTGTTTACGACCGTGCTCTGTTCAATGACTTGGAG
  41  GlnIleTyrAspThrSerCysLysGlyValTyrAspArgAlaLeuPheAsnAspLeuGlu
      CHH -->
 181  CACGTGTGTGACGATTGTTACAACCTCTACAGAACCTCCTATGTTGCCTCGGCCTGCAGA
  61  HisValCysAspAspCysTyrAsnLeuTyrArgThrSerTyrValAlaSerAlaCysArg

 241  TCAAACTGCTATAGCAACTTGGTGTTCCGGCAATGCATGGATGACCTTTTAATGATGGAC
  81  SerAsnCysTyrSerAsnLeuValPheArgGlnCysMetAspAspLeuLeuMetMetAsp

 301  GAGTTTGACCAATATGCCAGAAAGGTACAGATGGTTGGCAGGAAGAAGTAA......1500 bp..(A)n -3'
 101  GluPheAspGlnTyrAlaArgLysValGlnMetValGly[ArgLysLys]END
```

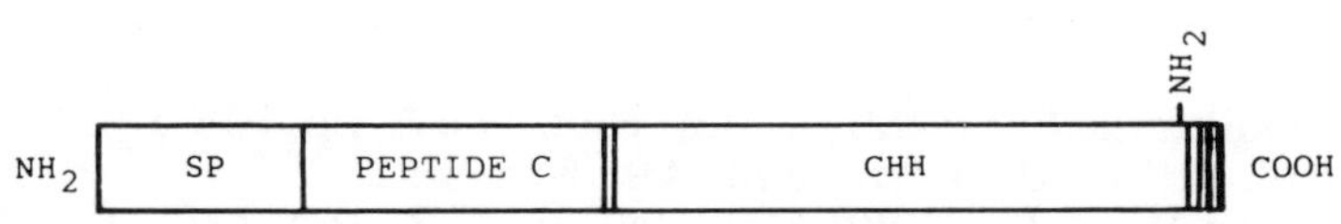

Fig.3.Part of the coding strand of the cDNA clone that contains the complete coding sequence for the CHH precursor, and the deduced amino acid sequence. The sequences of the mature CHH, including the putative amide-donating Gly, and peptide C are underlined. The numbers of nucleotides and amino acid residues appear at the beginning of each line, beginning with 1 at the start of the coding sequence for peptide C. Proteolytic processing sites are boxed. The partial CHH-sequence used for oligonucleotide probe construction is marked by a dotted line.

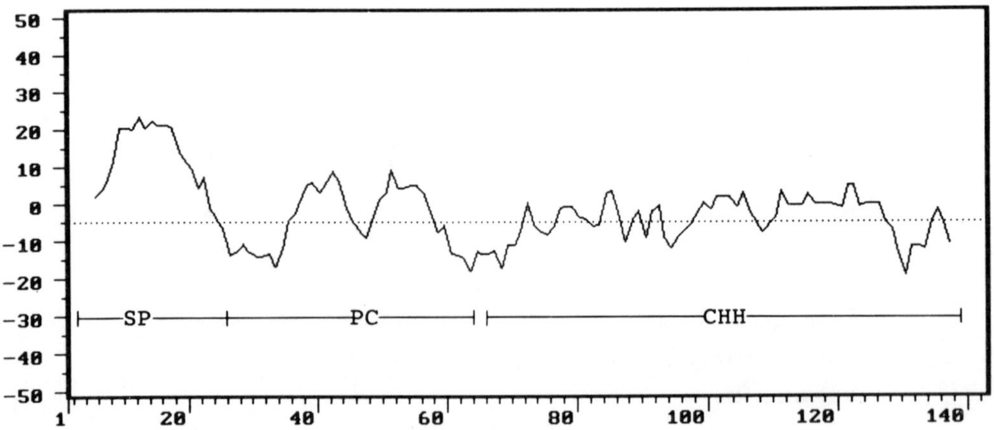

Fig.4. Hydropathy plot of the prepro CHH. The positions of the signal peptide (SP), peptide C (PC) and CHH are underlined. The values are calculated using the nonapeptide averaging method of Kyte (1982).

Another potential cleavage site is the dibasic Arg-Lys at positions 67 and 68, close to the C-terminus. This cleavage site could, if processed incompletely, generate two forms of CHH. However, there is so far no evidence of a truncated form of CHH in the sinus gland of *Carcinus maenas* (Kegel et al., 1989)

REFERENCES

Aviv, H and Leder, P. (1972) Proc. Natl. Acad. Sci. USA **69**,1408-1412.

Chirgwin, J.M., Pryzbyla, A.E., Mac Donald, R.J. and Rutter, W.J. (1979) Biochemistry **18**, 5294-5299.

Hanahan, D. and Meselson, M. (1983) Methods Enzymol. **100**, 333-342.

Kegel, G., Reichwein, B., Gaus, G., Peter- Katalinic, J. and Keller, R. (1989) FEBS-Letters (in press)

Keller,R. and Sedlmeier, D. (1988) in: Endocrinology of selected invertebrate types (Laufer, H. and Downer, R.G.H. eds.) pp. 235-258, Alan R. Liss Inc., New York.

Kyte,J. and Doolitle, R.F. (1982) J. Mol. Biol. **157,** pp 105-132

Newcomb, R.W. (1987) J.Neurochem. **49,** 574-583.

Okayama, H. and Berg, P. (1982) Mol. Cell. Biol. **2,** 161-170.

Pingoud, A. and Fliess, A. (1988) GIT Fachz. Lab. **5,** 475-478.

Sanger, F., Nicklen, S. and Coulsen, A.R. (1977) Proc. Nat. Acad. Sci. USA **74**, 5463-5467.

Stryer, L. Biochemistry (1988) Freeman, W.H. and Company; New York

Thorndyke, M.C. and Goldsworthy, G.J. (1988) Neurohormones in Invertebrates, Cambridge, New York.

Weidemann,W., Gromoll,J. and Keller, R. (1989) FEBS-Letters (in press)

Frontiers in Crustacean Neurobiology
Advances in Life Sciences

SYNAPTIC REGULATION OF NEUROSECRETORY CELL ACTIVITY IN THE CRAYFISH EYESTALK

Hugo Aréchiga*, Ubaldo García* and Luis Martínez-Millán+

*Centro de Investigación y de Estudios Avanzados, IPN Apdo. Postal.14-740, México, D.F. 07000, México.
+Departamento de Anatomía, Universidad del País Vasco, España.

SUMMARY

The neurosecretory cells in the crayfish X organ receive an excitatory synaptic input mediated by GABA. GABA can be released from the medulla terminalis in a Ca^{++}-dependent manner. Topical application of GABA and baclofen mimick the synaptically evoked excitation. This is blocked by picrotoxin. Light induces GABA release from the eyestalk. GABA-like immunoreactive neurones are present in the medulla terminalis

INTRODUCTION

The secretion of neurohormones form the crustacean eyestalk is known to be influenced by environmental factors and by endogenous mechanisms. Light and darkness are among the most important influences. The release of the distal pigment light adpating hormone (DPLH) is triggered by illumination (Aréchiga & Mena, 1974), whereas that of the red pigment concentrating hormone (RPCH) is induced by darkness (Aréchiga et al, 1985). Stressful stimuli enhance the release of the hyperglycaemic hormone (CHH) (Keller & Sedlmeier, 1988). Circadian rhythmicity is also a powerful modulating influence. Some neurohormones like DPLH and the neurodepressing hormone (NDH), are mostly secreted during the diurnal phase of the 24-hour cycle (Aréchiga & Menaa, 1974; Aréchiga & Huberman, 1980), whereas CHH and RPCH are secreted during the night phase (Hamman et al, 1974; Rodríguez-Sosa et al., In preparation). The secretion of peptides like the molt-inhibiting hormone (MIH) is presumably dependent on seasonal cycles (Skinner, 1985). Little is known about the pathways and transmitters conveying these physiological influences to the neurosecretory elements. Light-induced synaptic responses have been recorded from neurosecretory cells in the medulla terminalis (Glantz et al, 1983) and in the medulla externa of crayfish (Kirk et al., 1982). As to the origin of the light responses, direct illumination of the retina was found to trigger synaptic responses, both in the medulla externa and the medulla terminalis. On the other hand, a set of extra-retinal photoreceptors has been shown capable of initiating the light-induced release of DPLH (Aréchiga et al., 1985).

Various putative transmitters have been proposed to influence the release of eyestalk hormones. 5-HT appears to facilitate the secretion of CHH (Keller and Beyer, 1968), various amines and peptides were found to influence the release of chromatophorotropins (Quackenbush & Fingerman, 1984). The most complete set of data for a neurotransmitter characterization in the eyestalk are those for GABA, and a dual role has emerged for this transmitter. In cells in the medulla externa, Kirk et al., (1982) demonstrated that GABA application mimicked the light-induced hyperpolarization, whereas bicuculline blocked the effects of GABA and light. The same reversal potential was found for the light- and GABA-mediated responses i.e., near the chloride equilibrium potential. In contrast with these results, in the medulla terminalis, Iwasaki and Satow (1973) showed that the GABA-mediated response has a reversal potential far away from the chloride equilibrium potential.

RESULTS

The problem of GABA as a transmitter in neurosecretory cells at the medulla terminalis, like the one shown in Fig.IV, has been recently revised by García et al (In preparation), who have shown in a group of neurosecretory cells in the X organ-sinus gland system of the crayfish, that the stimulation of the protocerebral tract evokes a depolarizing potential (Fig. 2C) which can be suppressed by shifting the membrane potential to 0 mV.

see colour plate IV

This epsp is superimposed on a slow depolarizaton which may last for several seconds. The depolarization may be storng enough to induce spiking. Both depolarizing responses can be blocked by picrotoxin, but not by bicuculline. Since this latter antagonist has been proposed to act specifically on GABAA type of receptors, including some synapses in the crayfish visual system (see Pfeiffer-Linn and Glantz, 1989), the possibility of a different type of receptor was explored, and indeed, whereas the depolarization can be mimicked by GABA and baclofen, and agonist of GABAB type of receptors, it can not be induced by muscimol, a GABAA agonist (Fig. 3). Both the depolarization induced by tract stimulation and by GABA are generated at the neuropil, since both are abolished by severing the axon of the X organ neurone at a site proximal to the branching in the neuropil.. Further evidence for a role of GABA as a neurotransmitter is that the stimulation of the PR tract releases GABA in a calcium-dependent manner.

As seen in Fig. 4, the amount of GABA in the crayfish medulla terminalis is only second to that in the retina-lamina ganglionaris sytem, with a 25% of all GABA contained in the eyestalk. Fig. 5 illustrates that GABA can be released from the eyestalks by incubation in high [K^+] solutions. The reselase is abolished in Ca^{++} -free solutions.

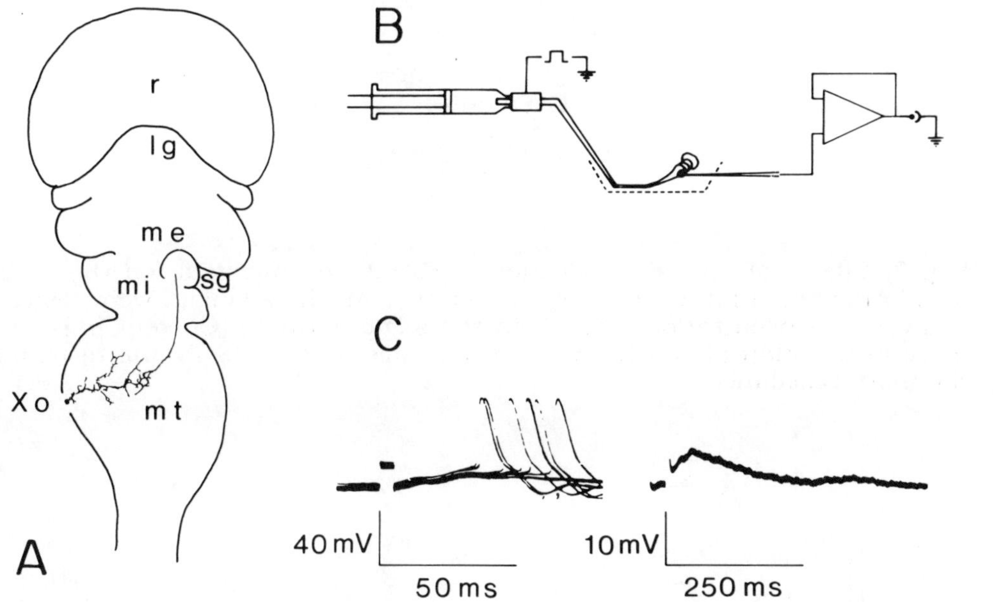

Fig. 2. A. Crayfish eyestalk diagram, retina (r) lamina ganglionaris (1g), medulla externa (me), medulla interna (mi), and medulla terminalis (mt). The cell bodies of the neurosecretory elements are located in the X organ (Xo) predominantly in the medial edge of the mt. Their axons branch extensively in the neuropil of mt and the main axon ends in a neurohemal organ, the sinus gland (sg). X-organ neurone is drawn from lucifer yellow injections as the one shown in Fig. 1. B. Diagram showing the preparation used to stimulate the protocerebral tract with a suction electrode in an isolated eyestalk while intracellular recordings were obtained from X-organ somata. C. Intracellular recordings of action potentials evoked in X-organ somata by electrical stimulation of the PR tract (left traces). Synaptic response recorded after PR tract stimulation (left trace).

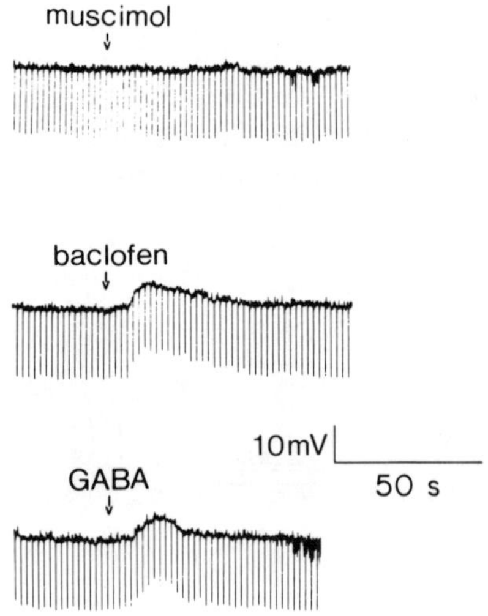

Fig. 3. Effects of topical application of GABA and agonists, on the resting membrane potential in an X-organ neurone. All the agonists were tested at equivalent concentrations (50 M) in the same neurone. Current pulses, 50 msec in duration at 0.5 Hz, were passed across the membrane to monitor the input resistance.

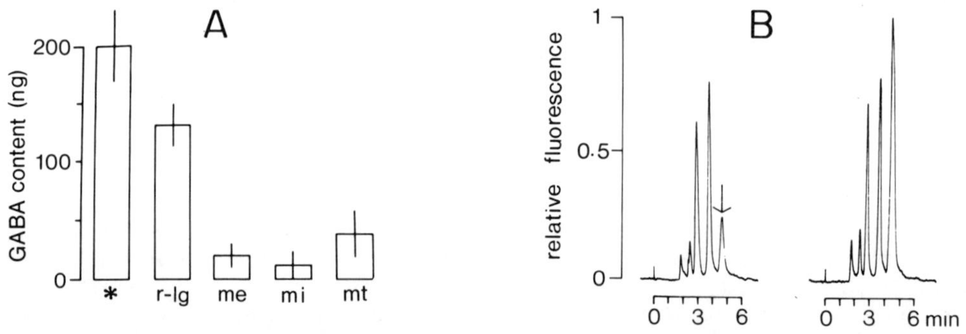

Fig. 4. Regional distribution of GABA content in the crayfish eyestalk, as determined by high-performance liquid chromatography. In A the first bar, signalled with the asterisk corresponds to the whole GABA content in the eyestalk. The following bars correspond to the GABA content per structure. B. Both chromatograms were obtained in the following conditions: Column: Microbandapak C18 (300 X 3-6 mm I.D.) Solvent: Na_2HPO_4 (20 mM)/CH_3 OH (90/10) pH 6.8 Sample: Left, GABA content in medulla terminalis. The peak signaled with the arrow. Right, the same sample added with aliquot of GABA standard solution.. Flow rate: 1.3 ml/min Detector: Fluorescence (420 Waters).

As to the ionic basis of the depolarizing response, in voltage-clamp experiments, with a whole-cell configuration, GABA was shown to enhance a slow inward cationic current. No effects on other currents have been detected (García et al., In preparation).

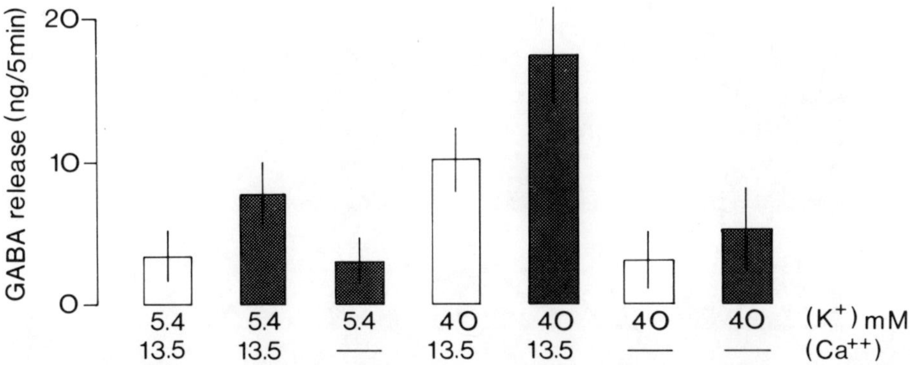

Fig. 5. GABA release from isolated eyestalk under various [K^+] - and [Ca^{++}]. Incubation in 40 mM [K^+] during 5 min, greatly enhances GABA release. This effect is abolished in Ca^{++} -free solution. Addition of nipecotic acid (5 mM, dark bars), increases both basal and evoked release. This effect is also abolished in Ca^{++} -free medium.

The anatomical origin of the GABA-ergic input to the X organ cells is yet to be determined. An immunocytochemical exploration in medulla terminalis with a monoclonal antibody against GABA, (raised by C. Matute) disclosed the presence of GABA-like immunoreactive axons and somata, thus suggesting a diverse origin (Fig. 6). It is likely that some of the GABA-ergic cells are in the PR tract, while part of the input is initiated in local GABA-ergic interneurons, since the severance of the PR tract reduces the GABA content in the medulla terminalis in a 70%. The existence of spontaneous epsp's, which are GABA mediated favors the local interneuron origin.

Although the precise physiological role of GABA is still to be clarified, there are good indications that GABA mediates light-induced changes in neurosecretory cells. As mentioned above, Kirk et al. (1982) in the medulla externa, were capable of blocking the light-induced hyperpolarization with picrotoxin. Light stimulation has also been shown to induce the release of GABA in isolated eyestalks. As seen in Fig. 7, within a range of light intensities from 240 to 670 lux, the amount of GABA released varies with the intensity of illumination.

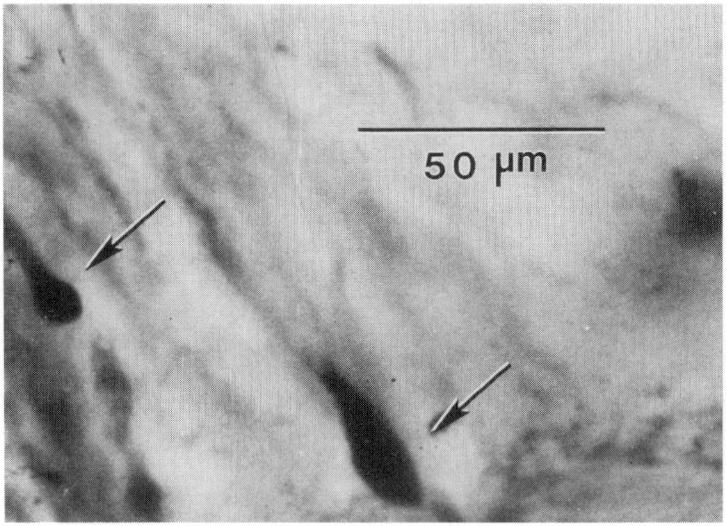

Fig. 6. Photomicrograph of a medulla terminalis, section stained with a monoclonal antibody against GABA

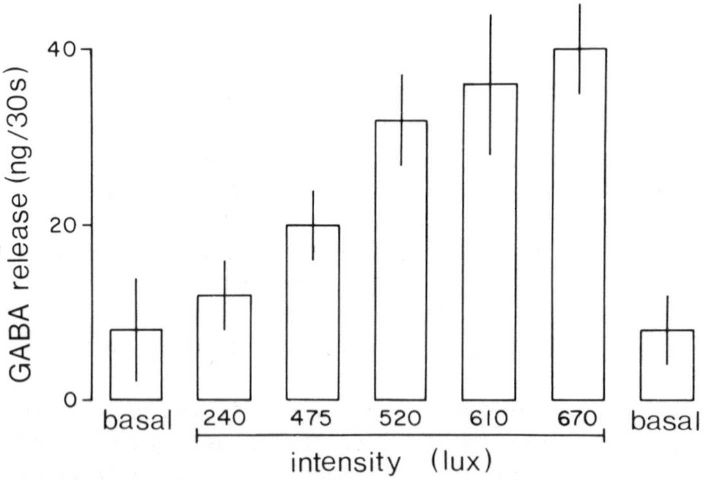

Fig. 7. Light-induced GABA release in isolated eyestalks, previously dark adapted. The basal release corresponds to the GABA released during 30 sec after 2 hour of dark-adaptation. Between successive light pulses the eyestalks were readapted to darness during 30 min.

DISCUSSION

The precise circuitry conveying light influence either to the medulla externa or the medulla terminalis neurosecretory cells is still to be determined. It is an interesting possibility however, that GABA may mediate both inhibitory and excitatory effects of light on n.s. cells. The former, by activation of a type A receptor, coupled to a chloride channel, and the latter by acting through a GABAB type receptor and a slow cationic channel. This arrangement could provide for light-induced increases or reductions in the release of the various eyestalk hormones with one common set of GABAergic interneurones.

Although these GABA effects on curstacean neurosecretory activity have been so far characterized only in the crayfish, it is likely that they are also present in other crustacenas, as suggested by the fact that GABA content in the eyestalk of the prawn Macrobrachium has been found to be very similar to that of the crayfish (Arámburo, 1983), and as mentioned above, injections of GABA have been found to suppress the release of RPCH induced by electrical stimulation of the eyestalk (Quackenbush & Fingerman, 1984).

At present, GABA is the most well known among the putative neurotransmitters acting on the eyestalk nuerosecretory cells, but it is by no means the only, as already mentioned, and only future studies will unravel the seemingly complex array of synaptic interactions regulating the activity of the various crustacean neurosecretory cells. One encouraging development is that intracellular staining and immunocytochemical characterization of the various peptide-containing neurons in the eyestalk (see Keller, this volume) may enable a more precise definition of the various neurones in terms of the peptide(s) they produce, their eletrophysiological properties and synaptic influences.

This work was partly supported by a CONACyT grant Nº P228CCOX681151, and a México-Spain exchange program grant.

REFERENCES

Arámburo, C. (1983). Correlación entre actividad neurodepresora y diferentes entidades químicas presentes en el tallo ocular de *Penaeus vannamei* (Boone). Ph. D. Thesis, U.N.A.M.

Aréchiga, H. & Mena, F. (1975). Circadian variations of hormonal content in the nervous system of the crayfish. Comp. Biochem. Physiol. **52A:** 581-584.

Aréchiga, H. and Huberman, A. (1980). Peptide modulation of neuronal activity in crustaceans. In J.F. Barker and T.G. Smith (eds.) The role of peptides in neuronal function. Marcel Dekker, Inc., New York. pp. 317-349.

Aréchiga, H., Cortés , J.J., García, U. & Rodríguez-Sosa, L. (1985). Neuroendocrine correlates of circadian rhythmicity in crustaceans. Amer. Zool. **25:** 265-274.

Glantz, R.M., Kirk, M.D. & Aréchiga, H. (1983). Light input to crustacean neurosecretory cells. Brain Res. **265**: 307-311.

Hamann, A. (1974). Die neuroendokrine Steuerung tagesrhythmischer blutzuckerschwankungen durch die Sinusdrüsse beim Flusskrebs. J. Comp. Physiol. 89: 197-214.

Iwasaki, S. and Satow, Y. (1973). Electrical characteristics of the membrane in neurosecretory neurons. In K. Yagi and S. Yoshida (eds.) Neuroendocrine control. Wiley, New York. pp. 85-109.

Keller, R. and Beyer, J. (1968). Zur hyperglykämischen Wirkung von Serotonin und Augenstielextrakt beim Flusskrebs *Orconectes limosus*. Z. Vergl. Physiol. **59:** 78-85.

Keller, R. and Sedlmeier, D. (1988). A metabolic hormone in crustaceans: The hyperglycaemic neuropeptide. In: Invertebrate Endocrinology (Endocrinology of Selected Invertebrate Types) Vol. 2. H. Lauger, & E.R.G.H. Downer, Eds. Alan R. Liss, Inc. New York. 315-326.

Kirk, M.D., Prugh, J.I. & Glantz, R.M. (1982). A visually induced GABA mediated IPSP in a crustacean neurosecretory cell. J. Neurobiol. 14: 473-480.

Pfeiffer-Linn, C. and Glantz, R.M. (1989). Acetylcholine and GABA mediate opposing actions on neuronal chloride channels in crayfish. Science **245**: 1249-1250.

Quackenbush. L.S. and Fingerman, M. (1984). Regulation of neurohormone release in the fiddler crab, *Uca pugilator*: effects of gamma-aminobutyric acid, octopamine, met-enkephalin, and beta-endorphin. Comp. Biochem. Physiol. **79C:** 77-84.

Skinner, D.E. (1985). Molting and regeneration. In D.E. Bliss and L. H. Mantel (ed.). The Biology of Crustacea. Vol. 9, Academic Press, New York, pp. 43-145.

Frontiers in Crustacean Neurobiology
Advances in Life Sciences

AMINE AND PEPTIDE MODULATION OF A VOLTAGE-SENSITIVE, PLASMA MEMBRANE Ca^{2+}-CHANNEL IN CRAYFISH SKELETAL MUSCLE

Cynthia A. Bishop, Mauri E. Krouse and Jeffrey J. Wine

Department of Psychology, Stanford University, Stanford, CA 94305, USA

SUMMARY

A large conductance channel in the plasma membrane of the crayfish tonic flexor muscle is modulated by the peptide proctolin. Proctolin alone has no effect on the channel, but renders it capable of sustained activity following a step depolarization. After depolarization induces activity, the open probability of the channel increases about 20 fold due to a marked decrease in the mean closed time at all voltages. Proctolin modulation occurs via an intracellular messenger, possibly cAMP. Modulation of the channel by proctolin varies seasonally, disappearing in the winter. Proctolin enhancement of channel activity can be restored in muscles from winter animals by pre-treating the muscles with octopamine.

INTRODUCTION

The regulation of cytosolic free Ca^{2+} is a powerful means by which biogenic substances may control cellular function. A commonly cited example is the control of cytosolic free Ca^{2+} and tension in the vertebrate heart by noradrenaline (Reuter 1983, 1984).

Recently, we have used patch-clamp techniques to show that a peptide neuromodulator activates a voltage sensitive, large conductance Ca^{2+} channel in the plasma membrane of crayfish skeletal muscle, leading to amplification of excitation-contraction coupling. Here we review some of the key features of the channel and its modulation by the peptide, including seasonal variability in the effect of the peptide, evidence for involvement of cAMP, synergistic effects of the peptide and octopamine.

Our preparation is the crayfish tonic flexor neuromuscular system which controls slow abdominal fexion. The system consists of 6 identified motoneurons and approximately 40 muscle fibers muscles in each hemisegment in the crayfish abdomen (Fig. 1A). Three of the excitatory motoneurons contain, in addition to the conventional neurotransmitter (L-glutamate), the peptide proctolin (H-Arg-Tyr-Leu-Pro-Thr-OH). Proctolin is released by these motoneurons in response to neural stimulation. Proctolin does not induce tension in resting muscles at any concentration, but acts directly on the muscle fibers to amplify depolarization-induced tension. The threshold for this effect is $5x10^{-11}$M with a maximum effect at $5x10^{-9}$M. Proctolin amplifies tension without observeable depolarizatio of the muscle or change in synaptic potential (Bishop et al., 1984;1987).

METHODS

Tonic flexor muscles were isolated from the crayfish,*Procambarus clarkii* and treated with collagenaseIA for 20min (2-4mg/5ml saline; Fig. 1A). For most experiments, muscles were bathed in 137 mM $BaCl_2$ (to enhance conductance of calcium channels), 1mM $CaCl_2$, 2.6 mM $MgCl_2$ and 10.1mM Trizma (pH7.0). Pipets contained 205mM $CaCl_2$ 2.6mM $MgCl_2$ and 10.1mM Trizma (pH 7.0). Experiments were performed at 21°C. The typical configuration was inside-out patches, with seal resistances over 50 G. When proctolin was used it was added at least 5 min prior to seal formation.

Currents records were usually filtered at 500 Hz with an 8 pole Bessel filter, digitized at 400 s/point, and analyzed on an IBM PC AT computer using the programs pClamp (Axon Instruments) and RS1 (BBN). Channel activity is expressed in terms of open probability (Mean Open Time/Mean Open Time+Mean Closed Time). We also indicate the percent of seals containing active channels, which reflects both channel activity and density. For cell-attached experiments the pipets contained the $BaCl_2$ solution and the bath was van Harreveld's physiological solution (van Harreveld, 1936).

RESULTS

Peptide channel activation. In control experiments from muscles not exposed to proctolin we recorded a channel with a chord conductance of 50 pS in 137 mM $BaCl_2$ (22 pS in 137 mM $CaCl_2$) in 5/29 (17%) of excised patches. Of the 5 patches with active channels, all had to be depolarized to at least 50 mV before the channel was activated (Fig. 1B). Even in depolarized patches the channel is mainly closed, with an open probability < 0.01.

When 5x10-9 M proctolin was added to the bath we still saw this channel only rarely in patches clamped at negative voltages, but when patches were depolarized by about 50 mV, we noted a 4 fold increase in the proportion of patches with active channels and an even larger increase in channel open probability (Fig. 1B). The peptide-induced increase in channel activity is mainly due to a dramatic (approximately 20 fold) decrease in the mean closed time; open times were increased less than 2 fold. Although the induction of channel activity required depolarization in most patches, once activity was initiated it became independent of voltage. The depolarization threshold in the proctolin-treated muscles did not appear to differ significantly from controls.

Depolarization-induced channel activity was dependent on the dose of proctolin in the bath. The dose-dependency perfectly paralleled the dose-dependency of proctolin's effect on muscle tension, which supports the involvement of the proctolin-dependent Ca^{2+} channel in the tension response of the muscle.

Proctolin acts via an intracellular messenger. In the above experiments, proctolin had access to the outside of the patch prior to seal formation, so we could not exclude a direct action of proctolin on the channel.

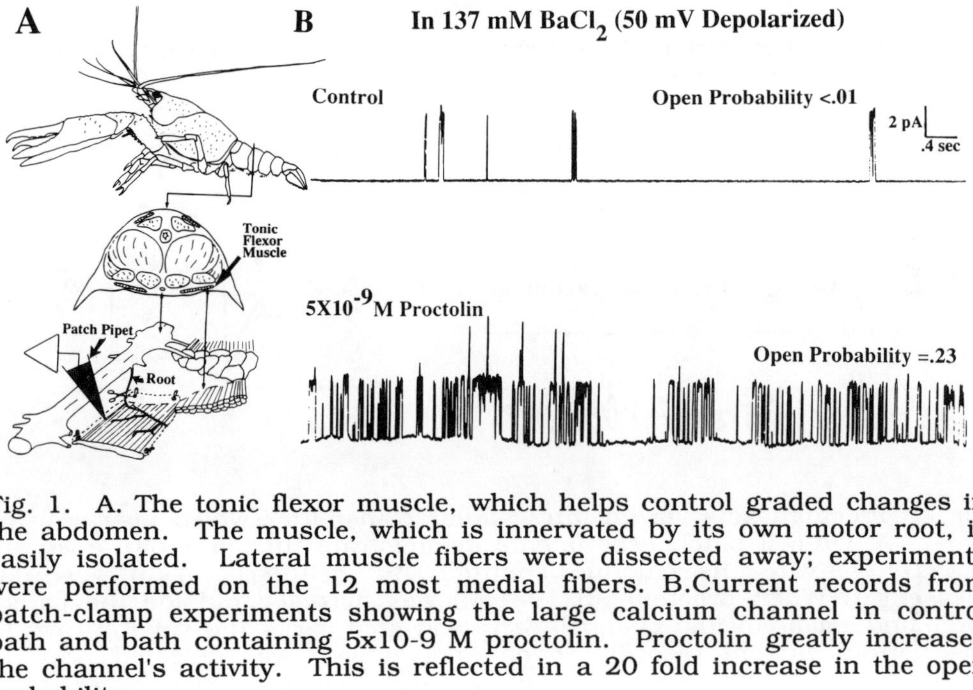

Fig. 1. A. The tonic flexor muscle, which helps control graded changes in the abdomen. The muscle, which is innervated by its own motor root, is easily isolated. Lateral muscle fibers were dissected away; experiments were performed on the 12 most medial fibers. B.Current records from patch-clamp experiments showing the large calcium channel in control bath and bath containing 5x10-9 M proctolin. Proctolin greatly increased the channel's activity. This is reflected in a 20 fold increase in the open probability.

We therefore formed cell-attached patches with pipets containing $BaCl_2$ and subsequently applied proctolin to the muscle fiber from a near-by pipet containing 5x10-9 M proctolin (Fig. 2A). In the absence of perfused proctolin no channels were observed in 3 patches, even after depolarizing steps. However, after proctolin perfusion and depolarization, channel openings were detected in all 3 patches.

We conclude that proctolin modulates the channel through an intracellular messenger. We have not yet identified the intracellular messenger(s) involved, but preliminary experiments suggest that cAMP may be involved. Following bath application of 50 M of 8-(4-chlorophenylthio) adenosine 3':5'-cyclic monophosphate (CPT-cAMP), a membrane-permeable cAMP analog, we recorded the large Ca^{2+} channel in 3 of 3 depolarized patches (Fig. 2B). No activity was detected in three patches examined prior to CPT-cAMP application.

Peptide modulation of channel activation is seasonal. Peptide modulation of the Ca^{2+} channel appears to be seasonal. The cyclicity of the effect is indicated by the percentage of seals with active channels in the presence of proctolin and depolarization (Fig. 3A). In the spring and summer of 1988,

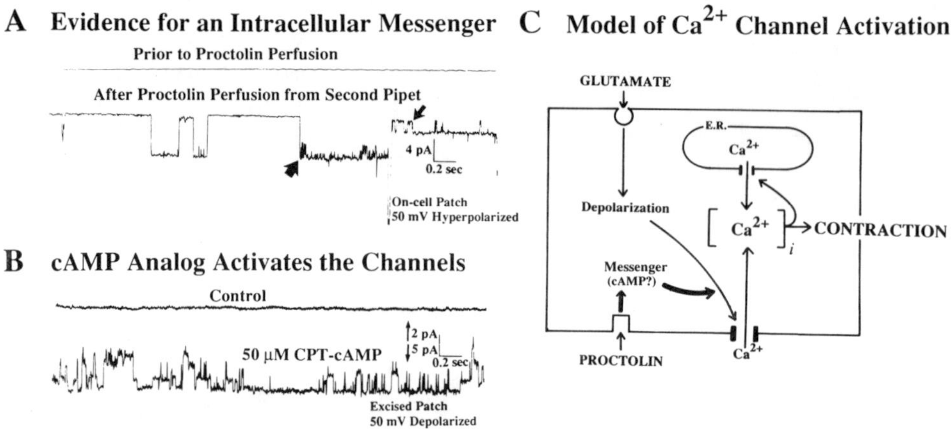

Fig. 2. Proctolin acts via an intracellular transmitter which may be cylic AMP. A. On-cell patch experiments demonstrate that proctolin does not directly activate the calcium channel, but requires an intracellular messenger: When proctolin (5x10-9 M) was perfused outside the patch, large and small calcium channels were activated (large and small arrows in the bottom current record). No channel activity was detected prior to proctolin perfusion (top current record). These experiments were conducted with 137 mM Ba in the patch èpipet, which reversed the direction of the channel compared to the excised experiments and barium currents were enlarged with hyperpolarizing steps instead of depolarizing steps. Channels required an initial depolarizing step of 25 mV for activation in the presence of proctolin in these on-cell experiments. This depolarization requirement was also seen in the excised patches. B. Bath application of 50 mM of the membrane-permeable cAMP analog CPT-cAMP prior to seal formation resulted in activation of two calcium channels in three out of three depolarized patches. No activity was detected in the three depolarized patches prior to CPT-cAMP application. C. Model of Ca^{2+} channel activation and its role in tension modulation in the tonic flexor muscle. Channel activation leads to an enhanced influx of Ca^{2+} into the muscle fiber and the subsequent potentiation of tension.

channel occurrence was 77% (17/22 patches). In November through March, 1988-89, channel occurrence was 15% (7/46 patches); in the spring of 1989 channel occurrence returned to 83% (10/12 patches).

Throughout this period, channel activity in control patches not exposed to proctolin was constant at about 15%. As expected, the seasonal cyclicity of proctolin's modulation is also apparent in the open probablity of the channel. The maximum open probability in 5x10-9 M proctolin was 0.23 in the spring and summer of 1988 and 0.28 the spring of 1989. The maximum open probability obtained in winter èanimals with this concentration of proctolin was only 0.06, which is not significantly different from the control value.

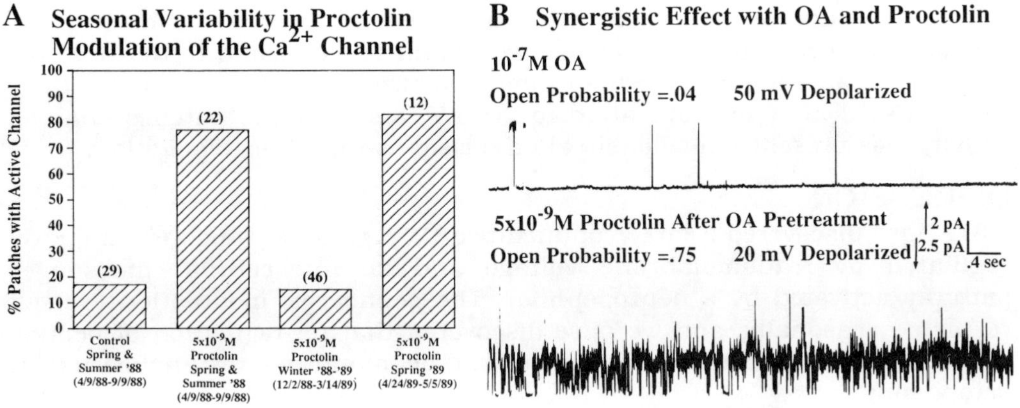

Fig. 3. A. Evidence for seasonal variability in proctolin response: Percent patches with active channels in 5x10-9 M proctolin was about four times greater in the spring and summer of 1988 and in the spring of 1989 than in the winter of 1988-89. Percentages for winter animals matched controls not exposed to proctolin. Specific dates over which experiments were conducted are indicated in parentheses below each bar. The total number of patches is indicated in parentheses above each bar. B. Octopamine and proctolin synergistically activated the Ca^{2+} channel. 10-7 M octopamine (OA) by itself had very little effect on channel activity. (Compare top current record to Fig. 1B.) However, when the muscle was washed with 10-7 M OA and then placed in a bath containing 5x10-9 M proctolin, channel activity was enormously enhanced (bottom channel record). Open probablity was at least three fold greater than the maximum recorded in proctolin alone (Fig. 1B).

Octopamine restores the proctolin sensitivity of Ca^{2+} channels in winter animals. What might be the basis for the seasonal changes in proctolin sensitivity of the Ca^{2+} channel? Octopamine is thought to have a neurohumoral role in crustacea and is also known to potentiate tension, like proctolin, by direct action on some muscles (Kravitz, 1988). In winter animals, the Ca^{2+} channel's sensitivity to proctolin modulation was greatly augmented by pretreatment with octopamine.

Octopamine alone had little effect on channel responsiveness in either winter or summer animals (Fig. 3B). However, a prewash in 10-7 M octopamine followed by a wash in 5x10-9 M proctolin returned the density of active channels in patches from winter animals to approximately that for proctolin-treated summer animals, and increased the maximum open probability to 0.75, which was triple the value for proctolin-treated summer animals. This very large response may be related to the high levels of octopamine used. (We have not yet determined dose-response curves for the octopamine effect.)

The octopamine pre-wash also appeared to decrease the level of depolarization required to activate Ca^{2+} channels, compared to that for only proctolin-treated animals. In the example shown in Fig. 3B, channel activity was initiated after depolarization to 20 mV, and in some patches channel activity was present immediately after excision without depolarization.

DISCUSSION

We have discovered a large conductance Ca^{2+} channel which is complexly regulated by transmembrane voltage and an intracellular messenger pathway activated by a neuropeptide. The peptidergic modulation is itself regulated seasonally, and we have discovered that up-regulation of peptide modulation that occurs in summer can be mimicked by application of octopamine.

Many questions about both mechanism and significance remain to be answered. Most of our experiments were conducted with excised, inside-out patches with èthe cytoplasmic face exposed to mM concentrations of $CaCa^{2+}$. It is likely that these conditions distort channel kinetics: for example, neither the need for strong levels of depolarization to induce channel activity nor the lack of voltage-dependency following activation are consistent with proctolin's effect on muscle tension. (Some hysteresis in the voltage dependence of open probability might account for aspects of catch tension).

Our hypothesis for the mechanism of peptide modulation is that proctolin binds to a specific membrane receptor, elevates cAMP levels, and phosphorylates either the channel itself or an associated regulatory molecule to increase the channel's sensitivity to depolarization (Fig. 2C). A host of pharmacological agents are available to assess this hypothesis.

The higher order modulation via octopamine is especially intriguing. Like proctolin, whose effects on tension or channel kinetics are only seen following depolarization, octopamine alone has little effect on channel activity in summer or winter animals. In winter animals, however, it appears to restore proctolin's enhancement of depolarization-induced channel activity. One way to relate the seasonal effects to octopamine is to hypothesize that octopamine levels in the blood vary seasonally. There is precedent for such a proposal; Roth (1978) has described a set of amine-containing (neutral red staining) neurons in crayfish ganglia that contain two populations of granules; the density of these granules are inversely correlated with the molt cycle. (It may be of interest that these neurons also appear to bind proctolin antibody [Bishop, Wine and Roth, unpublished results]). This hypothesis requires octopamine to work at much lower concentrations than we have used up to now, and also requires that octopamine induce a prolonged increase in proctolin responsiveness, since muscles removed from summer animals retain their responsiveness to proctolin for as long as we have tested them (more than 3 hours). The mechanism of the octopamine effect is unknown; it could act at any stage of the proctolin pathway from receptors to channel.

Among the hormonal actions proposed for octopamine in crustacea is central inhibition of tonic flexor motor neuron activity (Kravitz, 1988). The relation of that effect to the present one is unknown. We have no evidence that octopamine is present in the blood at levels needed to mediate these effects, nor that blood levels vary seasonally. Alternatives include mediation by a related hormone, or additional neuromodulation via one or more of the tonic flexor motoneurons that might also contain and release octopamine.

In conclusion, a multiply-regulated Ca^{2+} channel has been discovered in a well-studied crustacean nerve-muscle system. The large size and high density of the channel, the robustness of the peptide and amine modulatory effects, and the simplicity of the preparation recommend this system for further study.

REFERENCES

Bishop, C.A., Wine, J.J. and O'Shea, M. (1984) Neuropeptide proctolin in postural motoneurons of the crayfish. J. Neurosci. **4**: 2001-2009.

Bishop, C.A., Wine, J.J., Nagy, F. and O'Shea, M. (l987) Physiological consequences of a peptide co-transmitter in a crayfish nerve- muscle preparation. J. Neurosci. **7:** 1769-1779.

Kravitz, E.A. (1988) Hormonal control of behavior: amines and the biasing of behavioral output in lobsters. Sci. **241**: 1775-1781.

Reuter, H. (1983) Calcium channel modulation by neurotransmitters, enzymes and drugs. Nature **301**: 569-574.

Reuter, H. (1984) Ion channels in cardiac cell membrane. Ann. Rev. Physiol. **46**: 473-484.

Roth, R.L. (1978) Molt-related "neurosecretory" cells in the abdominal nerve cord of the crayfish, Procambarus clarkii. Soc. Neurosci. Abstr. **4:** 205.

van Harreveld, A. (1936) A physiological solution for freshwater crustaceans. Proc. Soc. Exptl. Biol. Med. **34**: 428-432.

Frontiers in Crustacean Neurobiology
Advances in Life Sciences

THE MODULATION OF THE OPTOKINETIC RESPONSE BY SEROTONIN AND OCTOPAMINE IN THE CRAB *LEPTOGRAPSUS VARIEGATUS*

J. Erber[1] and D.C. Sandeman[2]

[1] Institut für Biologie, TU Berlin, Franklinstr. 28/29, 1000 Berlin 10, FRG
[2] School of Biological Science, University of New South Wales, Kensington, N.S.W., Australia

SUMMARY:

Standard optokinetic responses were measured in the crab *Leptograpsus variegatus* during the application of serotonin and octopamine. The amines were either introduced into the blood stream or into the neural tissue of the optic lobes via a micropipette. Both amines enhance the optokinetic effect when applied in low doses. The effects of serotonin are maximal when the drug is applied in the medulla terminalis. The effects of octopamine appear not to be localized in the optic lobes.

INTRODUCTION:

Serotonin and octopamine can modulate the behavior of crustaceans (Kravitz et al., 1985). The modulatory role of these amines on sensory signal processing is largely unknown. The optokinetic reflex of the crab offers the possibility to study the effects of serotonin and octopamine in a well described sensory system (Sandeman et al., 1975 a). The eyes of many crustaceans show slow following movements interspersed with rapid return phases when the animal is positioned in a rotating striped drum. Many aspects of this behavior are similar to that of vertebrates. The movements of the two eyes are linked, a stimulated eye will drive the other eye which is covered with a little cap and the generation of the fast phase is controlled centrally and not governed by peripheral senory signals (Horridge and Sandeman, 1964) . The contributions of the two eyes can be separated and the effects of drugs in a treated eye can be compared with the contralateral untreated side.

METHODS

The animals were stimulated with a vertically striped drum moving sinusoidally in the horizontal plane. In a first series of experiments both eyes were unrestrained and eye movements were measured with a position sensor ("closed loop"). Drugs were introduced with a hypodermic syringe into the pericardium. These experiments evaluate the effects of the two amines applied into the blood stream of the animals.

In the second experimental series one eye of the crab was attached to a force tranducer, the other eye was fixed to the carapace. In this "open loop" experiment the effects of local drug application were evaluated. The fixed eye was injected with small volumes of the drugs (approximately 500 pl). Each animal was tested under three separate conditions: both eyes seeing, only the injected eye seeing and only the measured eye seeing. By comparing the results of these experiments it is possible to determine the contribution of each eye and also the effects of unilateral drug application.

RESULTS

Typical optokinetic responses of the crab for the "closed loop" and "open loop" experiments are shown in Fig. 1. When both eyes are able to move ("closed loop") the animals display slow following movements interspersed with fast phases for large oscillation amplitudes (Fig. 1a). For small stimulus amplitudes the animals respond with slow following movements (Fig. 1b).

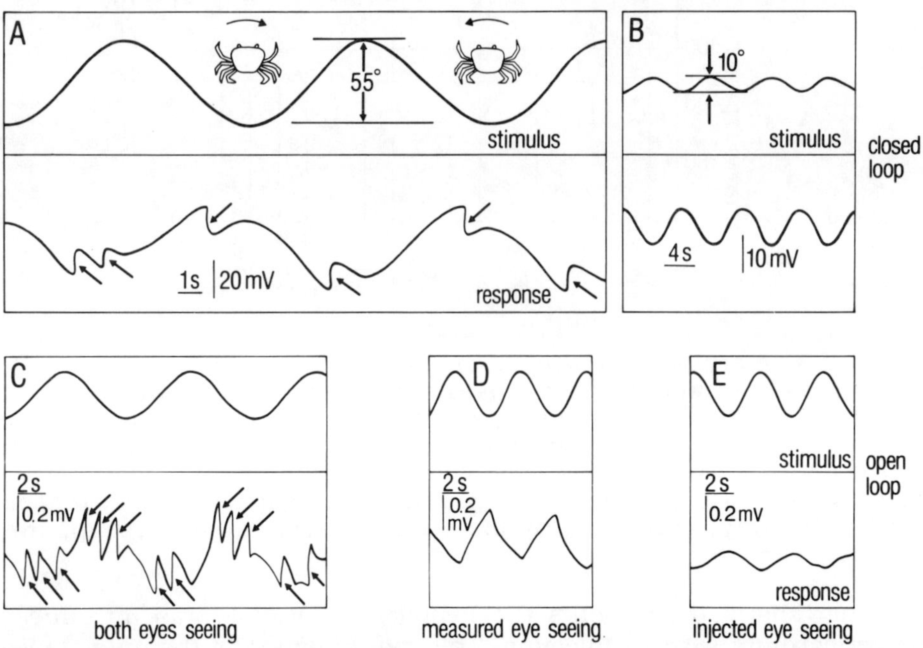

Fig. 1: Responses of the crabs for sinusoidal stimulation with a striped drum. In the closed loop experiment both eyes were able to move. In the open loop experiment one eye was attached to a force transducer and the other eye was fixed to the carapace. Stimulation amplitude for the open loop experiment was 12 degrees of arc. The arrows indicate fast return phases.

In the "open loop" experiment frequent fast phases can be registered when both eyes are seeing (Fig. 1 c), while the animals respond with slow following movements during unilateral stimulation (Fig. 1 d, e). The peak-to-peak amplitudes of the responses were measured to determine the effects of drug application.

Effects in the blood stream. Injection of serotonin into the blood stream leads to a dose-dependent enhancement of the response amplitude. The response modification reaches its maximum approximately 30 min after injection and lasts at least for 2 hours. Octopamine injection results in a much weaker enhancement of the optokinetic response.

The results of these experiments and the corresponding controls are summarized in Fig. 2. The mean relative response amplitudes measured between 40 and 120 min after injection are shown.

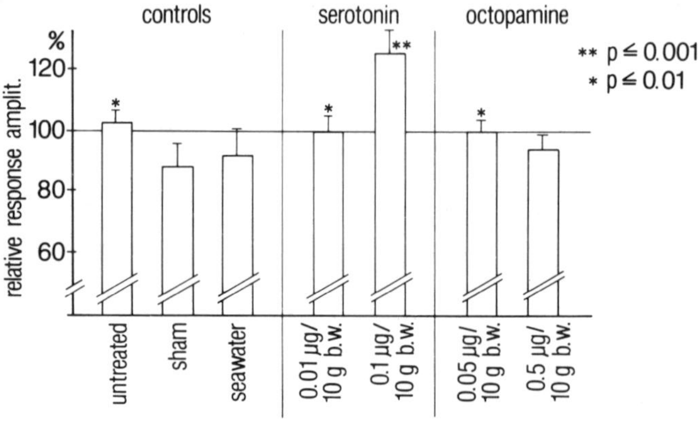

Fig. 2: Summary of the response amplitude changes after drug application to the blood stream. The responses were measured before (=100 %) and between 40 and 120 min after application into the pericardium. The doses refer to the amount of serotonin creatinine sulfate and octopamine hydrochloride / 10 g body weight. Volumes of 2.5 µl/10 g body weight were injected. The significance values refer to comparisons with seawater injection (2 way ANOVA). 5 animals were tested in each group, the bars indicate s.e.m.

In the "sham" experiments the hypodermic syringe was introduced into the pericardium without injection. This manipulation of the animals leads to similar reductions of the response amplitudes as do the seawater injections (2,5 µl/10 g body weight). Significant enhancements of the response amplitude compared to seawater injection were found for both serotonin doses and the lower dose of octopamine (2-way ANOVA test).

Local application in the optic lobes. In the open loop experiments the amines were pressure injected either into the medulla externa or medulla terminalis of the fixed eye. By covering one of the eyes the contributions of both sides can be evaluated separately. Injection of 500 pl serotonin (10 -5 M) into the medulla terminalis leads to an immediate and lasting increase in the optokinetic response generated by the injected eye only (Fig. 3a). The untreated eye appears to be unaffected by the contralateral injection (Fig. 3 b). If serotonin is injected into the medulla externa the enhancement is significantly weaker (2-way ANOVA test, $p < 0.025$). These findings suggest that serotonin is acting in the injected optic neuropile and that the maximum effects can be found in the medulla terminalis.

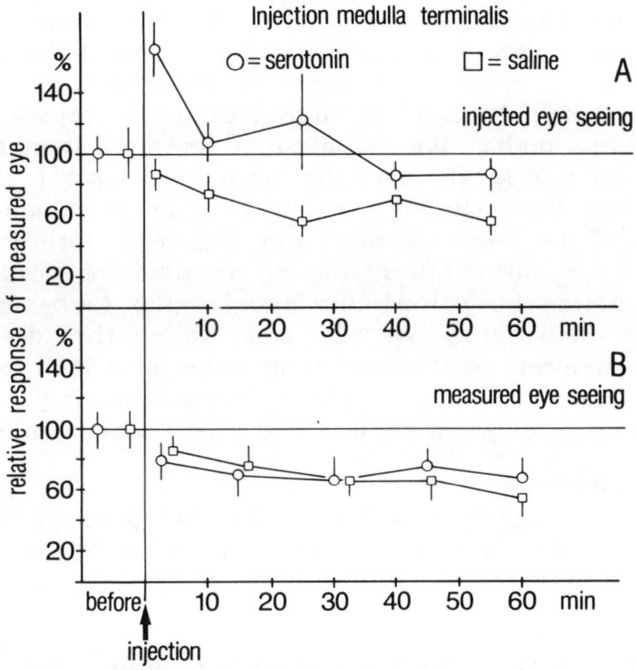

Fig. 3: Relative open loop response amplitudes after injection of approximately 500 pl of 10 -5 M serotonin or saline into the medulla terminalis. 6 animals were tested in each group, the bars indicate s.e.m.

Octopamine injection into the medulla externa (500 pl, 10 -5 M) does not lead to a similar enhancement of the response in the injected eye. When both eyes are able to see, an enlargement of the response amplitude is observed. We conclude from these experiments that the effects of octopamine can not be attributed to a local action within the injected eye stalk.

DISCUSSION

The optokinetic response of the crab is modulated by serotonin application into the blood stream and by local injection into the optic neuropiles. Earlier studies have shown that serotonin can modulate the posture of crustaceans and also several neuronal systems (Livingstone et al., 1980; Harris-Warrick and Kravitz, 1984; Kravitz et al., 1985; Flamm and Harris-Warrick, 1986). In addition, serotonin can act peripherally on muscles (Fischer and Florey, 1987) and on neurosecretory cells (Nagano, 1986). Although there appear to be many different target sites for the action of serotonin, our exeriments suggest that the enhancement of the optokinetic response is due to local effects in the optic neuropile.

Neural activity of motion sensitive interneurons which project from the medulla terminalis to the brain is closely correlated with the motor output underlying eye movements (Sandeman et al., 1975 b). Immunocytochemical studies in the eye stalks of Leptograpsus demonstrated that serotonin-like immunoreactivity can be found in all neuropiles of the optic system (Erber and Sandeman, 1989). Labelling of large neuronal processes was intensive in the medulla terminalis. We assume that serotonin is mainly acting on sensory interneurons in the medulla terminalis. Direct effects on the motoneurons can be excluded because in the open loop experiments enhancements of the response were only registered for the injected eye which itself was not moving but driving the contralateral eyestalk.

The site of action for octopamine appears not to be located in the injected optic neuropile. We do not know the distribution of octopaminergic neurons in the crab brain. The open loop experiments in which an enhancement of the optokinetic response is only apparent when both eyes are seeing suggest a not localized action of octopamine.

Acknowledgements

This work was supported by a Visiting Fellowship from the University of New South Wales to J.E., a grant from the ARGC to D.C.S. and a grant of the DFG to J.E.

REFERENCES

Erber, J., Sandeman, D.C. (1989) The effect of serotonin and octopamine on the optokinetic response of the crab *Leptograpsus variegatus*. J. Neurobiol. (in press).

Fischer, L., Florey, E. (1987) Octopamine action on the contractile system of crustacean skeletal muscle. Comp. Biochem. Physiol. **88C**: 335-342.

Flamm, R.E., Harris-Warrick, R.M. (1986) Aminergic modulation in lobster stomatogastric ganglion. I. Effects on motor pattern and activity of neurons within the pyloric circuit. J. Neurophysiol. **55:** 847-865.

Harris-Warrick, R.M., Kravitz, E.A. (1984) Cellular mechanisms for modulation of posture by octopamine and serotonin in the lobster. J. Neurosci. **4**: 1976-1993.

Horridge, G.A., Sandeman, D.C. (1964) Nervous control of optokinetic responses in the crab Carcinus. Proc. Roy. Soc. (B) **161**:216-246.

Kravitz, E.A., Beltz, B., Glusman, S., Goy, M., Harris-Warrick, R.M., Johnstone, M., Livingstone, M., Schwarz, R., King-Siwicki, K. (1985) The well modulated lobster. The roles of serotonin, octopamine and proctolin in the lobster nervous system. In Model neural networks and behavior. (ed. A.I. Selverston) pp 339-360. Plenum Press.

Livingstone, M.S., Harris-Warrick, R.M., Kravitz, E.A. (1980) Serotonin and octopamine produce opposite postures in lobsters. Science **208**: 76-79.

Nagano, M. (1986) Regional inhibitory effects of 5HT and GABA on the spontaneous electrical activity of a crab neurosecretory system. Biomed. Res. **7**: 267-277.

Sandeman, D.C., Erber, J., Kien, J. (1975 a) Optokinetic eye movements in the crab, *Carcinus maenas*. I. Eye torque. J.Comp. Physiol. **101**: 259-274.

Sandeman, D.C., Kien, J., Erber, J. (1975) Optokinetic eye movements in the crab, *Carcinus maenas* II. Responses of the optokinetic interneurons. J. Comp. Physiol. **101**: 259-274.

Frontiers in Crustacean Neurobiology
Advances in Life Sciences

OCCURENCE OF THE CRUSTACEAN CARDIOACTIVE PEPTIDE (CCAP) IN THE NERVOUS SYSTEM OF THE CRAYFISH *ORCONECTES LIMOSUS*

J.Stangier and R.Keller

Institut für Zoophysiologie der Universität Bonn, Endenicher Allee 11-13, D-5300 Bonn, F.R.G.

SUMMARY

The distribution of crustacean cardioactive peptide (CCAP) in the nervous system of the crayfish *Orconectes limosus* was investigated by radioimmunoassay. CCAP-like material was detected throughout the entire nervous system of the crayfish. The immunoreactive material, found to be highly abundant in the abdominal ganglia, was isolated and characterized by manual sequence analysis. In the crayfish, CCAP is not only a cardioactive agent but also enhances the motility of the isolated hindgut. It is concluded that the peptide may have a dual function as a neurotransmitter and neurohormone.

INTRODUCTION

Here we describe the identification, isolation and complete characterization of the recently discovered crustacean cardioactive peptide (CCAP) in the nervous system of the crayfish *Orconectes limosus*.

CCAP was origionally isolated from the neurohemal pericardial organs of the shore crab *Carcinus maenas* (Stangier et al.,1987). By means of a radioimmunoassay , CCAP was detected in several brachyuran species but no information was available according the occurence and distribution of CCAP in macruran crustaceans.

In brachyuran species, the pericardial organs represent the main source of CCAP. By radioimmunological investigations, 17-24 pmol CCAP/PO was detected. Additionally, the release of the neuropeptide from isolated pericardial organs in response to high potassium pulses was demonstrated (Stangier et al.,1988). Since application of CCAP to a semiisolated heart increased the frequency of heartbeat even at nanomolar concentration, it is suggested that CCAP is a neurohormone involved in the control of heartactivity. Immunocytochemical investigations revealed a complex system of CCAPimmunoreactive neurons that indicates an additional neurotransmitter function of CCAP (Dircksen and Keller, 1988).

The occurence of CCAP in *Orconectes limosus* indicates that the peptide may have neurotransmitter and/or neurohormonal functions in macruran crustaceans, too. First bioassay results substantiate this assumption.

MATERIAL AND METHODS

Animals. Crayfish, *Orconectes limosus*, were purchased from commercial dealer and maintained in large tanks at 12 °C. The animals were fed pelleted cat food.

Dissection of the nervous system. The ventral nerve cord was dissected in an ice-cooled petri dish and transferred to a chilled Reacti-Vial (Pierce) containing the extraction medium (5% formic acid/1% trifluoracetic acid/1% NaCl/1M HCl). For radioimmunoassay analysis, ganglia were dissected and stored separately in Eppendorf tubes.

Extraction procedure. Tissue was homogenized by repeated sonication and stirred on ice for 2h. After centrifugation, the pellet was resuspended in extraction medium, sonicated and stirred for 12h followed by centrifugation. The supernatants were combined and stored frozen.

High performance liquid chromatography. Prior to HPLC the supernatants were passed through a Sep-Pak C18 cartridge (Millipore-Waters), equilibrated and eluted with 0.11% trifluoracetic acid (TFA). The bound fraction was eluted with 60% acetonitrile in 0.1% TFA. The volume of the eluate was reduced to 0.1 ml in a Speed-Vac concentrator and subsequently separated on a phenyl column (4.6 x 250 mm) with a linear gradient from 10 to 80% B in 60 min. at a flow rate of 0.9 ml/min. Solvents were 0.11% TFA (solvent A) and 60% acetonitrile in 0.10% TFA (solvent B).

Radioimmunoassay. The radioimmunoassay used 125J-labeled (Tyr2)-CCAP as a tracer. The radioimmunoassay procedure is described in detail in an earlier paper (Stangier et al. 1988).

Sequence analysis. Carboxymethylated CCAP (CM-CCAP) was sequenced by the manual 4-N,N-dimethylaminoazobenzene-4'-isothiocyanate/ phenyliso-thiocyanate double-coupling technique (Chang et al.,1978). Details of peptide derivatisation and sequencing are given elsewhere (Stangier et al. 1987).

Bioassay experiments. Isolated hearts still attached to the dorsal carapace and the posterior ends of crayfish hindguts were fixed in a cylindrical perfusion chamber of volume 1.2 ml and connected to a force transducer (FT 03, Grass Instruments). Spontaneous contractions were amplified with a Grass preamplifier (7P122D) and recorded with a chart recorder. The chamber was constantly perfused with crayfish saline or test samples by means of a peristaltic pump.

RESULTS

In order to examine the distribution of CCAP in the crayfish ventral nerve cord, ganglia were dissected, extracted and analyzed by radioimmunoassay. CCAPir material was detected throughout the entire nervous system (fig.1).

CCAP turned out to be highly abundant in the abdominal ganglia (2.8-4.4 pmol CCAP) with the highest amount measured in the sixth abdominal ganglion (9.54 pmol CCAP). Relatively low levels were present in the thoracic ganglia 1-4 varying from 0.55 to 0.86 pmol CCAP/ ganglion. The 5th thoracic ganglion was found to contain about 1.78 pmol CCAP. The cerebral and suboesophagel ganglion diplayed levels of 0.8 pmol CCAP and 1.32 pmol, respectively.

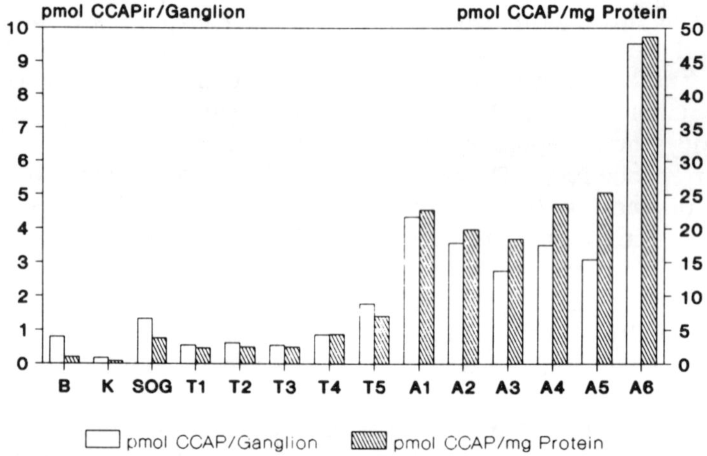

Fig.1 Distribution of CCAP immunoreactivity (CCAPir) in the crayfish nervous system, as determined by RIA. B.: Brain, K: Connectives, SOG: Subesophageal Ganglion, T1-T5: Thoracic Ganglia, A1-A5: Abdominal Ganglia

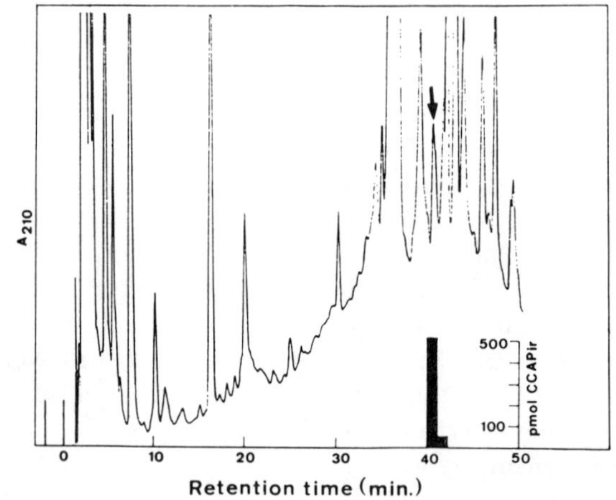

Fig.2 Reversed phase HPLC of an extract from 25 crayfish abdominal ganglia chains (A1-A5) and localisation of CCAPir material. Approximately 600 pmol CCAPir was detected in fractions 40/41, coinciding with the retention time of CCAP (arrow).

Characterization of the immunoreactive material.

In order to characterize the immunoreactive material 25 abdominal ganglia chains were dissected, extracted and subjected to HPLC.Radioimmunological screening of HPLC-fractions revealed two adjacent immunoreactive fractions (#40,41) (fig.2). The retention time of the material coincided with that of authentic CCAP. A total of 600 pmol CCAPir was recovered after the first chromatographic step.

Rechromatography of immunoreactive fractions on a different column (C18, Vydac) with a shallower gradient yielded a single, apparently pure peak (not shown). The purified immunoreactive material was carboxymethylated and subsequently subjected to manual sequence analysis. The following primary structure was deduced: PFCNAFTGC-NH2 (fig 3). Thus, the sequence is identical to *Carcinus*-CCAP.

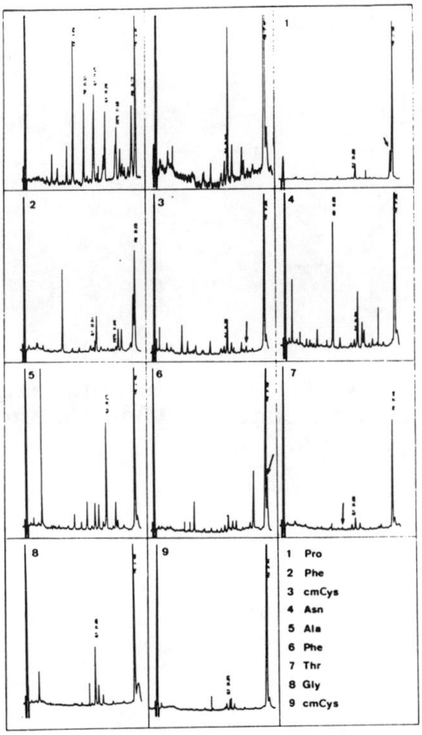

Fig.3 Sequence analysis of approximately 300 pmol of the carboxymethylated CCAP-like peptide. Included is a chromatogram of DABTH-amino acid standards and a blank (b). The N-terminal sequence is Pro (1), Phe (2), CM-Cys (3), Asn (4), Ala (5), Phe (6), Thr (7), Gly (8) and CM-Cys (9).

The presence of the C-terminal amide was ascertained by a comparison of the chromatographic behavior of carboxymethylated CCAP from *Orconectes* with synthetic standards. CM-CCAP-OH and CM-CCAP-NH2 differ in their retention times, and the *Orconectes* peptide cochromatographed with CM-CCAP-NH2.

In a first attempt to demonstrate a biological effect of CCAP in the crayfish, the peptide was applied to the isolated *Orconectes* heart. CCAP was found to accelerate the heartrate and increased the force of contraction, but the peptide was less effective than in *Carcinus*. The increase in force and frequency did not exceed 125% and 75%, respectively. In contrast, the heartrate of *Carcinus* showed a 250% increase at a hormone concentration of 10-6 M CCAP (data not shown).

The high level of CCAP in the terminal abdominal ganglion raised the question whether CCAP is involved in the control of hindgut motility. CCAP was tested on isolated posterior ends of the hindgut and turned out to be a highly effective agent accelerating the force and rate of spontaneous contractions. Additionally, it was observed that CCAP induced contractions in preparations not being spontaneously active (fig.4).

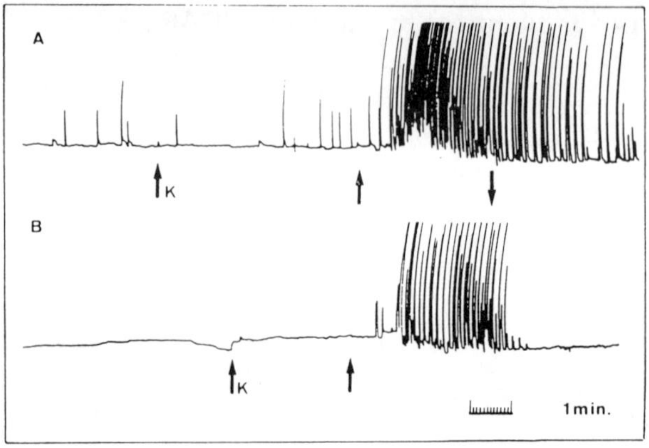

Fig.4 Recordings of the accelerating effect of CCAP on spontaneous contractions of the isolated crayfish (A) and induction of contractions in a quiescent preparation.

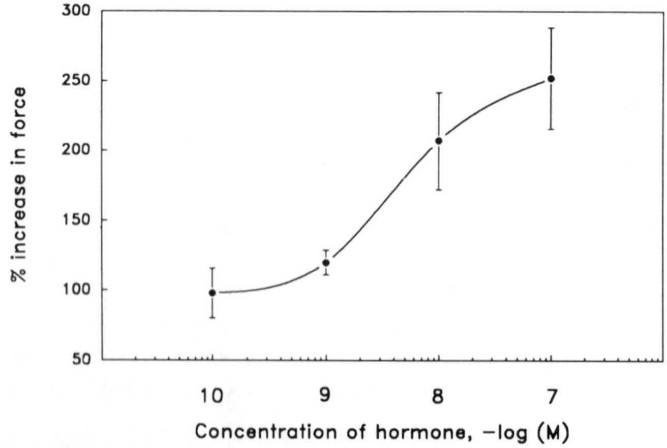

Fig.5 Dose-response relationship representing the effect of CCAP upon the crayfish hindgut.

A dose-response relationship was established which showed the concentration dependent inotropic effect of CCAP on the isolated hindgut. CCAP is active at a concentration of 10-10 M CCAP and led to an 250% increase in force at 10-7 M CCAP (fig.5).

DISCUSSION

In a recent paper, we reported the isolation and characterization of a cardioactive neuropeptide, CCAP, from the pericardial organs of the shore crab, *Carcinus maenas* (Stangier et al.,1987). The structure of the nonapeptide does not resemble that of of any other known peptide. The development of a radioimmunoassay offered the possibility to study the distribution of CCAP within the Arthropoda. The neuropeptide is present in all brachyuran species so far investigated and was recently isolated from the nervous system of an insect, the locust Locusta migratoria (Stangier et al.,1989). In the present paper we report the distribution of CCAP in a macruran species, the crayfish *Orconectes limosus.*

CCAP turned out to be present in the entire nervous system of the crayfish. In *Carcinus*, an immunocytochemical study revealed a complex system of CCAP immunoreactive neurons in the nervous system (Dircksen and Keller,1988). However, more than 80% of the total CCAP present in the central nervous system of the crab was detected in the neurohemal pericardial organs (Stangier et al.,1988). Thus, it was suggested that CCAP may have a dual role as a neurotransmitter/neurohormone. The occurence of CCAP in the central nervous system of the crayfish points to a neurotransmitter function, too.

First evidence indicating a neurohormonal role of CCAP in the crayfish came from RIA-investigations of blood samples. We were able to detect approximately 50 fmol CCAPir/ml hemolymph. So far, the source of CCAP in the circulation is unknown. Further investigations will show whether CCAP is present in macruran pericardial organs. Additionally, there may exist other neurohemal areas releasing CCAP into the circulation. Recently, Kobierski et al.(1987) reported the appearance of FMRFamide like immunoreactive neurosecretory endings in the connective tissue sheet surrounding the ventral nerve cord of the lobster. Obviously, it would be of interest to investigate the role of the connective tissue sheet as a release site of CCAP.

In addition to the previously known excitatory action on the crustacean heart that led to the identification of CCAP, we have shown that the peptide has a potent contraction enhancing effect on the crustacean hindgut. It remains to be established whether CCAP exerts this action under physiological conditions.

REFERENCES

Chang,J.Y., Brauer,D. and Wittmann-Liebold,B. (1978) Micro-sequence analysis of peptides and proteins using 4-NN-dimethylaminoazobenzen-4-isothiocyanate/phenylisothiocyanate double cuopling method FEBS Letters, **93**:205-214

Dircksen,H. and Keller,R. (1988) Immunocytochemical localization of CCAP, a novel crustacean cardioactive peptide, in the nervous system of the shore crab, *Carcinus maenas* L. Cell Tissue Res. **254**:347-360

Kobierski,L.A.,Beltz,B.S.,Trimmer,B.A.and Edward A. Kravitz (1987) FMRFamidelike Peptides of *Homarus americanus:* Distribution, Immunocytochemical Mapping, and Ultrastructural Localization in Terminal Varicosities J.Comp.Neurol. **266**:1-15

Schwarz,T.L., Lee,G.M.M., Siwicki,K., Standaert,D.G. and E.A. Kravitz (1984) Proctolin in the lobster: The distribution, release and chemical characterization of a likely neurohormone.J.Neuroscience **4**:1300-1311

Stangier,J.,C.Hilbich, K.Beyreuther and R.Keller. (1987) Unusual cardio-active peptide (CCAP) from pericardial organs of the shore crab *Carcinus maenas*. Proc.Natl.Acad.Sci. USA **84**:575-579

Stangier,J., C.Hilbich, H.Dircksen and R.Keller (1988) Distribution of a Novel Cardioactive Neuropeptide (CCAP) in the Nervous System of the Shore Crab *Carcinus maenas* Peptides, Vol.**9**:795-800

Stangier,J.,C.Hilbich and R.Keller (1989) Occurence of crustacean cardioactive peptide (CCAP) in the nervous system of an insect, *Locusta migratoria* J.Comp.Physiol.B **159**:5-11

Frontiers in Crustacean Neurobiology
Advances in Life Sciences

CHOLINERGIC, CATECHOLAMINERGIC AND GABAERGIC MECHANISMS OF SYNAPTIC TRANSMISSION IN THE HEART OF THE HERMIT CRAB

Tohru Yazawa and Kiyoaki Kuwasawa

Department of Biology, Tokyo Metropolitan University,
2-1-1 Fukazawa, Setagaya-ku, Tokyo 158, Japan

SUMMARY

Monoaminergic and cholinergic drugs accelerated bursting activity of the cardiac ganglion (CG). Dopaminergic antagonists suppressed accelerated CG activity by stimulation of extrinsic acceleratory nerves and also suppressed myocardial excitatory junctional potentials (EJPs) evoked by large ganglionic neurons (LGNs). Muscarinic antagonists suppressed excitatory postsynaptic potentials (EPSPs) of LGNs induced by small ganglionic neurons (SGNs), but nicotinic ones did not. γ-Aminobutylic acid (GABA) mimicked inhibitory effects on CG evoked by stimulation of extrinsic inhibitory nerves. The effects were suppressed by picrotoxin and bicuculline. LGNs and two of three regulatory axons in the dorsal cardiac nerve showed green fluorescence induced by glyoxylic acid. No neuronal processes in the heart showed immunoreactivity to anti-serotonin antibody. Our results suggest the following; SGNs are cholinergic, LGNs and the two acceleratory axons are catecholaminergic, and the single inhibitory axon is GABAergic.

INTRODUCTION

In decapods, heart rate is accelerated by acetylcholine (ACh) and some monoamines (review of Krijgsman, 1952; Matsui & Shibuya, 1958; Florey & Rathmayer, 1978; Miller et al., 1984) and inhibited by GABA (Maynard, 1961; Shimahara, 1969). These results indicate that neural components activated by the putative transmitters are contained in CG (Alexandrowicz, 1932). Otherwise, the neural components may be modulated by the substances as cardio-active hormones (Cooke & Sullivan, 1982). We have previously elucidated neural organization of the heart in hermit crabs (Yazawa and Kuwasawa, 1984a, b). We investigated effects of both the drugs and their antagonists on certain neural components and muscle cells within the heart. Some observations were obtained from fluorescence histochemical methods using glyoxylic acid and immuno-cytochemical methods using anti-serotonin antibody.

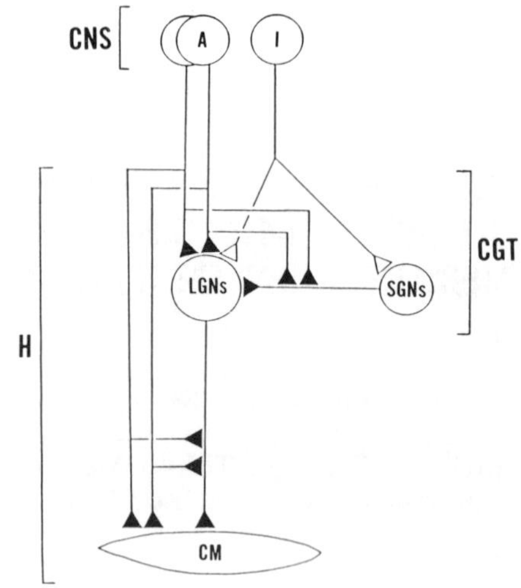

Fig. 1. Schematic diagram of a neural network of the cardiac ganglion. CNS, central nervous system; A and I, cardio-acceleratory and -inhibitory neurons, respectively; H, heart; LGNs and SGNs, large and small ganglionic neurons; CGT, trunk of the cardiac ganglion; CM, cardiac muscle cells.

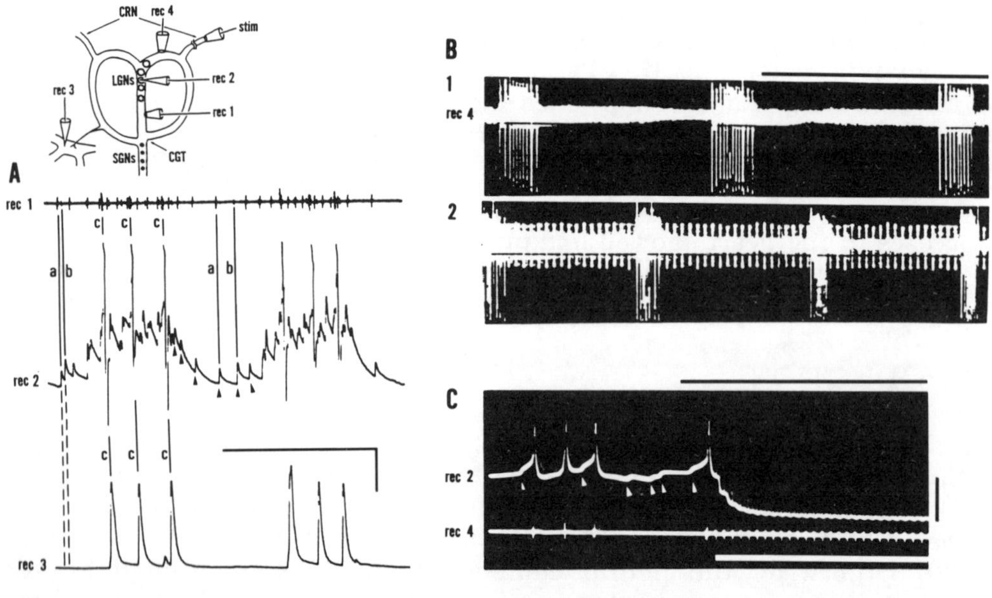

Fig. 2. A: simultaneous records from CGT (top), LGN (middle) and MC (bottom). B: records from CGT prior to (1) and during (2) stimulation of CA2 at 30 Hz. C: simultaneous records from LGN (upper) and CGT (lower) during CI stimulation at 30 Hz (underlined period). CRN, extrinsic cardio-regulatory nerve. Calibrations; 2mV (A rec2), 10 mV (A rec3 and C rec2) and 1 sec. See text for details.

MATERIALS AND METHODS

Heart preparations of marine hermit crabs (*Aniculus aniculus* and *Dardanus classimanus*) were made as described previously (Yazawa and Kuwasawa, 1984a). Electrophysiological methods were essentially the same as in the earlier investigation. Further, there was no apparent significant species difference.

The preparations were pinned to the bottom of a chamber (2 ml in volume), and perfused with filtered sea water containing the drugs.

The following drugs were used; acetylcholine, atropine, scopolamine, pilocarpine, hexamethonium, nicotine, picrotoxin, serotonin, dopamine, noradrenaline, yohimbine, L-glutamate (Wako); arecoline, carbamylcholine, muscarine, bicuculline, muscimol, cyproheptadine, octopamine, chlorpromazine (Sigma); methacholine (Nakarai); *d*-tubocurarine, decamethonium (Tokyo Kasei); mytolon (Smith, Kline & French Lab.); ergometrine (Takeda); tolazoline (Yamanouchi); phentolamine (Ciba Geigy); haloperidol (Dai-Nippon); fluphenazine (Yoshitomi); methysergide (Sandoz).

RESULTS AND DISCUSSION

Fig. 1 shows a neural network within the heart. Five LGNs are located in the trunk of the cardiac ganglion (CGT). LGNs receives synaptic input from four SGNs located posterior to a cluster of the cells. It has been believed that SGNs act as pacemaker cells and do not innervate the myocardium (Maynard, 1961). LGNs make synaptic contact with each other and send processes to cardiac muscle cells (CM). The LGNs and SGNs receive synaptic inputs from a pair of cardio-inhibitory and from two pairs of cardio-acceleratory axons (CI, CA1 and CA2, respectively) arising from the thoracic ganglion (Miyazaki et al., 1985). The CAs make direct synaptic contact with CM, LGNs and SGNs (Yazawa and Kuwasawa, 1984a, b).

The insertion of Fig. 2 shows schematically recording (rec1 to rec4) and stimulating (stim) sites on CGT. The activity of SGNs could be monitored intracellularly at rec2 by recording EPSPs of LGNs, evoked by SGNs. Fig. 2A and C contain arrowheads pointing out some of these EPSPs. SGN activity could also be monitored extracellularly at rec1 (A). LGN activity was recorded, extracellularly, at rec1 (A) and rec4 (B and C), and recorded intracellularly from a LGN soma itself at rec2 (A and C). Evoked impulses of CI and CAs in response to applied stimuli were observed extracellularly at rec4 (see B2 and C).

Fig. 2A shows two bursting discharges corresponding to two heart beats. Different SGN impulses in amplitude were recorded at rec1, which corresponded to different types of EPSPs at rec2 (lines a and b indicate this correspondence). There are no corresponding myocardial EJPs (rec2 and rec3, indicated by vertical broken lines). This suggests that SGNs do not innervate the myocardium. EJPs (rec3) corresponded to extracellular spikes (rec1) and intracellular spikes of LGNs (rec2) in a one-to-one manner, indicating that LGNs are motor neurons (showed by lines c). CA2 impulses (small impulses in Fig. 2B2) accelerated the bursting rate of LGNs. Bursting activity of LGNs was completely suppressed by summed IPSPs induced by CI stimulation (Fig. 2C). EPSPs of LGNs evoked by SGNs were blocked during the stimulation. This may show that CIs innervate both SGNs and LGNs.

Cholinergic drugs (ACh, nicotine and muscarine) and monoamines (dopamine, adrenaline, noradrenaline, octopamine and serotonin) enhanced heart rate and contraction force at threshold concentrations from 10^{-8} to 10^{-6} M for each drug. L-Glutamate (10^{-4} M) did not enhance them. GABA (10^{-4} to 10^{-3} M) and muscimol (10^{-5} to 10^{-4} M) mimicked effects of CIs on CG activity, and completely suppressed heart beat.

Table 1. Blocking effects of drugs on EPSPs and IPSPs of LGNs, myocardial EJPs, and excitatory effects of CAs on CG. (+, suppressed; -, no effect)

	EPSPs evoked by SGNs	IPSPs evoked by CIs	effects of CAs	EJPs evoked by LGN
SATROPINE	+	-	-	-
SCOPOLAMINE	+	-	-	-
CURARE	-	-	-	-
HEXAMETHONIUM	-	-	-	-
CHLORPROMAZINE		-	+	+
HALOPERIDOL		-	+	+
FLUPHENAZINE		-	+	+
PHENTOLAMINE	-	-	-	-
YOHIMBINE		-	-	-
METHYSERGIDE	-	-	-	-
PICROTOXIN	-	+	-	-
BICUCULLINE		+		

The effects of antagonists on synaptic potentials of LGN and myocardial EJPs were summarized in Table 1. Atropine and scopolamine suppressed EPSPs of LGNs transmitted from SGNs. Curare, hexamethonium and mytolon did not. Only dopaminergic blockers, haloperidol, chlorpromazine and fluphenazine suppressed myocardial EJPs transmitted from LGNs. Effects of either one of two CAs on CG activity were also antagonized only by dopaminergic blockers. Picrotoxin and bicuculline suppressed IPSPs induced by CIs.

Present results support the histochemical evidence suggesting that cholinesterase is present on the surface of LGNs in CG of the lobster (Maynard, 1971), as well as the biochemical evidence indicating the presence of catecholamines in LGNs (Ocorr & Berlind, 1983). Axons of LGNs and two of three axons in the dorsal cardiac nerve showed green fluorescence induced by glyoxylic acid. No serotonin immunoreactivity to anti-serotonin antibody was found in cardiac tissues although immunoreactive neuronal processes were observed in the central nervous system and in pericardial organs (see for method, Kurokawa et al., 1989). It has been observed that the stomatogastric system of the lobster synthesizes dopamine (Kushner & Barker,1983).

This study suggests that CIs are GABAergic and that both of LGNs and CAs are catecholaminergic, and probably contain dopamine or dopamine-like substances. ACh has been postulated to be a sensory (Barker et al., 1972) and a motor (Marder, 1976) transmitter in crustaceans. This study also suggests that ACh may be a transmitter of SGNs, functioning as pacemaker cells. (Contribution from the Shimoda Marine Res. Center, No.493.)

REFERENCES

Alexandrowicz, J.S. (1932) The innervation of the heart of the crustacea. I. Decapoda. Q. J. Microsc. Sci. **75**:181-249.

Barker, D. L., Herbert, E., Hildebrand, J.G. & Kravitz, E.A. (1972) Acetylcholine and lobster sensory neurones. J.Physiol. **226**:205-229.

Cooke, I.M. & Sullivan, R.E. (1982) Hormones and neurosecretion. In The biology of crustacea, Vol 3 (ed. Atwood, H.L. & Sandeman, D.C.) pp.205-290. New York: Academic.

Florey, E. & Rathmayer, M. (1978) The effects of octopamine and other amines on the heart and on neuromuscular transmission in decapod crustaceans: further evidence for a role as neurohormone. Comp. Biochem. Physiol. **61C**:229-237.

Krijgsman, B.J. (1952) Contractile and pacemaker mechanisms of the heart of arthropods. Biol. Rev. **27**:320-346.

Kurokawa, M., Kuwasawa, K., Otokawa, M., Yamada, C. & Kobayashi, H. (1989) Aminergic cellular organization in the gills of *Aplysia* species. J. Neurobiol. **20:**(in press).

Kushner, P.D. & Barker, D.L. (1983) A neurochemical description of the dopaminergic innervation of the stomatogastric ganglion of the spiny lobster. J. Neurobiol. **14**:17-28.

Marder, E. (1976) Cholinergic motor neurones in the stomatogastric system of the lobster. J. Physiol. **257**:63-86.

Matsui, K. & Shibuya, T. (1958) Effects of some drugs on the spontaneous activity of the isolated ganglionic trunk of the lobster heart (*Panulirus japonicus*). Jpn. J. Zool. *12*:189-201.

Maynard, D.M. (1961) Cardiac inhibition in decapod crustacea. In Nervous inhibition. (ed. Florey, E.) pp.144-178. Oxford: Pergamon.

Maynard, E.A. (1971) Microscopic localization of cholinesterases in the nervous systems of the lobsters, *Panulirus argus* and *Homarus americanus.* Tiss. Cell. 3:215-250.

Miller, M.W., Benson, J.A. & Berlind, A. (1984) Excitatory effects of dopamine on the cardiac ganglia of the crabs *Portunus sanguinolentus* and Podophthalmus vigil. J. Exp. Biol. **108**:97-118.

Miyazaki, T., Kuwasawa, K., Yazawa, T. & Mashimo, K. (1985) Identification of the cardio-regulator nerves in a marine hermit crab and the shadow-induced cardiac inhibition in some decapods. Zool. Sci. **2:**35-47.

Ocorr, K.A. & Berlind, A. (1983) The identification and localization of a catecholamine in the motor neurons of the lobster cardiac ganglion. J.Neurobiol. **14:**51-59.

Shimahara, T. (1969) The inhibitory post synaptic potential in the cardiac ganglion cell of the lobster, Panulirus japonicus. Sci. Rep. Tokyo Kyoiku Daigaku. Sec. B. **14**:9-26.

Yazawa, T. & Kuwasawa, K. (1984a) The cardio-regulator nerves of the hermit crabs: anatomical and electrophysiological identification of their distribution inside the heart. J. Comp. Physiol. A. **154**:871-881.

Yazawa, T. & Kuwasawa, K. (1984b) The cardio-regulator nerves of the hermit crabs: multimodal activation of the heart by the accelerator axons. J. Comp. Physiol. A. **155**:313-318.

Frontiers in Crustacean Neurobiology
Advances in Life Sciences

STOMATOGASTRIC GANGLION: NEUROMODULATORY ROLE OF A CHOLECYSTOKININ-LIKE PEPTIDE AND A RECURRENT BACK PROPAGATION MODEL OF THE GASTRIC RHYTHM

Gina Turrigiano and Allen Selverston

Department of Biology, B-022 University of California, San Diego La Jolla, California 92093 U.S.A.

SUMMARY

A peptide immunoreactive to mammalian cholecystokinin is shown by immunohistochemistry and RIA to be present in the lobster Panulirus interruptus. Bath application of mammalian CCK to the stomatogastric ganglion has characteristic effects on both the gastric and pyloric rhythms. Following feeding in unrestrained animals, the initiation of gastric mill activity is coincident with a rise in blood levels of a CCK-like peptide (CCKLP). Injection of CCK8 can activate the gastric mill although the pattern is not identical to food-induced activity. A specific blocker for CCK can inhibit feeding-induced gastric mill activity, suggesting CCK has a causal role in turning on the pattern. Preliminary studies using a fully-recurrent back propagation network model shows major features such as phase relationships of the gastric pattern can be attributed to simple cellular properties and the strengths of the synaptic connections. While the model mimics the normal pattern, it fails to duplicate experimental perturbations to the system suggesting that important parameters are missing.

INTRODUCTION

The *in vitro* lobster stomatogastric ganglion produces two stereotyped rhythmic motor patterns, the pyloric and gastric. When the ganglion is perfused with certain peptides or amines these patterns can be modulated so that the normal burst characteristics are significantly altered (for review see Marder, 1984; Harris-Warrick, 1988). Using immunohistochemical techniques, it has now been demonstrated that many putative modulators exist within fibers and neurons which terminate in the neuropil of the STG (see Marder, 1987). While the in vitro changes in the motor patterns have been well documented, nothing is known about whether the modulators which have identified play a role in normal behavior of the animal. Studies to date have emphasized the cellular and synaptic changes which occur following bath application of neuromodulatory substances or the changes induced by stimulation of identified modulator neurons (Nusbaum &

Marder, 1989a,b; Katz & Harris-Warrick, 1989). In this paper we show how a peptide similar to mammalian cholecystokinin is used by lobsters as part of their normal feeding behavior.

In a separate study, we look at some of the combined interactions of the gastric neurons with new network modeling techniques. In preliminary studies only synaptic strengths between units were modeled. The long term goal is to incorporate the biophysical changes which occur as a result of neuromodulatory action into the models so that they can be used as constraints or as ways of testing the computational assumptions. We describe some preliminary results using a recurrent back-propagation model to produce a testable model of the gastric rhythm.

RESULTS

CCK-like peptides. CCK is one of a family of peptides including the gastrin and caerulein peptide which share the same terminal amino acid sequence. In mammals CCK is thought to be involved in both the control of gut motility and the signaling of satiety (Dickray, 1978; Smith & Gibbs, 1985; Baile & Della-Fera, 1985). CCK has been demonstrated within the CNS of many vertebrates and has been shown to affect the excitability of some classes of vertebrate neurons (Skirboll et al., 1981; Brooks & Kelly, 1985). Antibodies specific to the terminal sequence of mammalian CCK have been used to identify CCK-like peptides in a number of invertebrates including arthropods (Larson & Vigna, 1983a). CCK-like peptides in insects have effects on gut motility (Nachman et al., 1986) suggesting they may act similarly to their vertebrate homologues. The presence of bioactive CCK-like material in arthropods makes this class of compounds likely candidates for modulators of the stomatogastric system.

CCK-like material in lobsters. The distribution of CCK-like material in the stomatogastric nervous system was determined by immunohistochemistry, using antisera raised against vertebrate CCK8. The stomatogastric nervous system shown diagramatically in Fig. 1 consists of paired commissural ganglia and an unpaired esophageal ganglion all connected to the stomatogastric ganglion via the stomatogastric nerve. The nerves leaving the stomatogastric ganglion contain axons which innervate the striated muscles of the gastric mill and pylorus. The inferior ventricular nerve (IVN) comes from the brain and enters the stomatogastric system near the esophageal ganglion. The commissural ganglia are connected to the entire CNS via the circumesophageal commissures.

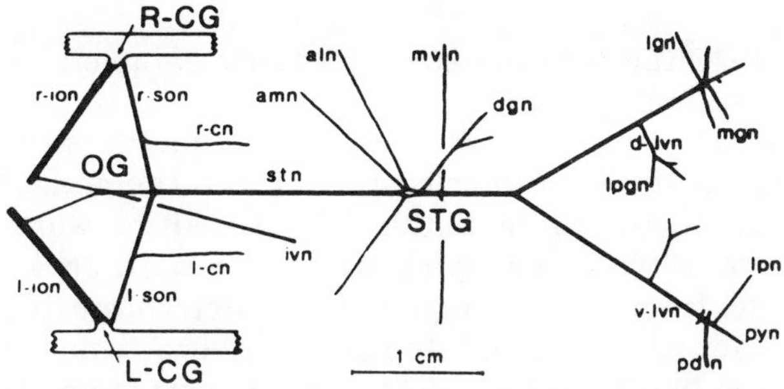

Fig. 1. Schematic diagram of the principle nerves and ganglia.

As with many other modulators, immunohistochemical staining reveals that only the neuropile is stained in the stomatogastric ganglion. Fibers from cell bodies in anterior ganglia enter the STG from the stomatogastric nerve. None of the somata in the stomatogastric or esophageal ganglia showed CCK-like immunoreactivity. This staining pattern indicates CCK-like material is contained in neurons outside the stomatogastric ganglion and can be released near or possibly directly onto the neuron making up the gastric and pyloric CPGs. In addition, there is strong immunohistochemical staining of the pericardial plexus surrounding the heart, and CCK-like peptide in the blood can be demonstrated by radioimmunoassay. The STG sites within an artery, where it is in a good position to respond to blood-borne factors. This suggests a second pathway by which CCK-like peptides have access to the STG.

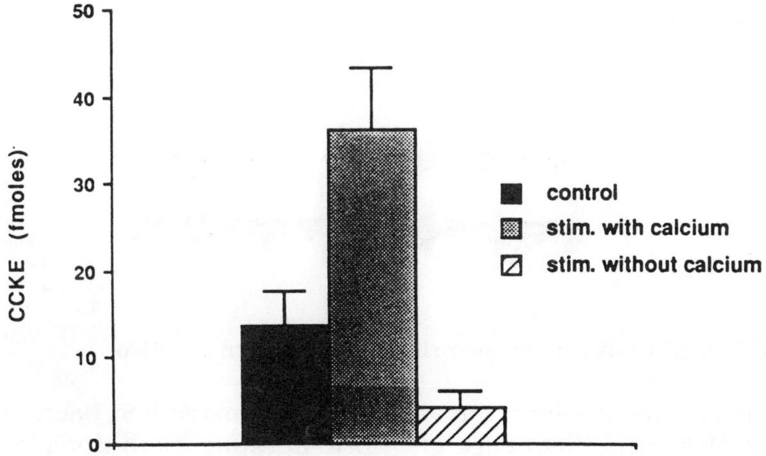

Fig. 2. Calcium dependent release of a CCKLP. Each bar represents the mean amount of CCKLP released into the medium in one hour ± SD.

The release of CCKLP into the stomatogastric ganglion was determined by stimulating the stomatogastric nerve and collecting the perfusate from the ganglion in a small well. This procedure presumably stimulates the CCK-containing axons in the STN to release CCK into the ganglion from where it diffuses into the surrounding bath. The procedure worked only when a protease inhibitor (PMSF) was present in the bath to keep the released CCK-like peptide from being degraded. To determine if the release was calcium dependent, the stomatogastric nerve was stimulated after magnesium was substituted for calcium in the perfusate. As can be seen in Fig. 2 the levels of CCKLP released under these conditions are not statistically different from zero.

Effect of CCK on motor patterns in vitro. After the presence of a CCK-like material had been confirmed within the stomatogastric system, the obvious next step was to determine how effective CCK agonists were in modulating the gastric and pyloric rhythms. Preliminary tests with gastrin 17 and unsulfated CCK by bath application gave negative results. However caerulein peptide and CCK8SO4 were able to modulate the output of both the pyloric and gastric mill motor pattern in characteristic ways.

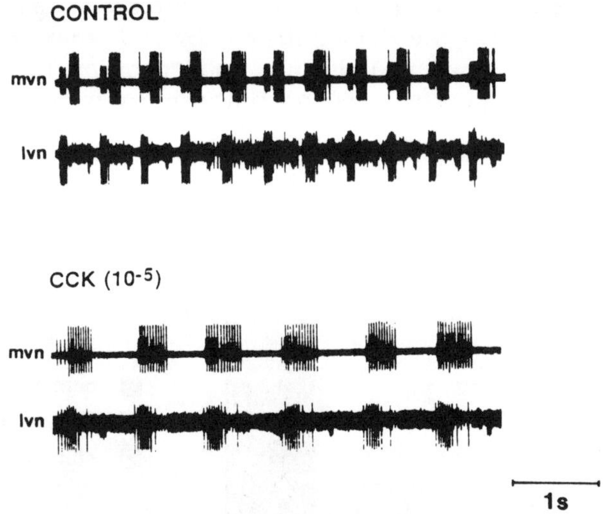

Fig. 3. Effect of CCK on the pyloric motor pattern in vitro.

In preparations in which the stomatogastric nerve had been blocked with sucrose to lower the frequency of pyloric bursting, bath application of CCK enhanced bursting in IC, VD, LP and PD (Fig. 3). Spike frequencies and number of spikes per burst were increased over the sucrose blocked condition for these neurons, but not for the PY neurons. Concentrations of CCK needed to obtain these results were quite high, on the order of 10^{-5} M suggesting these analogues were probably not equivalent in effectiveness to lobster CCK. Supporting this, we found a purified fraction of a CCK-like peptide from the shrimp Palaemon serratus (Faverel et al., 1987) had a far more potent effect than the mammalian form. The changes in the motor patterns were similar to those described for CCK8 but at much lower concentrations, approximately 10^{-8} M.

CCK8 could also modulate actively cycling pyloric rhythms. The IC neuron in particular shows increases in membrane potential oscillations and spike frequency with increasing concentrations of CCK.

CCK8 was not able to initiate gastric mill activity in a blocked preparation, but could start up a pattern in preparations which were spontaneously inactive with their commissural inputs intact. As with the pyloric rhythm, CCK could modulate ongoing GM activity, but relatively high concentrations were required. As well as increasing the spike frequencies of most of the gastric units, CCK increases the "duty cycle" of several units, i.e., the percentage of the period during which a particular unit fires. CCK increases the duty cycle of DG from .39 to .52 and that of LPG from .70 to .84. There is also a signficant phase shift in LG and GM relative to the beginning of the DG burst so that LG and GM fire later in the cycle. The phase of LG increases from .34 to .44 and that of GM from .40 to .47. These changes emphasize the phases of the gastric cycle which are responsible for opening the lateral and resetting the medial teeth.

Application of CCK had variable effects on the period which were dependent on the initial state of the system. In preparations in which the initial bursting was weak, CCK decreased the cycle period in a dose-dependent manner. However, in strongly cycling preparations, the period was lengthened by the application of CCK.

In vivo role of CCKLP. The demonstration of CCKLP within the stomatogastric nervous system and its effects in vitro does not, of course prove how or even if this substance is used by the lobster to control movements of the gastric mill in the intact animal. Using a radioimmunoassay to measure changes in blood CCK-like peptide levels following feeding, as well as chronic EMG recording of gastric mill muscles, it was possible to correlate CCK-like peptide concentrations in the blood with activation of the gastric mill before, during and after feeding. On average there was a four-fold increase in CCK-like peptide levels following feeding and these levels remained elevated for approximately four hours. This corresponds well with the time-course of GM activation (Fig. 4) and the amounts of time food remains in the stomach (Fleischer, 1981).

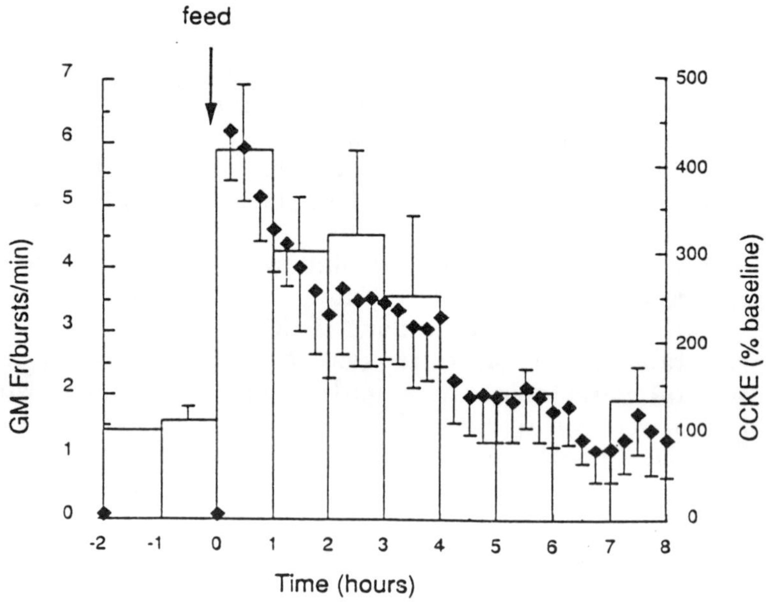

Fig. 4. Increases in CCLP in blood and increased GM muscle activity following feeding.

Injections of mammalian CCK8 into lobsters sufficient to raise hemolymph levels to between 10^{-7} and 10^{-6} M initiated cycling in 8 out of 9 animals. The GM activity produced in this way was in general slower with longer burst lengths and lower spike frequencies than GM activity following feeding. Similar results were obtained by injection of proctolin and RPCH. It is possible that rapid GM activity following feeding is produced by several factors acting synergistically.

That CCKLP play a major role in the activation of the GM can be shown by the use of a specific CCK antagonist. Proglumide is a specific competitive antagonist of CCK which has been used to block effects of endogenous and exogenous CCK in mammals. Proglumide injected within the first two hours after feeding produced a long-lasting decrease in GM activity, whereas injection of vehicle alone or disturbances caused by turning on the lights produced only brief interruptions of gastric mill activity (Fig. 5). Proglumide blocked the in vivo effects of CCK when injected into the hemolymph but did not block the effects of injected RPCH.

Proglumide was able to block the effects of CCK bath-applied in vitro but did not block the in vitro effects of proctolin or RPCH. These data suggest that proglumide acts specifically to antagonize the effects of CCK-like peptides in lobsters.

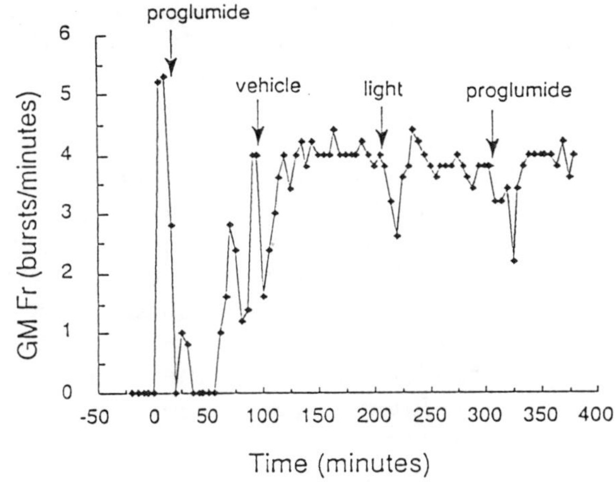

Fig. 5. The CCK antagonist proglumide inhibits GM activity following ingestion.

Modeling the gastric mill network. Both the unmodulated and the CCK-modulated gastric mill pattern represent the collective interactions between thousands of synaptic and cellular properties. A fundamental question about this and other small networks is what properties are essential, i.e. both necessary and sufficient, to generate a particular pattern. Previous modeling efforts have stressed realism by incorporating as many phenomenological parameters as possible into the model. By judicious manipulation of parameter values it is not too difficult to simulate a known circuit. But all of the "realism" fails to get at the most fundamental question, what are the essential components of the basic mechanisms? This is due to the fact that because so many parameters are used in the model, one cannot tell which are the crucial components of the system.

Another approach is to model extremely simplified neuronal elements to see how well they reproduce real biological systems. More biological "realism" can be added incrementally when such "abstract" models fail to perform properly. Modeling is only helpful in explaining mechanisms when it can predict perturbations to a system, tuning the parameters to achieve some fixed pattern is by itself inadequate to explain how a system functions.

We have therefore begun to model the gastric system taking an entirely new approach. Using a new recurrent back propagation algorithm, and very simple "neurons", we can ask if a network like the gastric can be taught to produce a normal motor pattern. If so, does the model adjust its synaptic strengths so that they are like those found in the biological system? Our initial hypothesis was that unlike the pyloric system, the pattern was generated by virtue of the synaptic interactions alone. Only one neuron, the

DG appeared to have intrinsic bursting capability and we had shown previously that it could be deleted from the network and the overall oscillation would persist. Since it has also been shown that stomatogastric neurons can release transmitter in a graded fashion without spiking, we modeled the slow intracellular potentials only. Our hypothesis was that the synaptic strength parameters along with a sigmoidal activation function for each neuron was sufficient to explain the normal gastric mill oscillatory pattern. The DG neuron was modeled as two reciprocally connected units which were trained to oscillate with only one of the units making connections to the rest of the network. In our initial experiments, all of the neurons in the gastric network were totally connected to one another and their synaptic strengths randomized. All of the neurons were taught their correct pattern with a Williams-Zipser algorithm. After about 25-30 periods, the network learned the pattern so that when the "teacher" was removed the model would continue to generate the correct pattern based on the synaptic "weights" it had learned. Repeating the procedures gave similar results, but specific connection strengths between known cells differed on each trial. The network was then constrained to have only the actual number of synapses present in the biological network and to have the known polarity (excitatory or inhibitory) as well. When trained under these conditions, the network took somewhat longer to learn the correct pattern, but the weight distributions were more consistent. This means that without constraints, the model had so many degrees of freedom that a large number of solutions could be found but than when constrained, the number of solutions was far fewer. Furthermore, the weights learned under the constrained condition showed a 70% match with the biological weights in terms of strong or weak. This is remarkable given the fact that the many electrotonic weights present in the biological circuit as well as A-currents, postinhibitory rebound, plateau potentials and a myriad of other biophysical properties were not present in the model. This suggests that much of the basis for generating the gastric rhythm can be attributed to the connectivity matrix alone. Preliminary tests of the model have unfortunately not had much predictive value. Simulated cell-killing and voltage pulse experiments do not match similar experiments in the biological system. This means that while the network can be tuned to generate a correct stable output pattern, there must be features missing from the model which are still necessary if the model is to perform correctly under a variety of conditions including being able to mimic the effects of different neuromodulators. One hopes that by the judicious addition of more biological features to the model it will become better able to correct these deficiencies.

Supported by ONR contract N00014-88-K-0328 and NIH grant NS25916. We thank Gary Cottrell and Fu-Sheng Tsung for collaborating in the modeling studies

REFERENCES

Baile, C.A. & Della-Fera, M.A. (1985) Central nervous system cholecystokinin and the control of feeding. Ann. NY Acad. Sci. **448**: 424-430.

Brooks, P.A. & Kelley, J.S. (1985) Cholecystokinin as a potent excitant of neurons in the dentate gyrus of rats. Ann. NY Acad. Sci. **448:** 361-374.

Dockray, G.J. (1978) Comparative biochemistry and physiology of gut hormones. Ann. Rev. Physiol. **41**: 83-95.

Harris-Warrick, R.M. (1988) Chemical modulation of central pattern generators. In Neural Control of Rhythmic Movements in Vertebrates (eds. A.H. Cohen, S. Rossignol & S. Grillner) pp. 232-285. New York: Wiley.

Favrel, P., Van Wormhoudt, A., Studler, J.M. & Bellows, C. (1987) Immunochemical and biochemical characterization of gastrin/CCK-like peptides in *Palaemon serratus* (crustacea, decapoda): Intermolt variations. Gen. Comp. Endocrin. **65**: 363-372.

Fleischer, A.G. (1981) The effect of eyestalk hormones on the gastric mill in the intact lobster *Panulirus interruptus*. J. Comp. Physiol. **141**: 363-368.

Katz, P.G. & Harris-Warrick, R.M. (1989) Serotonergic/cholinergic muscle receptor cells in the crab stomatogastric nervous system. II. Rapid nicotinic and prolonged modulatory effects on neurons in the stomatogastric ganglion. J. Neurophysiol. **62**: 571-581.

Larson, B.A. & Vigna, S.R. (1983) Gastrin/cholecystokinin-like immunoreactive peptides in the dungeness crab, *Cancer magister* (Dana): Immunochemical and biological characterization. Reg. Peptides **7:** 155-170.

Marder, E. (1987) Neurotransmitters and modulators. In The Crustacean Stomatogastric System (eds. A.I. Selverston & M. Moulins) pp. 263-306. Berlin: Srpinger-Verlag.z

Nachman, R.J., Holman, G.M., Haddon, W.R. & Ling, N. (1986) Leucosulfakinin, a sulfated insect neuropeptide with homology to gastrin and cholecystokinin. Science **234**: 71-73.

Nusbaum, M. & Marder, E. (1989a) A modulatory proctolin-containing neuron (MPN). I. Identification and characterization. J. Neurosci. **9**: 1591-1599.

Nusbaum, M. & Marder, E. (1989b) A modulatory proctolin-containing neuron (MPN). II. State-dependent modulation of rhythmic motor activity. J. Neurosci. **9**: 1600-1607.

Skirboll, L.R., Grace, A.A., Hommer, D.W., Rehfeld, J., Goldstein, M., Hokfelt, T. & Bunney, B.S. (1981) Peptide-monoamine coexistence: Studies of the actions of cholecystokinin-like peptide on the electrical activity of midbrain dopamine neurons. Neuroscience **6**: 2111-2124.

Smith, G.P. & Gibbs, F. (1985) The satiety effect of cholecystokinin: Recent progress and current problems. Ann. NY Acad. Sci. **448**: 417-423.

Williams, R. & Zipser, D. (1989) A learning algorithm for continually running fully recurrent neural networks. Neural Computation **1:** 270-280.

APPENDIX

List of Abbreviations

AB	anterior burster neuron
aln	anterior lateral nerve
AM	anterior medial neuron
amn	anterior medial nerve
CCK	cholecystokinin
CCK8SO4	cholecystokinin 8 sulfate
CCKE	cholecystokinin molar equivalents
CCKLI	cholecystokinin-like immunoreactivity
CG	commissural ganglion
CPG	central pattern generator
DG	dorsal gastric neuron
dgn	dorsal gastric nerve
d-lvn	dorsal lateral ventricular nerve
FMRFamide	phe-met-arg-phe-amide
GM	gastric mill neuron
IC	inferior cardiac neuron
ion	inferior eosophageal nerve
LG	lateral gastric neuron
LP	lateral pyloric neuron
LPG	lateral posterior gastric neuron
lvn	lateral ventricular nerve
MG	medial gastric neuron
mvn	medial ventricular nerve
OG	eosophageal ganglion
ON	eosophageal nerve
PY	pyloric neuron
RIA	radioimmunoassay
RPCH	red pigment concentrating hormone
son	superior eosophageal nerve
STG	stomatogastric ganglion
stn	stomatogastric nerve
VD	ventral dilator
v-lvn	ventral lateral ventricular nerve

Frontiers in Crustacean Neurobiology
Advances in Life Sciences

MEMBRANE CURRENTS IN RHYTHMIC NEURONS

Jorge Golowasch, Wanita Kumar and Eve Marder

Biology Department, Brandeis University, Waltham, MA 02254, USA

SUMMARY

The peptide proctolin can initiate strong pyloric and gastric rhythms from the stomatogastric ganglion (STG) of lobsters and crabs. To account for the effects of proctolin on the neural networks that produce the pyloric rhythms, we have attempted to determine the specific neural targets for proctolin, and to describe the membrane currents influenced by it. To this end, we have placed individual STG neurons in dissociated cell culture. We find that many of these neurons oscillate subsequent to hyperpolarizing pulses, and that proctolin increases the oscillatory activity of these neurons.

INTRODUCTION

A fundamental question in neuroscience is understanding how neuronal networks that generate rhythmic behaviors are activated and modulated. The stomatogastric ganglion (STG) of decapod crustaceans contains about 30 neurons, and is capable of generating two different motor patterns, the pyloric rhythm and the gastric mill rhythm. Previous work showed that the neuropeptide proctolin is present in identified modulatory inputs to the STG, the MPNs (Nusbaum & Marder, 1989a, b), and that stimulation of the MPNs or bath application of proctolin can initiate robust pyloric activity in quiescent preparations (Hooper & Marder, 1984, 1987; Marder et al., 1986; Nusbaum & Marder, 1989a, b).

Ultimately we would like to account for proctolin and MPN's actions on the pyloric network at the cellular level. That is, we would like to know which cells are responsive to proctolin, and which membrane currents proctolin is influencing. As a first step towards this goal, Hooper & Marder (1987) determined in the lobster, *Panulirus interruptus*, that the Anterior Burster (AB), and the Lateral Pyloric (LP) neurons are direct targets of proctolin action. Indeed, in this species, proctolin strongly activates the ability of the AB neuron to generate rhythmic oscillatory activity (Hooper & Marder, 1987). In this paper, we describe some of the biophysical actions of proctolin on individual neurons of the STG of the crab, *Cancer borealis*, analyzed in situ, and after the neurons were placed in dissociated cell culture.

METHODS

All experiments were performed using *Cancer borealis*. The effects of proctolin on LP neurons were studied by isolating the STG with a sucrose block around the stomatogastric nerve, and then placing the ganglion in 10^{-7}M TTX and 10^{-5}M picrotoxin (PTX). Two electrodes were placed in the LP neuron for two electrode voltage or current clamp analyses. Proctolin was applied by pressure onto the central neuropil.

STG neurons were placed in dissociated cell culture by a modification of the method of Krenz (personal communication, Krenz & Fischer, 1988; see this volume). Ganglia were treated with 2% collagenase-dispase solution in Ca^{++}-free, Mg^{++}-free crab saline for 90-120 min at room temperature. Cells were dissociated by suction and plated directly on plastic dishes (Nunclon) in salt-balanced L-15 medium containing 1mg/ml gentamicin. Cells were kept for 1-7 days in this medium without changes, in which time they attached (usually in less than 24 h) and grew processes. Recordings from cultured neurons were made using either a discontinuous single electrode current or voltage clamp with an intracellular microelectrode. All measurements in cultured cells were done at room temperature; and at 12°C in the in situ preparations. Crab saline composition: 440mM NaCl, 11mM KCl, 26mM $MgCl_2$, 13mM $CaCl_2$, 5mM maleic acid, 11mM Trizma base, pH 7.4-7.5.

RESULTS

The LP neuron in *Cancer borealis* responds to proctolin with a slow depolarization (Fig. 1). In some preparations the depolarization is accompanied by slow oscillations of membrane potential that ride on the peak and falling phase of the response (e.g. Fig. 1). The amplitude of these oscillations is strongly dependent on the membrane potential of the LP neuron. When the LP is placed in voltage clamp, and proctolin is applied, the steady-state current voltage curves seen in proctolin show an increased negative resistance region (bottom panel, Fig. 1). Together, the data shown in Fig. 1 argue that proctolin may enhance the ability of the LP neuron to oscillate when it is part of the functional pyloric network.

Although it is possible to voltage clamp the soma of the LP neuron, and to isolate it, at least partially using pharmacological tools, the complex branching structure of the neuron, and the presence of presynaptic terminals of other cells makes it difficult to establish unambiguously that all proctolin effects are direct on the cell recorded, and that all proctolin effects are measurable. Therefore, we studied the effects of proctolin on neurons in dissociated cell culture that would be, by definition, isolated, and which might be better suited for biophysical analyses. To this end, we have adapted the method of Krenz and Fischer (1988; this volume) for crayfish neurons to crab neurons, and have recorded from unidentified STG neurons in primary cell culture.

The top panel in Fig. 2 shows a recording from a cultured STG neuron that responded to proctolin with a slow depolarization and rapid oscillations. Note that these oscillations are similar but faster than those seen in the intact LP neuron shown in Fig. 1. When proctolin was washed out of the dish these oscillations stopped and the cell repolarized. The

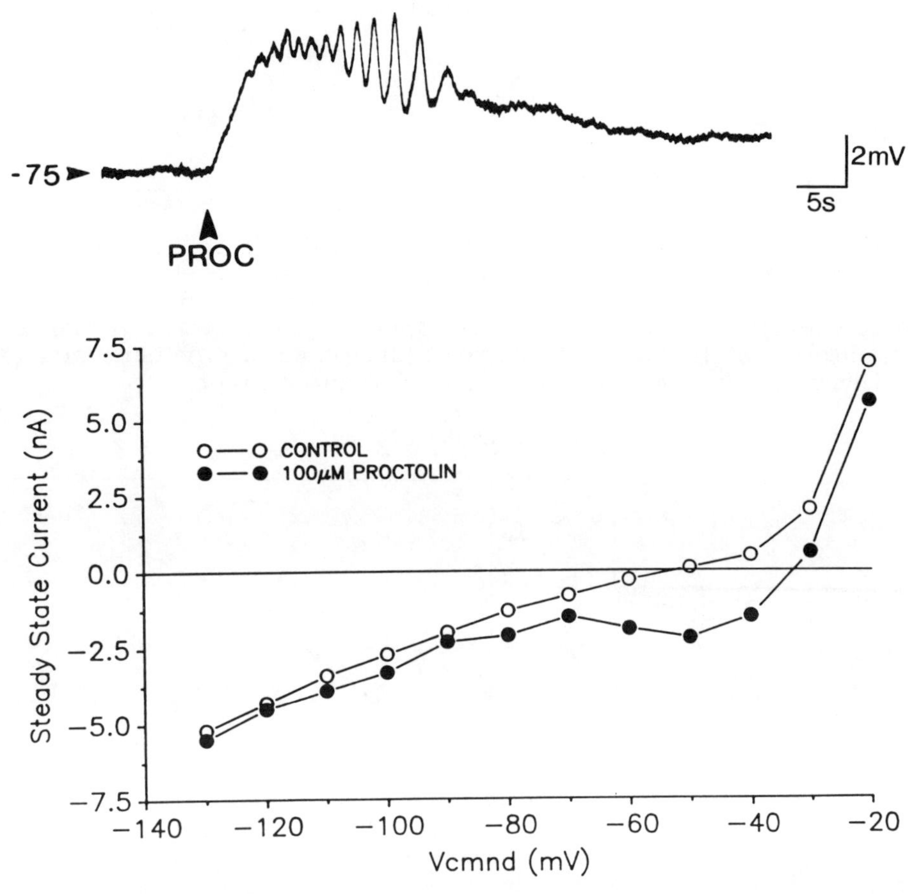

Fig. 1. Proctolin response of LP neuron. LP cell impaled with two electrodes in situ in crab saline containing 0.1μM TTX and 10μM Picrotoxin. Upper panel: response in current clamp to 100μM Proctolin puffed onto the neuropil for 0.5 sec at the arrow. Lower panel: currents measured in voltage clamp at the end of 1 sec pulses to the voltages indicated, both in control saline (TTX-Picrotoxin) and in the presence of Proctolin.

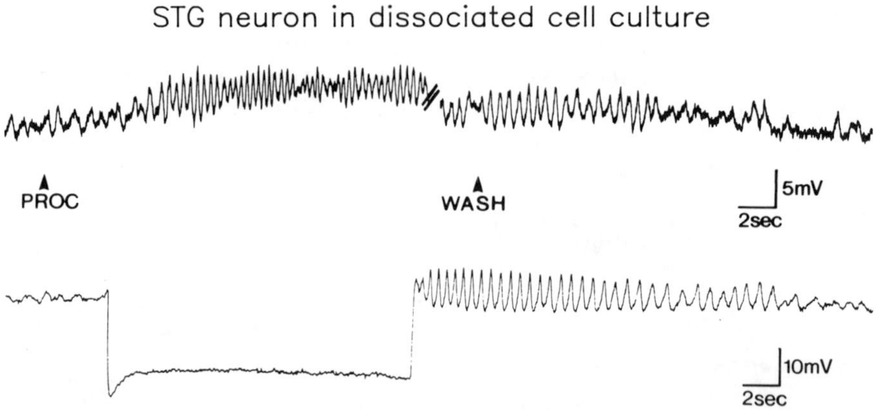

Fig. 2. Unidentified STG neuron in dissociated cell culture. Cell in normal crab saline at room temperature and impaled with one electrode, under discontinuous current clamp; sampling frequency, 7.5kHz. Control membrane potential in both panels is -36mV. Upper panel: response to bath application of 1μM Proctolin (arrows show time of proctolin entry and wash). Lower panel: response to injection of -0.2nA current.

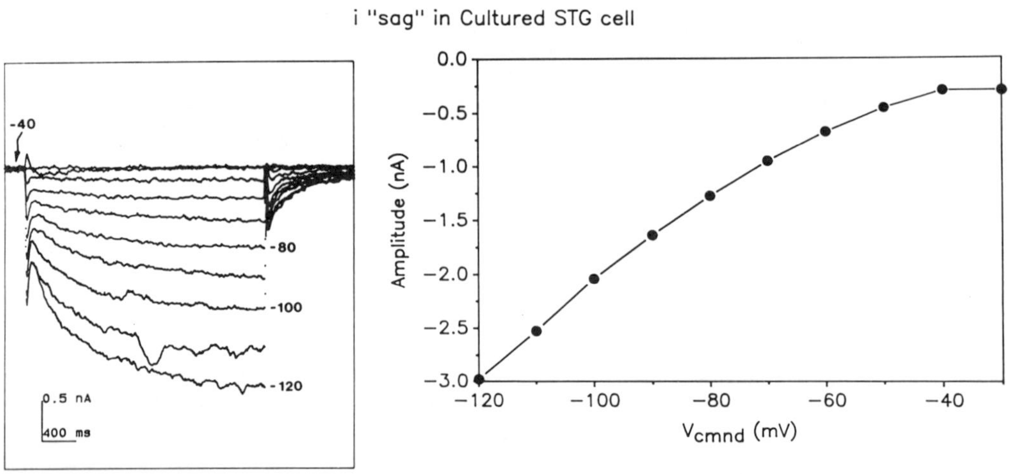

Fig. 3. Hyperpolarization activated inward current in cultured STG neuron. Same cell as shown in Fig. 2. Single electrode voltage clamp (sampling frequency 7.5kHz). Left: Raw currents obtained from a holding potential of -40mV to step voltages of -120mV to -40mV in increments of 10mV (no leak subtraction). Right: Current-voltage relationship of currents measured at 2.5sec after the onset of the voltage pulse (150 msec averaged).

bottom panel in Fig. 2 illustrates a common feature of the cultured STG neurons; they routinely oscillate upon release from a long hyperpolarizing pulse. We suspected that this might be due to the presence of a "sag" current, an inward current activated by hyperpolarization (Difrancesco et al., 1986). Therefore, we voltage-clamped cultured STG neurons and measured the "sag" current, as shown in Fig. 3.

The left hand panel in Fig. 3 shows voltage clamp records of the sag current that developed when the cell pulsed from a holding potential of -40mV to membrane potentials of -40mV to -120 mV. In all cases a slow inward current developed. The plot on the right in Fig. 3 shows that the amplitude of the sag current (measured after 2.5 sec) increases as the cell is hyperpolarized. This current is abolished by treatment with 5-10mM Cs^+ (not shown). Oscillations can not be induced after even very strong hyperpolarizations in the presence of 5mM Cs^+.

Other experiments on cultured neurons have shown a voltage-dependent Ca^{++} current, a delayed rectifier-like K^+ current, and a Ca^{++}-activated K^+ current. Since bathing the cell in 200μM Cd^{++}, known to block Ca^{++} and Ca^{++}-activated K^+ currents in situ, also blocks the generation of oscillations in these cells, we assume that these currents are capable of producing the membrane oscillations when the cell is activated either by proctolin or in response to hyperpolarization.

DISCUSSION

One of the most salient features of proctolin's actions on the pyloric and gastric networks of the STG is that it can activate full rhythmic activity from previously silent networks (Hooper & Marder, 1984, 1987; Marder et al., 1986; Nusbaum & Marder, 1989a, b; Heinzel & Selverston, 1988). Even the preliminary results presented make several important points.

First, isolated STG neurons in dissociated cell culture retain their sensitivity to proctolin. Only a small number of neurons that we have thus far recorded from have shown proctolin sensitivity; this is consistent with what we would predict from the number of neurons that are thought to be direct targets for proctolin action in the intact ganglion (Hooper & Marder, 1987). Since we have not yet been able to identify STG neurons before culturing them, we do not know if the proctolin-sensitive neurons in culture are those which are thought to be direct targets in the animal. The possibility remains that time in culture or length of neurite outgrowth is the determining factor in the expression of proctolin sensitivity, although we have as of yet seen no evidence that this is the case.

Second, a large number of healthy STG neurons in dissociated cell culture have the ability to oscillate following release from a long hyperpolarizing pulse. We presume that this is due to the slow activation of the inward sag current, as well as the existence of a number of other currents. These oscillations are relatively small in amplitude, and are interesting because they are considerably more rapid than those produced by neurons in the intact network, or even by neurons isolated from presynaptic inputs in the STG (Marder & Eisen, 1984; Flamm & Harris-

Warrick, 1986; Harris-Warrick & Flamm, 1987; Hooper & Marder, 1987; Bal et al., 1989). One possibility is that all STG neurons have the ability to generate oscillations (Bal et al., 1989) and that the frequency of the oscillatory processes depends critically on the anatomy of the neurons, and on the extent of electrical coupling among the neurons (Hooper & Marder, 1987; Kepler et al., 1989). In this context it is interesting that the neurons of the STG are thought to be conditional oscillators, and depend on extrinsic inputs to generate oscillatory activity (Moulins & Cournil, 1982; Bal et al., 1989) while the cultured neurons oscillate in the absence of input from other neurons. Perhaps this is in response to culture conditions (e.g. something in the culture medium), or to the new synthesis of membrane subsequent to culturing.

REFERENCES

Bal, T., Nagy, F. & Moulins, M. (1988) The pyloric central pattern generator in Crustacea: a set of conditional neuronal oscillators. J. Comp. Physiol. A. **163**:715-727.

Difrancesco, D., Ferroni, A., Mazzanti, & Tromba, C. (1986) Properties of the hyperpolarizing-activated current (if) in cells isolated from the rabbit sino-atrial node. J. Physiol. **377:**61-88.

Flamm, R.E. & Harris-Warrick, R.M. (1986) Aminergic modulation in lobster stomatogastric ganglion. II. Target neurons of dopamine, octopamine, and serotonin within the pyloric circuit. J. Neurophysiol. **55**:866-881.

Harris-Warrick, R.M. & Flamm, R.E. (1987) Multiple mechanisms of bursting in a conditional bursting neuron. J. Neurosci. **7:**2113-2128.

Heinzel, H.-G. & Selverston, A.I. (1988) Gastric mill activity in the lobster. III. Effects of proctolin on the isolated central pattern generator. J. Neurophysiol. **59**:515-522.

Hooper, S.L. & Marder, E. (1984) Modulation of a central pattern generator by two neuropeptides, proctolin and FMRFamide. Brain Res. **305:**186-191.

Hooper, S.L. & Marder, E. (1987) Modulation of the lobster pyloric rhythm by the peptide proctolin. J. Neurosci. **7**:2097-2112.

Kepler, T.B., Abbott, L.F. & Marder, E. (1989) The role of electrical coupling on the emergent frequency of a neuronal oscillator. In preparation.

Krenz, W.D. & Fischer, P. (1988) Ionic conductances in crustacean stomatogastric neurons in primary culture. Soc. Neurosci. Abst. **14**:295.

Marder, E. & Eisen, J.S. (1984) Transmitter identification of pyloric neurons: electrically coupled neurons use different transmitters. J. Neurophysiol. **51**:1345-1361.

Marder, E., Hooper, S.L. & Siwicki, K.K. (1986) Modulatory action and distribution of the neuropeptide proctolin in the crustacean stomatogastric nervous system. J. Comp. Neurol. **243**:454-467.

Moulins, M & Cournil, I. (1982) All-or-none control of the bursting properties of the pacemaker neurons of the lobster pyloric pattern generator. J. Neurobiol. **13**:447-458.

Nusbaum, M.P. & Marder, E. (1989a) A modulatory proctolin-containing neuron (MPN). I. Identification and characterization. J. Neurosci. **9**:1591-1599.

Nusbaum, M.P. & Marder, E. (1989b) A modulatory proctolin-containing neuron (MPN). II. State-dependent modulation of rhythmic motor activity. J. Neurosci. **9**:1600-1607.

Frontiers in Crustacean Neurobiology
Advances in Life Sciences

NEURONS THAT PARTICIPATE IN SEVERAL BEHAVIORS

James M. Weimann, Pierre Meyrand and Eve Marder

Biology Department, Brandeis University, Waltham, MA, 02254

SUMMARY

The pyloric and gastric mill rhythms of the stomatogastric ganglion (STG) were thought to be independently generated by separate groups of neurons with only weak coupling between neurons of the two networks. However, we now report that neurons which are integral components of the pyloric central pattern generating (CPG) network can become rhythmically active in the gastric rhythm, while elements of the gastric CPG can play a role in pyloric pattern generation. This flexibility in neuron motor output provides the network with many different outputs from a small set of neurons.

INTRODUCTION

There are about 30 neurons in the STG, most of which are motor neurons that innervate the striated muscles of the gastric mill and pyloric chamber of the foregut (Maynard and Dando, 1974). The gastric rhythm has a period of about 5-10 seconds, while the period of the pyloric rhythm is about 1 second. Motor neurons are named and identified physiologically on the basis of which muscles they innervate (Maynard and Dando, 1974). An important property of the STG is that synaptic connections among the STG motor neurons are critical to the generation of both the gastric mill and pyloric patterns (Selverston and Moulins, 1987).

We study the STG of the crab, *Cancer borealis*. After careful identification of the STG motor neurons on the basis of the muscle innervation pattern, we observed many neurons that spontaneously became active with both the pyloric and gastric mill rhythms. Indeed, many of these neurons were observed to display several different motor outputs and change between these outputs during the course of an experiment. Many neurons that innervate the gastric muscles can produce pyloric outputs while some pyloric neurons show strong gastric output. We were interested to determine the mechanisms that account for the ability of these neurons to switch between the pyloric and gastric motor patterns. In principle, these switches could arise from changes in: a) the intrinsic membrane properties of a cell such as its ability to produce bursting pacemaker potentials, plateau properties, or post inhibitory rebound and/or b) efficacy of the synaptic interactions among the STG neurons.

METHODS

All experiments were done using standard procedures for intracellular and extracellular recording in the stomatogastric nervous system (Selverston and Moulins, 1987).

RESULTS

The pyloric rhythm is triphasic: first PD-AB followed by LP-IC and then PY-VD (Selverston and Moulins, 1987). During spontaneous activity many gastric motor neurons masquerade as pyloric neurons (Meyrand et al., 1988). Specifically, the LPG neuron is active during the AB-PD phase, MG and AM fire in LP time, and Interneuron 1 is similar in its activity to PY and VD. As a consequence of this, it is easy to misidentify MG as LP or Int 1 as a PY if proper muscle innervation patterns are not used for identification. The LPG neurons are those previously called PDin (Hooper et al., 1986), as for many years their close resemblance to PD neurons caused them to be classified as PD neurons.

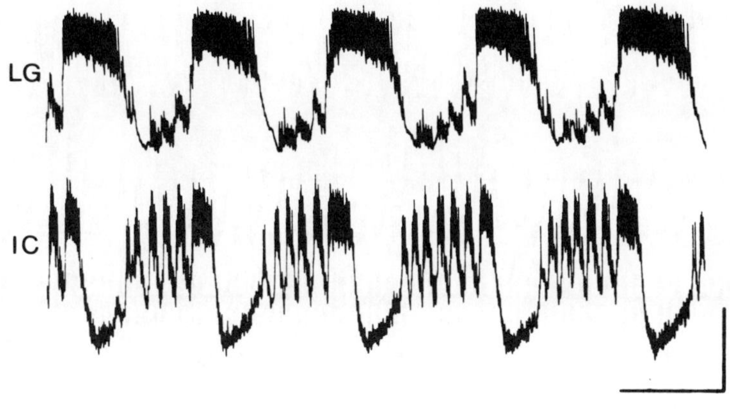

Figure 1. Simultaneous intracellular recordings from a gastric neuron LG and a pyloric neuron IC during spontaneous gastric activity. The most hyperpolarized points of membrane potentials: LG, -72mV; IC, -63mV. (Cal. bars, time=5sec; voltage=10mV LG; 20mV IC)

During gastric activity two pyloric neurons, the VD and IC, can become part of the gastric CPG. When the gastric rhythm is active the IC neuron fires strongly at the beginning of the LG neuron burst and then is inhibited later in the LG burst (figure 1). The VD neuron produces large bursts of activity in antiphase to the LG neuron but before the IC activity becomes strong. The strong inhibition from LG to VD ensures that VD never fires during a LG burst.

When the anterior ganglia are connected to the STG the situation seen in figure 2 can be observed in control saline. In this case the gastric neurons Interneuron 1, LPG, and LG are all participating in the pyloric CPG. Two of the three phases of the pyloric rhythm are seen in the simultaneous intracellular recordings of Int 1 and LPG- the PY and AB phases.

The first two figures illustrate some of the switches that can occur between pyloric and gastric motor neurons. These examples are of neurons which were spontaneously producing these activities. We are now capable of experimentally inducing some of these switches. After bath application of 10^{-7}M SDRNFLRFamide, a FMRFamide-like peptide isolated

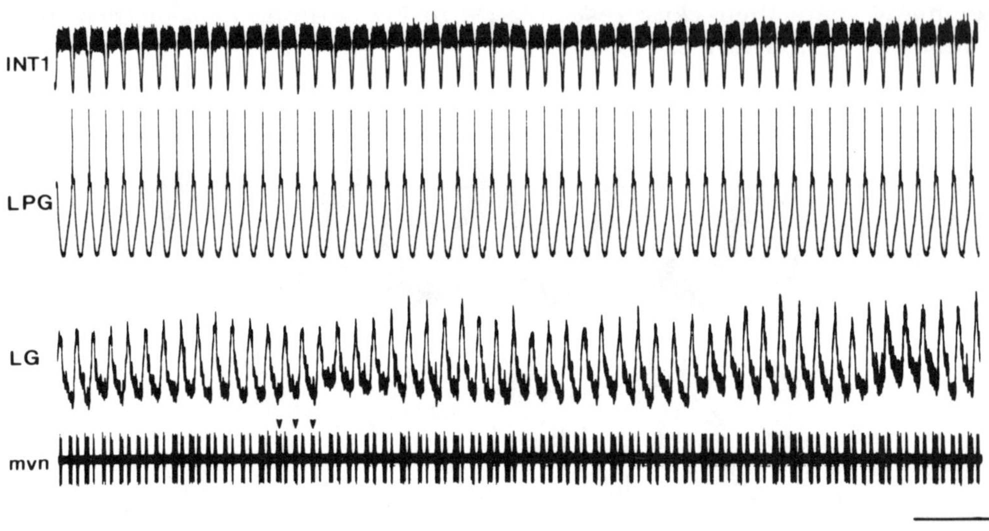

Figure 2. Simultaneous intracellular recordings from Int 1, LPG, LG, and an extracellular recording of the mvn show the gastric motor neurons active in the pyloric rhythm. The VD and IC neurons are firing alternately on the mvn. The action potentials shown by the arrowheads are VD. Most hyperpolarized points of membrane potentials: LG, -80mV; LPG, -80mV; Int 1, -40mV. (Cal. bars, time=5sec; voltage=7mV Int 1; 20mV LPG; 10mV LG)

from the lobster, *Homarus americanus* (Trimmer et al., 1987), a strong gastric rhythm emerges (Figure 3; Weimann & Marder, 1989). Concurrent with the activation of gastric activity many neurons switch from the pyloric rhythm to the gastric rhythm. The activation of the gastric CPG causes all the gastric motor neurons except LPG to be pulled into this CPG.

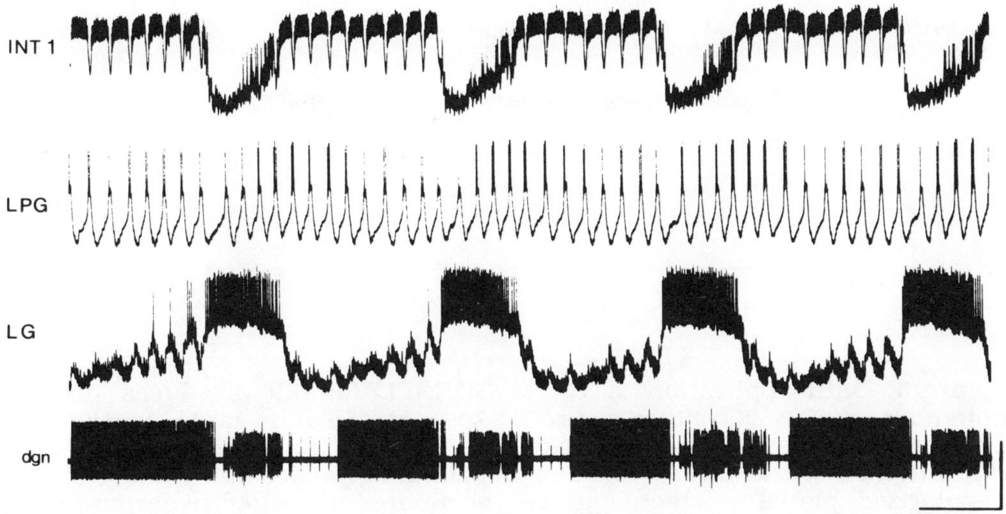

Figure 3. The same preparation as Figure 2 after bath application of 10^{-7}M SDRNFLRFamide to the STG. All of the gastric motor neurons are producing gastric motor outputs except LPG. Small perturbations from LG are seen in LPG. The DG neuron is bursting strongly (large spikes on dgn) in antiphase to the GM (small spikes on the dgn). Most hyperpolarized point of membrane potential: Int 1, -48mV; LPG, -80mV; LG, -80mV. (Cal. bars, time=5sec; voltage=9mV Int 1; 20mV LPG; 10mV LG)

We do not yet have a complete understanding of the mechanisms underlying these pyloric-gastric switches. However, it is already readily apparent that peptides that are present in inputs to the STG can modify either intrinsic membrane properties of some of these neurons and/or modulate the strength of synaptic interactions in the network.

The STG of *Cancer borealis* receives a dense neuropilar projection from fibers that contain FMRFamide-like peptides (Hooper and Marder, 1984; Marder et al., 1987). Although the exact sequence of these peptides is not known, there is at least one which is biochemically similar to SDRNFLRFamide (Marder et al., 1987). SDRNFLRFamide can elicit plateau potentials in the DG neuron (Figure 4). These oscillations have a period of 10-15 seconds and can be initiated or terminated with short current pulses. It is likely that the endogenous properties of other cells are also affected by this peptide.

Proctolin is a peptide found in inputs to the STG of *Cancer borealis* (Hooper and Marder, 1984; Marder et al., 1986; Nusbaum and Marder, 1989a,b).

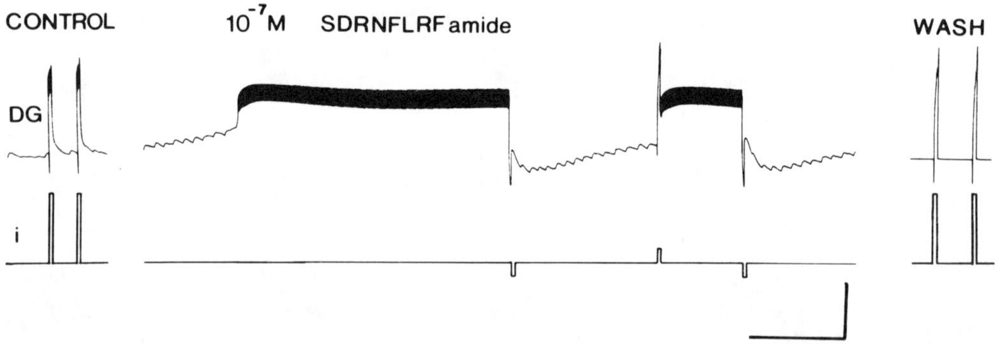

Figure 4. Bath application of 10^{-7}M SDRNFLRFamide produces plateau potentials in the DG motor neuron. In control saline large depolarizing current injections into the DG evoke firing only during the current pulse. In the presence of the peptide smaller depolarizing pulses can initiate a long depolarized plateau, which can be terminated by brief hyperpolarizing current pulses. Membrane potential of DG at most hyperpolarized point, -68mV. (Cal. bars, time=5sec; voltage=40mV; current=2nA)

In spontaneously active preparations the GM neurons can fire in pyloric time with strong inhibition during the LP-IC phase. In the control condition without spontaneous pyloric activity in the GM neurons, the IPSP from the IC neuron to the GM neurons is not apparent at any GM membrane potential. However, in proctolin (10^{-6}M) the IC neuron evokes a large IPSP in the GM neurons with a reversal potential of -58mV. This argues that proctolin can modulate the switch of the GM neurons into the pyloric CPG by changing the synaptic strength between these two neurons.

DISCUSSION

We have shown that many of the neurons of the crab STG can participate in the generation of both the pyloric and gastric rhythms. We have evidence that suggests that modulation of the ability of these neurons to generate plateau potentials is an important determinant of whether these neurons show pyloric or gastric activity. Likewise it appears that the efficacy of some and perhaps many of the synaptic connections among the STG neurons is modulated. This strengthens or weakens the connections of a given neuron with other elements of the gastric and pyloric pattern generating neurons, producing switches of neurons back and forth between the pyloric and gastric rhythms.

Two other studies have described situations in which neurons change their activity patterns. Hooper & Moulins (1989) showed that the VD neuron in Palinurus vulgaris can become active in time with the cardiac sac network. In this case the switch involves the control of plateau properties in the VD neuron. Dickinson et al. (1989a,b) showed in *Panulirus interruptus* that the peptide RPCH can cause neurons of the gastric mill network to become coordinately active with the cardiac sac rhythm. In this example, the switch involves a strong modulation of the efficacy of a given set of synaptic interactions.

In the two cases involving the cardiac sac network, pyloric and gastric network neurons are becoming active along with the cardiac sac, but it is not clear whether they are able to influence the frequency of the cardiac sac oscillator. Despite this, it is clear that the specific firing pattern of these neurons is still influenced by their synaptic connections to other pyloric and gastric neurons.

The switches described in this paper involve neurons that are part of the central pattern generators for the pyloric and gastric rhythms. In the case of Int 1 it is clear that it is an integral member of the gastric CPG (Selverston & Moulins, 1987). However, it is as much a member of the pyloric CPG as VD due to its very strong coupling to VD. LPG is also strongly coupled to AB and PD and is normally so pyloric in activity that for many years the LPGs were thought to be PD neurons (Hooper et al., 1986). Also, short current pulses injected into the IC or VD neurons can phase shift the gastric rhythm. Likewise, the gastric neurons LG or the LPGs can reset and change the period of the pyloric rhythm (Weimann and Marder, 1989). For these reasons it is clear that these neurons are not just passive followers of a different rhythm but are becoming integral members of a different CPG.

Further work needs to be done to determine, for each neuron of the STG, to what extent it can modify both the gastric and pyloric rhythms. Since many of the neurons in the STG can independently switch between CPGs it may be more profitable to speak of a single large neural network which is very flexible. This network now contains all the elements necessary to produce multiple forms of the pyloric and gastric rhythms. These elements (intrinsic membrane properties and synaptic efficacies) can be turned on or off by modulatory inputs to the network.

REFERENCES

Dickinson, P.S., Mecsas, C. & Marder, E. (1989a) Control of the interactions of two motor pattern generators by red pigment concentrating hormone. Soc. Neurosci. Abst. **15:**1119.

Dickinson, P.S., Mecsas, C. & Marder, E. (1989b) Neuropeptide fusion of two motor pattern generator circuits, submitted for publication.

Hooper, S.L. & Marder, E. (1984) Modulation of a central pattern generator by two neuropeptides, proctolin and FMRFamide. Brain Res. **305**:186-191.

Hooper, S.L. & Moulins, M. (1989) Switching of a neuron from one network to another by sensory-induced changes in membrane properties. Science **244**:1587-1589.

Hooper, S.L., O'Neil, M.B., Wagner, R., Ewer, J., Golowasch, J. & Marder, E. (1986) The innervation of the pyloric region of the crab, *Cancer borealis*: homologous muscles in decapod species are differently innervated. J. Comp. Physiol. A. **159**:227-240.

Marder, E., Hooper, S.L. & Siwicki, K.K. (1986) Modulatory action and distribution of the neuropeptide proctolin in the crustacean stomatogastric nervous system. J. Comp. Neurol. **243**:454-467.

Marder, E., Calabrese, R.L., Nusbaum, M.P. & Trimmer, B. (1987) Distribution and partial characterization of FMRFamide-like peptides in the stomatogastric nervous systems of the rock crab, *Cancer borealis*, and the spiny lobster, *Panulirus interruptus*. J. Comp. Neurol. **259**:150-163.

Maynard, D.M. & Dando, M.R. (1974) The structure of the stomatogastric neuromuscular system in *Callinectes sapidus*, *Homarus americanus* and *Panulirus argus* (Decapoda Crustacea). Phil. Trans. Roy. Soc. Lond.B. **268**:161-220.

Meyrand, P., Weimann, J.M. & Marder, E. (1988) Pattern generating neurons switch between different neural circuits. Soc. Neurosci. Abst. **14**:257.

Nusbaum, M.P. & Marder, E. (1989a) A modulatory proctolin-containing neuron (MPN). I. Identification and characterization. J. Neurosci. **9**:1591-1599.

Nusbaum, M.P. & Marder, E. (1989b) A modulatory proctolin-containing neuron (MPN). II. State-dependent modulation of rhythmic motor activity. J. Neurosci **9**:1600-1607.

Selverston, A.I. & Moulins, M. (1987) The Crustacean Stomatogastric Nervous System, Springer-Verlag.

Trimmer, B.A., Kobierski, L.A. & Kravitz, E.A. (1987) Purification and characterization of FMRFamidelike immunoreactive substances from the lobster nervous system: isolation and sequence analysis of two closely related peptides. J. Comp. Neurol. **266**:16-26.

Weimann, J.M. & Marder, E. (1989) Activation of the gastric rhythm of the crab stomatogastric ganglion by SDRNFLRFamide. Soc. Neurosci. Abst. **15**:1047.

Frontiers in Crustacean Neurobiology
Advances in Life Sciences

SENSORY MODULATION OF MOTOR PATTERN GENERATORS IN THE CRAB STOMATOGASTRIC GANGLION

Ronald M. Harris-Warrick and Paul S. Katz[1]

Section of Neurobiology and Behavior, Cornell University, Ithaca NY, 14853 U.S.A.

SUMMARY

The gastro-pyloric receptor (GPR) cells are proprioceptors monitoring muscle tension at the border of the gastric mill and pyloric regions in the foregut of the crab, *Cancer borealis*. These cells use both acetylcholine and serotonin (5-hydroxytryptamine) as co-transmitters. They evoke rapid nicotinic epsps and a variety of slow neuromodulatory serotonergic responses in neurons in the stomatogastric ganglion. The modulatory effects profoundly alter the motor patterns generated by the gastric mill and pyloric central pattern generators (CPGs) as well as interactions between the two CPGs. Thus, motor pattern generators can be modulated by sensory neurons for prolonged periods of time in a phase-independent fashion.

INTRODUCTION

It is now generally agreed that neural circuits in the central nervous system (called Central Pattern Generators, or CPGs) are capable of generating timing and phasing commands for simple rhythmic movements (Delcomyn, 1980). However, the motor patterns generated by these anatomically defined circuits are not at all stereotyped or rigid; instead, they show an astonishing plasticity. For example, sensory feedback can play important roles in determining exact phasing and intensity of activity. Such feedback is generally thought to occur on a cycle-by-cycle basis utilizing classical rapid synaptic mechanisms (Pearson, 1987). In addition, work in a number of invertebrate systems has shown that slow neuromodulatory inputs, using such transmitters as peptides and monoamines, can alter the properties of these circuits in three very general ways: 1) they can define which cells in the circuit are physiologically active components of the CPG; 2) they can alter the intrinsic response properties of the component neurons, such as rhythmic bursting, plateau potentials and post-inhibitory rebound; and 3) they can alter the synaptic efficacy and thus change the "wiring diagram" of the circuit (Harris-Warrick, 1988).

---

[1]Current address: Department of Biochemistry, Brandeis University, Waltham, MA 02254

Most of the effects of neuromodulators have been studied using bath application. The relevance of such experimental results for the intact animal is not always clear. A neuroethologically more satisfying approach is to identify the neurons that release these neuromodulators and to study the effects of stimulating those neurons on CPG performance. In addition, one would like to know what activates the modulatory neurons, and thus put the release of known neuromodulators in some behavioral context.

We have begun this approach with a study of the effects of the monoamine serotonin (5HT) on neurons in the stomatogastric ganglion (STG) of the Jonah crab, *Cancer borealis*. The STG is a tiny ganglion of only 30 neurons which contains two CPGs, the gastric mill and the pyloric circuits. All of the serotonergic innervation of the STG arises from a set of sensory proprioceptors which use both 5HT and acetylcholine (ACh) as co-transmitters. These muscle receptors, called the gastro-pyloric receptor (GPR) cells, have both rapid cycle-by-cycle and prolonged modulatory effects on the CPG circuits in the STG. Thus, neuromodulatory input can arise from sensory neurons, and sensory feedback is not limited to cycle-by-cycle effects on the motor pattern

RESULTS

Anatomy of the Gastro-Pyloric Receptor (GPR) cells. Beltz et al. (1984) identified fibers showing serotonin-like immunoreactivity (5HT-LIR) in the STG of the crab. The source of these fibers was not determined, although peripheral 5HT-LIR cell bodies were observed in motor nerves. We have shown that these peripheral cells are the sole neuronal source of serotonergic input to the crab STG (Fig.1; Katz et al.,1989). There are four

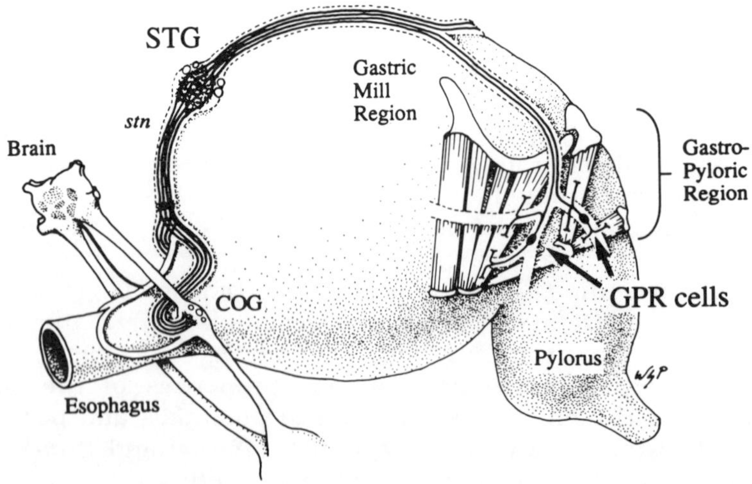

Fig. 1. Projection pattern of the GPR cells in relation to the foregut of the crab.

such cells in two bilaterally symmetrical pairs in each animal. Each cell has dendritic processes that extend over a specific set of muscles along the border between the gastric mill and pyloric regions of the foregut. Their axons ascend to the STG, where they branch profusely throughout the neuropil. The axons continue to other ganglia, where they terminate (Fig.1).

The GPR cells are proprioceptors which use both acetylcholine and serotonin as co-transmitters. We initially expected that the serotonergic GPR cells would have some effect on the muscles that they contact, as has been demonstrated in other systems (Kupfermann and Weiss, 1981; Kravitz et al.,1981). However, stimulating these cells had no detectable effect on muscle tension or neuromuscular transmission (Katz et al., 1989). Instead, the GPR cells are proprioceptors, responding to changes in tension of the muscles that they innervate.HPLC measurements with electrochemical detection confirmed that the GPR cells contain authentic 5HT (Beltz et al., 1984). Since crustacean proprioceptors are generally thought to be cholinergic, we performed choline acetyltransferase assays and confirmed that the GPR cells also synthesize ACh as well. Combining these results with the pharmacological studies described below, we conclude that the GPR cells use both ACh and 5HT as co-transmitters.

Actions of the GPR cells on gastric mill and pyloric neurons in the STG. We have studied the effects of GPR stimulation on all the neurons in the pyloric and the gastric mill CPG circuits of the crab STG (Katz and Harris-Warrick, 1989; Katz and Harris-Warrick, 1990a, b). The synaptic responses vary widely between different postsynaptic cells. Two general classes of synaptic responses are seen: 1) rapid nicotinic cholinergic epsps; 2) slow modulatory input that changes intrinsic cellular properties by a noncholinergic mechanism that is partially mimicked by bath application of 5HT. These two classes of synaptic responses are seen in varying combinations in different cells. Most of the gastric mill CPG neurons, for example, have a dual response to GPR stimulation: a rapid nicotinic epsp and a slow, prolonged noncholinergic excitation that is mimicked by bath-applied 5HT. On the other hand, most of the pyloric CPG neurons had no detectable rapid cholinergic response, but they still showed prolonged modulatory responses mimicked by serotonin. These responses included slow excitation, slow inhibition, enhancement of rhythmic bursting and plateau potential induction. One pyloric neuron responded with a nicotinic epsp but no modulatory response, and a few gastric mill neurons did not respond at all.

Figure 2 shows a typical response of the gastric mill motoneuron, DG (Katz and Harris-Warrick, 1989). GPR stimulation at low frequency evokes a rapid and probably monosynaptic epsp of about 1 mV amplitude (Fig.2A).

It shows a typical nicotinic pharmacological profile, being reversibly blocked by

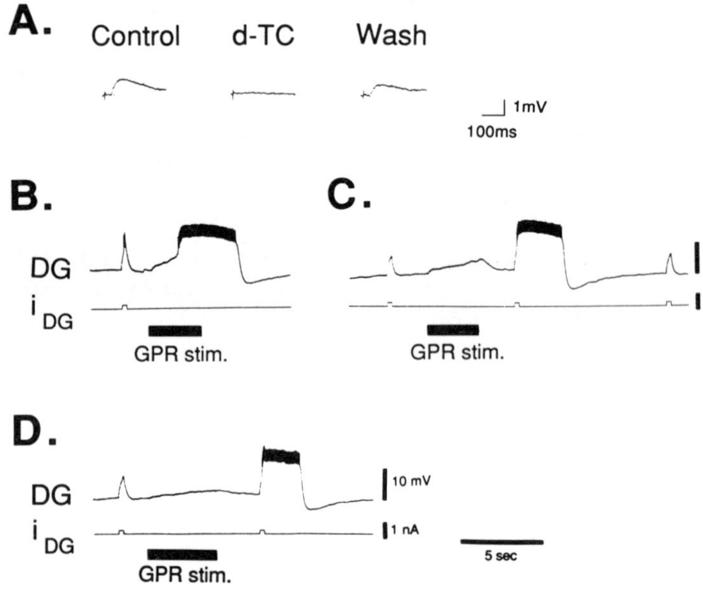

Fig. 2. Effects of GPR stimulation on the DG neuron. **A.** A GPR-evoked epsp is eliminated by 0.1 mM d-tubocurarine (d-TC). **B**. A 10 Hz GPR train produces epsps which summate to trigger a plateau potential. **C**. A 10 Hz GPR train does not elicit a plateau, but immediately afterwards a small current pulse (which was ineffective before GPR stimulation) elicits a plateau potential. **D**. 0.1 mM d-TC eliminates the GPR-evoked rapid epsps but does not block a slow depolarization and a plateau potential upon current injection.

d-tubocurarine (Fig.2A), decamethonium, hexamethonium and mecamylamine. In addition to this classical epsp, GPR stimulation modulates the intrinsic properties of the DG neuron. Trains of GPR impulses evoke epsps that summate to trigger a plateau potential lasting several seconds (Fig. 2B). Occasionally a GPR train does not evoke a plateau potential, but only the summating epsps superimposed on a low amplitude depolarization; in these cases, a short depolarizing pulse (which was ineffective before GPR stimulation) elicits a full plateau potential (Fig. 2C). If the nicotinic epsps are suppressed with d-tubocurarine, the GPR train induces only the small prolonged depolarization. However, the cell can still fire a plateau potential when excited by a short depolarizing current pulse which was below threshold before GPR stimulation (Fig.2D). Bath-applied serotonin (10 μM) induces a similar prolonged depolarization with tonic action potential activity. Thus the two GPR neurotransmitters play complementary roles to generate DG plateau potentials. Serotonin elicits the capability for plateau potential generation, provided that the cell is depolarized above a specific threshold. Acetylcholine evokes rapid epsps which summate to exceed this threshold.

The modulatory effect of GPR stimulation on the pyloric CPG neuron, PD, is shown in Fig. 3. This cell receives no detectable rapid epsp upon GPR stimulation (Katz and Harris-Warrick,1989,1990b). However, a GPR stimulus train can induce rhythmic oscillations in a quiescent PD neuron (Fig.3B). Bath-applied serotonin has the same effect. Due to technical difficulties, we could not determine whether this reflects a direct GPR effect on the PD neuron or on the tightly electrically coupled AB neuron. The electrically coupled PD/AB group are the most important cells for induction of rhythmic cycling in the pyloric pattern, and this initiation of PD/AB bursting underlies the activation of the pyloric rhythm after GPR stimulation (Fig. 3). The pyloric LP motoneuron is also highly excited by GPR stimulation (Fig. 3).

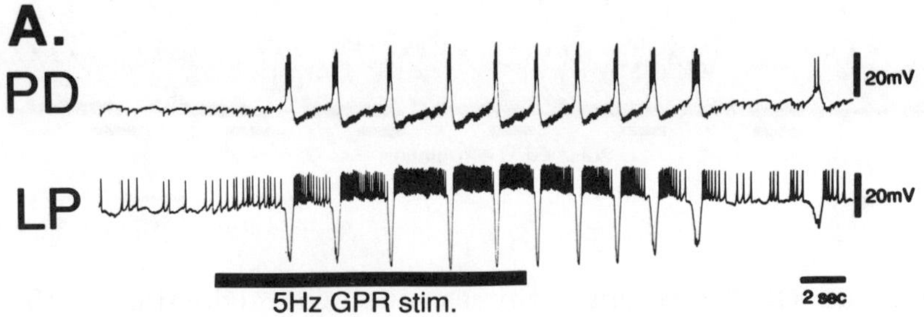

Fig. 3.
GPR stimulation activates the pyloric rhythm. The quiescent PD neuron begins to burst rhythmically and the LP neuron is highly excited except when inhibited by the PD/AB group.

Effect of GPR activity on the pyloric rhythm. When the pyloric rhythm was silent or cycling weakly and irregularly, a single GPR train activated a rhythmic pyloric motor pattern (Fig.3). This result led us to study the normal activity pattern of the GPR cells relative to the pyloric rhythm *in situ.* Observations of GPR activity in a semi-intact foregut preparation reveal that these proprioceptors do not respond to the movements of the faster pyloric rhythm, but they do fire in rhythmic bursts in phase with the slower gastric mill pattern. In addition, the GPR cells often display spontaneous rhythmic bursts with a frequency similar to that of the gastric mill rhythm. Even though the GPR cells do not fire rhythmically with the pyloric cycle, their activity can profoundly alter the ongoing pyloric pattern. We mimicked the normal firing pattern of the GPR cells in an *in vitro* preparation, with all other extrinsic inputs to the STG eliminated (Katz and Harris-Warrick, 1990b,c). Under these conditions, the GPR train caused the ongoing pyloric rhythm to pause, due to excitation of the LP neuron which inhibited the pacemaker AB and PD cells, and direct GPR inhibition of the PY neurons (Fig. 4). For a few cycles immediately following the end of each GPR train, there were several rapid changes in phasing and activity of pyloric neurons. With a series of GPR trains mimicking the gastric mill rhythm, a prolonged increase in cycle frequency and intensity was observed which could last for over a minute after cessation of GPR stimulation.

Thus, rhythmic activity in the sensory GPR cells, which are normally activated by gastric mill movements, can impart an envelope of modulation

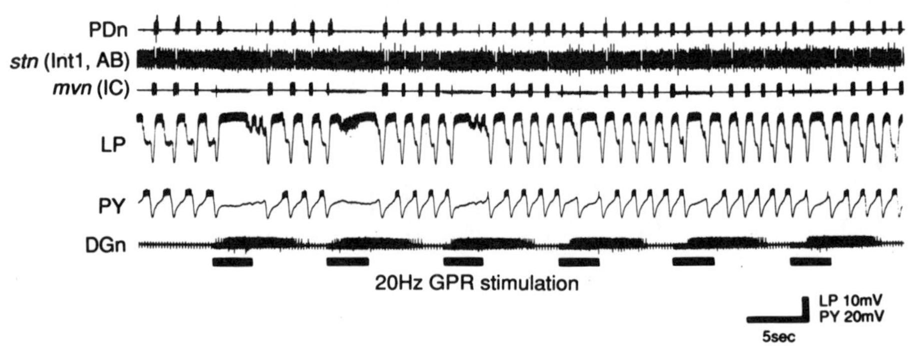

Fig. 4. Periodic GPR stimulation causes repetitive modulation of the pyloric rhythm. A single GPR cell is stimulated in its *in situ* firing pattern (3 sec. at 20 Hz every 10 sec.), causing a periodic excitation of LP and periodic inhibition of the other pyloric neurons, followed by enhanced cycle frequency and altered phase relations. The gastric mill neurons, DG and Int1, are also excited.

entrained to the gastric mill rhythm onto ongoing pyloric activity. This allows the gastric mill CPG to modify the pyloric pattern even though there are no strong functional synapses from the gastric mill neurons onto the pyloric neurons. This modulation is phase-independent because it does not need to occur at a certain phase of the pyloric cycle to be effective. The direct modulation of one CPG by another CPG through a peripheral feedback loop has not been previously described (Katz and Harris-Warrick, 1990c).

GPR-evoked prolonged modulatory excitation can also cause certain gastric mill motoneurons to fire in the pyloric motor pattern. When other extrinsic inputs to the STG are removed, the gastric mill CPG always stops cycling. After GPR stimulation, a number of gastric cells are excited for prolonged periods of time. Due to synaptic inputs from the pyloric circuit, these excited gastric cells begin to fire rhythmically in phase with the pyloric pattern. Thus, under certain conditions, neurons that are components of one CPG circuit can switch allegiance and fire in phase with a different CPG circuit. Similar switches in allegiance from one CPG to another have been observed after stimulation of another sensory input to the stomatogastric nervous system (Hooper and Moulins, 1987), and after bath application of the peptide Red Pigment Concentrating Hormone (Dickinson and Marder, 1989).

CONCLUSION

We began this study to understand the context for serotonergic modulation in the crab STG. We found that instead of descending from higher integrative neural centers, serotonergic input to the STG is provided by a set of peripheral sensory neurons that monitor muscle tension. The GPR neurons fire rhythmically in phase with the slower gastric mill motor pattern, but provide synaptic inputs to both the gastric mill and the faster pyloric CPGs. They use at least two different neurotransmitters, ACh and 5HT, enabling them to provide both rapid cycle-by-cycle corrective feedback to the gastric mill neurons, through release of ACh onto classical nicotinic receptors, and slow modulatory input to neurons in both CPGs. These modulatory effects change the state of the CPG circuits for prolonged times, and are probably mediated by serotonin, which mimics most of the effects.GPR-evoked neuromodulation can alter the overall organization of the motor patterns evoked by the two STG CPGs, affecting the frequency, intensity and relative phasing of muscle contractions. The modulatory sensory feedback loop can also affect interactions between the two CPGs in two important ways. First, it provides a communication bridge from the gastric mill to the pyloric motor pattern. Second, it can recruit neurons from the gastric mill into the pyloric rhythm under certain conditions.

our work shows that sensory neurons can have all the interesting and prolonged modulatory effects on motor circuits that have been ascribed to central modulatory neurons. Many sensory neurons in both invertebrates and vertebrates contain peptides or monoamines and synapse upon neurons related to motor function. This suggests that prolonged modulation of motor circuits by sensory afferents will be found in other systems as well as our own.

REFERENCES

Beltz, B.S., Eisen, J.S., Flamm, R., Harris-Warrick, R.M., Hooper, S. & Marder, E. (1984) Serotonergic innervation and modulation of the stomatogastric ganglion of three decapod crustaceans (*Homarus americanus, Cancer irroratus* and *Panulirus interruptus*). *J. Exp. Biol.* **109**: 35-54.

Delcomyn, F. (1980) Neural basis of rhythmic behavior in animals. *Science* **210**:492-498.

Dickinson, P.S. & Marder, E. (1989) Peptidergic modulation of a multioscillator system in the lobster. I. Activation of the cardiac sac motor pattern by the neuropeptides proctolin and red pigment-concentrating hormone. *J. Neurophysiol.* **61**: 833-844.

Harris-Warrick, R.M. (1988) Chemical modulation of central pattern generators. In *Neural Control of Rhythmic Movements in Vertebrates* (ed. A.H. Cohen, S. Rossignol & S. Grillner) pp. 285-331. New York: John Wiley and Sons.

Hooper, S.L. & Moulins, M. (1987) Sensory input or spontaneous central rhythmicity can "switch" a neuron from one neural network to another. *Soc. Neurosci. Abst.* **13**: 821.

Katz, P.S., Eigg, M.H. & Harris-Warrick, R.M. (1989) Serotonergic/ cholinergic muscle receptor cells in the crab stomatogastric nervous system: I. Identification and characterization of the gastro-pyloric receptor cells. *J. Neurophysiol.*, in press.

Katz, P.S. & Harris-Warrick, R.M. (1989) Serotonergic/ cholinergic muscle receptor cells in the crab stomatogastric nervous system: II. Rapid nicotinic and prolonged modulatory effects on neurons in the stomatogastric ganglion. *J. Neurophysiol.*, in press.

Katz, P.S. & Harris-Warrick, R.M. (1990a) A neuromodulatory role for proprioceptive input to motor pattern generators: I. Mechanosensory afferents evoke both rapid synaptic and prolonged modulatory effects in gastric mill neurons of the stomatogastric ganglion. Submitted to *J. Neurosci.*

Katz, P.S. & Harris-Warrick, R.M. (1990b) A neuromodulatory role for proprioceptive input to motor pattern generators: II. Modulation of the rhythmically active pyloric CPG by sensory afferents. Submitted to *J. Neurosci.*

Katz, P.S. & Harris-Warrick, R.M. (1990c) A neuromodulatory role for proprioceptive input to motor pattern generators: III. Peripheral feedback coordinates two central pattern generator circuits. Submitted to *J. Neurosci.*

Kravitz, E.A., Glusman, S., Livingstone, M. & Harris-Warrick R.M. (1981) Serotonin and octopamine in the lobster nervous system: mechanisms of action at neuromuscular junctions and preliminary behavioral studies. In *Serotonin Neurotransmission and Behavior* (ed. B.L. Jacobs & A. Gelperin) pp. 188-210. MIT Press, Cambridge.

Kupfermann, I. & Weiss K.R. (1981) The role of serotonin in arousal of feeding behavior in *Aplysia*. In *Serotonin Neurotransmission and Behavior* (ed. B.L. Jacobs & A. Gelperin) pp. 255-287. MIT Press, Cambridge.

Pearson, K.G. (1987) Central pattern generation: a concept under scrutiny. In *Advances in Physiological Research* (ed. H. McLennan, J.R. Ledsome, C.H.S. McIntosh & D.R. Jones) pp. 167-185. New York: Plenum Press.

Frontiers in Crustacean Neurobiology
Advances in Life Sciences

A CONFEDERATION OF NEURAL CIRCUITS: CONTROL OF SWIMMERET MOVEMENTS BY A MODULAR SYSTEM OF PATTERN GENERATORS

Brian Mulloney, Larisa D. Acevedo, Abdesslam Chrachri, Wendy M. Hall and Carolyn M. Sherff

Department of Zoology, and Neurobiology Graduate Group, University of California, Davis CA 95616 USA

SUMMARY

The motor pattern produced by swimmeret motor neurons in isolated ventral nerve cords of the crayfish, *Pacifastacus leniusculus*, is described quantitatively. The evidence is reviewed that each swimmeret has its own motor center, which produces the alternating power-stroke and return-stroke activity needed for rhythmic movements. The anatomy of the power-stroke and return-stroke pools of swimmeret motor neurons is described in terms of the architectonics of segmental ganglia. The responses of individual ganglia to command neurons and to their putative transmitters are reviewed. The ability of individual hemiganglionic centers to oscillate independently is described. Properties of the circuit of interneurons that coordinates these motor centers are discussed in terms of the integrated performance of the swimmeret system.

INTRODUCTION

Since an intact crayfish uses its swimmerets in a coordinated manner, and since rhythmic beating of the swimmerets almost always begins with bursts of impulses in power-stroke (PS) motor axons in the fifth segment (Ikeda & Wiersma, 1964; Heitler, 1985), we might expect that there would be one controlling center in the CNS that would regulate expression of the swimmeret motor pattern. This is not the case. The great early investigators of the neural basis of crayfish behavior suggested that each swimmeret had its own motor center (Hughes & Wiersma, 1960; Ikeda & Wiersma, 1964; Wiersma & Ikeda, 1964), and this suggestion was used by the next generation to design and interpret experiments on control of swimmeret movements (Davis, 1969; Stein, 1971). Results of our more recent experiments, using techniques not available to our predecessors, are assembled here to examine this suggestion critically. We have marshaled structural, physiological and pharmacological evidence to support our working model of the crayfish swimmeret system as a set of ten equivalent neural modules, one modular pattern-generating circuit for each of ten swimmerets. Individual modules are anatomically restricted to half a segmental ganglion. In segments that bear swimmerets, each ganglion has a pair of modules, and activities of these modules are coordinated by a concatenated network of interneurons.

METHODS

The anatomical procedures have been described (Leise et al., 1986, 1987; Mulloney & Hall, in press). Physiological procedures (Paul & Mulloney, 1985a; Paul & Mulloney, 1985b; Paul & Mulloney, 1986; Mulloney et al., 1987) and analytical procedures (Mulloney & Hall, 1987) have also been described . The legend for each figure summarizes the methods used to generate it.

RESULTS AND DISCUSSION

The motor pattern produced by isolated ventral nerve cords. When the chain of six abdominal ganglia is removed from the abdomen and placed in a saline-filled dish, the swimmeret motor neurons often fire long, rhythmic trains of bursts of impulses. The temporal properties of these trains are like those recorded from intact animals when they beat their swimmerets (Hughes & Wiersma, 1960; Ikeda & Wiersma, 1964; Wiersma & Ikeda, 1964; Mulloney et al., 1987). The pattern recorded from each nerve that innervates a swimmeret, segmental nerve N1, consists of alternating bursts of impulses in power-stroke (PS) and return-stroke (RS) axons (Fig. 1A). The periods, durations and phases of this activity are within the range observed when intact crayfish beat their swimmerets (Table 1).

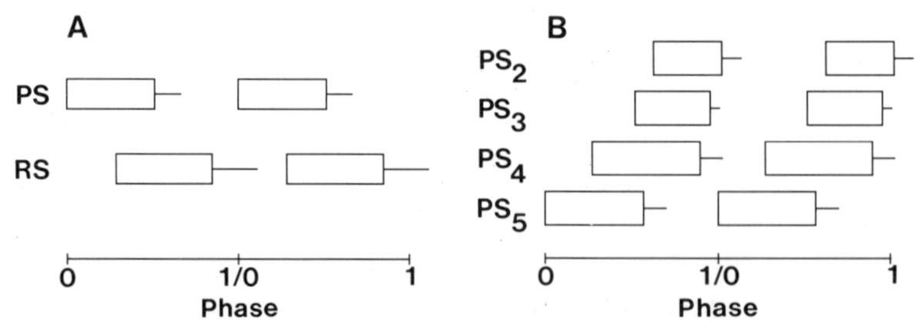

Fig. 1. Durations and phases of bursts of impulses recorded from swimmeret motor axons in isolated abdominal cords during spontaneous episodes of swimmeret motor pattern generation. A. Two cycles of the pattern in each N1. B. Two cycles of the pattern in PS axons from abdominal ganglia 2, 3 , 4 and 5. Each bar represents the mean duration ± S.D. Each bar begins at the mean phase, in A relative to PS, in B relative to PS_5. Each cycle was normalized to the mean period (Mulloney & Hall, 1987).

Bursts of PS impulses in contralateral N1s of the same ganglion occur simultaneously in these isolated nerve cords, as they normally do when an intact animal beats its swimmerets.

Bursts of impulses in motor neurons from different ganglia have an almost constant phase-relation (Fig. 1B). Posterior ganglia lead their more anterior neighbors. The mean values of period, duration and phase for each ganglion in these isolated cords fall within the ranges observed in behaviors that involve swimmeret beating, and show less variability than does beating during these behaviors (Table 1).

Table 1. Temporal Characteristics of Bursts of Impulses in Swimmeret Motor Patterns Generated by Isolated Ventral Nerve Cords of *Pacifastacus leniusculus*.

To one swimmeret, e.g. on abdominal segment 4:

Burst Source	Period (msec)	Duration (msec)	Phase	N
PS_4	666 ± 137	343 ± 99	0.278 ± 0.019	5
RS_4	667 ± 139	375 ± 176	0.563 ± 0.027	5

To swimmerets on each segment:

Burst Source	Period (msec)	Duration (msec)	Phase	N
PS_2	635 ± 76	251 ± 71	0.629 ± 0.099	6
PS_3	635 ± 89	277 ± 34	0.520 ± 0.125	6
PS_4	625 ± 85	396 ± 81	0.273 ± 0.142	6
PS_5	643 ± 88	360 ± 83	0 .0	6

Data are expressed as Mean ± S.D.
Phase is calculated relative to PS bursts in segment 5.

The motor innervation of pairs of swimmerets. The innervation of swimmerets is duplicated in each half of each segment. Each swimmeret is innervated through one N1. Each N1 branches initially into anterior and posterior branches that contain, respectively, axons of RS and PS motor neurons. All the motor neurons innervating each swimmeret have cell bodies located in the same ganglion. Within each ganglion, the cell bodies of motor neurons with axons in the same N1 form clusters near that N1's root (Fig. 2A). Clusters on the left and right sides of the ganglion do not overlap; only one RS motor neuron has a cell body contralateral to the swimmeret it innervates (Fig. 2B). We estimate 33 RS motor neurons and 36 PS motor neurons innervate each swimmeret, from maxima of cell-body counts in Co^{++} backfilled ganglia, after subtracting the two axons of nonspiking stretch receptors (Heitler, 1982) and the segmental giant neuron (Kramer et al., 1981). Three RS motor neurons and two PS motor neurons are GABAergic, and so are probably the peripheral inhibitors of the swimmeret musculature (Mulloney & Hall, in press). This ipsilateral clustering of PS and RS cell bodies is consistent with the idea that each ganglion has two separate circuits, or modules, that control the pair of swimmerets in that segment.

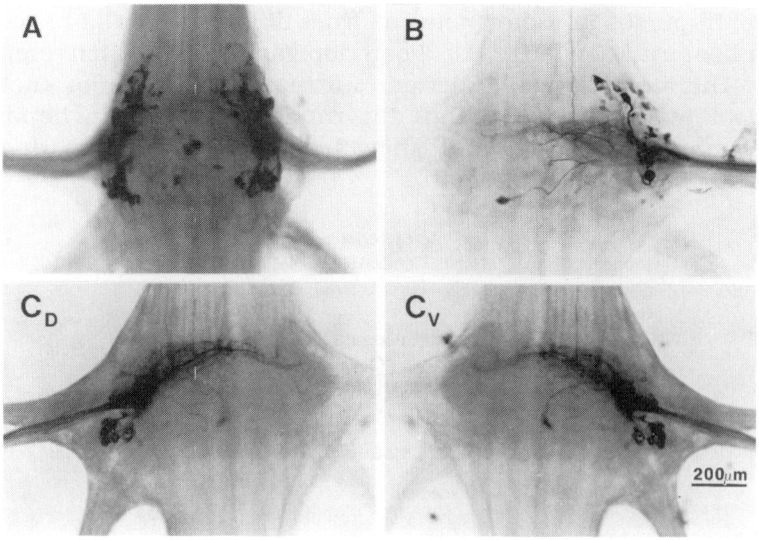

Fig. 2. Wholemounts of abdominal ganglia (A4) with swimmeret motor neurons that had been backfilled with Co^{++} and later intensified with silver (Leise et al., 1987). Anterior is at the top, and A, B, and C_V are ventral, frontal views. A. A fill of both N1s, showing the full bilateral complement of motor neurons. B. A fill of the anterior branch of the left N1, showing one left swimmeret's RS motor neurons. C_V. A fill of the posterior branch of the left N1, showing one left swimmeret's PS motor neurons. C_D. Dorsal view of the same ganglion, focused on the processes that project to the opposite lateral neuropil.

These motor neurons have major branches in the lateral neuropil (Skinner, 1985a), above the base of the N1 out which their axons project (Fig. 2). However, many motor neurons also have branches that project across the midline, in Dorsal Commissures (Skinner, 1985b), to the opposite lateral neuropil (Fig. 1C_D), so left and right swimmerets might be controlled by a single circuit with bilateral components.

Local interneurons in the swimmeret system. A small number of distinctive local interneurons occurs in each swimmeret-bearing ganglion. Unilateral local interneurons, with branches largely restricted to the lateral neuropil, are components of each pattern-generating circuit (Paul & Mulloney, 1985b; Paul & Mulloney, 1985a). At least one type of neuron in this category occurs as an identifiable bilateral pair in each segment (Paul & Mulloney, 1985a). These neurons have strong effects on the activity of the motor neurons ipsilateral to them, and weaker effects on the contralateral pools of motor neurons.

Bilateral local interneurons also occur, but their influence on the activities of the two modules in their ganglion is characteristically weaker than that of the unilateral interneurons. We have argued elsewhere that these bilateral interneurons be considered not as components of the pattern-generating circuits in each ganglion, but rather as coordinating interneurons that synchronize the phases of two hemisegmental pattern-generating circuits (Paul & Mulloney, 1985b). The structures of the unilateral locals and the differences in the physiology of the unilateral and bilateral local interneurons suggests to us that separate modules exist on opposite sides of each ganglion.

Modules in each ganglion respond directly to command interneurons and to their putative transmitters. Both excitatory and inhibitory command interneurons that affect the swimmerets occur in these animals (Hughes & Wiersma, 1960; Wiersma & Ikeda, 1964). Although intact crayfish normally begin to beat their swimmerets with a power-stroke movement in abdominal segment five, and command-driven motor patterns in isolated cords begin with a PS-burst in the fifth abdominal ganglion, the system still responds to stimulation of command axons if the connectives are severed between the fourth and fifth ganglia or between the third and fourth ganglia, and the ganglia anterior to the cut still respond to stimulation of command interneurons (Wiersma & Ikeda, 1964). The period and phase relations of the resulting motor patterns are similar to those produced by intact nerve cords (Wiersma & Ikeda, 1964). This observation was the basis for the original suggestion that each swimmeret had its own motor center.

Bath application of proctolin, a pentapeptide that occurs as a transmitter in the CNS of crustaceans, mimics stimulation of excitatory command interneurons in isolated ventral nerve cords, and motor patterns produced under the influence of proctolin have periods and phases within the normal range of spontaneous and command-driven patterns(Mulloney et al., 1987). We used proctolin solutions to activate swimmeret motor activity in otherwise silent isolated ventral nerve cords.

When proctolin is applied to single, isolated ganglia, they sometimes will produced bilaterally coordinated alternating bursts of PS and RS impulses, although the stability of the output from these single ganglia is not as great as that from longer chains of ganglia (Paul & Mulloney, 1986). Conversely, if proctolin is applied to individual ganglia in an intact, isolated ventral cord that is not actively producing a swimmeret motor pattern (Fig. 3), the entire cord is induced to produce a coordinated swimmeret motor pattern (Acevedo & Mulloney, in manuscript). In the first episode (left), proctolin was applied to all four ganglia, and the preparation produced a vigorous, coordinated motor pattern in every ganglion. After proctolin was washed out from each well, the preparation returned to its original silent state (not shown). The same proctolin solution was then applied to each ganglion in turn (+P). In each of these four individual bath applications, the ganglion exposed to proctolin responded with a vigorous swimmeret motor pattern. The others were also activated in the normal metachronous pattern (Fig. 1B). In the absence of proctolin or of command stimulation, this preparation did not produce swimmeret motor patterns, and when the proctolin solution was washed out between each episode, the swimmeret activity stopped (not shown). These observations suggest that the swimmeret modules in each ganglion have receptors for proctolin, and can respond to command activation.

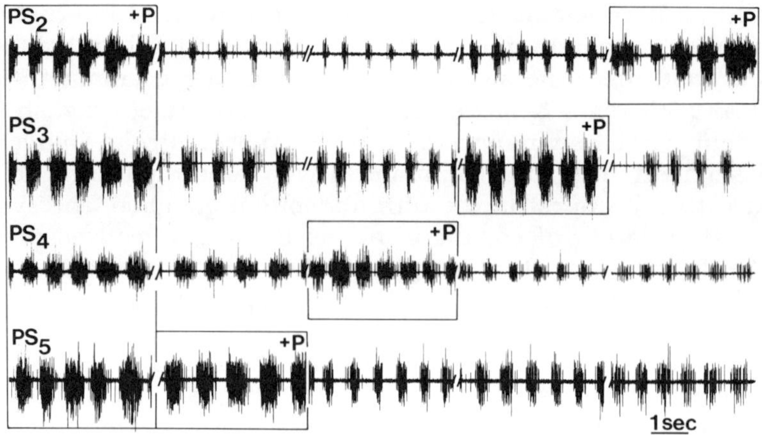

Fig. 3. PS activity recorded simultaneously from abdominal ganglia 2,3,4 and 5 during five separate episodes of swimmeret activity induced by bath application of 5 μM proctolin to an isolated abdominal cord (left panel), and then to each of its ganglia individually. The boxes surrounding different traces show which ganglion was bathed with proctolin solution (+P) during each episode. Each ganglion was isolated by Vaseline wells, but the connectives between ganglia were intact (Acevedo & Mulloney, in manuscript).

Blocking impulses exposes independent oscillation of individual modules. Swimming lobsters and crayfish normally beat swimmerets in the same segment in phase, but when they roll about their long axis, they right themselves in part by an asymmetric, out-of-phase beating of their swimmerets (Davis, 1968; Takahata & Hisada, 1982). Experimental perturbation of swimmeret interneurons can also produce phase differences between activity on opposite sides of a ganglion (Paul & Mulloney, 1985b). Both of these observations suggest that normally phase-locked pairs of modules could be uncoupled, and might not need contralateral input to generate the basic pattern that drives each swimmeret (Fig. 1A). To test whether the pattern-generating circuits on opposite sides of each ganglion could actually operate independently, we recorded from swimmeret motor neurons with microelectrodes, activated the swimmeret system with proctolin and then blocked impulse-conduction with tetrodotoxin (TTX). Under normal conditions, the membrane potentials of these two motor neurons, and all other PS neurons in the same ganglion, oscillate in phase. Of course, TTX stopped all impulse activity in the peripheral nerves and in the interganglionic connectives. In the absence of proctolin, TTX also halted all oscillations of the membrane potentials of the recorded neurons. However, in the presence of proctolin, oscillations continued in some neurons (Fig. 4). If the recorded neurons were in different ganglia, or on opposite sides of one ganglion, their persistent oscillations had different periods and no constant phase (Fig. 4B). If they were on the same side of one ganglion, their persistent oscillation had the same phase as they had demonstrated before TTX was applied (Chrachri et al. in manuscript). We interpret these results to mean that the pattern-generating circuits on opposite sides of one ganglion could operate without impulse conduction between the two circuits, and that under these conditions, they had somewhat different inherent periods.

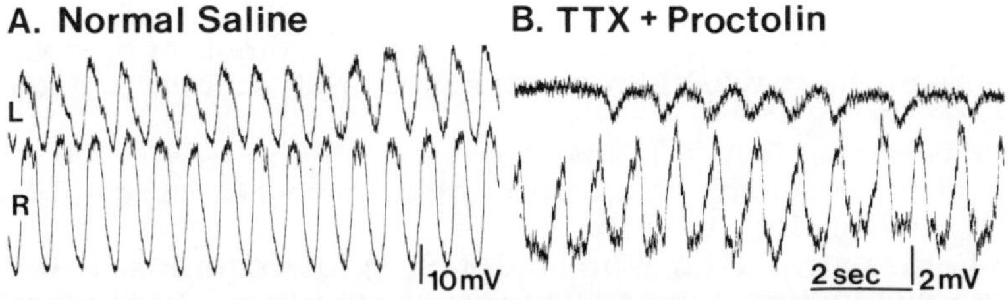

Fig. 4. Simultaneous intracellular recordings from PS motor neurons in the left and right modules of A4. A. Synchronous oscillations of PS motor neurons on opposite sides (L: left; R: right) of the ganglion, recorded in normal saline. B. Independent oscillations of PS motor neurons on opposite sides of the ganglion recorded 45 min after bath application of 5 x 10^{-7} M TTX + 10^{-6}M proctolin. Note the different amplitudes and periods of oscillations in these two recordings.

Conclusions. Although the swimmeret system works in a coordinated way, the evidence is consistent with the model that each ganglion in a swimmeret-bearing segment has a bilateral pair of pattern-generating circuits -- one neural module for each swimmeret. Each module has a similar number of motor neurons and unilateral local interneurons, and produces alternating bursts of PS and RS impulses with similar periods. Except in the most anterior segments, which show sex-specific modification of swimmerets, it is appropriate to view these modules as equivalent, and their coordinated activity as the product of a network of bilateral local interneurons and intersegmental interneurons that impose on these modules the synchronizing information needed to generate their characteristic metachronous rhythm.

If the modules are equivalent, why then does PS5 activity usually start each bout of swimmeret beating? We think that the network of intersegmental synaptic connections is inherently polarized, that swimmeret activity in every ganglion actually begins with excitation of interneurons whose axons project posteriorly, and that the convergent excitation by these descending axons brings the swimmeret modules in A5 to threshold first. The experimental test of this hypothesis should clarify our understanding of this elegant nervous system.

References

Davis, W.J. (1968) Lobster righting responses and their neural control. Proc. Roy. Soc. Lond. B. 70: 435-456.

Davis, W.J. (1969) Neural control of swimmeret beating in the lobster. J. Exp. Zool. 50: 99-117.

Heitler, W.J. (1982) Non-spiking stretch receptors in the crayfish swimmeret system. J. Exp. Biol. 96: 355-366.

Heitler, W.J. (1985) Motor programme switching in the crayfish swimmeret system. J. Exp. Biol. 114: 521-549.

Hughes, G.M. & Wiersma, C.A.G. (1960) The co-ordination of swimmeret movements in the crayfish, Procambarus clarkii. J. Exp. Biol. 37: 657-670.

Ikeda, K. & Wiersma, C.A.G. (1964) Autogenic rhythmicity in the abdominal ganglion of the crayfish: Th e control of swimmeret movements. Comp. Biochem. Physiol. 12: 107-115.

Kramer, A.P., Krasne, F.B. & Wine, J.J. (1981) Interneurons between giant axons and motoneurons in crayfish escape circuity. J. Neurophysiol. 45: 550-573.

Leise, E.M., Hall, W.M. & Mulloney, B. (1986) Functional Organization of Crayfish Abdominal Ganglia: I. The Flexor Systems. J. Comp. Neurol. 266: 495-518.

Leise, E.M., Hall, W.M. & Mulloney, B. (1987) Functional Organization of Crayfish Abdominal Ganglia: II. Sensory Afferents and Extensor Motor Neurons. J. Comp. Neurol. 266: 495-518.

Mulloney, B. & Hall, W.M. (1987) The PD Programs: a Method for the Quantitative Description of Motor Patterns. J. Neurosci. Meth. 19: 47-59.

Mulloney, B., Acevedo, L.D. & Bradbury, A.G. (1987) Modulation of the Crayfish Swimmeret Rhythm by Octopamine and the Neuropeptide Proctolin. J. Neurophysiol. 58: 584-597.

Mulloney, B. & Hall, W.M. (in press) GABAergic neurons in the crayfish nervous system: An immunocytochemical census of the segmental ganglia and stomatogastric system. J. Comp. Neurol.

Paul, D.H. & Mulloney, B. (1985a) Nonspiking Local Interneuron in the Motor Pattern Generator for the Crayfish Swimmeret System. J. Neurophysiol. 54: 28-39.

Paul, D.H. & Mulloney, B. (1985b) Local interneurons in the swimmeret system of the crayfish. J. Comp. Physiol. 156: 489-502.

Paul, D.H. & Mulloney, B. (1986) Intersegmental Coordination of Swimmeret Rhythms in Isolated Nerve Cords of Crayfish. J. Comp. Physiol. 158: 215-224.

Skinner, K. (1985a) The Structure of the Fourth Abdominal Ganglion of the Crayfish, Procambarus clarkii II. Synaptic Neuropils. J. Comp. Neurol. 234: 182-191.

Skinner, K. (1985b) The Structure of the Fourth Abdominal Ganglion of the Crayfish, Procambarus clarkii I. Tracts in the Ganglionic Core. J. Comp. Neurol. 234: 168-181.

Stein, P.S.G. (1971) Intersegmental coordination of swimmeret motor neuron activity in crayfish. J. Neurophysiol. 34: 310-318.

Takahata, M. & Hisada, M. (1982) Statocyst interneurons in the crayfish, Procambarus clarkii. I Identification and response characteristics. J. Comp. Physiol. 149: 287-300.

Wiersma, C.A.G. & Ikeda, K. (1964) Interneurons commanding swimmeret movements in the crayfish, Procambarus clarkii. Comp. Biochem. Physiol. 12: 509-525.

Frontiers in Crustacean Neurobiology
Advances in Life Sciences

LOBSTER STOMATOGASTRIC GABA SYSTEM

Isabelle Cournil, Pierre Meyrand and Maurice Moulins

Laboratoire de Neurobiologie et Physiologie Comparées,
Université de Bordeaux I et CNRS, Place Peyneau, 33120 Arcachon, France.

SUMMARY

GABA immunodetection on paraffin serial sections coupled with (1) Lucifer yellow intracellular staining to obtain double labelling (2) nickel chloride axonal backfilling to suppress GABA immunoreactivity and (3) electrophysiological techniques, has allowed identification of all 8 GABAergic neurones that project to the lobster stomatogastric ganglion (STG). It will now be possible to examine whether these neurones containing the same neurotransmitter, constitute a functionally discrete input system.

INTRODUCTION

Immunohistochemical studies have demonstrated that the lobster stomatogastric ganglion (STG) receives via the stomatogastric nerve (stn), a large number of extrinsic inputs containing a wide variety of neurotransmitters. Moreover, bath application experiments on in vitro preparations have shown that several of these transmitters are able to evoke different motor patterns from the STG pyloric and gastric networks (Marder, 1987). Until now, however, only a few of these extrinsic input neurones have been identified electrophysiologically (Nagy et Moulins, 1987), and this considerably limits the possibility to determine the physiological context in which they influence on their target networks. In this work we use the combination of immunohistochemical analysis, retrograde tracing, and electrophysiological methods to identify all neurones projecting to the STG that use the same transmitter, GABA.

RESULTS

GABA immunodetection in the stomatogastric nervous system of lobsters. It was shown previously that GABA immunoreactive terminals are present in the STG neuropile and that bath applied GABA has considerable effects on the activity of the pyloric network in the STG (Cazalets et al., 1987). Using specific GABA antibody (Seguela et al., 1984) treatment of paraffin serial sections, it has been possible to confirm that the STG neuropiles of both *Homarus gammarus* and *Jasus lalandii* contain numerous immunoreactive terminals (Fig. 1A), and that 10 immunoreactive axons are present in the single input nerve (stn) to the STG (Fig. 1B). Since the STG itself does not contain any GABA-reactive cell body, the labelled terminals arise uniquely from these 10 fibres in the stn that connects the STG to the more rostral oesophageal (OG) and commissural (COG) ganglia (see Fig. 5). With serial sections it has been possible to show that the OG contains 4 GABA immunoreactive cell bodies (Fig. 1C and D) while each COG contains more than 40 immunoreactive cell bodies. Moreover the bilateral superior (son) and inferior (ion) oesophageal nerves which connect the OG to the COGs, contain 5 and 4 labelled axons, respectively (see Fig. 5).

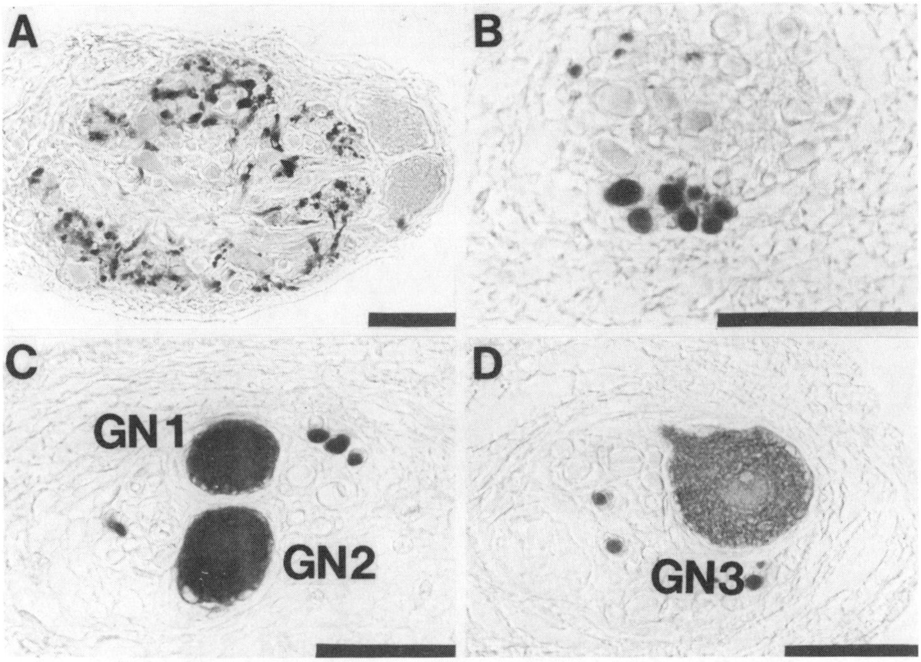

Fig. 1. GABA immunodetection in the stomatogastric system. A: GABA immunoreactivity in the neuropile of the STG; B: Cross section of the stn showing 10 immunoreactive fibres which can be followed along the length of the nerves. C: 2 GABA immunoreactive cell body in the OG, and named GN1 and GN2; D: GN3 is one of 2 bipolar GABA immunoreactive cell bodies also found in OG (see Fig. 5). Calibration bar: 50 μm.

Identification of the GABA immunoreactive projections to STG. Retrograde axonal migration in combination with GABA labelling has demonstrated that the 10 stn axons projecting to the STG belong to the 4 OG labelled neurones (GN1-GN4) and to 2 of the 40 labelled neurones (GN5 and GN6) in each COG. These results are summarized in Figure 5 and to illustrate the method in this short paper, the complete identification of GN1 and GN2 as GABAergic input neurones to the STG is presented here.

Lucifer yellow migration and GABA immunodetection. Lucifer yellow migration from the cut end of the stn toward the rostral ganglia (after section of the son's) stains 3 cell bodies in the OG (which can be observed in whole mount preparations; Fig. 2A). After fixation and embedding, serial sections were made and used alternately to detect either Lucifer yellow fluorescence or GABA immunoreactivity. Only 2 of the 3 fluorescent OG cell bodies exhibit GABA immunoreaction, as evident in the successive sections of Fig. 2B and C. These 2 GABAergic neurones projecting to the stn from the OG are referred to as GN1 and GN2.

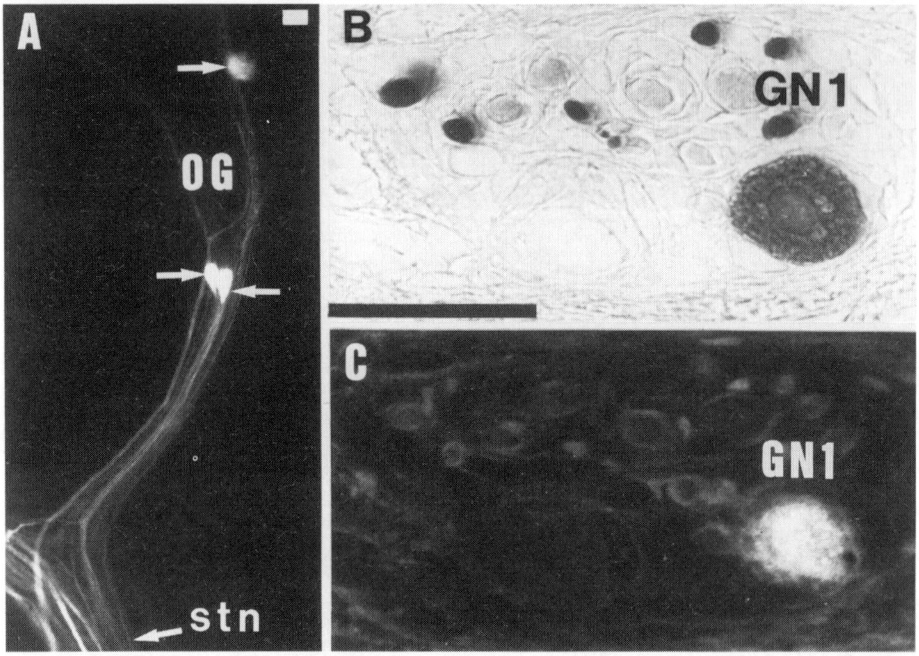

Fig. 2. Lucifer yellow backfill and immunodetection. A: Low magnification whole mount of OG following Lucifer yellow backfill of the stn; 3 cell bodies were fluorescent ( ). Subsequent serial sectionning and GABA immunostaining reveled 2 cell bodies with both GABA immunoreaction and fluorescence as illustrated respectively in B and C for GN1. Calibration bar: 50 μm.

Nickel chloride migration and GABA immunodetection. We have found recently that the presence of nickel chloride in GABAergic neurones completely inhibits subsequent GABA immunodetection procedures. On this basis, and to bypass the limitations of double labelling procedures, nickel chloride axonal migrations were carried out from the cut end of the stn and the preparations where then processed for GABA immunodetection. With such backfills, the GN1 and GN2 cell bodies are no longer GABA reactive, a result which confirms that their axons project into the stn. Moreover, of the 8 fibres traversing the OG and which are reactive in control conditions (Fig. 3B), only 2 (X) remain labelled after nickel chloride migration in the stn (Fig. 3A). Two of the 6 missing fibres belong to GN1 and GN2 while the 4 others are axonal projections of GN5 and GN6 (see Fig. 5) Furthermore, after nickel chloride migration from the cut end of the son's toward the OG, the cell bodies of GN1 and GN2 are also unreactive to GABA antibody indicating that these neurones also send an axonal branch into each son (see Fig. 5).

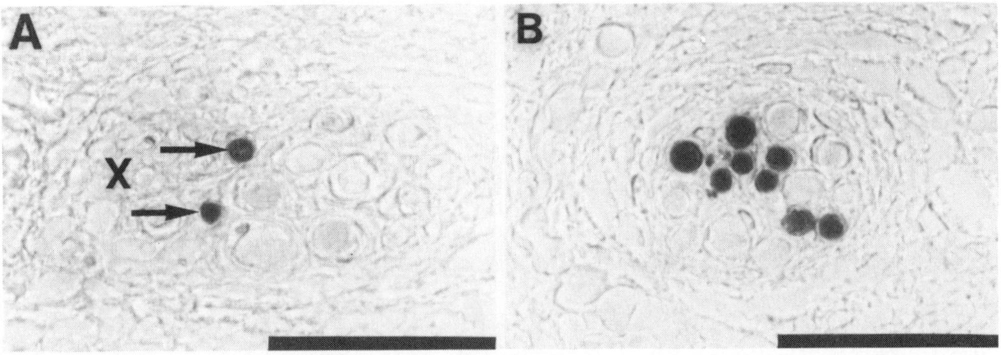

Fig. 3. Nickel chloride backfill and immunodetection. A: After nickel chloride backfill from the stn and GABA immunodetection, only 2 fibres (X) were labelled in the OG; B: in control conditions (without nickel chloride backfill), 8 large fibres are GABA immunoreactive in the OG (see Fig. 5). Calibration bar: 50 µm.

Electrophysiological identification of GABA neurones projecting to STG. The following criteria identify and characterize GN1 and GN2 in microelectrode recordings from the cell bodies of OG neurones. First, consistent with its axonal geometry described above (see Fig. 4A), each action potential recorded in the soma of GN1 or 2 is time-locked to an extracellularly recorded action potential in the stn and both son's (Fig 4B). Secondly, and as again suggested by the presence of their axons in the stn, GN1 and 2 have postsynaptic effects in the STG. Figure 4C shows that firing of GN1 by intrasomatic current injection produces a modification in the ongoing activity of neurones in the pyloric (PD) and gastric (LPG) networks. Moreover, spikes in GN give rise to discrete, constant latency EPSP's in STG neurones (Fig. 4D1). Thirdly pharmacological tests suggests the GABAergic nature of the penetrated GN neurone. Picrotoxin (PTX) is known to block the action of the GABA in many preparations (Takeuchi, 1976 ; Cazalets et al., 1987) and Fig. 4D show that the probable monosynaptic EPSP in LPG (Fig. 4D1) disappears completely (Fig. 4D2), though reversibly, after bath application of 2.10-4M PTX.

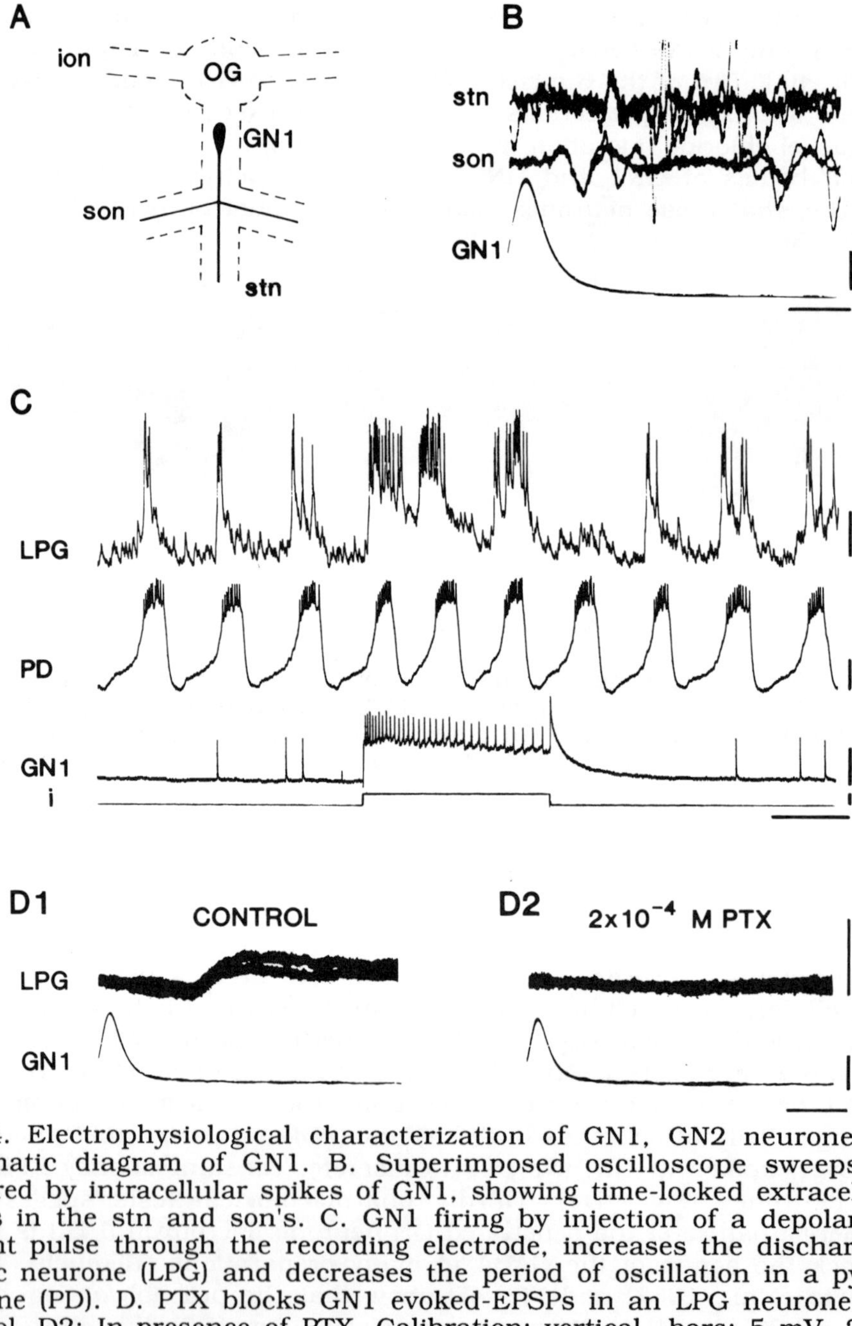

Fig. 4. Electrophysiological characterization of GN1, GN2 neurones. A. Schematic diagram of GN1. B. Superimposed oscilloscope sweeps (3), triggered by intracellular spikes of GN1, showing time-locked extracellular spikes in the stn and son's. C. GN1 firing by injection of a depolarizing current pulse through the recording electrode, increases the discharge of gastric neurone (LPG) and decreases the period of oscillation in a pyloric neurone (PD). D. PTX blocks GN1 evoked-EPSPs in an LPG neurone. D1: Control. D2: In presence of PTX. Calibration: vertical bars: 5 mV, 2 nA; horizontal bars: 10 ms B and D, 2 sec C.

Fourthly at the end of an experiment the neurone was injected with Lucifer yellow and the preparation treated for GABA immunoreactivity of the Lucifer stained cell. This procedure has been successfully applied to GN3-GN4 and GN5-GN6.

CONCLUSION

This work shows that the combined application of different experimental techniques to a model crustacean preparation has allowed complete identification of all GABAergic neurones projecting to a central ganglion. Since the target neurones in this ganglion (STG) are components of well defined rhythm generating networks, it will now be possible to examine the influence of GABAergic inputs both individually and in combination. In the latter context, moreover, it will be possible to determine whether these inputs constitute a physiologically significant system, i.e. can an ensemble of chemically related of neurones behave as a functional unit.

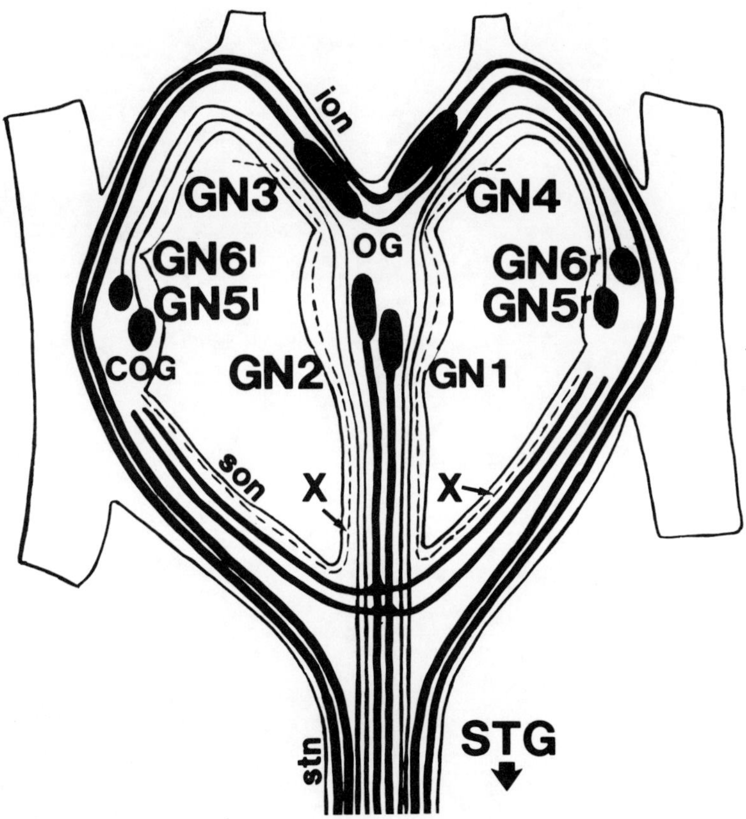

Fig. 5. Diagrammatic representation of all GABA immunoreactive neurones projecting to the STG.

REFERENCES

Cazalets, J.R., Cournil, I., Geffard, M. & Moulins, M. (1987). Suppression of oscillatory activity in Crustacean pyloric neurons: Implication of GABAergic inputs. J. Neurosci. **7:** 2884-2893.

Marder, E. (1987) Neurotransmitters and neuromodulators in the Crustacean stomatogastric system. A.I. Selverston and M. Moulins Eds. 263-300. Springer Verlag Heidelberg.

Nagy, F. & Moulins, M. (1987) Extrinsic inputs. In : The Crustacean Stomatogastric System. A Model for the Study of Central Nervous Systems (eds. A.I. Selverston & M. Moulins), pp. 205-262, Heidelberg : Springer Verlag.

Seguela, P., Geffard, M., Buijes, R.M. & Le Moal, M. (1984) Antibodies against g-aminobutyric acid: specificity studies and immunocytochemical results. Proc. Natl. Acad. Sci. USA **81:** 3888-3892.

Takeuchi, A. (1976) Studies of inhibitory effects of GABA in invertebrate nervous system. In GABA in Nervous System Function, E. Roberts, T.N., and B. Towers, eds, pp.225-267, Raven, New York.

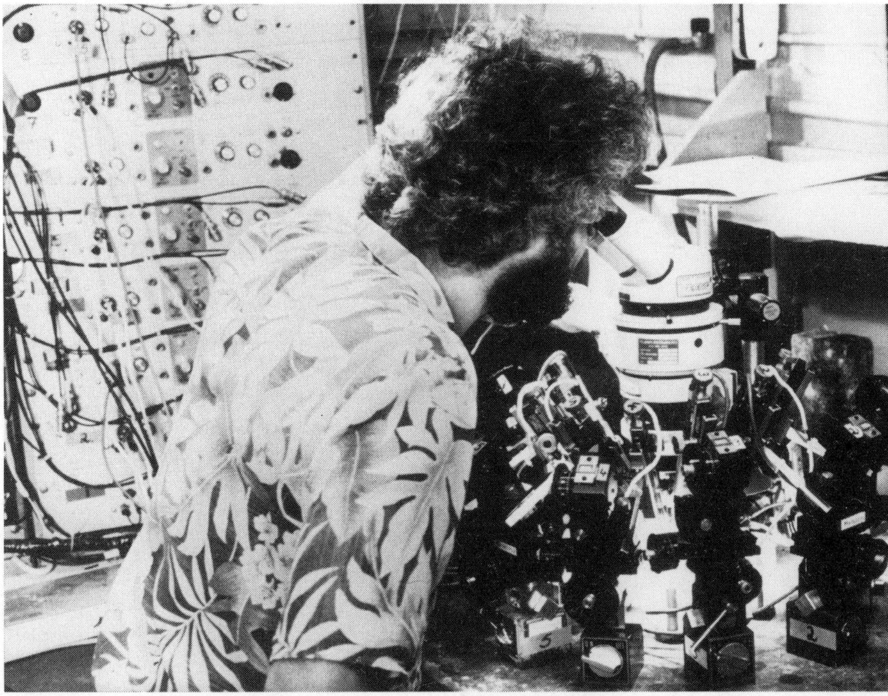

The Selverston lab in 1985, George Heinzel recording from 8 Neurons of the Stomatogastric System

Frontiers in Crustacean Neurobiology
Advances in Life Sciences

THE COOPERATION OF SEVERAL OSCILLATORS IN THE STOMATOGASTRIC SYSTEM OF THE CRAB *CANCER PAGURUS*

Hans-Georg Heinzel

Institute of Zoology, University Cologne, Weyertal 119, 5000 Köln 41, Federal Republic of Germany

SUMMARY

The pentapeptide proctolin can, first, strengthen an ongoing rhythm of the pyloric filter apparatus in intact crabs and, secondly, start rhythmic activity of the cardiac sac and the gastric mill. The pyloric rhythm then shows changes which are phase-locked to the slower cardiac sac and gastric rhythms. The cooperation of the three underlying central pattern generators (CPGs) can be interpreted as an opening of the cardio-pyloric valve of the pyloric apparatus which is coordinated with the movements of the three teeth of the gastric mill and the contractions of the cardiac sac, both pushing food into the filter system.

Stimulation of the anterior gastric stretch receptor can strengthen the gastric rhythm. Cobalt stainings have revealed that this receptor has its endings in the stomach wall near the insertion of a gastric muscle. Interestingly, these endings can generate autonomous burst activity which in turn is modulated by gastric activity.

INTRODUCTION

Endoscopic studies of gastric mill movements in the lobster (Heinzel, 1988a,b) have bridged the gap in our understanding of the operation of the gastric CPG at the cellular level (Selverston & Moulins, 1987) and the relation to the gastric motor behaviour. Two separate studies have shown that proctolin can change cellular and network properties of this CPG in isolated preparations (Heinzel & Selverston, 1988) as well as induce a corresponding change of chewing modes in the animal (Heinzel, 1988b). These analyses have also demonstrated that a deeper insight into the function of the whole system can only be obtained by simultaneous studies of both cellular activities and motor performance in the intact animal. Such studies have been proven to be difficult in the lobster. I succeeded, however, in developing a crab preparation (Fig. 1) which allows endoscopic observations of stomach movements and, simultaneously, extra- and intracellular recordings from cells of the intact stomatogastric system.

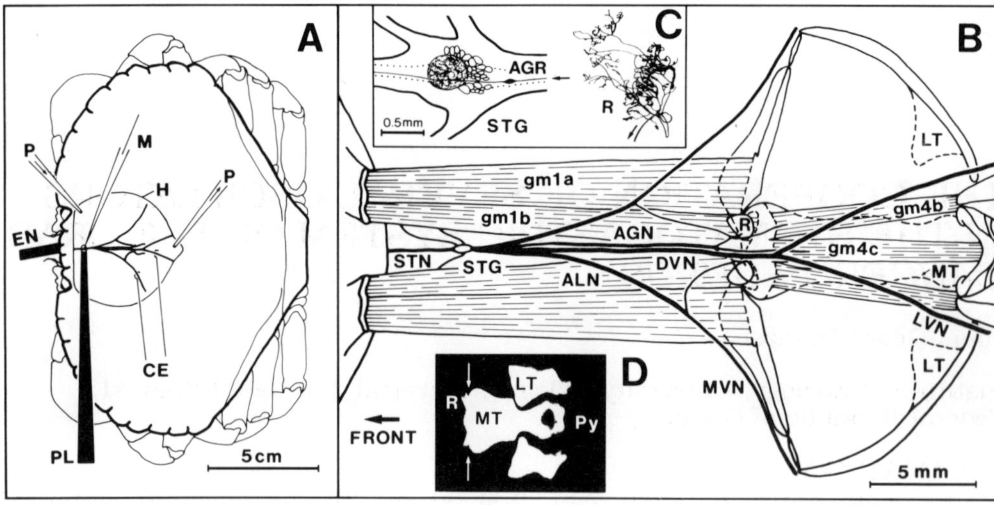

Fig.1. The strategy for studying the stomatogastric system in *Cancer pagurus*. A. A hole (H) in the carapace gives access for cuff- (CE) and microelectrodes (M). PL = platform stabilizing the stomatogastric ganglion (STG); P = perfusion system; EN = endoscope. B. Detailed view of muscles, nerves, and ossicles. Muscles gm1a/b pull the medial tooth (MT) forward, gm4b/c backward. STN = stomatogastric nerve, DVN/LVN/MVN = dorsal/lateral/median ventricular nerve; ALN = anterior lateral nerve; AGN = anterior gastric nerve. C. Soma and one of the two symmetrical receptor endings (R) of the anterior gastric receptor. D. Endoscopic view of the two lateral (LT) and the single medial tooth (MT); Py = position of the cardiopyloric valve.

This preparation should first enable us to analyse the cooperation of the several CPGs which drive different parts of the stomach, and second will permit the study of receptor action under closed loop conditions.

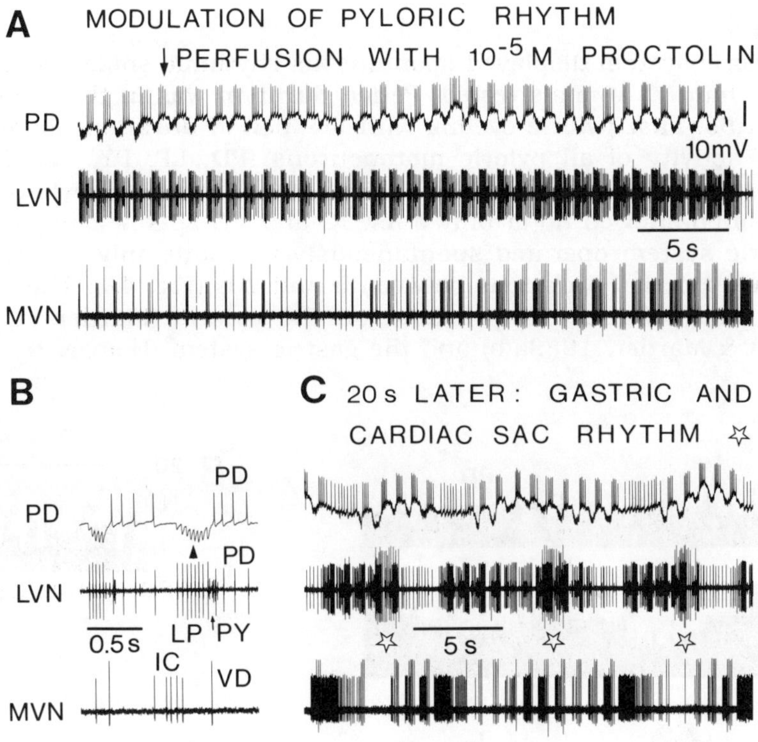

Fig. 2. The response of the pyloric, cardiac sac, and gastric system to perfusion with proctolin. Intracellular recordings of the pyloric PD-cell; cuff-electrode recordings from the LVN and MVN showing the rhythmic activity of other pyloric motoneurons (see details in B).

METHODS

The legs and claws of crabs (*Cancer pagurus*) were fixed with rubber bands, and the animal was mounted in a small aquarium connected to a filter system with cold (16 °C) sea-water. A hole was cut into the carapace, and floating cuff-electrodes with insulated stainless steel wires were used to record both the activity of motoneurons of the pyloric and gastric systems as well as the spike activity of a gastric stretch receptor (Fig. 1). Additional intracellular recordings were made after stabilizing the ganglion on a platform. The opening in the carapace was perfused either with saline or with saline containing Proctolin (Sigma). Movements of the stomach were observed from the outside or monitored with a video camera connected to an endoscope (Heinzel, 1988a). The soma and the receptor endings of the anterior gastric receptor (AGR) were stained by migration of cobalt chloride (5%) from the cut ends of the anterior gastric nerve (AGN) and by subsequent silver intensification.

RESULTS

The pyloric system displayed spontaneous rhythmic spike activity in all of the more than 30 animals tested. Period duration was in the range between 0.5 and 1.5s. Fast pyloric cycling with low period duration usually showed rhythmic activity of all pyloric motoneurons (PD, LP, PY, and IC, VD) as recorded from the LVN and MVN (Fig. 2A, beginning), whereas slower rhythms often showed no or only a few IC and VD spikes (compare Fig. 5A). The gastric system operated spontaneously in about only one third of the animals with period durations between 5 and 20s (Fig. 4A). The well-known presence and influence of proctolin on the pyloric (Marder et al., 1986; Nusbaum & Marder, 1989a,b) and the gastric system (Heinzel & Selverston, 1988) of isolated preparations of lobsters was analysed in such almost intact crabs. In most studies proctolin perfusion was limited to the stomatogastric ganglion (STG) of isolated combined preparations (the STG together with the single oesophageal and the paired commissural

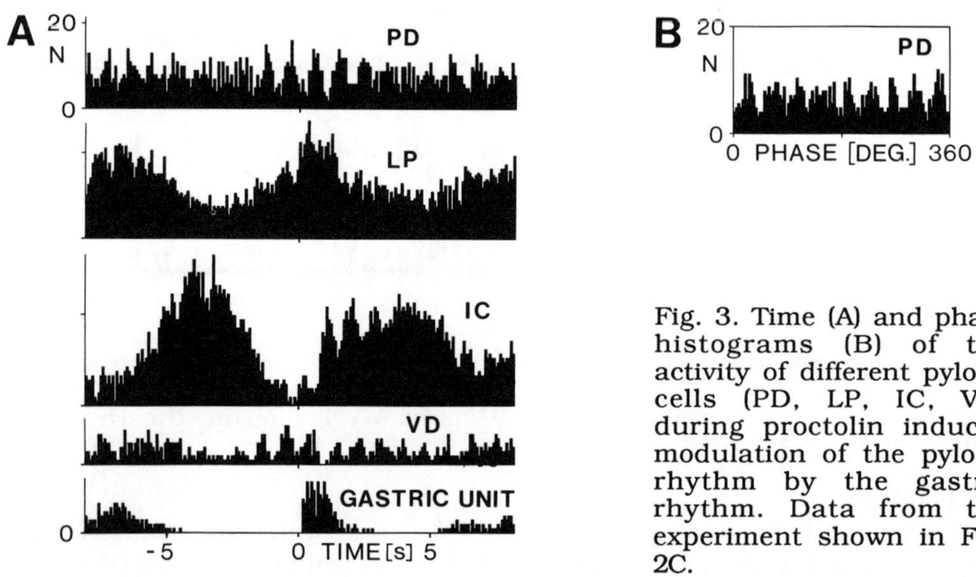

Fig. 3. Time (A) and phase histograms (B) of the activity of different pyloric cells (PD, LP, IC, VD) during proctolin induced modulation of the pyloric rhythm by the gastric rhythm. Data from the experiment shown in Fig. 2C.

ganglia). In the intact crab preparation proctolin perfusion was applied to the whole animal, thus mimicking release from the known storage sites in the pericardial organ (Schwarz et al., 1984).

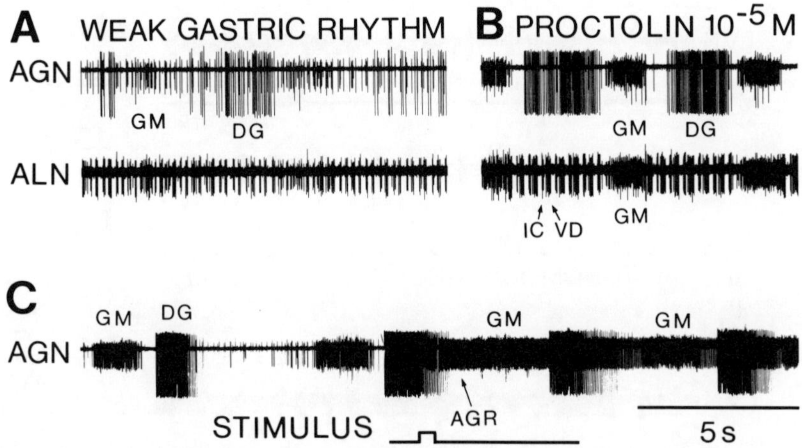

Fig. 4. A weak and irregular spontaneous gastric rhythm (A) is converted into a strong and regular alternation (B) of the antagonists GM and DG by the application of proctolin, whereas the pyloric IC and VD motoneurons are completely silenced during GM activity. Such gastric activity slows down after a few minutes, but is here (C) accelerated again by brief mechanical stimulation of a gastric stretch receptor (AGR, see Fig. 1) which fires a long burst upon stimulation.

Such application of proctolin first acted on the pyloric system by strengthening ongoing pyloric regular cycling with the induction of more spikes per burst in all pyloric cells (Fig. 2A). This regular pyloric cyling was, however, interrupted rhythmically as soon as proctolin initiated cardiac sac contractions and gastric mill movements which were observed to be in synchrony with the appearance of the large spikes in the LVN recording (Fig. 4C). The inferior cardiac motoneuron (IC), which controls the cardio-pyloric valve, was phasically inhibited in synchrony with this gastric activity (Fig. 3A). The two coupled pyloric dilator motoneurons (PD) showed less modulation of their spike frequency, but their activity nevertheless demonstrated that the whole pyloric oscillator was phasically influenced by the gastric system, since an integer number (here 9, see Fig. 3B) of pyloric PD cycles matched one gastric cycle. In cases with especially strong gastric activity, not only the IC but also the other motoneuron (VD) operating the cardio-pyloric valve were completely inhibited during the GM activity of the gastric cycle (Fig. 5B).

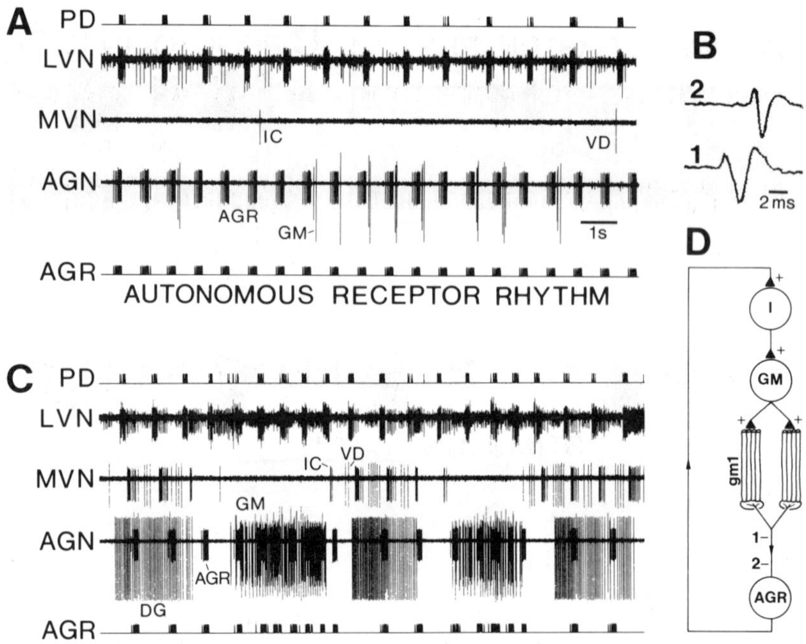

Fig. 5. Rhythm generation within a receptor ending. A. The anterior gastric receptor (AGR) can spontaneously generate an autonomous rhythm as shown by the spikes recorded in the AGN. Spike activity of the pyloric PD cell and the AGR was extracted from the LVN respectively AGN recordings by electronic filtering. B. Recordings from two sites (see 1, 2 in D) of the AGN demonstrate that the AGR spikes are generated at the receptor ending and travel towards the soma in the stomatogastric ganglion. C. Modulation of AGR rhythm by strong spontaneous gastric activity. D. Sensorimotor circuit (suggested by the circuit worked out for Hommarus by Simmers and Moulins 1988b) involving AGR and the muscle gm1b which is innervated by the GM motoneurons. See text for details.

Recordings from these GM motoneurons and their antagonistic DG motoneuron were made from the anterior gastric nerve (AGN). Recordings from this nerve of the crab also show small spikes of a sensory cell which travel towards the STG (Figs. 4C; 5A,B). A brief mechanical stimulus with a glass probe applied to the base of the gastric gm1b muscle elicited a long lasting train of such spikes and an acceleration of gastric mill activity. Cobalt stainings revealed that the sensory cell has its bipolar soma within the STG and that it has two symmetrical receptor endings in the stomach wall near the base of each gm1b muscle. Its axon leaves the STG via the stomatogastric nerve and travels towards the commissural ganglia.

All these findings suggest that this receptor cell of the crab is homologous to the anterior gastric receptor (AGR) which has been described in Homarus (Simmers & Moulins, 1988a,b). The AGR of the crab normally displays spontaneous continuous spiking (around 5Hz) similar to the AGR of Homarus, but its receptor endings also can generate autonomous rhythmic bursting with period durations slightly faster than the pyloric rhythm (Fig. 5A,B). Such receptor spike bursts are often followed by bursts of GM motoneuron spikes with a latency of about 80ms (Fig. 5A). This spontaneous positive effect of AGR on GM is consistent with the positive effect of AGR stimulation on the gastric rhythm (shown in Fig. 4C). Spontaneous gastric cycling demonstrates the reverse effect, namely the stimulation of the AGR (here, acceleration of its spontaneous rhythm, Fig. 5C) during each GM burst.

DISCUSSION

The results suggest that the anterior gastric receptor of the crab has similar connections as that of Homarus (Simmers & Moulins, 1988a,b). The AGR cell has no branches within the STG and no direct connections to the motoneurons of the STG, but instead has a positive connection to an interneuron (I, Fig. 5D) in each commissural ganglion which then excites the GM motoneurons driving the gm1 muscle. The function of such a positive feedback loop - suggested by Simmers & Moulins' (1988a,b) experiments with semi-intact preparations with non operating gastric mills - has here been proven to operate under realistic closed loop conditions in an intact animal. The generation of an autonomous receptor rhythm within such a positive feedback loop is unproblematic if the gain is low, i.e. if only a few reflectory spikes are generated in the GM motoneurons (Fig. 5A). It becomes, however, problematic if the gain gets too high since this might lead to a lock up of the whole system. This could be avoided by a sign reversal which has been demonstrated to occur in the interneuron of this circuit in Homarus (Simmers & Moulins, 1988a,b).

The consequences of an autonomous receptor rhythm of a gastric receptor running at a slightly faster frequency than the pyloric rhythm is not yet clear. The receptor rhythm might contribute to the cooperation of the gastric and pyloric CPGs which occurs either spontaneously or under the influence of proctolin perfusion (Figs. 2,3,4) in the intact crab. Interestingly, autonomous receptor rhythms have also been demonstrated for the gastro-pyloric receptor (GPR) near the pyloric region (see Harris-

Warrick, this volume) and recently for the AGR of Hommarus (Moulins, personal communication).

ACKNOWLEDGMENTS

I would like to thank Mrs. Ingrid Anders and Mr. Waldemar Gibner for their technical help, especially the cobalt stainings, and Mr. Fred McKitrick for his editorial assistance. This study has been supported by the German Research Foundation He1118/7.

REFERENCES

Heinzel, H.G. (1988a) Gastric mill activity in the lobster. I. Spontaneous modes of chewing. J. Neurophysiol. **59:** 528-550.

Heinzel, H.G. (1988b) Gastric mill activity in the lobster. II. Proctolin and Octopamine initiate and modulate chewing. J. Neurophysiol. **59**: 551-565.

Heinzel, H.G. & Selverston, A.I. (1988) Gastric mill activity in the lobster. III. Effects of Proctolin on the isolated central pattern generator. J. Neurophysiol. **59**: 566-585.

Marder, E., Hooper, S.L. & Siwicki, K.K. (1986) Modulatory action and distribution of the neuropeptide proctolin in the crustacean stomatogastric nervous system. J. comp. Neurol. **242:** 454-467.

Nusbaum, M.P. & Marder, E. (1988a) A modulatory proctolin-containing neuron (MPN). I. Identification and characterization. J. Neurosci. **9**: 1591-1599.

Nusbaum, M.P. & Marder, E. (1988b) A modulatory proctolin-containing neuron (MPN). II. State-dependent modulation of rhythmic motor activity. J. Neurosci. **9:** 1600-1607.

Schwarz, T.L., Lee, G.M.-H., Siwicki, K.K., Standaert, D.G. & Kravitz, E.A. (1984) Proctolin in the lobster: The distribution, release, and chemical characterization of a likely neurohormone. J. Neurosci. **4**: 1300-1312.

Selverston, A.I. & Moulins, M. (eds.) (1987) The crustacean stomatogastric system. Berlin: Springer.

Simmers, J. & Moulins, M. (1988a) A disynaptic sensorimotor pathway in the lobster stomatogastric system. J. Neurophysiol. **59:** 740-756.

Simmers, J. & Moulins, M. (1988b) Nonlinear interneuronal properties underlie integrative flexibility in a lobster disynaptic sensorimotor pathway. J. Neurophysiol. **59**: 757-777.

Frontiers in Crustacean Neurobiology
Advances in Life Sciences

CELLULAR PROPERTIES AND FUNCTIONAL FLEXIBILITY IN THE CRUSTACEAN STOMATOGASTRIC NERVOUS SYSTEM

Maurice Moulins

Laboratoire de Neurobiologie et Physiologie Comparées. Université de Bordeaux I and CNRS, Place Peyneau, 33120 Arcachon, France

SUMMARY

Flexibility occuring in a sensory-motor pathway and an endogenously-active motor network have been studied using electrophysiological techniques on in vitro preparations of the stomatogastric nervous system of lobsters. It is illustrated first that intrinsic neuronal properties can play a major role in the non-linear performance of a disynaptic reflex pathway. Secondly, it is shown that a neuromodulatory neuron projecting to the pyloric network is able to modify ongoing pyloric activity by changing the expression of intrinsic properties of the pyloric neurons. Finally, it is demonstrated that such changes in intrinsic properties can allow a neuron belonging to the pyloric network to switch to another network.

INTRODUCTION

Centrally-generated motor activity must be flexible to adapt animal behavior to environmental contingencies. Changes occuring in motoneuron output can be induced either by peripheral sensory inputs or by central "descending" inputs. In many cases, the same input can lead to different outputs and to explain such flexibility, it is generally necessary to postulate that afferent information can be routed to motoneurons via multisynaptic pathways operating in parallel and which are selected as a function of behavioral requirements (Reichert & Rowell, 1985; Rossignol et al., 1988). This problem has been recently investigated in the lobster stomatogastric nervous system where synaptic relationships are well documented (see Selverston & Moulins, 1987). Reported here are results concerning changes in motor output induced by sensory inputs and by "descending" afferents, and the underlying role played by intrinsic neuronal properties in motor flexibility, i.e. that flexibility can be an inbuilt feature of hardwired circuits.

METHODS

Results were obtained from *Homarus gammarus, Jasus lalandii* and *Panulirus vulgaris,* using standard electrophysiological techniques on in vitro preparations of the stomatogastric nervous system (see Fig. 1A) as described in Selverston et al. (1976). In situ isolation of neurons (see Fig. 2C) was achieved with the photoinactivation method described by Miller & Selverston (1979).

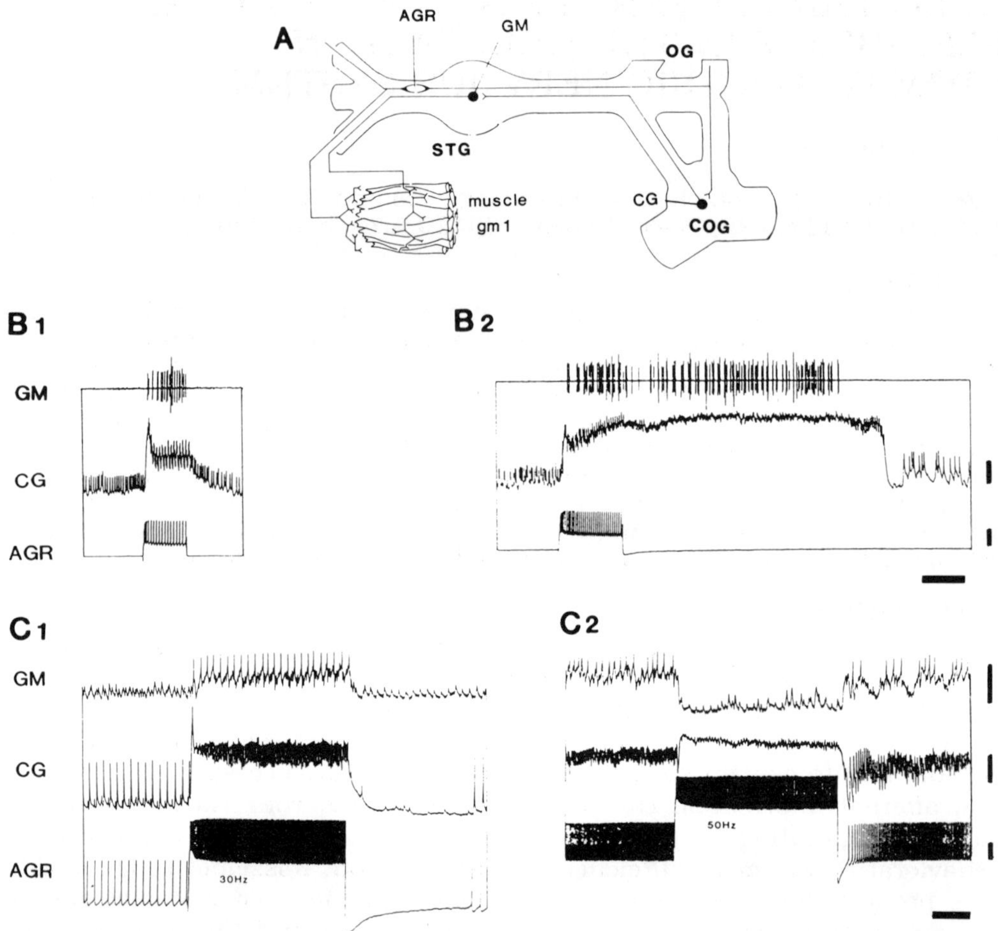

Fig. 1. Non-linearity in the AGR (sensory)-GM (motor) pathway. A. Schematic drawing of the cellular pathway through the stomatogastric nervous system. B. Change in gain. C. Change in sign (see text). AGR, anterior gastric receptor; CG, commissural gastric neuron; COG, commissural ganglion; GM, gastric motoneuron; OG, oesophageal ganglion; STG, stomatogastric ganglion. Horizontal bar: 1 s, vertical bars: 10 mV.

RESULTS

Non linear integration in a gastric sensori-motor pathway. In *Homarus*, the stretch-sensitive dendrites of a recently described mechanosensory neuron (the Anterior Gastric Receptor, AGR; see Simmers & Moulins, 1988a) terminate near the insertion of the gastric teeth muscle gm1 (Fig. 1A). Activation of this neuron produces a reflex excitation of GM motoneurons (Fig. 1B) whose somata are located in the stomatogastric ganglion (STG) and which innervate gm1. This reflex occurs uniquely via an intercalated neuron, the Commissural Gastric neuron (CG) which is excited by AGR and, in turn, excites GM (Fig. 1A). Using different paradigms of AGR stimulation, it has been possible to show that discontinuities can occur between AGR input and the GM response (Simmers & Moulins, 1988b). Firstly, abrupt gain changes can be observed with slight increases in AGR activation whereby the GM response, which is of the same duration as that of AGR stimulation (Fig. 1B1), switches to a response that considerably outlasts AGR activation (Fig. 1B2). Secondly abrupt changes in sign can occur with increased discharge frequencies of AGR whereby the GM response switches from activation (Fig. 1C1) to inactivation (Fig. 1C2).

These non-linearities in the input-output relationships can be explained solely by the intervention of intrinsic properties of the intercalated CG neuron. Firstly CG has bistable plateau properties, i.e. the ability to actively depolarize from a given threshold and to remain depolarized (and firing) before spontaneously repolarizing. In Figure 1B1, AGR activation was not sufficient to reach this threshold: CG (and hence GM) fires only during AGR discharge. In Figure 1B2 however, synaptic excitation from AGR is sufficient to reach plateau threshold: CG (and GM) fires throughout the intrinsic plateau, and thus for a duration which considerably outlasts the original AGR stimulus. Secondly CG is known to produce action potentials only within a window of membrane potential (Robertson & Moulins, 1981). When AGR activation drives CG into this window, the latter fires and excites GM (Fig. 1C1). When AGR drives CG out of this window (above its upper threshold for firing), the interneuron stops firing and GM, which is no longer excited, repolarizes and remains silent (Fig. 1C2).

Centrally-induced changes in pyloric network pattern. The STG contains the extensively-studied pyloric network (Selverston & Moulins, 1987) comprising 14 neurons (Fig. 2A) that generate and organize rhythmic motor activity of the pyloric chamber. In the oesophageal ganglion of *Panulirus* and *Jasus* (see Fig. 1A), Nagy & Dickinson (1983) have identified a neuron, the Anterior Pyloric Modulator (APM), which projects to the STG (Fig. 2A) and whose firing can produce radical changes in the pyloric pattern. For example, APM firing is able to induce a long term change in the phase at which the constrictor neuron LP is active in the cycle of the dilator neuron PD (Fig. 2B). It has been shown recently that such flexibility is due solely to

APM-induced changes in membrane properties of the LP neuron (T. Bal & F. Nagy, unpublished). All pyloric neurons are endogenous oscillatory neurons (Bal et al., 1988), i.e. neurons which develop a slow spontaneous depolarization (the pacemaker potential) until a threshold is reached from where a sudden regenerative depolarization produces a burst of action potentials (see Fig. 2C2). The experiment of Figure 2C, in which LP was isolated from its partners in the network (Fig. 2C1), shows that APM discharge results in an increase in slope of the LP pacemaker potential in a frequency-dependent manner (Fig. 2C2).

In other words, APM discharge enables LP to actively depolarize more rapidly. When LP is still coupled to the pyloric network (Fig. 2B), it is strongly inhibited by PD during the development of its pacemaker potential,

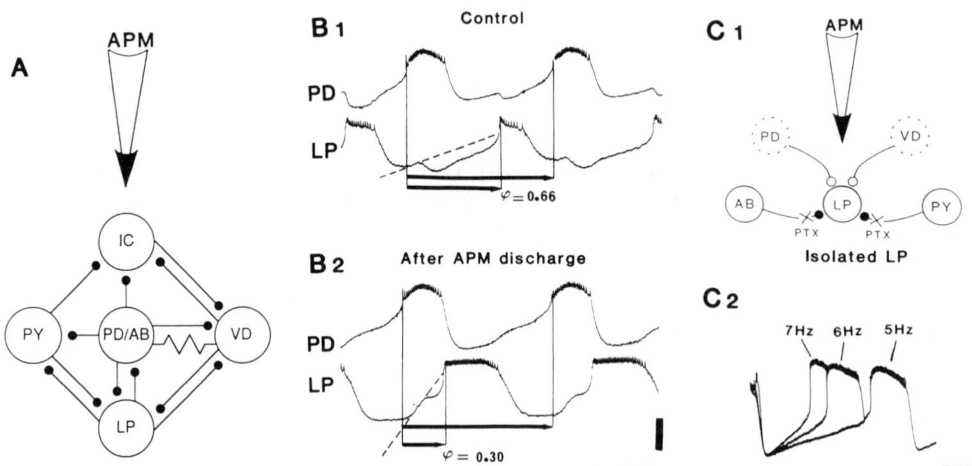

Fig. 2. Centrally-induced changes in the output of the pyloric network. A. The anterior pyloric modulator neuron (APM) of the oesophageal ganglion projects to the pyloric network in the STG. B. APM discharge induces long lasting changes in the phase (j) of LP bursts in PD period (compare B2 to B1). Note changes in slope (dotted lines) of LP pacemaker potential. C. APM discharge induces long lasting frequency-dependent changes in the pacemaker slope of isolated LP. C1. Method used to isolate LP from other pyloric circuit neurons (photoinactivation of PD and VD, plus bath application of picrotoxin (PTX) to abolish synaptic input from AB and PY). C2. Progressive increase in slope of LP's pacemaker potential with APM discharge frequencies of 5, 6 and 7Hz. Horizontal bars: 0.5 s, vertical bars: 10 mV (C from T. Bal and F. Nagy, unpublished).

and the cell's ongoing depolarization is retarded. Because this depolarization is faster and stronger after APM discharge (Fig. 2B2), LP reaches its firing threshold much earlier than in the control situation (Fig. 2B1). Thus, changes induced in the kinetics of LP's intrinsic pacemaker potential by APM discharge are sufficient to explain changes occuring in the phase relationships of LP activity in the PD cycle.

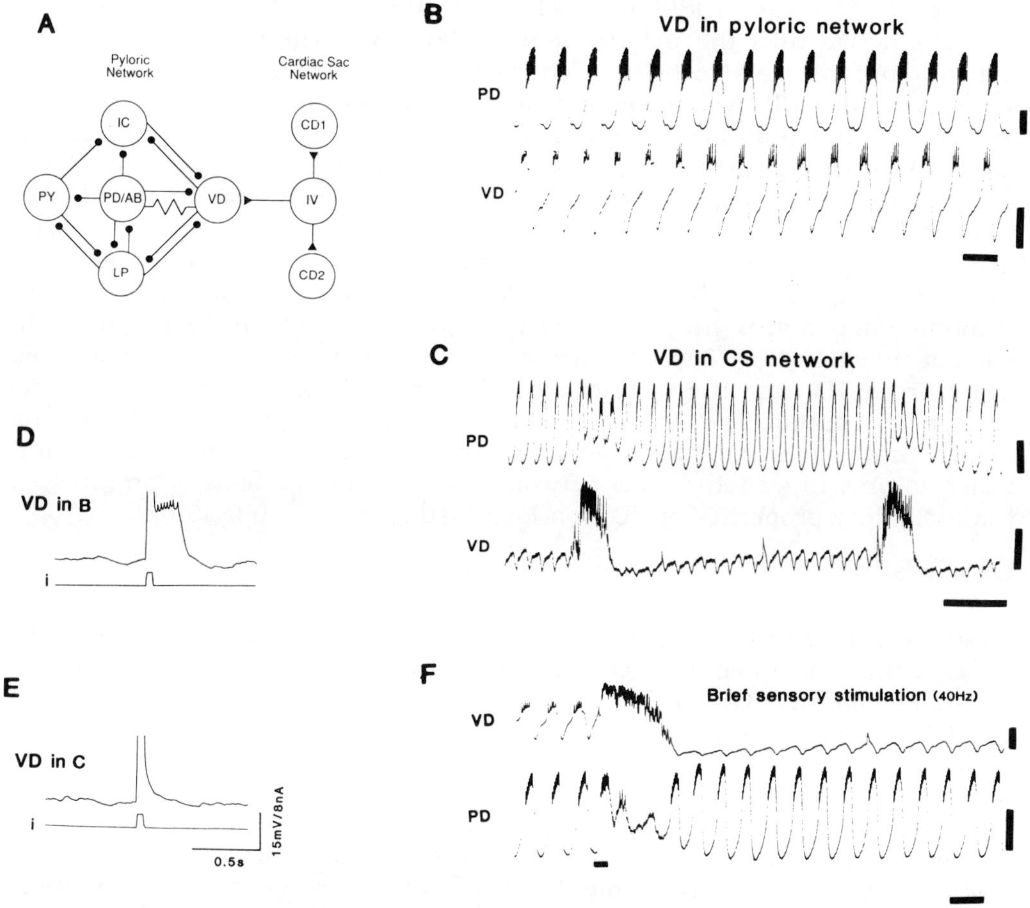

Fig. 3. Switching of VD activity from the pyloric circuit to the cardiac sac circuit. A. VD is a member of the pyloric circuit, but also receives excitatory input from cardiac sac circuit neurons. B-E. VD is normally active with the pyloric circuit (B) but can leave this circuit to become active with the cardiac sac circuit (C). This change is correlated with the suppression of regenerative (plateau) properties in VD (compare D to E). F. The loss of VD's regenerative properties (giving rise to its ability to leave the pyloric circuit) can be induced by a brief stimulation of a stomach sensory nerve (bar). Horizontal bars: 1 s except in C : 5 s, vertical bars: 10 mV.

Switching a pyloric neuron to another network. The Ventral Dilator (VD) neuron innervates the dilator muscle of the cardio-pyloric valve (the valve between the cardiac sac (CS) and the pyloric chamber). While VD is a full member of the pyloric circuit, it also receives excitatory input from cardiac sac network neurons (Fig. 3A). It has been shown recently in *Panulirus* (Hooper & Moulins, 1989) that whenever the CS network is silent, VD remains active with the pyloric network (Fig. 3B). However, when the CS network becomes active (with a characteristic period of more than 10 s), VD leaves the still cycling pyloric network to become active in time with the CS network (Fig. 3C). This complete change in allegiance of VD is due to a radical change in intrinsic properties expressed by the neuron. When active with the pyloric network, VD exhibits regenerative oscillatory properties. This can be demonstrated by intrasomatic injection of brief depolarizing current pulses which always give rise to a full regenerative oscillation (Fig. 3D). When active with the CS network however, VD never exhibits such active properties either spontaneously, or in response to current injection (Fig. 3E). In other words, it is the loss of these properties which frees VD from the pyloric network and enables it to passively follow synaptic excitation from the active CS network. Interestingly we have also shown that a mechanosensory input arising from the stomach wall, and which is able to switch on CS network activity, simultaneously suppresses the oscillatory properties of VD in a long lasting manner (Fig. 3F).

DISCUSSION

At least three conclusions can be drawn from the results presented here. Firstly, intrinsic neuronal properties can underly flexibility in sensori-motor relationships. All integrative changes (i.e. in gain, or sign) which can occur in the disynaptic AGR to GM sensori-motor pathway can be explained by special membrane properties of the intercalated CG interneuron. Neurons with such complex transfer functions are probably not an exception. It is now well known for example, that Ia afferent activation in the cat can produce either a brief discharge or a long-lasting response in lumbar a motoneurons. The unexpected change in temporal gain of this monosynaptic reflex has now been directly correlated with intrinsic plateauing properties of the motoneurons themselves (Hounsgaard et al., 1984).

Secondly, changes in intrinsic neuronal properties can underly flexibility in the rhythmic output of a central motor circuit. In the example described here, the phase shift of LP in the pyloric cycle after APM firing has been found, by isolating LP from its partners in the pyloric network, to be directly correlated with a change in the expression of LP intrinsic properties and specifically, the kinetics of its pacemaker potential. It is now clear that neurons of the pyloric circuit in the stomatogastric system receive a large number of "modulatory" inputs (Nagy & Moulins, 1987; Marder, 1987; Harris-Warrick, 1988), many of which probably control pyloric neuron properties in a manner similar to APM. Such flexibility induced by changes in neuronal properties may also be a widespread phenomenon, as in the case of locomotory behavior in lower vertebrates where excitatory amino acid inputs acting on spinal neurons induce regenerative oscillatory properties via NMDA receptor activation (Sigvardt et al., 1985; Grillner & Wallen, 1985).

Thirdly, and probably the most novel conclusion is that, flexibility induced by changes in intrinsic neuronal properties is not limited to a restructuring of the activity pattern of a single network (such as the pyloric network), but can result in a completely new circuit configuration involving neurons previously belonging to different networks. That circuit reconfiguration can be induced by sensory inputs, moreover, opens new perspectives in the study of sensori-motor relationships. If such mechanisms prove to be a generality, it will be no longer possible to consider the CNS in terms of discrete, hardwired circuits.

REFERENCES

Bal, T., Nagy, F. & Moulins, M. (1988) The pyloric central pattern generator : a set of conditional neuronal oscillators. J. comp. Physiol., **163:** 715-727.

Grillner, S. & Wallen, P. (1985) The ionic mechanisms underlying N-methyl-D-aspartate receptor-induced, tetrodotoxin-resistant membrane potential oscillations in lamprey neurons active during locomotion. Neurosci. Lett., **60**: 289-294.

Harris-Warrick, R.M. (1988) Chemical modulation of central pattern generators. In Neural control of rhythmic movements in Vertebrates (eds. A.H. Cohen, S. Rossignol & S. Grillner) pp. 285-331. Wiley: New York.

Hooper, S. & Moulins, M. (1989) Switching of a neuron from one network to another by sensory-induced changes in membrane properties. Science, 244: 1587-1589.

Hounsgaard, J., Hultborn, H., Jesperen, B. & Kiehn, O. (1984) Intrinsic membrane properties causing a bistable behaviour of a motoneurons. Exp. Brain Res., **55:** 391-394.

Marder, E. (1987) Neurotransmitters and neuromodulators. In The crustacean stomatogastric system (eds. A.I. Selverston & M. Moulins) pp. 263-300. Springer: Heidelberg.

Miller, & Selverston, A.I. (1979) Rapid killing of single neurons by irradiation of intracellular injected dye. Science, **206:** 702-704.

Nagy, F. & Dickinson, P. (1983) Control of a central pattern generator by an identified interneurone in Crustacea. I. Modulation of the pyloric motor output. J. Exp. Biol., **105**: 33-58.

Reichert, H. & Rowell, C.H.F. (1985) Integration of monophase locked exteroceptive information in the control of rhythmic flight in the locust. J. Neurophysiol., **53**: 1201-1218.

Robertson, & Moulins, M. (1981) Firing between two spike thresholds: implications for oscillating lobster interneurons. Science, **214:** 941-943.

Rossignol, S., Lund, J.P. & Drew, T. (1988) The role of sensory inputs in regulating patterns of rhythmical movements in higher vertebrates. In Neural control of rhythmic movements in Vertebrates (eds. A.H. Cohen, S. Rossignol & S. Grillner) pp. 210-284. Wiley: New York.

Sigvardt, K.A., Grillner, S., Wallen, P. & Van Dongen, P.A.M. (1985) Activation of NMDA receptors elicit fictive locomotion and bistable membrane properties in the lamprey spinal cord. Brain Res., **336**: 390-395.

Simmers, J. & Moulins, M. (1988a) A disynaptic sensori-motor pathway in the lobster stomatogastric system. J. Neurophysiol., **59**: 740-756.

Simmers, J. & Moulins, M. (1988b) Non linear interneuronal properties underlie integrative flexibility in a lobster disynaptic sensori-motor pathway. J. Neurophysiol., **59**: 757-777.

Selverston, A.I. & Moulins, M. (1987) The crustacean stomatogastric system: a model for the study of central nervous systems. Springer Verlag, Heidelberg, 330 pp.

Selverston, A.I., Russell, D.F., Miller, J.P. & King, D.G. (1976) The stomatogastric nervous system: structure and function of a small neural network. Progress. Neurobiol., **7**: 215-290.

Frontiers in Crustacean Neurobiology
Advances in Life Sciences

ENKEPHALINS, BIOLOGICALLY ACTIVE NEUROPEPTIDES IN INVERTEBRATES, WITH SPECIAL REFERENCE TO CRUSTACEANS

Peter P. Jaros

Universität Oldenburg, Abt. Zoophysiologie,
Postfach 2503,2900 Oldenburg, FRG

SUMMARY

Peptides biochemically and/or immunologically related to enkephalins are present in the nervous system of crustaceans and the recent findings are reviewed in this chapter. In addition, the physiological effect of leu-enkephalin on the blood sugar level is reported. In vivo and in vitro studies support the view that endogenous enkephalin inhibits the exocytotic release of the hyperglycemic neurohormone from the sinus gland. High performance liquid chromatography and characterization of endogenous enkephalins by radioimmunoassay is described. The contribution should give access to crustaceans as a versatile model system for studies in neurobiology and endocrinology.

INTRODUCTION

Considerable research has been done attempting to delineate the presence and physiological significance of endogenous enkephalins in invertebrates. Although former studies suggested that opioid peptides existed solely within vertebrates (Pert et al., 1974), it has become evident that enkephalins are present in various tissues of non-vertebrate phyla.

In terms of immunoreactivity several peptides of the enkephalin family have been described in various invertebrate groups: In coelenterates Grimmelikhuijzen (1983) found FMRFamide in numerous species of different taxa. In plathelminthes Kerschbaum et al. (1984) detected ß-endorphin in *Crenobia alpina* and Jennings et al. (1987) presented evidence for the existence of FMRFamide in several species of turbellaria and in addition in nemertean worms. In annelids, Remy & Dubois (1979) demonstrated β-endorphin in *Dendrobaena subrubicunda* and Alumets et al. (1979) β-endorphin and enkephalin in *Lumbricus terrestris*. In the same species Rzasa et al. (1984) detected leu- and met-enkephalin by radioimmunoassay (RIA) in nerves and various tissues and Gesser & Larsson (1986) studied these enkephalins as putative sensory transmitters. Zipser (1980) investigated the leech Haemopsis marmorata and revealed the presence of leu- and met-enkephalin reactive neurones, while Verger-

Bocquet et al. (1987) found additionally dynorphin and α-neoendorphin in the leech Theromyzon tessulatum by immunohistochemical methods.

The initial report on met-enkephalins in molluscs (*Octopus vulgaris*) was published by Martin et al. (1979) followed by the detection of leu-enkephalin and FMRFamide (Martin et al. 1981), the latter has first been characterized by Price & Greenberg (1977) (for review see Price et al., 1987). Further evidence for enkephalins was given by Schot et al. (1981) in neurones of *Lymnea stagnalis* and in *Mytilus edulis* by Stefano & Martin (1983) (for review see Greenberg & Price, 1983). Alterations of the cyclic nucleotide and dopamin level by enkephalins were reported by Stefano & Catapane (1979) and Stefano & Hiripi (1979). Osborne & Neuhoff (1979) suggested the presence of an invertebrate opioid receptor as a result of studies on molluscs. Finally the primary structure of three endogenous enkephalins from *Mytilus edulis* have been identified as leu- and met-enkephalin and met-enkephalin-arg^6-phe^7 (Leung & Stefano, 1983).

The first reports on the presence of enkephalin-like peptides in insects were those of Remy et al. (1978) who found ß-endorphin neurones in the suboesophageal ganglion of the lepidopteran *Thaumetopoea pityocampa* and of Gros et al. (1978), who detected met-enkephalin by RIA in extracts of optic lobes from *Locusta migratoria*. Stefano & Scharrer (1981) demonstrated high affinity binding of an enkephalin analogue in the brain of Leucophaea maderae. Subsequently, a considerable number of studies have provided evidence of the occurrence of opioid-immunoreactive peptides in various taxa of insects (for review see Duve & Thorpe, 1988).

The occurrence of opioid-like peptides in crustacea has been reported by Mancillas et al. (1981) who found leu-enkephalin immunoreaction in all retinular cells of the ommatidia and in axons between the medulla interna and medulla terminalis of *Panulirus interruptus* and *Procambarus sp.* By means of immunofluorescence Jaros & Keller (1983) detected leu-enkephalin in the sinus gland, the eyestalk ganglia and the brain of *Carcinus maenas* and *Orconectes limosus* and subsequently Jacobs & van Herp (1984) localized FMRFamide immunocytochemically in the eyestalk of Palaemon serratus. 25 to 30 FMRFamide positive cells were found in the lamina ganglionaris and the medulla terminalis. Multiple stained axons are attached to the medulla terminalis ganglionic X-organ (MTXO)-sinus gland (SG)-tract, indicating a neuroendocrine transmission area (for review: Jaros, 1986). Neither Jacobs & van Herp (1984) nor van Deijnen et al. (1985) found any anti-FMRFamide binding to the axon terminals of the SG. The distribution of enkephalin-like peptides was confused by the results, that immunocytochemically anti-α-melanocyte stimulating hormone (MSH) binds to the SG, but extracts of the material were negative in RIA. In addition cross-reactivity was observed in neurones of the lamina ganglionaris with anti-α MSH and anti-FMRFamide and in the crustacean hyperglycemic hormone (CHH)-producing perikarya of the MTXO with anti-

CHH and anti-α MSH (van Deijnen et al., 1985). Mangerich et al. (1987) observed a co-localization of FMRFamide- and pigment-dispersing hormone (PDH)-immunoreactivities in *C. maenas* and *O. limosus* eyestalk ganglia. In the cerebral ganglion, the circumoesophageal connectives and commissural ganglia no co-localization has been reported, although numerous FMRFamide- and PDH-immunopositive neurones and axons were evaluated (Mangerich & Keller, 1988). However, in the brain and the stomatogastric nervous system of Cancer gracilus and C. productus anti-FMRFamide co-labeled all neurones, which were immunopositive for a monoclonal antibody against the molluscan small cardioactive peptide B (Callaway et al., 1987). Finally FMRFamide-like immunoreactive substances were purified and characterized by Trimmer et al. (1987) from *Homarus americanus* and tentatively identified as octapeptides (Table 1).

The carboxy-terminal -Arg-Phe-amide sequence seems to be common for the members of this putative family. It is the main antigenic epitope for most of the antisera applied to immunopositive FMRFamide structures and in addition the most critical sequence of the pharmacological effects of the peptides (Trimmer et al., 1987). The occurrence of immunoreactive enkephalins was the subject of a scrutiny by Jaros et al. (1985). They reported the distribution of the material from the lamina ganglionaris to the

Table 1: Peptides of the supposed enkephalin family reported for crustaceans

Peptide	Animal	Method	Author
FMRF	*Palaemon serratus*	ICC	Jacobs & van Herp, 1984
YGGFMRF	*C. maenas*	HPLC, RIA, ICC	Jaros et al., 1985
YGGFM	*C. maenas*	HPLC, RIA, ICC	Jaros et al., 1985
YGGFL	*C. maenas*	HPLC, RIA, ICC	Jaros et al., 1985
SDRNFLRF-NH_2	*H. americanus*	SA	Trimmer et al., 1987
TDRNFLRF-NH_2	*H. americanus*	SA	Trimmer et al., 1987
pEGRF-NH_2	*Anthozoa*	SA	Grimmelikhuijzen & Groeger, 1987

The anthozoa peptide, identified from Renilla köllikeri, might join a group of amidated, N-terminally blocked pentapeptides, isolated by Graff & Grimmelikhuijzen (1988a,b). HPLC: high performance liquid chromatography; ICC immunocytochemistry; RIA: radioimmunoassay; SA: sequence analysis.

medulla terminalis and the presence in the neurohemal organ, the sinus gland. Endogenous enkephalin-like peptides, extracted from sinus glands, fractionated by HPLC, detected by RIA, co-eluted with synthetic met- and leu-enkephalin and with enkephalin-arg-phe. In *Uca pugilator* Fingerman et al. (1985) reported the occurrence of leu- and met-enkephalin as well as FMRFamide immunoreactivity in the eyestalk ganglia and in addition Keller et al. (1985) gave evidence for the presence of an enkephalin-like peptide in the pericardial organs of *C. maenas*, suggesting that it could be released as a neurohormone at this site or that it contains regulatory functions (for further details see the contribution of H. Dircksen in this volume). Recently Leung et al. (1987) demonstrated the presence of RIA-detected met-enkephalin after HPLC from total brain and eyestalk extracts of *Gecarcinus lateralis*, which confirms the previous investigations.

In the present contribution attention is focused on the physiological significance of enkephalin-like peptides in crustacea, because their occurrence seemed to have been sufficiently elucidated.

METHODS

Endogenous enkephalin-like peptides have been isolated as described earlier (Jaros et al., 1985), using a LKB HPLC system consisting of two pumps No 2150, solvent controller No 2152, UV-monitor No 2151, Rheodyne injector No 7161, a Shimadzu C-R3A data processor and Waters µ Bondapak Phenyl columns. For rechromatography a C 18 reverse phase column was used. The leu-enkephalin-like peptide peak was collected according to retention time of synthetic leu-enkephalin (Serva) and identified by RIA as described previously. Tracer and antiserum was obtained from Amersham Ltd.

The action of endogenous enkephalin-like substance and synthetic leu-enkephalin on the CHH-release was estimated by measuring the hemolymph glucose level in *Uca pugilator*. The hemolymph sample (10 µl) was mixed with 500 µl of glucose oxidase reagent (GOD Perid test kit, Boehringer) and the absorption was read at 436 nm after 45 min. Control animals were subjected to naloxone and enkephalin to test the specific blockade effect on the opioid binding sites. In order to differentiate the site of action of enkephalin on the CHH-dependent blood glucose level, complete eyestalk ganglia with sinus gland were used to recognize, whether enkephalin acts directly on the glucose metabolism or decreases the CHH-release from the sinus glands. The *C. maenas* eyestalk ganglia were incubated at 12 °C in sterile enkephalin-containing saline (3.5 % artificial sea-water + 1 mM EDTA + 100 mM KCl). The released CHH was separated from enkephalin by G25 chromatography, injected into *U. pugilator* and the blood glucose level has been determined and compared to controls.

RESULTS

Intact *Uca pugilator* were injected with a dose of $1.8x10^{-8}$ mol synthetic leu-enkephalin per crab, with $2.7x10^{-8}$ mol naloxone or with a combination of both, respectively. As shown in Table 2, neither naloxone nor the naloxone/enkephalin mixture injection alters the blood glucose level compared to saline injected animals. Alone enkephalin decreased the basal glucose concentration in the hemolymph to almost zero.

Table 2: Action of synthetic leu-enkephalin on blood glucose level in intact *U. pugilator*

Agent	Dose/crab 10^{-8} M	n	Glucose conc. mg/100 ml	Standard deviation mg/1ooml
Saline	-	8	4.8	± 0.6
LE	1.8	8	0.8	± 1.4
LE/Naloxone	1.8/2.7	7	9.1	± 5.4
Naloxone	2.7	8	5.0	± 0.6

LE: leu-enkephalin;

In addition the opioid antagonist naloxone abolished the effect of synthetic enkephalin. In order to evaluate the site of action of the peptide, *C. maenas* eyestalk ganglia were incubated in a sterile 3.5 % sea-water saline, containing 1 mM EDTA and 100 mM KCl according to Nordmann & Morris (1988) who demonstrated that potassium-containing calcium-free medium induces no higher hormone release compared to controls. 72 ganglia were used to receive suitable amounts of released CHH. 36 of them were incubated in 1.8 mM enkephalin-supplemented saline, the others in enkephalin-free saline. After 4 h the bath volume, 1.8 ml each, was desalted on a PD 10 Pharmacia column, lyophilized and 10 µl of the CHH fraction, redissolved in 100 µl aqua dest., were injected into destalked *U. pugilator*. Saline, processed as the samples, was given as additional control. Table 3 shows the result of this experiment, elucidating the inhibitory action of synthetic leu-enkephalin on the CHH-release from sinus glands of *C. maenas*.

Table 3: Inhibition of CHH-release from sinus glands in vitro by synthetic leu-enkephalin

Incubation	Incubated eyestalk ganglia	Glucose conc. ± S.D. mg/100 ml
Eyestalk ganglia	36	7.2 ± 3.2
dito with 1.8 mM leu-enkephalin	36	0.4 ± 0.6
Saline without leu-enkephalin	--	0.8 ± 0.4

Note that 10 % of the released CHH has been used for the bioassay. Endogenous enkephalin-like peptide isolated from *C. maenas* as described before (Jaros et al., 1985) has been compared with synthetic leu-enkephalin by bioassay in intact *U. pugilator* (Table 4).

Table 4: CHH-release inhibited by synthetic and endogenous enkephalin

Dose/crab	n	Glucose conc. ± S.D.
Saline	6	4.5 ± 0.7
1.8×10^{-8} M synth. LE	6	0.8 ± 1.4
0.2 SGE endog. Enkephalin	6	0.2 ± 0.3

LE: synthetic leu-enkephalin; SGE: sinus gland equivalent

Synthetic as well as endogenous enkephalin reduces the basal hemolymph glucose level to the limit of detection.

DISCUSSION

Even if accepting the hypothesis that the isolated endogenous enkephalin-like peptide might be identical with leu-enkephalin, as it is indicated by the co-elution of rechromatographed Carcinus enkephalin-like peptide with synthetic leu-enkephalin (data not shown) and by the rather indirect indication of successful identification of leu-, met-enkephalin and met-enkephalin-arg^{6}-phe^{7} in molluscs, our knowledge of the metabolism and function of these peptides is still very poor. No information is available on precursor molecules. This implies that no investigations on the biosynthesis of opioid-like peptides in invertebrates in general have been made. The same is true of the degradation of these peptides in invertebrates. In vertebrates, half-lives of enkephalins are in a range of a few seconds up to several minutes (for review see Roda et al., 1986). Binding to receptors has been investigated in molluscs and in insects only (for references see Introduction).

The present study is the first report on the physiological action of an enkephalin-like peptide isolated from sinus glands of the shore crab. No suggestion concerning the structure of the peptide can be given due to the limited amount of material isolated so far. But compared to synthetic leu-enkephalin the endogenous substance is a strong inhibitor of CHH-exocytosis. The amount of approximately 0.2 SGE induces a response similar to that of 10^{-8} M leu-enkephalin and it can be hypothesized that this might be the action of a neuropeptidergic transmitter or neuromodulator. This speculation is confirmed by the localization of immunoreactive enkephalin in granules of sinus gland axon terminals (Jaros et al., 1985) and by the demonstration of axo-axonal junctions in the sinus gland of *Palaemon paucidens* (Hisano, 1978).

Recently a number of observations gave further evidence for the integrative modulation of synthetic enkephalin derivates on various endocrine and behavioural mechanisms. Martinez et al. (1988) reported a naloxone blockable excitatory action of FK 33824, a stable opioid analog, on the locomotory activity of *Gecarcinus lateralis*. Brunner & Maldonado (1988) studied the influence of morphine and naloxone on habituation in the crab *Chasmagnathus granulatus*. They observed an anterograde detrimental effect on responsiveness at high doses, not antagonized by naloxone. However, Valeggia et al. (1989) showed that naloxone increases the escape response of the same species, supporting the view of a participation of opioid receptors. In this context it might be worth while mentioning that Spector (1989) presented proofs for the existence of endogenous morphine in rat brain identical with the alkaloid by means of GC-mass spectrometry.

Kulkarni & Fingerman (1987) injected synthetic met-enkephalin and FMRF-NH_2 into *Uca pugilator*. They hypothesized that the evoked dark adaptation of the distal retinal pigment is caused by stimulating release of the dark-adapting neurohormone. Previously Quackenbush & Fingerman (1984) reported an enhanced release of melanophore- and erythrophore-concentrating hormone caused by GABA, octopamine, met-enkephalin and ß-endorphin. These findings are in accordance with an immunocytochemical study of Fingerman et al. (1985).

Manifold questions are open for further investigations. Unpublished observations (cited by Kavaliers & Hirst, 1987) on the feeding behaviour of Orconectes immunis suggest that the opioid system is involved in its regulation. Interestingly, deJesus & Renaud (1989) reported the naloxone-reversible inhibition of phagocytosis by enkephalins in the protozoan *Tetrahymena thermophila*. Enkephalin peptides may also be involved in cardiovascular regulation, as demonstrated by Ruth et al. (1984) in mammals. Likewise the participation of enkephalins and other opioids as putative neurotransmitters in the light perception of the optical system is evident (Weiler, 1985), but has not been studied in crustaceans so far, although Mancillas et al. (1981) demonstrated enkephalin immunoreactivity in the retina of the lobster.

An exciting feature of neurohormone research is the growing body of results on the "integrated communication between the nervous, endocrine and immune systems" (Kordon & Bihoreau, 1989). Opioid peptides affect numerous immuno-competent cell-mediated events such as natural killer cell activity, antibody production, macrophage chemotaxis and CD 8 cell generation (for review see Carr et al., 1988). The exploration of this neuroendocrine-immunological axis will be a real challenge for the physiologist. First attempts have been made by Stefano et al. (1989) who demonstrated the involvement of an enkephalin derivate in the adherence and chemokinesis of immuno-competent hemocytes in *Mytillus edulis* and *Leucophaea maderae.*

ACKNOWLEDGEMENT

The author would like to thank Mrs. H. Rothe and Mr. W. Lüschen for their contribution in the studies, Mr. K. Köbrich for expert technical and Mrs. A. Sievers for excellent clerical assistance. The work was supported by the Deutsche Forschungsgemeinschaft (Ja 397/2-1).

REFERENCES

Alumets, J., Håkanson, R., Sundler, F. & Thorell, J. (1979) Neuronal localisation of immunoreactive enkephalin and ß-endorphin in the earthworm. Nature **279:**805-806.

Brunner, D. & Maldonado, H. (1988) Habituation in the crab *Chasmagnathus granulatus*: Effect of morphine and naloxone. J.comp.Physiol.A **162**: 687-694.

Callaway, J.C., Masinovsky, B. & Graubard, K. (1987) Co-localization of SCP B-like and FMRFamide-like immunoreactivities in crustacean nervous systems. Brain Research**405**:295-304.

Carr, D.J.J., Kim, C.-H., DeCosta, B., Jacobson, E., Rice, K.C. & Blalock, J.E. (1988) Evidence for a ∂-class opioid receptor on cells of the immune system. Cell.Immunol. **116**:44-51.

DeJesus, S. & Renaud, F.C. (1989) Phagocytosis in Tetrahymena thermophila: Naloxone-reversible inhibition by opiates. Comp.Biochem.Physiol. **92C**:139-142.

Duve, H. & Thorpe, A. (1988) Mapping of enkephalin-related peptides in the nervous system of the blowfly, Calliphora vomitoria, and their co-localization with cholecystokinin (CCK)- and pancreatic polypeptide (PP)-like peptides. Cell Tiss.Res. **251**:399-415.

Fingerman, M., Hanumante, M.M., Deshpande, U.D. & Nagabhushanam, R. (1985) Localization of substance P-like, leucin-enkephalin-like, methionine-enkephalin-like, and FMRF-amide-like immunoreactivity in the eyestalk of the fiddler crab, *Uca pugilator.* Cell Tiss.Res. **241**:473-477.

Gesser, B.P. & Larsson, L.L. (1986) Enkephalins may act as sensory transmitters in earthworms. Cell Tiss.Res. **246**:33-37.

Graff, D. & Grimmelikhuijzen, C.J.P. (1988) Isolation of <Glu-Ser-Leu-Arg-Trp-NH 2, a novel neuropeptide from sea anemones. Brain Research **442**:354-358.

Greenberg, M.J. & Price, D.A. (1983) Invertebrate neuropeptides: Native and naturalized. Ann.Rev.Physiol. 45:271-288.

Grimmelikhuijzen, C.J.P. (1983) FMRFamide immunoreactivity is generally occurring in the nervous system of coelenterates. Histochem. **78**:361-381.

Grimmelikhuijzen, C.J.P. & Groeger, A. (1987) Isolation of the neuropeptide pGlu-Gly-Arg-Phe-amide from the pennatulid *Renilla köllikeri.* FEBS Letters **211**:105-108.

Gros, C., Lafon-Cazal, M. & Dray, F. (1978) Présence de substances immunoréactivement apparentées aux enképhalines chez un insecte, *Locusta migratoria.* C.R.Acad.Sc.Paris **287**: Ser.D, 647-650.

Hisano, S. (1978) Synaptic junctions in the sinus gland of the fresh-water prawn Palaemon paucidens. Cell Tiss.Res. **189**:435-440.

Jacobs, A.A.C. & van Herp, F. (1984) Immunocytochemical localization of a substance in the eyestalk of the prawn, *Palaemon serratus,* reactive with an anti-FMRFamide rabbit serum. Cell Tiss.Res. **235**:601.

Jaros, P.P. (1986) Neuropeptides in crustaceans with special reference to opioid-like peptides. In Handbook of comparative opioid and related neuropeptide mechanism, Vol I, (ed. G.B. Stefano) pp. 181-195. Boca Raton: CRC-Press.

Jaros, P.P., Dircksen, H. & Keller, R. (1985) Occurrence of immunoreactive enkephalins in a neurohemal organ and other nervous structures in the eyestalk of the shore crab, *Carcinus maenas* L. (Crustacea, Decapoda). Cell Tiss.Res. **241**:111-117.

Jaros, P.P. & Keller, R. (1983) Localization of leu-enkephalin-like material in the brain and neurohaemal organ of the brachyuran *Carcinus maenas* and the astacidean *Orconectes limosus.* 12th Congr.Europ.Comp.Endocrinologists, Sheffield.

Jennings, J.B., Davenport, T.R.B. & Varndell, I.M. (1987) FMRFamide-like immunoreactivity and acrylamidase activity in turbellarians and nemerteans - Evidence for a novel neurovascular coordinating system in nemerteans. Comp.Biochem.Physiol. **86** C:425-430.

Kavaliers, M. & Hirst, M. (1987) Slugs and snails and opiate tales: Opioids and feeding behavior in invertebrates. Fed.Proc. **46**:168-172.

Keller, R., Dircksen, H., Mangerich, S. & Jaros, P.P. (1985) Hyperglycemic hormone and other neuropeptides in crustacean neurosecretory structures. In Neurosecretions and the biology of neuropeptides, (ed. H. Kobayashi, H.A. Bern & A. Urano) pp. 60-69. Tokyo: Sci.Soc.Press.

Kerschbaum, H., Pohlhammer, K., Hacker, G., Treiblmayr, K. & Adam, H. (1984) ß-Endorphin-ähnliche Immunreaktivität bei *Crenobia alpina* (Turbellaria, Tricladia). Mikroskopie **41**:30-33.

Kordon, C. & Bihoreau, C. (1989) Integrated communication between the nervous, endocrine and immune systems. Horm.Res. **31**:100-104.

Kulkarni, G.O. & Fingerman, M. (1987) Distal retinal pigment of the fiddler crab, *Uca pugilator*: Release of the dark-adapting hormone by methionine enkephalin and FMRFamide. Pigment Cell Res. **1**:51-56.

Leung, M.K., Kessler, H., Whitefield, K., Murray, M., Martinez, E.A. & Stefano, G.B. (1987) The presence of enkephalin-like substances in the eyestalk and brain of the land crab *Gecarcinus lateralis*. Cell.Mol.Neurobiol. **7**:91-96.

Leung, M. & Stefano, G.B. (1983) Isolation of molluscan opioid peptides. Life Sciences **33**:77-80.

Mancillas, J.R., McGinty, J.F., Selverston, A.I., Karten, H. & Bloom, F.E. (1981) Immunocytochemical localization of enkephalin and substance P in retina and eyestalk neurones of lobster. Nature **293**:576.

Mangerich, S. & Keller, R. (1988) Localization of pigment-dispersing hormone (PDH) immunoreactivity in the central nervous system of *Carcinus maenas* and *Orconectes limosus* (Crustacea), with reference to FMRFamide immunoreactivity in *O. limosus*. Cell Tiss.Res. **253**:199-208.

Mangerich, S., Keller, R., Dircksen, H., Rao, K.R. & Riehm, J.P. (1987) Immunocytochemical localization of pigment-dispersing hormone (PDH) and its coexistence with FMRFamide immunoreactive material in the eyestalks of the decapod crustaceans *Carcinus maenas* and *Orconectes limosus*. Cell Tiss.Res. **250** :365-375.

Martin, R., Frösch, D., Weber, E. & Voigt, K.H. (1979) Met-enkephalin-like immunoreactivity in a cephalopod neurohemal organ. Neurosci.Lett. **15**:253-257.

Martin, R., Frösch, D., Kiehling, C. & Voigt, K.H. (1981) Molluscan neuropeptide-like and enkephalin-like material coexists in octopus nerve. Neuropeptides **2**:141-150.

Martinez, E.A., Murray, M., Leung, M.K. & Stefano, G.B. (1988) Evidence for dopaminergic and opioid involvement in the regulation of locomotory activity in the land crab *Gecarcinus lateralis*. Comp.Biochem.Physiol. **90** C:89-93.

Nordmann, J.J. & Morris, J.F. (1980) Depletion of neurosecretory granules and membrane retrieval in the sinus gland of the crab. Cell Tiss.Res. **205**:31-42.

Osborne, N.N. & Neuhoff, V. (1979) Are there opiate receptors in the invertebrates? J.Pharm.Pharmacol. **31**:481.

Pert, C.B., Aposhian, D. & Snyder, S.H. (1974) Phylogenetic distribution of opiate receptor binding. Brain Res. **75**:356-361.

Price, D.A., Davies, N., Doble, K & Greenberg, M.J. (1987) Review: The variety and distribution of the FMRFamide-related peptides in molluscs. Zool.Sci. **4**:395-410.

Price, D.A. & Greenberg, M.J. (1977) The structure of a molluscan cardioexcitatory neuropeptide. Science **197**:670-671.

Quackenbush, L.S. & Fingerman, M. (1984) Regulation of neurohormone release in the fiddler crab, *Uca pugilator*: Effects of gamma-aminobutyric acid, octopamine, met-enkephalin and beta-endorphin. Comp.Biochem.Physiol. **79** C:77-84.

Remy, C. & Dubois, M.P. (1979) Localisation par immunofluorescence de peptides analogues à l' -endorphine dans les glanglions infraoesophagiens du Lombricidé *Dendrobaena subrubicunda* Eisen. Experientia **35**:137-138.

Remy, C., Girardie, J. & Dubois, M.P. (1978) Présence dans le ganglion sous-oesophagien de la Chenille processionaire du Pin (*Thaumetopoea pityocampa* Schiff) de cellules révélées en immunofluorescence par un anticorps anti- -endorphine. C.R.Acad.Sc., Ser.D **2 8 6**:651-653.

Roda, L.G., Venturelli, F. & Roscetti, G. (1986) Hydrolysis and protection from hydrolysis of circulating enkephalins. Comp.Biochem.Physiol. **8 5** C:449-454.

Ruth, J.A., Cuizon, J.V. & Eiden, L.E. (1984) Leucine-enkephalin increases norepinephrin-stimulated chronotropy. Neuropeptides **4**:185-191.

Rzasa, P., Kaloustian, K.V. & Prokop, E.K. (1984) Immunochemical evidence for Met-enkephalin-like and Leu-enkephalin-like peptides in tissues of the earthworm, *Lumbricus terrestris*. Comp.Biochem.Physiol. **7 7 C**:345-350.

Schot, L.P.C., Boer, H.H., Swaab, D.F. & van Noorden, S. (1981) Immunocytochemical demonstration of peptidergic neurones in the central nervous system of the pond snail *Lymnaea stagnalis* with antisera raised to biologically active peptides of vertebrates. Cell Tiss.Res **2 1 6**:273-291.

Spector, S. (1989) Endogenous opiate alkaloids. XI Internatl.Symp.Comp.Endocrinol., Malaga, Spain, M 11.

Stefano, G.B. & Catapane, E.J. (1979) Enkephalins increase dopamine levels in the CNS of a marine mollusc. Life Sci. **2 4**:1617-1622.

Stefano, G.B. & Hiripi, L. (1979) Methionine enkephalin and morphine alter monoamine and cyclic nucleotide levels in the cerebral ganglia of the freshwater bivalve *Anodonta cygnea*. Life Sci. **2 5:**291-298.

Stefano, G.B., Leung, M.K., Zhao, X. & Scharrer, B. (1989) Evidence for the involvement of opioid neuropeptides in the adherence and migration of immunocompetent invertebrate hemocytes. Proc.Natl.Acad.Sci.USA **8 6**:626-630.

Stefano, G.B. & Martin, R. (1983) Enkephalin-like immunoreactivity in the pedal ganglion of *Mytilus edulis* (Bivalvia) and its proximity to dopamin-containing structures. Cell Tiss.Res. **2 3** 0:147-153.

Stefano, G.B. & Scharrer, B. (1981) High affinity binding of an enkephalin analog in the cerebral ganglion of the insect *Leucophaea maderae* (Blattaria). Brain Res. **2 2 5**:107-114.

Trimmer, R.A., Kobierski, L.A. & Kravitz, E.A. (1987) Purification and characterization of FMRFamide-like immunoreactive substances from the lobster nervous system: Isolation and sequence analysis of two closely related peptides. J.comp.Neurol. **2 6 6:**16-26.

Valleggia, C., Fernandez-Duque, E. & Maldonado, H. (1989) Danger stimulus-induced analgesia in the crab *Chasmagnathus granulatus*. Brain Res. **4 8 1**:304-308.

VanDeijnen, J.E., Vek, F. & Van Herp, F. (1985) An immunocytochemical study of the optic ganglia of the crayfish Astacus leptodactylus (Nordmann 1842) with antisera against biologically active peptides of vertebrates and invertebrates. Cell Tiss.Res. **2 4 0**:175-183.

Verger-Bocqet, M., Malecha, J. & Tramu, G. (1987) Immunohistochemical localization of opioid peptides in the brain of the leech *Theromyzon tessulatum*. Cell Tiss.Res. **2 5 0**:63-71.

Weiler, R. (1985) Afferent and efferent peptidergic pathways in the turtle retina. In Neurocircuit of the retina. A Cajal memorial, (ed. A. Gallego & P. Gouras) pp. 245-256. New York: Elsevier.

Zipser, B. (1980) Identification of specific leech neurones immunoreactive to enkephalin. Nature **283**:857-858.

Frontiers in Crustacean Neurobiology
Advances in Life Sciences

GASTRIN/CCK-LIKE PEPTIDES IN THE NERVOUS SYSTEM AND THE STOMACH OF CRUSTACEANS

Alain Van Wormhoudt[1] and Heinrich Dircksen[2]

[1]Laboratoire de Biologie Marine, College de France, 29110 Concarneau, France; [2] Institut für Zoophysiologie der Universität Bonn, 5300 Bonn 1, FRG

INTRODUCTION

The mammalian peptide gastrin and cholecytokinine (CCK) share a common C-terminal pentapeptide sequence which contains the minimal biologically active fragment. Gastrin/CCK-like material has been described in invertebrates generally by use of gastrin/CCK-antisera specific for the C-terminus.

In crustaceans, Larsson & Vigna (1983) began to study these peptides in crabs. We studied these peptides in shrimps and in Norway lobsters. Important variations related to the moulting cycle (Favrel et al.1987) and postprandial increases of the concentrations of these peptides in the hemolymph were shown (Van Wormhoudt et al.1989). We have purified these peptides from the stomachs of *Palaemon serratus* and *Nephrops norvegicus*. In this paper we present recent results on the localization and the separation of these peptides in the nervous system and propose possible biological functions.

METHODS

Gastrin/CCK-like peptides were extracted in boiling water from the stomachs and the central nervous systems of *Palaemon serratus* and *Nephrops norvegicus* and estimated by RIA with an antiserum against the common C-terminus of Gastrin and CCK using Leu-Gastrin as the standard (Favrel et al.1987).

By use of immunocytochemistry, Gastrin/ CCK-like immunoreactive structures were demonstrated using indirect FITC-immunofluorescence methods in whole mount preparations of the central nervous systems and on sections through the eyestalk and stomach by the PAP-technique (Dircksen et al.1988).

Reversed phase HPLC-fractionations of the different tissues were realized on a Vydac-column using a 0.11 % aqueous TFA/acetonitrile gradient.

Purification and characterization by amino acid analysis of the four major G/CCK-like peptides was performed on a Biotronic LC 50 analyzer by Dr.G.Kegel, Bonn.

Biological activities on the function of the digestive tract were investigated. Protein synthesis was measured in vivo in the hepatopancreas of *Palaemon serratus* after injection of 3H-Leu (50 Ci/mmole) together with peptides (Van Wormhoudt et al.1988). Secretagogue effects were measured according to Resch & Sedlmeier (1989) in the *Orconectes limosus* system.

RESULTS AND DISCUSSION

Radioimmunoreactivity was present in all investigated tissues. Maximum values of the total amount were found in the digestive tract (50 pg equivalent of Leu-Gastrin), the eyestalks (5 pg eq.) and the thoracic ganglia (2 pg eq.). The maximum concentration occurs in the stomatogastric ganglia and the circumoesophageal connectives.

Whole mount immunocytochemistry revealed immunoreactive cells in the eyestalks and the cerebral, thoracic and abdominal ganglia whereas long fibers and plexus but no cells were found in other structures (e.g.the stomatogastric ganglia).

By HPLC-fractionation, the same immunoreactive peptides were shown in the stomach and in the central nervous system. However, their relative proportion is very different in the tissues under investigation. 7 different peptides could be identified. 4 of them were purified from the stomachs and their amino acid compositions given.

Seven amino acids are common to the four analyzed peptides. Thus, these peptides seem to belong to one family which is probably different from the G/CCk-family (only 0.04 % of cross-reactivity).

Concerning their biological activities, preliminary results have shown a possible role of the purified peptides on hepatopancreatic protein synthesis (Favrel & Van Wormhoudt 1986), a secretagogue effect on the hepatopancreas of Orconectes (in collaboration with Dr.D.Sedlmeier, Bonn) and a promising role in the modulation of the stomatogastric nervous system (in collaboration with G.Turrigiano and Prof.Selverston, La Jolla, USA: data not shown).

No stimulatory effect was observed on the pancreatic amylase secretion in the rat. All these effects should be confirmed with purified peptides in the described model systems.

REFERENCES

Dircksen H, Webster SG, Keller R (1988) Cell Tissue Res **251**:3-12

Larsson BA, Vigna SR (1983) Gen Comp Endocrinol **50**:469-475

Favrel P, Van Wormhoudt A (1986) Cah Biol Mar Abstr **17**:377

Favrel P, Van Wormhoudt A, Studler JM, Bellon C (1987) Gen Comp Endocrinol **65**:363-372

Resch G, Sedlmeier D (1989) Gen Comp Endocrinol **74**:262

Turrigiano G, Selverston AI (1987) Soc Neurosci Abstr Mai 1987

Van Wormhoudt A, Favrel P, Guillaume J, Cruz-Suarez E (1988) Oceanis **12**(4):304-319

Van Wormhoudt A, Favrel P, Guillaume J (1989) J Comp Physiol, in press

Frontiers in Crustacean Neurobiology
Advances in Life Sciences

IMMUNOCYTOCHEMICAL IDENTIFICATION OF THE NEUROSECRETORY PRODUCTS OF THE PERICARDIAL ORGANS OF *CARCINUS MAENAS*

Heinrich Dircksen

Institut für Zoophysiologie, Rheinische Friedrich-Wilhelms Universität, Endenicher Allee 11-13, 5300 Bonn 1, Federal Republic of Germany

SUMMARY

Whole mount immunocytochemistry revealed distinct patterns of distribution of CCAP-, Proctolin-, FMRFamide- and Leu-enkephalin-immunoreactive axons and nerve endings in the neurohemal pericardial organs (PO) of Carcinus maenas. Based on morphological criteria six different types of endings could be classified which contain distinct neurosecretory granules and/or vacuoles and vesicles. Using a combination of light and electron microscopical immunolabeling techniques CCAP-, Proctolin- and FMRFamide-immunoreactivities were attributed to four different neurosecretory granule types in endings of traced axons.

INTRODUCTION

The pericardial organs (PO) are complex neurohemal organs in the pericardial cavity of crustaceans containing numerous neurosecretory endings abutting on the surface of the nerve plexuses and anastomosing trunks. The neurosecretory nature of the PO was discovered by Alexandrowicz (1953) in several crustacean species, and Maynard (1961) was the first to describe different cell clusters in the thoracic ganglia of brachyuran crustaceans as the origin of neurosecretory neurons projecting through at least seven segmental nerves to the PO. In addition, Maynard (1961) described a large nerve plexus on respiratory muscles, the so-called anterior ramifications (AR), branching off from the first segmental nerve.

The PO became known as neurohemal release sites of several cardioactive factors, the biogenic amines dopamine, octopamine, and serotonin, and at least two cardioactive neuropeptides (see for review: Cooke & Sullivan 1982).

Sullivan (1979) first suggested one of them to be Proctolin, Arg-Tyr-Leu-Pro-Thr, a neuropeptide known from insects (Brown & Starratt 1975, Starratt & Brown 1975). The existence of Proctolin in the PO was biochemically confirmed by Schwarz et al. (1984) in the astacuran Homarus americanus and by Stangier et al.(1986) in the brachyuran Carcinus maenas.

In both studies, proctolin was demonstrated in axons and neurosecretory terminals by indirect immunofluorescence methods.

In the PO of *Carcinus maenas*, Stangier et al. (1987) recently identified a novel crustacean cardioactive peptide (CCAP), a potent cardioacceleratory substance with the cyclic nonapeptide structure: Pro-Phe-Cys-Asn-Ala-Phe-Thr-Gly-Cys-NH2. The production of antisera against this peptide and their use in an immunocytochemical study (Dircksen & Keller 1988) revealed a complex distribution of CCAP-neurons in the central nervous system of this species. CCAP-neurons of the thoracic ganglia project to the AR and the PO via the segmental nerves. These results were corroborated by radioimmunological studies (Stangier et al., 1988) showing the high specificity of the antiCCAP-sera and providing evidence for the release of CCAP from PO in vitro.

Evidence for the existence of further peptides probably related to the families of the molluscan cardioactive peptides, the FMRFamides, and vertebrate-type enkephalins in axons and nerve terminals of the PO of *Carcinus maenas* has been provided by the immunocytochemical demonstration of peptide-material immuno-reactive with antiserea against FMRFamide and Leu-enkephalin (Dircksen et al., 1987a; Dircksen & Keller 1988).

The aim of this study was to provide neuropeptide-specific morphological and biochemical data for the identification of neurosecretory products of the PO.

RESULTS AND CONCLUSIONS

Using whole mount immunocytochemistry patterns of distribution of neuropeptide-immunoreactive (IR) axons were traced throughout the SNs, anterior and posterior bars, dorsal and ventral trunks of the PO of Carcinus maenas. CCAP-IR axons enter the PO via all segmental nerves and exhibit numerous endings with strand-like or umbellate immunofluorescent structures (Dircksen & Keller 1988). Less numerous Proctolin-, FMRFamide-, and Leu-enkephalin (LENK)-IR axons occur throughout the PO forming umbellate and other forms of endings on the inner surface of the organ. Axons showing immunoreactivity to the first two peptides enter the PO exclusively via the first SN, whereas LENK-IR axons enter the PO via SN 1,3 and 7 (Fig.1).

By comparisons of serial semithin sections through trunks of the PO PAP-labeled with antisera against the different neuropeptides colocalizations of immunoreactive structures could not be detected (Fig.2).

The basis for the immunocytochemical identification of neurosecretory products of the PO of Carcinus maenas was the fine structural analysis of traced immunoreactive axons and endings.

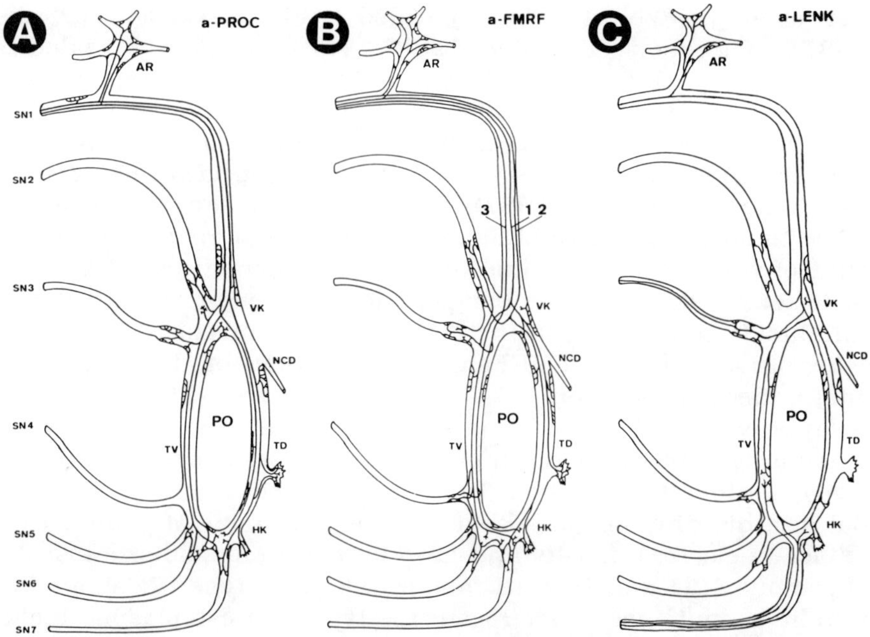

Fig.1. Principal patterns of distribution of Proctolin- (A), FMRFamide- (B) and Leu-enkephalin- (C) immunoreactive axons and endings in the right PO of Carcinus maenas.

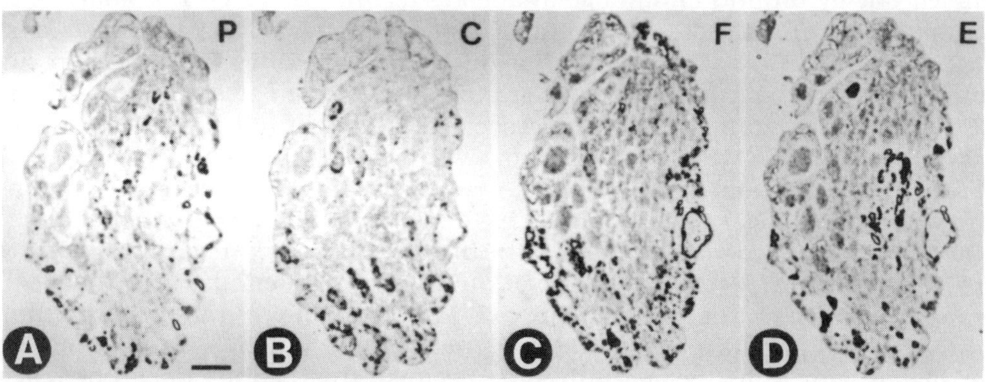

Fig.2. Serial semithin cross-sections through the dorsal trunk of a PO of Carcinus maenas (unosmicated tissue) PAP-stained using antisera against Proctolin (A,P), CCAP (B,C), FMRFamide (C,F) and Leu-enkephalin (D,L); bar: 10 μm.

Dircksen et al., 1987b) of HPLC-separated crude PO-extracts (Dircksen et al., 1987a; Dircksen & Keller 1988). These assays revealed single immunoreactive peak-fractions eluting at the retention times of authentic Proctolin and CCAP, but two different FMRFamide-IR HPLC-fractions at retention times different from authentic FMRFamide. The latter result indicates the presence of at least two different peptides related to FMRF-amides. Trimmer et al. (1987) recently identified the octapeptides SDRNFLRFamide and TNRNFLRFamide in the PO of Homarus americanus, the latter of which exhibiting ino- and chronotropic effects on semiisolated hearts. It seems likely that similar peptides cross-reactive with the applied antiFMRFamide-serum exist in the PO of Carcinus maenas. The biochemical characterizations of both FMRFamide-IR fractions and the LENK-IR are currently under investigation.

Size (approximate diameter) and other morphological criteria were used to preliminarily define four types of electron-dense neurosecretory granules observed in different endings. Type I contained granules that show a bimodal size distribution (Ia: about 70 nm, Ib: about 160 nm), the other types differ in electron-density and have normal unimodal size distributions (type II: about 120 nm, type III: about 100 nm, type IV: about 90 nm). Other endings contained a heterogeneous type V of cytoplasmic inclusions: small electron-lucent vesicles (about 40 nm), granules (about 90 nm) with a dense core of generally paracrystalline appearance and electron-dense granules (about 110 nm). The endings of type VI exclusively contain small electron lucent vesicles (about 40 nm). These granule types were also found in cross-sections of the segmental nerves (SN).

The ultrastructural, neuropeptide-specific identification of endings was carried out by on-grid immunogold-labeling techniques or by the analysis of combinations of labeled semithin and adjacent unlabeled ultrathin sections. Fine structural characteristics of identified endings could then be compared with the known types of granules and vesicular structures. Thus, CCAP-IR was attributed to the neurosecretory granule type I, Proctolin-IR to granule type II, FMRFamide-IR, however, was associated with the two different types III and V (Fig.3). Since both FMRFamide-IR types of endings showed almost the same PAP-labeling density in semithin sections, these differences were not detectable at the light-microscopic level. The results are in agreement with the observation of three different FMRFamide-IR types of axons in the SN 1 (compare Fig.1), axons 1 and 2 containing granule type III and axon 3 containing granule type V. LENK-IR could not be correlated with a distinct granule type because this peptide does not resist pretreatment with osmic acid. This pretreatment, however, is essential to preserve e.g. the membrane structures of granule and vesicle types.

The immunocytochemical results were confirmed by preabsorption controls and immunodot-blotting assays (methodology described by

Dircksen et al., 1987b) of HPLC-separated crude PO-extracts (Dircksen et al., 1987a; Dircksen & Keller 1988).

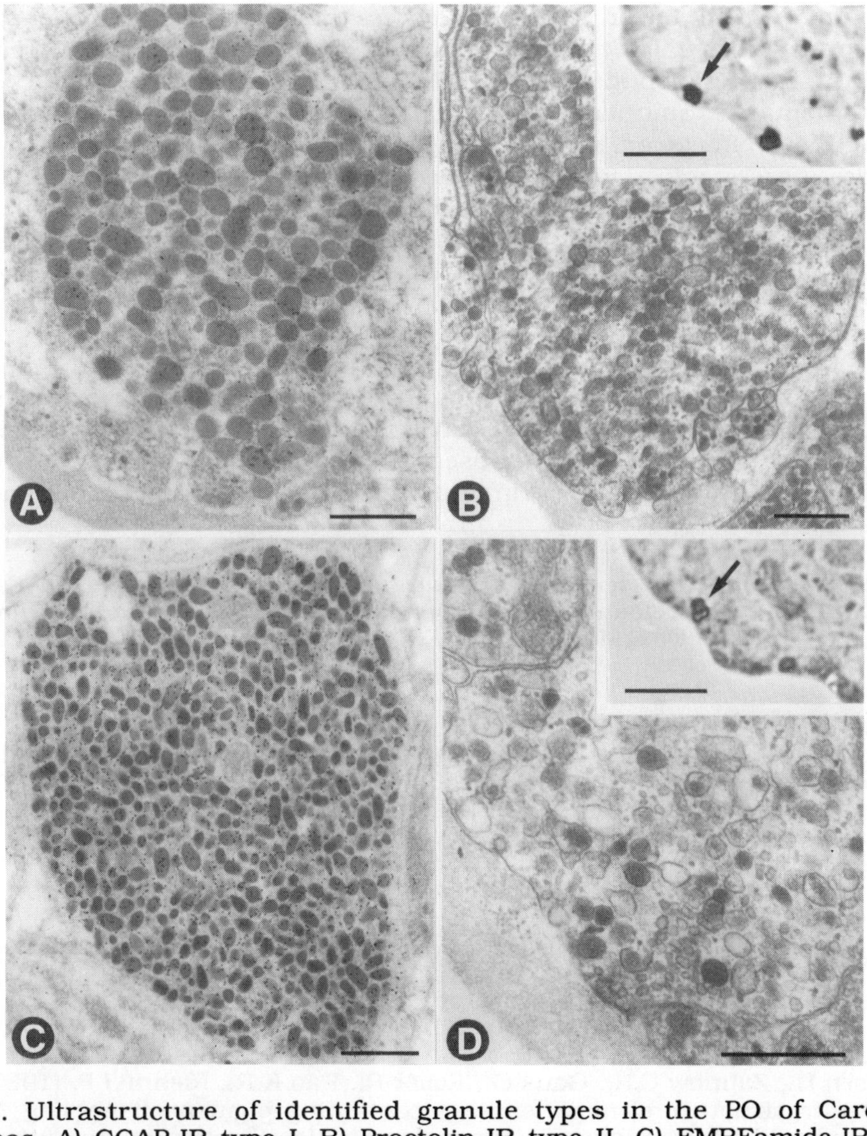

Fig.3. Ultrastructure of identified granule types in the PO of Carcinus maenas. A) CCAP-IR type I, B) Proctolin-IR type II, C) FMRFamide-IR type III, D) FMRFamide-IR granule type V. On-grid immunogold-labeling in A),C). Insets in B) and D) show PAP-labeled axon endings in semithin sections adjacent to the ultrathin sections. For methodological details see Dircksen & Keller (1988). bars: 500 nm; bars in insets.10 μm.

These assays revealed single immunoreactive peak-fractions eluting at the retention times of authentic Proctolin and CCAP, but two different FMRFamide-IR HPLC-fractions at retention times different from authentic FMRFamide. The latter result indicates the presence of at least two different peptides related to FMRFamides. Trimmer et al. (1987) recently identified the octapeptides SDRNFLRFamide and TNRNFLRFamide in the PO of Homarus americanus, the latter of which exhibiting ino- and chronotropic effects on semiisolated hearts. It seems likely that similar peptides cross-reactive with the applied antiFMRFamide-serum exist in the PO of Carcinus maenas. The biochemical characterizations of both FMRFamide-IR fractions and the LENK-IR are currently under investigation.

The anatomical distributions of peptidergic axons in the AR and PO suggest that FMRFamide- and LENK-IR peptides together with the identified neuropeptides proctolin and CCAP may participate in the complex control of heartbeat and respiration in the shore crab. Since the source of these peptides are neurons in the thoracic ganglia projecting to the AR and PO via the segmental nerves (Dircksen et al.1987a; Dircksen & Keller 1988), the identified neurosecretory systems may serve as model systems for the study of peripheral release of neurosecretion and its regulation.

Three of the antisera used in this study were generous gifts of Dr.M.Eckert, Jena, GDR (antiProctolin), Dr.H.H.Boer, Amsterdam, NL (antiFMRFamide) and Dr.R.Martin, Ulm, FRG(antiLeu-enkephalin)

REFERENCES

Alexandrowicz J.S. (1953) Nervous organs in the pericardial cavity of the decapod. J.Mar.Biol.Assoz.U.K. 31:563-580

Brown B.E. & Starratt A.N. (1975) Isolation of proctolin, a myotropic peptide from *Periplaneta americana.* J.Insect.Physiol. **21**:1879-1881

Cooke I.M. & Sullivan R.E. (1982) Hormones and neurosecretion. In: The Biology of Crustacea, Vol 2 (eds. D.E.Bliss, L.H.Mantel) pp. 205-290. Academic Press, New York

Dircksen H., Stangier J., Keller R. (1987a) Proctolin-like, FMRFamide-like, and Leu-enkephalin-like immunoreactovity in the pericardial organs of brachyuran crustaceans. Abstract of the 13th Conf.Europ.Comp.Endocrinologists, Belgrade, Yugoslavia, Gen.Comp. Endocrinol. **66**:42

Dircksen H., Zahnow C.A., Gaus G., Keller R., Rao K.R., Riehm J.P. (1987b) The ultrastructure of nerve endings containing pigment-dispersing hormone (PDH) in crustacean sinus glands: Identification by an antiserum against synthetic PDH. Cell Tissue Res. **250**:377-387

Dircksen H.& Keller R. (1988) Immunocytochemical localization of CCAP, a novel crustacean cardioactive peptide, in the nervous system of the shore crab, Carcinus maenas L. Cell Tissue Res. **254:**347-360

Maynard D.M. (1961) Thoracic neurosecretory structures in Brachyura. I.Gross anatomy. Biol.Bull. **121**:316-329

Schwarz T.L., Lee G.M.H., Siwicki K.K., Standaert D.G., Kravitz E.A. (1984) Proctolin in the lobster: The distribution, release, and chemical characterization of a likely neurohormone. J. Neurosci. **4**:1300-1311

Stangier J., Dircksen H., Keller R. (1986) Identification and immunocytochemical localization of Proctolin in the pericardial organs of the shore crab, *Carcinus maenas*. Peptides **7**:67-72

Stangier J., Hilbich C., Beyreuther K., Keller R. (1987) Unusual cardioactive peptide (CCAP) from pericardial organs of the shore crab *Carcinus maenas*. Proc.Natl.Acad.Sci.USA **84**:575-579

Stangier J., Hilbich C., Dircksen H., Keller R. (1988) Distribution of a novel cardioactive neuropeptide (CCAP) in the nervous system of the shore crab, *Carcinus maenas* L. Peptides **9**:795-800

Starratt A.N. & Brown B.E. (1975) Structure of the pentapeptide proctolin, a proposed neurotransmitter in insects. Life Sci. **17**:1253-1256

Sullivan R.E. (1979) A proctolin-like peptide in crab pericardial organs. J.Exp.Zool. **210**:543-552

Trimmer B.A., Kobierski C.A., Kravitz E.A. (1987) Purification and characterization of immunoreactive substances from the lobster nervous system: Isolation and sequence analysis of two closely related peptides. J.Comp.Neurol. **266**:16-26

Frontiers in Crustacean Neurobiology
Advances in Life Sciences

BRADYCARDIA AND TACHYCARDIA INDUCED BY EXTRINSIC CARDIAC NERVES IN AN ISOPOD, *BATHYNOMUS DOEDERLEINI*

Kosuke Tanaka and Kiyoaki Kuwasawa

Department of Biology, Tokyo Metropolitan University, 2-1-1 Fukazawa, Setagaya-ku, Tokyo 158, Japan

SUMMARY

We elucidated in *Bathynomus doederleini* that one extrinsic cardio-inhibitory (CI) and two cardio-acceleratory axons (CAs) contained in one of paired anterior cardiac nerves were found to originate from, respectively, the first, second and third thoracic ganglia. Using restrained and unrestrained animals, correlations among activity of the heart, impulses of the extrinsic nerves, and animal movements were investigated. Optical and mechanical external stimuli induced instantaneous bradycardia or cardiac arrest. Such cardiac inhibition resulted from reciprocal activation of CIs and inactivation of CAs.

An increase of swimmeret rate accompanied instantaneous tachycardia, which was induced by activation of CAs. Once CAs were cut, heart rate did not immediately increase along with the increase of swimmeret rate. Our results suggest that the neural mechanism (i.e., activation of CAs) is indispensable in order to produce tachycardia and that inactivation of CIs may contribute, in part, to tachycardia.

INTRODUCTION

It has been long known that, in crustaceans, heartbeat is driven by the cardiac ganglion located in the heart. In decapods a pair of extrinsic cardio-regulatory nerves referred to as dorsal nerves innervate the heart (Alexandrowicz, 1932; reviewed by Maynard, 1960). It has been reported in decapods that external stimuli such as mechanical and optical stimuli evoked bradycardia or cardiac arrest (Florey & Kriebel, 1974; Miyazaki et al., 1985), and that activation of CIs and inactivation of CAs decreased heart rate (Field & Larimer, 1975; Miyazaki et al. , 1985).

In decapods, tachycardia was accompanied by animal movements (Larimer & Tindel, 1966; Smatresk & Cameron, 1981; Wood & Randall, 1981; Booth et al., 1982). However, it has not been verified that the cardio-regulatory nerves are involved in the mechanisms of tachycardia which are accompanied by animal movements.

In an isopod *Ligia*, the heart is innervated by a pair of extrinsic cardiac nerves (Alexandrowicz, 1952). In *Porcellio*, the cardiac nerves running along the anterior artery contain both inhibitory and acceleratory axons, which regulate the cardiac ganglion and myocardium (Holley & Delaleu, 1972; Delaleu & Holley, 1976). In the present material, *Bathynomus doederleini*, one of paired anterior cardiac nerves contains one inhibitory axon (CI) and two acceleratory axons (CA1 and CA2), as well as two axons innervating cardio-arterial valves of anterior arteries (Kihara & Kuwasawa, 1984, 1985).

In this study, we first identified routes of CI, CA1 and CA2 from the periphery to the central ganglia. Then, using restrained and unrestrained animals, we investigated correlations between changes in heart rate induced by a variety of external stimuli or accompanied by animal movements, and activity of the cardio-regulatory axons. Preliminary accounts of part of this study have appeared (Tanaka et al., 1986).

MATERIAL & METHODS

The giant marine isopod, *Bathynomus doederleini* (8-15 cm in body length), was used. They were collected at the bottom of the sea off Tokyo Bay in traps and were kept in laboratory aquaria at 15-18°C. Unrestrained animals were used to investigate correlations between, variously, heart rate and external stimuli, or heart rate and animal movements. We recorded electrocardiogram (EKG) and electromyogram (EMG) of the swimmerets which have tufts of branchial filaments functioning as the gill (cf. McLaughlin, 1983). Fire-polished Ag-AgCl electrodes connected with AC amplifiers through an enamel-coated copper wire (50 cm in length) were used for recording EKG and EMG. The electrodes inserted through artificial openings in the exoskeleton were attached to the dorsal surface of the heart and to a certain muscle bundle of swimmeret responsible for return stroke. The openings were obturated with plastic glue in order to fix the electrodes to the exoskeleton. In studies of restrained animals, impulses of cardio-regulatory axons were recorded by means of glass capillary suction electrodes and at the same time EKG and EMG were recorded in order to investigate correlations between impulses of the axons and heart rate, or swimmeret rate. Methods of gross dissection were similar to those described previously (Kihara & Kuwasawa, 1984).

RESULTS & DISCUSSION

We anatomically and electrophysiologically identified the central ganglia from which CI and CAs originate. CI, CA1 and CA2 (cf. Kihara & Kuwasawa, 1984 for neural anatomy) originate from, respectively, the fourth root of the first thoracic ganglion, the third root of the second thoracic ganglion, and the third root of the third thoracic ganglion. Even after each of the single ganglia from which the axons originate was isolated from other central ganglia, spontaneous impulses of the axons were still recorded at the periphery. Cell bodies of CI, CA1 and CA2 may, therefore, be located in the ganglia from which they originate.

We recorded impulses of both left- and right-side CIs and left-side CA1 from the bundle composed of a pair of anterior cardiac nerves in the heart, and impulses of a single left-side CA2 (Fig. 1). A tactile stimulus was applied to the first thoracic limb. Immediately after the stimulus, CI impulse rate accelerated, while, contrarily, impulse rates of CA1 and CA2 decreased. After a while, their impulse rates reverted to the level prior to stimulation. Since such reciprocal correlation between activity of CI and CAs has been observed in decapods as well (Field & Larimer, 1975; Miyazaki et al., 1985), this reciprocal correlation might be common in a variety of Malacostraca (cf. Bowman & Abele, 1982 for classification of Crustacea).

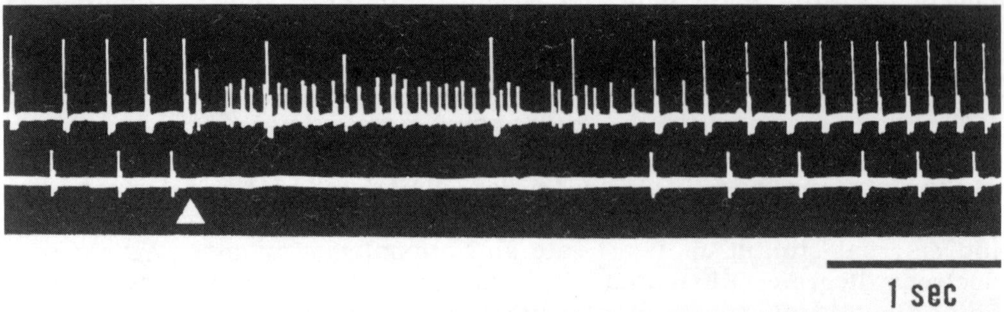

Fig. 1. Simultaneous records of impulses obtained from the bundle composed of a pair of anterior cardiac nerves in the heart (upper trace) and from a single left-side CA2 (lower trace). In the upper trace, the large impulses were recorded from left-side CA1 and the two small types of impulses from left and right CIs. A tactile stimulus was applied to the first thoracic limb at the point indicated by an arrowhead.

A variety of external stimuli (including light-on and -off, tactile, pressure and vibration stimuli) produced bradycardia or cardiac arrest. Fig. 2 A shows simultaneous records of EKG and EMG of a swimmeret obtained from an unrestrained animal in response to tactile stimulation applied to the tergum of the thorax. Simultaneous inhibition of EKG and swimmeret EMG were observed accompanying the stimulation. Such response of EKG was never evoked by any external stimuli once a pair of anterior cardiac nerves had been severed. Therefore, it is suggested that the cardio-inhibitory response resulted from both activation of CI and inactivation of CA1 and CA2 (see Fig. 1). Cardiac inhibition resulted only from the neuronal mechanisms of the cardiac nerves. In decapods, cardiac inhibitory reflexes were induced by such external stimuli (Florey & Kriebel, 1974; Miyazaki et al., 1985).

External stimuli produced not only cardiac inhibition but also inhibition of swimmeret movements. In the shore crab, heartbeat and scaphognathite movements were inhibited by external stimuli (Cumberlidge & Uglow,

1977). Young (1978) suggested that a common system might govern the correlation between cardio-inhibitory nerves and inhibition of scaphognathites. Wilkens (1976) suggested that, in decapods, inhibitory inputs to the cardiac ganglion and scaphognathite system were commonly mediated by cardio-inhibitory neurons. Since our study failed to inhibit respiratory swimmeret movements by antidromic stimulation of cardio-inhibitory axons, we consider it unlikely that CIs commonly innervate both the heart and swimmerets.

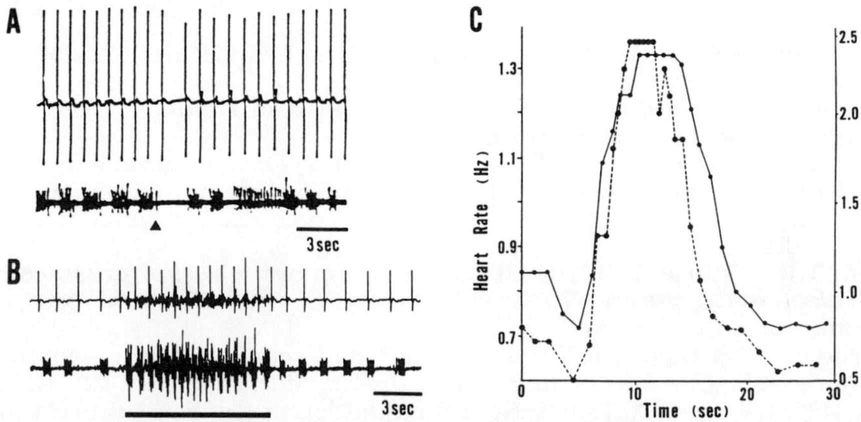

Fig. 2. Simultaneous recordings of EKG (upper traces) and swimmeret EMG (lower traces) obtained from unrestrained animals. A tactile stimulus (indicated by an arrowhead) evoked cardiac inhibition (A). Paddling (hyperventilation) accompanied cardiac acceleration (underlined period in B). Graph C shows changes in heart rate (solid line) and swimmeret rate (broken line) in the paddling movement.

In decapods, tachycardia was accompanied by various animal movements, including walking (in the crayfish, Larimer & Tindel, 1966), exercise on a treadmill (in the coconut crab, Smatresk & Cameron, 1981; in the land crab, Wood & Randall, 1981), and swimming (in the blue crab, Booth et al., 1982). We used unrestrained animals to investigate the correlation between heart rate and animal movements. The three types of movements observed were paddling (hyperventilation), walking, and swimming, accompanied by an increase in swimmeret rate and in heart rate. Fig. 2 B shows simultaneous recordings of EKG and swimmeret EMG in the paddling movement. Fig. 2 C shows temporal patterns of heart and swimmeret rates resulting from paddling. Heart rate increased by 78% and swimmeret rate by 400 % in the animal movement.

We recorded CA2 impulses using restrained animals when tachycardia occurred in the paddling movement. An increase of CA2 impulse frequency was accompanied by the increase in swimmeret rate, nearly instantaneously (not shown). Once CAs had been severed, heart rate did not immediately increase along with the increase in swimmeret rate. Activation of CAs may be indispensable in order to tachycardia accompanied by an increase in swimmeret rate. Inactivation of CIs may contribute, in part, to tachycardia.

Acknowledgements. This study was supported in part by Grants-in-Aid for Co-operative Research (No. 61304006) from the Ministry of Education, Science and Culture of Japan. Contribution from the Shimoda Marine Research Center, No. 494.

REFERENCES

Alexandrowicz, J.S. (1932) The innervation of the heart of the crustacea. I. Decapoda. *Q. J. Microsc. Sci.* **75**: 181 - 249.

Alexandrowicz, J.S. (1952) Innervation of the heart of *Ligia oceanica. J. Mar. Biol. Assoc. UK* **31**: 85-96.

Booth, C.E., McMahon, B.R. & Pinder, A.W. (1982) Oxygen uptake and the potentiating effects of increaseed hemolymph lactate on oxygen transport during exercise in the blue crab, *Callinectes sapidus.. J. Comp. Physiol.* **148**: 111-121.

Bowman, T.E. & Abele, L.G. (1982) Classification of the recent crustacea. In *The biology of Crustacea* , Vol 1, (ed. D.E. Bliss) pp. 1-27. New York: Academic press.

Cumberlidge, N. & Uglow, R.F. (1977) Heart and scaphognathite activity in the shore crab, *Carcinus maenas* (L.). *J. Exp. Mar. Biol. Ecol.* **28**: 87-107.

Delaleu, J.C. & Holley, A. (1976) Neural regulation of the heart muscle in an isopod crustacean: acceleration and peripheral inhibition. *J. Exp. Biol.* **64**: 345-356.

Field, L.H. & Larimer, J.L. (1975) The cardioregulatory system of crayfish: Neuroanatomy and physiology. *J. Exp. Biol.* **62**: 519- 530.

Florey, E. & Kriebel, M.E. (1974) The effects of temperature, anoxia and sensory stimulation on the heart rate of unrestrained crabs. *Comp. Biochem. Physiol.* **48** A: 285-300.

Holley, A. & Delaleu, J.C. (1972) Electrophysiology of the heart of an isopod crustacean: I. general properties. *J. Exp. Biol.* **57**: 589-608.

Kihara, A. & Kuwasawa, K. (1984) A neuroanatomical and electrophysiological analysis of nervous regulation in the heart of an isopod crustacean, *Bathynomus doederleini. J. Comp. Physiol.* A **154**: 883-894.

Kihara, A. & Kuwasawa, K. (1985) Neural control of the cardio-arterial valves in an isopod crustacean, *Bathynomus doederleini* : Excitatory and inhibitory junctional potentials. *J. Comp. Physiol.* A **157**: 529-536.

Larimer, J.L. & Tindel, J.R. (1966) Sensory modifications of heart rate in crayfish. *Anim. Behav.* **14**: 239- 245.

Maynard, D.M. (1960) Circulation and heart function. In *The physiology of crustacea* , Vol I, (ed. T.H. Waterman) pp. 161-226. New York: Academic press.

McLaughlin, P.A. (1983) Internal anatomy. In *The biology of crustacea* , Vol 5, (ed. D.E. Bliss) pp. 1-52. New York: Academic press.

Miyazaki, T., Kuwasawa, K., Yazawa, T. & Mashimo, K. (1985) Identification of the cardio-regulator nerves in a marine hermit crab and the shadow-induced cardiac inhibition in some decapods. *Zool. Sci.* **2**: 35-47.

Smatresk, N.J.& Cameron, J.N. (1981) Post-exercise acid-base balance and ventilatory control in *Birgus latro* , the coconut crab. *J. Exp. Zool.* **218**: 75-82.

Tanaka, K., Kuwasawa, K. & Fujiwara, Y. (1986) Inhibitory and acceleratory cardiac reflexes in *Bathynomus doederleini. Zool. Sci.* **3**: 968.

Wilkens, J.L. (1976) Neuronal control of respiration in decapod crustacea. *Fed. Proc.* **35**: 2000-2006.

Wood, C.M. & Randall, D.J. (1981) Oxygen and carbon dioxide exchange during exercise in the land crab (*Cardisoma carnifex*). *J. Exp. Zool.* **218**:7-22.

Young, R.E. (1978) Correlated activities in the cardioregulator nerves and ventilatory system in the Norwegian lobster, *Nephrops norvegicus* (L.). *Comp. Biochem. Physiol.* **61** A: 387-394.

Frontiers in Crustacean Neurobiology
Advances in Life Sciences

DEVELOPMENT AND IDENTIFIED NEURAL SYSTEMS IN THE CRAYFISH BRAIN

Renate Sandeman and David Sandeman

School of Biological Science, University of New South Wales, Sydney, Australia.

SUMMARY

Serotonin immunoreactivity is first expressed in neurons in the brain of crayfish at 75% development, increases in the two postembryonic stages, and is complete in the first adult stage. Early ablations of the antennules of early postembryos, reared in isolation from their mothers, affects the development of the olfactory lobes and the large serotonin immunoreactive neurons within them.

INTRODUCTION

Investigations of the brains of adult arthropods have revealed the precision with which individual components of the nervous system are connected together and the search for rules that govern the correct assembly of neurons has been a continuing and challenging one. The advent of immunocytochemical and molecular genetic techniques has provided us with some powerful tools and reawakened the study of neuronal development in a number of different species. Developmental studies on crustaceans have lagged behind those on insects probably because of the short generation times of many insects and relative ease with which they can be reared. Freshwater crayfish nevertheless offer some unique possibilities. Their embryos are available throughout development, and are cared for by the mother. Their development in the egg can easily be observed through the tough transparent chorion, and free swimming larval stages through which marine crustaceans pass, are considerably modified and take place in the egg (Zehnder 1934a,b). There are also some drawbacks: 1, there is no published account of the developmental stages of freshwater crayfish, reared at constant temperature and expressed as a percentage of their total development. 2, when they hatch, the young are still attached to the inside of the chorion and to the mother (Chantran 1872) and so are not practically accessible to manipulation. 3, it has been reported that eggs detached from the swimmerets, develop but fail to hatch (Droscher 1906) and do not undergo subsequent postembryonic moults to turn into miniature adults. Attempts to raise eggs, isolated in dishes, from an early stage through to adults do not seem to have been very successful, although the importance of suspending eggs above the substrate was noted to be important for their survival (Bieber 1940). We have developed a method for rearing embryos of Australian freshwater crayfish *Cherax destructor* in isolation from their mothers and have begun to explore the development of the nervous system in these animals. The crayfish brain is a complex organ and for developmental studies one is constrained to choose an identifiable system or neuron set. The olfactory lobe with its monomodal sensory input (Sandeman and Denburg 1976, Mellon et al 1989) presented itself as a possibility, particularly as it contains large neurons that label reliably with antibodies raised against serotonin (Sandeman and Sandeman 1987). Also, an identifiable set of about 100 neurons in adult animals label consistently with antibodies to serotonin and our ability to select these neurons out of the brain, makes them attractive for such a study (Sandeman et al 1988). In this report we describe initial results that have been obtained in an immunocytochemical study of developing serotonin immunoreactive neurons and the effect on them and the olfactory lobes, of antennular ablation in the early postembryonic stage.

METHODS

Australian freshwater crayfish, *Cherax destructor* will reproduce throughout 9 months of the year in controlled conditions of light, temperature and pH of the water in which they live. The developmental stages of *Cherax* embryos were observed under controlled conditions by removing eggs from mothers every day during the period from their fertilization to hatching. In this way a description of the total development, in 5% steps, has been obtained for embryos from 48 different mothers (Sandeman and Sandeman in preparation). Using this information we were able to determine the stage at which serotonin immunoreactivity first appeared and monitor its subsequent development. Methods used for immunocytochemical treatment of whole-mounted and sectioned brains have been described in detail in a previous publication (Sandeman et al 1988). Micrographs of the first postembryonic stage were made using cryo-scanning electron microscopy and of later stages using material fixed in glutaraldehyde and dried from xylene over several days in a dust proof container.

Access to the first postembryonic stage (POI) which is normally still attached to the mother was critical for the ablation studies, and so we developed the following procedure for rearing eggs in isolation: A small block (8mm x 8mm x 1.5mm thick) of Sylgard (Dow Corning U.S.A.) was prepared by cutting a slit into its surface. An egg was removed from the mother by cutting through the short stalk that binds it to the swimmeret. The Sylgard block was bent over a small bar, opening the slit in its surface enough to admit the stalk of the egg. Releasing the block firmly clamps the egg stalk in the slit and the block with the egg were then placed in a tissue culture well (35mm wide, 18mm deep. Cell Well, Corning. U.S.A.) containing dechlorinated tap water. The Sylgard block with egg hanging beneath it, floats on the surface of the water in the well like a small raft. Surface tension fortuitously keeps it in the center and away from the walls of the cell well. The floor of each well was covered with a disc of nylon plankton net (0.25mm mesh, see Results). Water in the wells was changed every 2 to 3 days, but was neither oxygenated nor agitated between changes. More than two thirds of embryos reared in this way reached the first adult stage. 90% of all fatalities occured during moulting.

Antennular ablations were carried out on the first postembryonic stage, while they were still attached to the chorion. No operations were performed on the healed stumps of the second embryonic stage (POII), but regenerated appendages in the first adult stage (ADI) were removed immediately after the moult from the second postembryonic stage to the adult. The animals were kept until the subsequent moult (ADII), about 30 days later, and then fixed for sectioning. Sectioned brains were reacted with antibodies raised against serotonin to examine the effect of antennular ablation on serotonin immunoreactive cells in the olfactory lobe.

RESULTS

Developmental stages: Shortly before hatching, embryos appear to be compressed against the inside walls of the chorion. The chorion splits longitudinally and the hatchling hangs between the two halves of the chorion and divests itself of a second, internal membrane. We have called this stage the first postembryo, or POI. Its large cephalothorax is filled with egg yolk, its eyes appear to be sessile, and only about one quarter of the photoreceptors contain pigment. Antenna and antennules are curved posteriorly. The lateral flagellum of the antennule is larger than the medial and both are without sensory hairs although in some animals small raised areas on the distal annuli of the lateral flagellum may represent developing chemoreceptors. Sections taken through the base of the antennules and examined with light and electron microscopes revealed no axons, from which we conclude that even if peripheral development of receptor hairs is already underway at this stage, the ingrowing afferent axons have not yet reached the base of the antennule or central nervous system. The antennae are also hairless. The dactyls of the last two walking legs are hooked. The telson and uropods, contained within the membranous sheath attaching the postembryo to the chorion, are not yet differentiated into separate appendages.

The first moult occurs 5 to 8 days after hatching at 20~C. Very few animals lying on the floor of their dishes survive this moult, but almost all those suspended from Sylgard rafts free themselves from their exuvia and drop to the floor of the wells.

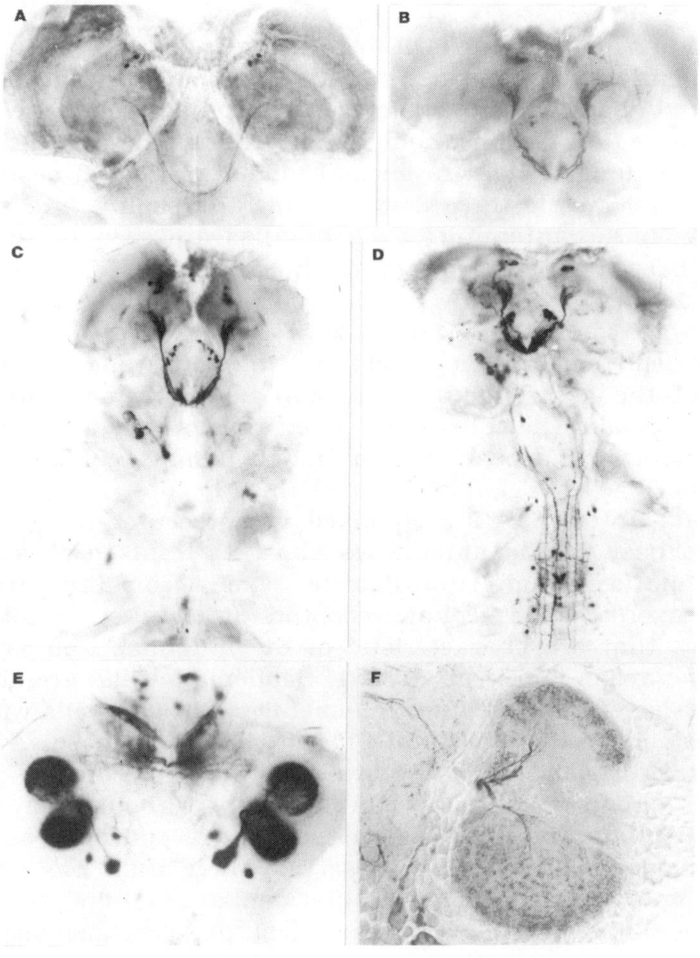

Fig 1. A, at 75-85% development, axons of immunoreactive neurons with their cell somata in the terminal medulla on each side, pass across the median protocerebrum. B, by 85-95%, the primary neurites between the cell somata and the synaptic field in the terminal medulla can be seen. Immunoreactivity develops in the internal medulla and in cell somata along the anterior edge of the median protocerebrum. C, large serotonin immunoreactive cells that branch in the olfactory and accessory lobes are visible just before hatching. D, by POI, immunoreactive cells in the thoracic ganglia label clearly as do most cells in the protocerebrum that are present in the adult. E, in POII, the first large serotonin immunoreactive cells branching in the olfactory and accessory lobes are joined by up to four other cell somata. F, by ADI the structure of the axon branching in the olfactory and accessory lobes has been established as column-like in the olfactory lobes or as small round glomeruli in the accessory lobe.

The second postembryo, or POII, has less yolk stored in its cephalothorax and consequently a more slender appearance. The eyes can now be seen to be stalked and about half the photoreceptors contain pigment. Antennae are longer than in POI but still without receptor hairs. The lateral flagella of the antennules are longer than the medial, and bear 5 to 6 aesthetasc hairs (chemoreceptors) on the three distal annuli. In keeping with the presence of receptors on the antennule, axon bundles are seen in sections taken through its base. POII animals are able to move around freely but are not particularly active.

The POII stage lasts from 10 to 14 days at 20~C and the end is signalled by the near depletion of the egg yolk and the appearance of gastroliths on each side of the gastric mill which can be easily seen in the almost transparent animals. The subsequent moult results in a miniature adult that is highly mobile and accepts food although it may still have yolk stored alongside the digestive glands. We call this the first adult stage or ADI. Antennae and antennules are equipped with receptor hairs and sections through the base of the antennules show at least three axon bundles containing fine (less than 1um diameter) axons from the chemoreceptors and larger axons from mechanoreceptors (Mellon et al 1989). Sessile feather hairs that are characteristic of the antennae and antennules of larger adult crayfish (Tautz et al 1981, Sandeman 1989) are absent except at the very base of the flagellum. Animals living in cell wells with a smooth floor did not survive the POII to ADI moult as well as those where the floor was covered with nylon mesh to provide them with an anchor point for the exuvia. Also, miniature adults raised in cell wells without nylon mesh on the floor, were frequently found lying on their backs and often succumbed to fungal infections. This was never observed when mesh was provided. Our rationalisation of this phenomenon is that miniature adults require a surface to which they can cling to with their feet to keep themselves upright, particularly when using their anterior chelate walking legs to clean themselves.

Development of the serotonin immunoreactive neurons: With our methods we detect the first expression of serotonin immunoreactivity in neurons in the protocerebrum in whole mounted preparations at 75% to 80% development (Fig. 1A). Up to 6 cell somata appear on the medial edge of the terminal medulla. A synaptic field of serotonin immunoreactive fibers, lying in the center of the terminal medulla can be detected, as can fine fibers in a network in the internal medulla. Labelled axons pass from the terminal medulla down along the short protocerebral tracts to the median protocerebrum and cross to the contralateral side. A synaptic field of serotonin immunoreactive neurons develops just anterior to the axons that cross the brain. No connections between these and the axons crossing the brain can be made out in the early stages, and nor do cell somata in the median protocerebrum react to the antibody at this stage. No other neurons in the lateral or median protocerebrum or ventral nerve cord showed immunoreactivity to serotonin antibodies at this stage. The early development of serotonin immunoreactive cells in crayfish are remarkably similar to those occurring during larval development of the moth *Manduca* (Granger et al 1989)

By 85-95% development, primary neurites from the cell bodies in the terminal medulla can be traced down to the synaptic fields in the neuropile. Fine fibers extend laterally from the terminal medulla to end in the internal medulla and some cell somata in the median protocerebrum label (Fig. 1B). In some preparations, fine fibers can be detected extending posteriorly from the anterior median protocerebral network to the deutocerebrum. Segmentally arranged cell bodies make an appearance in the thoracic ganglia, together with short stretches of labelled axons. Serotonin immunoreactivity in the olfactory and accessory lobes becomes clearly established between 95% and hatching (Fig 1C).

Many of the features of the adult system (Sandeman et al 1988) can be recognised in the brain and thoracic ganglia of the POI stage (Fig. 1D). In the terminal medulla, the large median complex of serotonin immunoreactive fibers is clearly established and the projection of axons from this complex to the protocerebral bridge can be determined. Large axons that in the adult run between the median protocerebrum and the lateral part of the terminal medulla and internal medulla, are also present in POI. Dorsal to the protocerebral bridge, a network of immunoreactive fibers spreads out laterally and caudally. The somata of these neurons, lying in the anterior median cluster of cells in the median protocerebrum, also label at this stage. Fibers in lateral portions of the median protocerebrum label in POI. These can be recognised as terminals of large elements that cross the central body in adults, although at this stage neither the cell bodies of these neurons nor their complex branching in the central body can be seen.

The giant serotonin immunoreactive neurons in the olfactory lobe are the dominant features of the median protocerebrum after hatching. Initially, one large cell appears on each side and this branches into the olfactory and accessory lobes which have already taken on their spherical appearance, although the olfactory lobes are larger than the accessory lobes at this stage. Terminal branches of serotonin immunoreactive giants in the olfactory and accessory lobes all have the same bulbous appearance at this stage. There is no sign of the very different glomerular structure that later distinguishes the two neuropiles from one another. Branches from the primary neurites of the giant neurons, that end in small neuropiles just medial to the olfactory lobe, are a characteristic of fully formed neurons in adults and are also conspicuous at this stage.

By POII, nearly all features of the adult serotonin immunoreactive system are present. Lateral branches of the axons traversing the central body are clear to see, branching in the lateral lobes of the median protocerebrum. Olfactory and accessory lobes are about the same size in POII and the terminals of the giant neuron still end in small bulbs although they appear more tightly packed in the accessory lobes. The first large serotonin immunoreactive giant cells to appear on each side are now joined by up to four smaller cell somata whose axons also project into the accessory and olfactory lobes (Fig. 1E).

All components of the serotonin system are present in the ADI stage including fine fibers that project from the deutocerebrum down into the antennular lobes, not visible in the POII animals. The developmental stages of serotonin neurons in the protocerebrum can only be judged by the extent of their branching and not by the form taken by the terminals in the synaptic fields. The terminals of the olfactory giant cells however, take on a different form depending on whether they end in the olfactory or accessory lobe. In the olfactory lobe they branch within large column-like glomeruli, whereas in the accessory lobe they form small round glomeruli. This difference is first observable in ADI animals, and is best seen in sections through the lobes (Fig. 1D). The serotonin immunoreactive network is extensive in thoracic ganglia of ADI animals.

Ablation experiments: Removal of the antennule on one side at the POI stage resulted in a smooth stump in POII animals in nearly all cases. Large receptor hairs were sometimes found on healed stumps. These animals were not included in the experiment. Smooth stumps of POII animals were not treated in any way. After moulting from POII to ADI, most animals exhibited a biramous, regenerated antennule bearing chemoreceptor and mechanoreceptor hairs. Annuli of both medial and lateral regenerated flagella were often irregular in comparison with unablated appendages.

Removal of the antennule from the POI, and again of the regenerate from the ADI, reduces the size of the olfactory lobe on the ablated side in ADII animals by about 30%. The lateral antennular neuropile on the ablated side is also reduced. Large serotonin immunoreactive neurons are present on both sides of the brain and branch within normal and reduced olfactory lobes. Sections through the center of the lobe on the unablated side show branches of serotonin immunoreactive cells to be separated by unlabelled elements that could be glial cells, large axons or blood vessels (Fig. 2A). Neuropile in the olfactory lobe on the ablated side, however, is not divided into columns by these unlabelled elements and serotonin immunoreactive branches diffuse evenly through the lobe (Fig. 2B). A sheath of fine axons, presumably from the antennular chemoreceptors, encloses the olfactory lobes of <u>both</u> unablated and ablated sides in ADII animals.

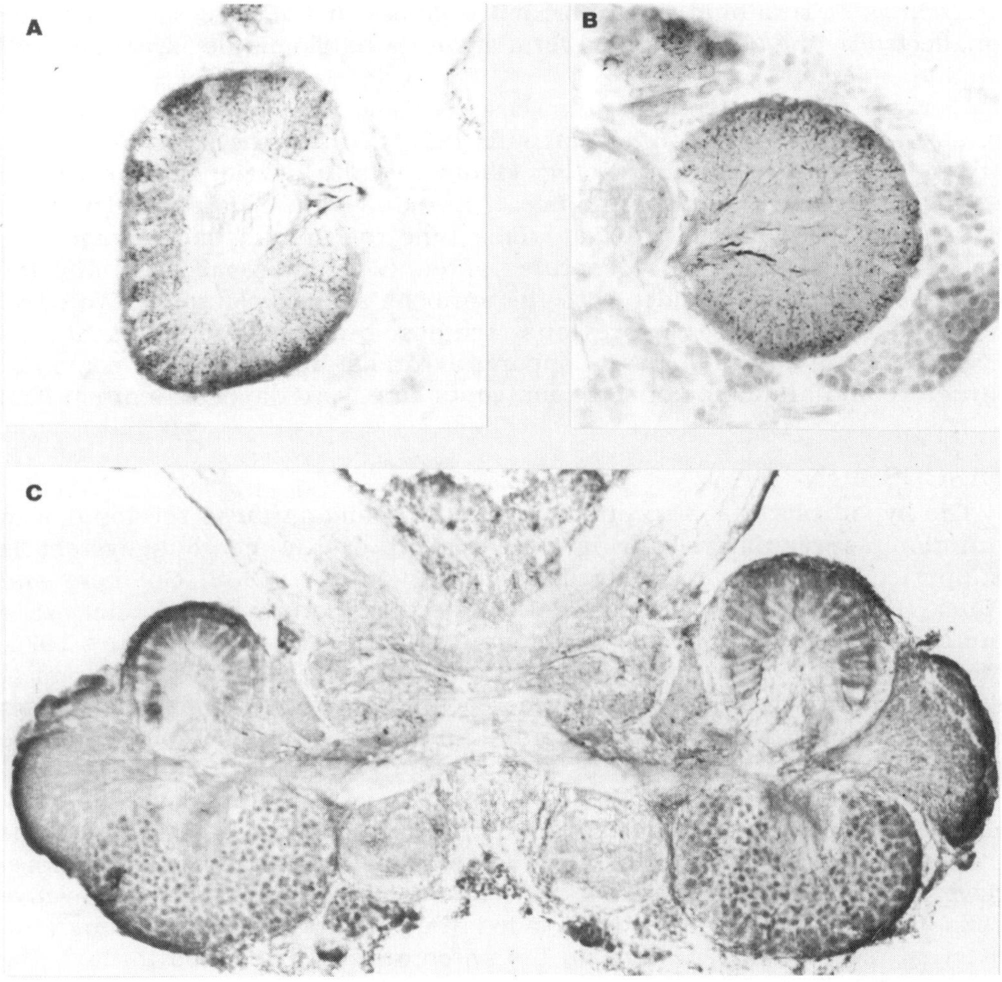

Fig. 2. A, a section through the olfactory lobe of an ADII animal whose left antennule had been ablated at POI and again at ADI. The neuropile is divided into columns by unlabelled elements. B, on the ablated side of the brain of the same animal, the olfactory lobe neuropile is not columnar. Branches of serotonin immunoreactive cells penetrate both lobes. C, olfactory lobes of an adult animal whose left antennule had been ablated. The olfactory lobe on the ablated side is much smaller than that on the untreated side, but still exhibits a columnar structure.

Endings of serotonin immunoreactive giants in the accessory lobes are unaffected by the ablations, and form small round glomerular synaptic fields on both sides.

Removal of the antennules from large animals is followed by a reduction in size of the olfactory lobes (Maynard 1973). To test the effect of ablation on the serotonin immunoreactive giants in fully developed *Cherax*, we removed the antennule on one side of an adult with a carapace length of 5cm. After three months during which time the animal had not moulted and had not produced a regenerated antennule, it was sacrificed and the brain sectioned and labelled with the antibody against serotonin. We could confirm the results of previous studies but also found that the cytoarchitecture of the lobes is apparently undisturbed, and the columnar structure and branching of serotonin containing giants appears normal (Fig. 2C).

DISCUSSION

The hypothesis that neurotransmitters, and among these serotonin, can function as regulators during development of the nervous system is supported by a growing body of evidence (Mattson 1988, Goldberg and Kater 1989). The only afferents that project to the crayfish olfactory lobe are from chemoreceptors on the antennules (Sandeman and Denburg 1976, Mellon et al 1989) and the suggestion has been made, on purely anatomical grounds, that large serotonin immunoreactive neurons in the olfactory lobes are presynaptic to sensory afferents and constitute part of a positive feedback system that amplifies chemoreceptive signals (Sandeman et al 1988). Do these serotonin cells also play a role in regulating development in the olfactory lobe? In order to qualify for such a role, they need to be present in the olfactory lobes before ingrowing afferents arrive. Our studies have shown that in POI animals, the first large serotonin immunoreactive cells to appear have already invaded the olfactory lobes, although no external receptors are present on the antennules and sections through the base of the antennules reveal no axons. If, like similar cells in *Helisoma* embryos (Goldberg and Kater 1985, Goldberg et al 1986), ingrowing afferents in crayfish are arrested by the serotonin immunoreactive giants, a neuroregulatory role for these cells is feasible.

A related question is whether the serotonin immunoreactive giants have an effect on the overall cytoarchitecture of the olfactory and accessory lobes. During their development, the serotonin immunoreactive giants send separate branches into the olfactory and accessory lobes. In POI and POII, endings in the two lobes do not take on a distinct form but by ADI the neuropile of the two lobes is distinctly different, the accessory lobe glomeruli being small and round and those in the olfactory lobes being arranged as radiating columns. Our ablation experiments provide us with some indication that the serotonin immunoreactive giants are perhaps not responsible for the induction of different types of architecture because the columnar structure of the olfactory lobe is absent on the ablated side in ADII animals, although the dichotomously branching serotonin immunoreactive neuron is present. We suggest that, like in the moth *Manduca*, it is probably the afferents, and associated glial cells in crayfish, that are important for the induction of the columnar structure (Camazine and Hildebrand 1979, Hildebrand et al 1979, Oland and Tolbert 1988). In our experiments however, removal of the antennules at the POI stage served only to delay the ingrowth of afferent fibers to the olfactory lobe, not completely remove them. The absence of columns despite the reappearance of afferents may be indicative of a critical time window during which ingrowing afferents exert their control over the cytoarchitecture of the olfactory neuropile. Once columnar architecture has been established in the olfactory lobe, the removal of afferents does not alter it. This is perhaps not unexpected because the columnar appearance reflects the structural organization of endogenous elements in the lobe which do not necessarily degenerate in the absence of the afferent input. The developmental flexibility of second order systems in the olfactory lobe has been dramatically demonstrated in animals with supernumerary, homeotic antennules. In such a case the olfactory lobe targeted by ingrowing chemoreceptors from the extra antennule, increases in size over the normal contralateral lobe, and behavioural tests indicate the addition of functional chemoreceptive input (Mellon et al 1989). The early appearance of serotonin immunoreactive neurons in crayfish brain and their persistence throughout the life of the animals, may be related not only to their function as neuromodulators of various neural systems, but to the maintained ability of crayfish to regenerate appendages and receptors and to regulate the correct connection of ingrowing afferents from such receptors in the brain.

REFERENCES

Bieber, A (1940) Beitrage zur Kenntnis der Jugendphasen desFlusskrebses *Astacus fluviatilis* (Rond.) L. mit besondere Berucksichtigung der Metamorphose. *Rev. Suisse de Zoologie* **47**:391-470

Chantran, S. (1872) Sur la fecondation des ecrevisses. *C.R. Acad. Sci.Paris* **74**:201-202

Camazine, S.M. & Hildebrand J.G. (1979) Central projections of antennal sensory neurons in mature and developing *Manduca sexta*. *Soc. Neurosci. Abst.* **5**:155

Droscher, W. (1906) Der Krebs und seine Zucht. J. Neumann, Neudamm.Goldberg, J.I. & Kater, S.B. (1989) Expression and function of the neurotransmitter serotonin during development of the *Helisoma* nervous system. *Developmental Biology* **131**:483-495

Goldberg, J.I. & Kater, S.B. (1985) Experimental reduction of serotonin content during embryogenesis alters morphology and connectivity of specific identified *Helisoma* neurons. *Soc. Neurosci. Abstr.* **11**:158

Goldberg, J.I., Natvig, P. & Kater, S.B. (1986) Embryonic and postembryonic development of the serotonin phenotype in *Helisoma*. *Soc. Neurosci. Abstr.* **12**:1163

Granger, N.A., Homberg, U., Henderson, P., Towle, A. & Lauder, J.M. (1989) Serotonin-immunoreactive neurons in the brain of *Manduca sexta* during larval development and larval-pupal metamorphosis. *Int. J. Neuroscience* **7**:55-72

Hildebrand, J.G., Hall, L.M. & Osmond, B.C. (1979) Distribution of binding sites for 125 I-labeled alphabungarotoxin in normal and deafferented antennal lobes of *Manduca sexta*. *Proc. Natl. Acad. Sci. USA* **76**:499-503

Mattson, M.P. (1988) Neurotransmitters in the regulation of neuronal cytoarchitecture. *Brain Research Reviews* **13**:179-212

Maynard, E.A. (1973) Microscopic studies of degeneration in the crayfish brain following antennule removal. *Society for Neuroscience, 3rd annual Meeting San Diego Abstr.*, p 39

Mellon, D., Tuten, H.R. & Redick, J. (1989) Distribution of radioactive leucine following uptake by olfactory sensory neurons in normal and heteromorphic crayfish antennules. *J. Comp. Neurol.* **230**:645-662

Mellon, D., Tuten, H.R., Hurley, L.M. & Easley, M.E. (1989) Acquisition of central targets by olfactory sensory neurons in homeotic antennules: Functional consequences. *Soc. Neurosci. Abstr.* **13**:1140

Oland, L.A. & Tolbert, L.P. (1988) Effects of hydroxyurea parallel the effects of radiation in developing olfactory glomeruli in insects. *J. Comp. Neurol.* **278**:377-387

Sandeman, D.C. (1989) Physical properties, sensory receptors and tactile reflexes of the antenna of the Australian freshwater crayfish *Cherax destructor*. *J. exp. Biol.* **141**:197-217

Sandeman, D.C. & Denburg, (1976) The central projections of chemoreceptor axons in the crayfish revealed by axoplasmic transport. *Brain Res.* **115**:492-496

Sandeman, D.C., Sandeman, R.E. & Aitken, A.R. (1988) Atlas of serotonin-containing neurons in the optic lobes and brain of the crayfish *Cherax destructor*. *J. Comp. Neurol.* **269**:465-478

Sandeman, R.E. & Sandeman, D.C. (1987) Serotonin-like immunoreactivity of giant olfactory interneurons in the crayfish brain. *Brain Res.* **403**:371-374

Tautz, J., Masters, W.M., Aicher, B. & Markl, H. (1981) A new type of water vibration reeptor on the crayfish antenna. I. Sensory Physiology. *J. Comp. Physiol.* **144**:533-541

Zehnder, H. (1934a) Uber die Embryonalentwicklung des Flusskrebses. Teil I. Die ersten Stadien der Embryonalentwicklung von *Astacus fluviatilis* (Rond.) L. und *Astacus torrentium* (Schrank) vom unbefruchteten Ei bis zur Gastrulation. *Acta Zool.* **15**:1-83

Zehnder, H. (1934b) Uber die Embryonalentwicklung des Flusskrebses. Teil II. Die Ausbildung der ausseren Korperform von *Astacus fluviatilis* (Rond.) L. und *Astacus torrentium* (Schrank) von der Gastrulation zum entwickelten Tier. *Acta Zool.* **15**:85-148

Frontiers in Crustacean Neurobiology
Advances in Life Sciences

CRUSTACEAN NERVE CELLS IN PRIMARY CULTURE

Wulf Dieter Krenz, Franco Del Principe and Pamela Fischer

Zoologisches Institut, Universität Basel, Rheinsprung 9, CH-4051 Basel, Switzerland

SUMMARY

We describe a primary culture system for neurones from the central nervous system of adult crayfish. After enzymatic treatment individual neurones were isolated by suction from abdominal ganglia and the stomatogastric ganglion. On poly-L-lysine as substrate they survived for up to 24 days and grew neuritic processes. Results from current and voltage clamp experiments show that functionally important electrophysiological properties are at least partly maintained or regenerated by cultured neurones.

INTRODUCTION

In arthropod nervous systems cellular events underlying neuronal network function are not easily investigated quantitatively due to the extensive branching of the neurites where most of the voltage and ligand dependent membrane ion channels are localized. The stomatogastric system of crustacea, one of the most thoroughly studied and best understood central pattern generating networks (Selverston & Moulins, 1987) represents an example in which the inaccessibility of membrane properties has in the past rendered impossible the answering of important questions on the cellular basis of the generation, maintenance, and modulation of motor rhythms. To overcome this constraint we have developed a technique that allows one to isolate individual cells from the stomatogastric ganglion (STG) of adult crayfish, keep them alive in primary culture, and let them regenerate electrophysiological behaviour in vitro. Primary culture of neurones isolated from adult nervous systems of invertebrates has become a powerful tool in cellular and developmental neurobiology which among other approaches allows one to investigate physiologically relevant biophysical and pharmacological properties of the membranes of cell bodies and growing neurites with powerful techniques as voltage and patch clamp (e.g. Belardetti et al., 1986; Stewart et al., 1989).

METHODS

Desheathed abdominal ganglia and STGs of adult crayfish (*Pacifastacus leniusculus* and *Procambarus clarkii*) were incubated for 1.5 to 2 hours in 2 mg/ml collagenase/dispase in culture medium containing 5-10 % fetal calf serum (M500 FCS: M500 was prepared by mixing Leibovitz L-15 tissue culture medium [GIBCO-BRL, Basel, Switzerland] 1:1 with a stock salt solution to yield the same final ionic composition as Van Harreveld crayfish saline. Osmolarity was elevated to 500 mOsmol by adding NaCl).

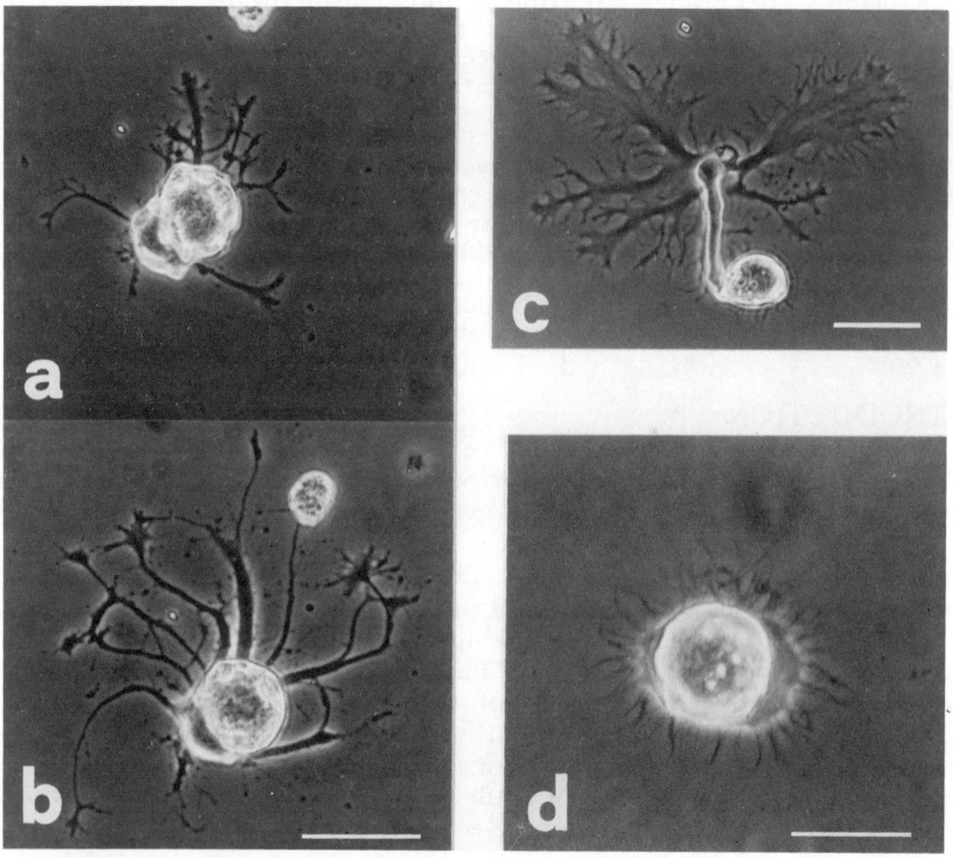

Fig. 1. a. b.: Neurone explanted from an abdominal ganglion growing several neurites multipolarly from the soma, photographed on day 2(a) and 4(b) after explantation. c.: STG neurone explanted with part of the primary neurite attached, photographed on day 5 after explantation. d. Apolar growth in an STG neurone photographed on day 7 after explantation. Bars: 100 μm.

Individual neuronal somata were isolated by suction with siliconized fire-polished pipettes as described by Ready & Nicholls (1979). After careful washing through three drops of sterile medium (M500 FCS) the cells were plated on poly-L-lysine-coated glass coverslips (Ready & Nicholls, 1979) and incubated in 4-well multidishes (NUNC 134673) in M500 lacking FCS but containing 0.05 mg/ml gentamycin or streptomycin. FCS was added after 12 hours. All procedures were performed in a laminar flow hood. The culture wells were kept in a moist chamber at room temperature (22-25 °C).

RESULTS

Survival and growth. Under the conditions described above an average of 43% of the explanted cells survived and of those 32% started growing often as early as 8 hours after plating. Survival as well as neurite growth were inhibited when the cell membranes were covered with microglial cells and extracellular material. Three types of growth patterns were distinguished. Multipolar growth (Fig. 1 a and b) originating directly from the soma, growth out of the distal tip of the primary neurite that was left attached to the soma during isolation (Fig. 1c), and apolar growth forming vast lamellipodia around the cell body from which filopodia were stretching out into all directions (Fig. 1d). No systematic factors determining growth patterns were observed and growth was not a prerequisite for electrophysiological behaviour.

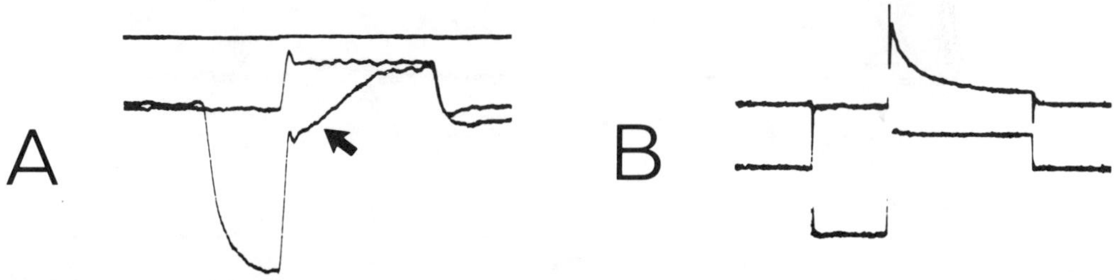

Fig. 2. A. Response of an STG neurone to depolarizing current without and with preceding hyperpolarization. The prehyperpolarization led to a substantial delay in the depolarizing response (arrow). B. The same cell under voltage clamp. A transient outward current resembling I(A) was recorded when the depolarizing command voltage pulse was preceded by a hyperpolarizing prepulse. Calibrations: A: 10 mV, 20 nA, 50 ms; B: 20 mV, 20 nA, 50 ms. Upper traces: current; lower traces: voltage.

Electrophysiology. Cultured crayfish neurones had resting membrane potentials (RMP) of -40 to -60 mV. While almost all cells isolated from abdominal ganglia became excitable after 2 days in culture (data not shown here) those from the STG displayed more specific electrophysiological behaviour which is described below.

In most cultured STG neurones depolarizing current injection resulted in a fast depolarizing response which was subject to strong outward rectification (Fig. 2A). Normally no action potentials (AP) were evoked under these conditions. In voltage clamp experiments a slow outward current was measured whose kinetics and voltage dependence resembled the Hodgkin/Huxley-type delayed rectifier current.

When a hyperpolarizing current pulse preceded the depolarizing one the depolarization could be delayed by more than 150 ms (Fig. 2A arrow). In cells that were able to generate APs a conditioning hyperpolarization would delay AP firing. Figure 2B shows the same cell as the one in figure 2A under voltage clamp. Application of a similar prepulse paradigm as in current clamp experiments uncovered a fast transient outward current with kinetics and voltage dependence closely resembling the transient potassium current (IA) described first by Neher (1971) and Connor & Stevens (1971) in molluscan neurone somata. Today this kind of current is known to be present in many neurones in vertebrates and invertebrates (Hille, 1984). It was also found in neuronal somata from the crustacean STG in situ (Hartline et al., 1985; Hartline & Gassie, 1986). Its possible role involves the regulation of phase relationships between bursts fired by connected neurones and the regulation of AP firing frequency within bursts.

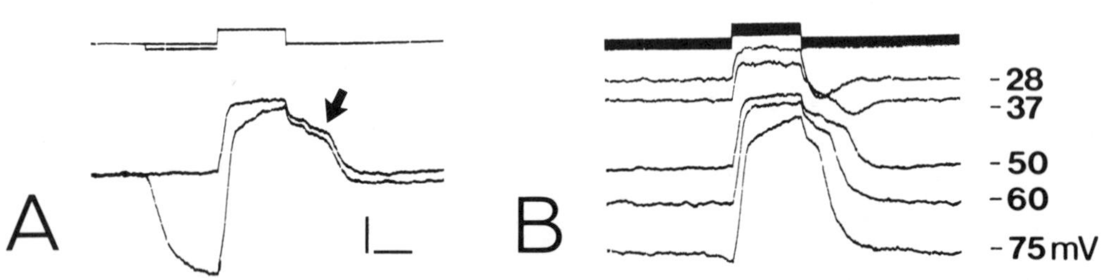

Fig. 3. A. Plateau-like afterpotentials in cultured STG cells following termination of a depolarizing current pulse. The arrow indicates step-like phases that may be due to generation of the plateaus at different locations within the growing neurites. B. Dependence of the duration of the plateau phase on membrane potential. Calibrations A, B: 10 mV, 50 nA, 50 ms. Upper traces: current; lower traces: voltage.

It may also be involved in the regulation of the bursting properties of the conditional bursting cells of the STG (Harris-Warrick & Johnson, 1987; Russel & Graubard, 1987). As described in situ this transient current was present to different extents in different STG neurones.

Some of the STG neurones were able to generate plateau-like afterpotentials at the end of a depolarizing current clamp pulse (Fig. 3). Expression of plateau potentials is thought to be one important factor in the generation of the conditional bursting capability of the different neurones of the STG but also in other rhythmically active neurones. Although not as powerfully expressed as in situ the plateau potentials in cultured STG neurones showed similar dependence on membrane potential as in situ (Dickinson & Nagy, 1983). When the membrane holding potential was depolarized above -30 mV then they were reduced in amplitude or even abolished (Fig. 3B). When voltage pulses were delivered from more hyperpolarized potentials than -50 mV, the plateaus were again shortened. Step-like phases in their time course (Fig. 3A arrow) suggest that in growing cells plateaus may be generated at different locations within the neuritic arborization.

Many of the isolated STG neurones showed low-amplitude, subthreshold oscillations around their RMP (data not shown here) and in a few cells more prominent cyclic behaviour was observed (Fig. 4). In situ the induction and maintenance of oscillatory behaviour depends on the presence of neuromodulatory substances released from specific neurones. This behaviour is referred to as conditional bursting capability (Harris-Warrick & Flamm, 1987) and it has been shown to be present in all of the pyloric (Bal et al., 1988) and many of the gastric neurones (Russel & Hartline, 1984) in the STG . In the cultured STG cells membrane potential oscillations were generated in complete isolation and in the absence of any modulatory substances. Figures 4A and B show an example of a cell that was able to generate bursts of APs. The individual bursts appeared at irregular intervals and were terminated by an apparently active hyperpolarization. The arrowheads in figure 4B mark fluctuations in AP firing frequency. The interburst intervals were characterized by a slow depolarization that resembled a pacemaker potential. In figures 4C and D a recording from another cell is shown that did not generate APs but instead generated slow membrane potential oscillations at a frequency of about 1.5 Hz. Each oscillatory cycle was characterized by a more gradual phase that was followed by a more rapid depolarization which resulted in a semi-stable plateau with small oscillations. Each cycle was terminated by a steep, apparently active hyperpolarization.

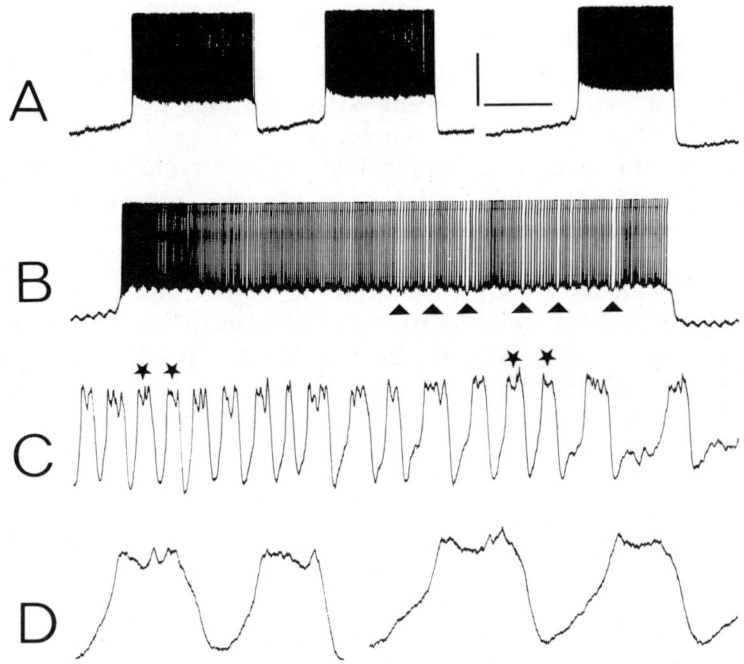

Fig. 4. Recordings from oscillating STG neurones in culture. The cell in A was firing bursts of APs at irregular intervals. The interburst phases were characterized by a pacemaker-like depolarization. Bursts were terminated by an apparently active hyperpolarization. In B a single burst is shown at higher sweep speed. In C a cell performing slow oscillations of its membrane potential is shown, the cycles marked by asterisks are displayed at higher sweep speed in D. The individual cycles were characterized by a biphasic depolarization and a rapid, apparently active hyperpolarization. Calibrations: A, C: 5 mV, 5 s; B, D: 5 mV, 1 s.

DISCUSSION

Our results demonstrate for the first time that individual neurones can be isolated from the crustacean nervous system, be kept alive in primary cell culture, grow processes, and are able to maintain or regenerate part of their specific electrophysiological properties. Although all the data presented here are from cells that were not identified prior to explantation the results demonstrate clearly that not all isolated neurones behave in the same way in response to culture conditions. Instead, many of them express specific properties which in many respect are similar although not identical to those shown in situ. Some possess more IA-like current than others, others express plateau potentials, and another group is capable to oscillate. We conclude that individual STG neurones retain at least part of the specific set of ion channels determining their electrophysiological personality. Our culture system may thus allow studies leading to a more complete understanding of cellular and molecular events underlying the conditional bursting properties of the neurones of the STG.

(Supported by the Swiss National Foundation and the Roche Research Foundation)

REFERENCES

Bal, T., Nagy, F. & Moulins, M. (1988) The pyloric central pattern generator in crustacea: A set of conditional neuronal oscillators.

Belardetti, F., Schacher, S. & Siegelbaum, S.A. (1986). Action potentials, macroscopic and single channel currents recorded from growth cones of Aplysia neurones in culture. J. Physiol. **374**, 289-313.

Connor, J.A. & Stevens, C.F. (1971) Voltage clamp studies of a transient outward membrane current in gastropod neural somata. J. Physiol. **213**, 21-30

Dickinson, P.S. & Nagy, F. (1983) Control of a central pattern generator by an identified modulatory interneurone in crustacea II. Induction and modification of plateau properties in pyloric neurones. J. exp. Biol. **105**, 59-82

Hartline, D.K., Palacio, J.Y. & Gassie, D.V. (1985) Voltage clamp studies of isolated somata from identified pattern generator neurons in the lobster stomatogastric ganglion. Soc. Neurosci. Abstr. **11**, 1023

Hartline, D.K. & Gassie, D.V. (1986) Voltage-clamp analysis of outward currents in identified somata of the gastric mill pattern generator of Panulirus marginatus stomatogastric ganglion. Soc. Neurosci. Abstr. **12**, 358

Harris-Warrick, R.M. & Flamm, R.E. (1987). Multiple mechanisms of bursting in a conditional bursting neuron. J. Neuroscience 7, 2113-2128.

Harris-Warrick, R.M. & Johnson, B.R. (1987) Potassium channel blockade induces rhythmic activity in a conditional burster neuron. Brain Research **416**, 381-386

Hille, B. (1984) Ionic channels of excitable membranes. Sinauer Associates, Inc., Sunderland, Mass.

Neher, E. (1971) Two fast transient current components during voltage clamp on snail neurons. J. Gen. Physiol. **58**, 36-53

Ready, D.F. & Nicholls, J. (1979) Identified neurones isolated from leech CNS make selective connections in culture. Nature **281**, 67-69

Russell, D.F. & Graubard, K. (1987) Cellular and synaptic properties. In The crustacean stomatogastric system (ed. A.I. Selverston & M. Moulins), pp. 79-100. Berlin-Heidelberg-New York: Springer Verlag.

Russel, D.F. & Hartline, D.K. (1984) Synaptic regulation of cellular properties and burst oscillations of neurons in gastric mill system of spiny lobsters, *Panulirus interruptus*. J. Neurophysiol. **52**, 54-73

Selverston, A.I. & Moulins, M. (eds.) The crustacean stomatogastric system. Springer Verlag, Berlin-Heidelberg-New York 1987

Stewart, R.R., Nicholls, J.G. & Adams, W.B. (1989) Na+, K+ and Ca2+ currents in identified leech neurones in culture. J. exp. Biol. **141**, 1-20

Frontiers in Crustacean Neurobiology
Advances in Life Sciences

ISOLATING DEVELOPMENTALLY IMPORTANT GENES FROM THE LOBSTER NERVOUS SYSTEM

Lisa N. Geller, Linda Kobierski, H. Willi Honegger*, Grace Pien, Huntington Potter and Edward A. Kravitz

Department of Neurobiology, Harvard Medical School, Boston, MA, USA.
* Present address: Institut für Zoologie, Technische Universität München, 8046 Garching, FRG

SUMMARY

We are examining the roles that specific gene expression play in development and behavior in the nervous system of the American lobster, *Homarus americanus*. In particular, we have isolated genomic DNA sequences that encompass several putative lobster genes—one possibly encoding a receptor for the steroid molting hormone, 20-hydroxyecdysone, and at least one homologous to the family of mammalian genes encoding the biopterin-dependent amine hydroxylases (tryptophan hydroxylase, tyrosine hydroxylase, and phenylalanine hydroxylase). Tryptophan hydroxylase is the rate-limiting enzyme for the synthesis of serotonin, a developmentally regulated lobster neurohormone. The control of expression of these genes in individual lobster neurons can be assayed by in situ hybridization and could provide insights into the linkage between behavior, development, and gene expression in this organism.

INTRODUCTION

The use of modern molecular genetic techniques has allowed entirely new areas of study within traditional experimental systems. Thus the lobster, with its relatively long generation time and lack of inbred strains, both of which preclude classical genetic analysis, is easily amenable to study with the new molecular approaches. Indeed, in lobsters, as in all species, there are strong indications that changes in gene expression underlie important changes in neuronal function. With lobsters, one has the additional advantage of analyzing such changes at the level of single, functionally identified cells. At this meeting, papers were presened showing changes in function that probably depend on altered gene expression. For example, C. Bishop described a substantial seasonal change in the responsiveness of lobster muscle fibers to the peptide proctolin (this volume). While some part of that change may depend on second messenger mechanisms, it also is possible that altered rates of receptor synthesis are important. Activity also can influence gene expression in crustaceans, as demonstrated in the paper by Atwood presented at this symposium (this volume).

There are several examples of modifications in structural anatomy or cellular physiology that probably involve the readout of new programs of gene expression during lobster development. The differentiation of the cutter and crusher claws is one classic example (Govind, 1984). At the end of the fourth larval stage of development, when animals settle to the bottom they must handle items from the substrate with their claws to allow differentiation. Without this handling, claws remain symmetrical. In another example, removal of an eyestalk from a young lobster often results in the regeneration of an antennule (Maynard & Dingle, 1963). A further example comes from our recent studies demonstrating that in certain serotonin/proctolin-containing neurons in juvenile and adult animals, there are very different rates of appearance of the two substances during development (Beltz & Kravitz, 1987). Serotonin is found in these neurons by about half way through embryonic development, while the peptide proctolin does not appear until larval stages 1 through 5, which occur some 4-5 months later in the wild.

Our studies focus on the suggestion that long-term influences on behavior of animals will be represented by activity and use-dependent changes in gene expression. In this brief presentation we describe preliminary results of our attempts to isolate several genes that may be subjected to developmental or use-dependent regulation in lobsters. These genes include hydroxylases (tryptophan hydroxylase, tyrosine hydroxylase, phenylalanine hydroxylase, and possibly tyramine b-hydroxylase) and the gene for the receptor for the arthropod molting hormone, 20-hydroxyecdysone.

METHODS

Construction of a Complete Lobster Genomic Library. A lobster genomic library was constructed from a partial Mbo I digest of lobster ovarian DNA. The products of the Mbo I digest were size-selected for those fragments in the 15-20 kb size range and ligated to Bam HI- and Eco RI-digested EMBL3 DNA. The ligated DNA was packaged into virions and plated. A library size of 3 x 106 recombinant plaques was obtained.

Construction of a Lobster cDNA Library. RNA was isolated from first stage lobster larvae by the guanidine isothiocyanate/cesium chloride method (Chirgwin et al., 1979). Poly A+ RNA was fractionated on oligo-dT cellulose columns (Aviv & Leder, 1972), primed with oligo-dT and reverse transcribed. Following synthesis of a second strand, the cDNA was methylated with Eco R1 methylase, Eco R1 linkers were added and the linkered cDNA digested with the EcoR1 restriction enzyme. The resulting fragments were ligated into the lgt11 expression vector. A library of approximately 1 x 106 recombinant clones was obtained.

Library Screens. Phage were used to infect LE392 or Y1090 cells and 5 x 105 plaques plated for each screen. Plaques were lifted in duplicate onto nitrocellulose filters, the DNA fixed, and filters hybridized in 40% formamide, 4X SSC, 10% dextran sulfate, 10 mM Tris pH 7.5, 5X Denhardt's solution, 50 mg/ml sonicated herring sperm DNA at 37°. After washing in 1X SSC and 0.1% SDS, filters were placed against x-ray films for autoradiographic analysis.

Sequencing. DNA sequencing was performed using T7 DNA polymerase or Sequenase (U.S. Biochemical Corp.) in a modification of the dideoxy sequencing technique described by Sanger et al. (1977). Sequences were analyzed using the software package available from the University of Wisconsin Genetics Computer Group (Madison, Wisconsin).

In situ Hybridization. Nerve cords were dissected from juvenile lobsters and fixed in fresh 4% paraformaldehyde, washed in PBS, dehydrated through an isopropanol series, embedded in Paraplast, sectioned, and fixed to subbed slides. After deparaffination and rehydration, the sections were prehybridized in a solution containing formamide, SSC, salmon sperm DNA, dextran sulphate, yeast tRNA, Denhardt's reagent, and dithiothreitol. For hybridizations, denatured radioactive probe was added to the prehybridization solution. Hybridized slides were washed in SSC solutions containing b-mercaptoethanol and sodium thiosulphate, air dried, coated with nuclear track emulsion (NTB2, Kodak), and exposed for 4-8 weeks.

The oligonucleotides used as probes in the in situ hybridizations were labeled at their 3' ends with terminal transferase using (35S)-dATP (Deng & Wu, 1983).

RESULTS

Cloning lobster steroid hormone receptors. As in all arthropods, lobsters grow in a discontinuous process that involves periodic shedding of the exoskeleton (molting), and is mediated by the steroid hormone 20-hydroxyecdysone. This hormone is known to regulate many developmental processes besides molting, including aspects of nervous system development (for example Weeks and Truman, 1986). Because of our interest in lobster development and the acquisition of stage-specific behaviors, we are attempting to clone the lobster 20-hydroxyecdysone receptor. This will be used to identify cells in the nervous system that are targets for the hormone.

To identify clones containing sequences likely to encode the lobster 20-hydroxyecdysone receptor, the lobster genomic library was screened with a DNA fragment isolated from a clone of the E75 sequence from Drosophila (generously provided by W. Seagraves and D. Hogness). E75, isolated from an early induced puff site in polytene chromosomes, was found to be closely related to vertebrate steroid hormone receptors, notably in the DNA binding domain which contains the diagnostic zinc-finger structure for the steroid hormone receptor family (Evans & Hollenberg, 1988). Although we originally screened the library using a 382 bp fragment which includes both zinc-fingers and extends into both of the flanking exons, we found that the results were clearer when a smaller fragment was used which did not contain any sequence 5' to the zinc-finger-containing exons (Figure 1). Several unique clones were identified by restriction mapping and by Southern analysis. Portions of two of these have been sequenced and appear to contain open reading frames. One (L1) contains some homology to the region of the E75 sequence that is adjacent to the DNA binding domain (Figure 1). Probes from one of these clones are being prepared to screen the lobster larval stage 1 library.

Cloning the biopterin-dependent amine hydroxylase gene family. When injected into freely moving lobsters, serotonin generates a stable stereotypical posture resembling that seen in dominant lobsters—the animals stand on the tips of their walking legs with the claws open in front of them and their abdomens loosely tucked downward. These and other experiments suggest that serotonin may play an important role as a neurohormone in the regulation of lobster aggressive behavior. Tryptophan hydroxylase is the rate-limiting enzyme in serotonin synthesis. Therefore, any understanding of the regulation of serotonin accumulation in lobsters must include an understanding of the regulation of expression of this enzyme. Genomic clones from a lobster library were isolated by their homology to a 582 bp sequence from the highly conserved active site region of the rabbit tryptophan hydroxylase gene (Grenett et al., 1987, generously given to us by S.L.C. Woo). Several of these clones are different by their restriction maps. The active site region of tryptophan hydroxylase is highly conserved between species and between other biopterin-dependent amine hydroxylases (tyrosine hydroxylase and phenylalanine hydroxylase—Grenett et al., 1987; Neckameyer & Quinn, 1989). Thus it is expected that genes related to tryptophan hydroxylase also may be recovered using this screening procedure.

We also have isolated a genomic clone for a putative tryptophan hydroxylase gene from Drosophila. Partial sequencing of this clone reveals a region homologous to human phenylalanine hydroxylase and rat tryptophan hydroxylase. Two oligonucleotides corresponding to this region were synthesized and used as probes for in situ hybridization in nerve cords from juvenile lobsters (with kind help from Leonard G. Davis). The pattern of hybridization was surprising; labeling was seen in glia surrounding neurons, in neuronal nuclei, and in teh cytoplasm of certain neurons. In addition, these oligonucleotides were used to screen the lobster genomic library and a number of positive clones have been identified. These clones also hybridize to the rabbit tryptophan hydroxylase sequence, providing further indications that they probably encode an enzyme related to lobster tryptophan hydroxylase.

```
  1  ttactgatctatgcgctgattgttgcaggaatggtggtgttgttttacgtcttccgtct   60
     LeuLeuIleTyrAlaLeuIleValAlaGlyMetValValLeuPheLeuArgLeuProSer

 61  tccttcttacctgaagaggatcagggtgtctttctgaccatgattcagttacccgctggc  120
     SerPheLeuProGluGluAspGlnGlyValPheLeuThrMetIleGlnLeuProAlaGly

121  agcgacgcaagagcggacgaaaaagtgttggatcaagttacggattactatctgaagaac  180
     SerAspAlaArgAlaAspGluLysValLeuAspGlnValThrAspTyrTyrLeuLysAsn

181  gagaaagcgaacgttgaaagtgctttacggttaacggctttacttcagcgccaggcacaa  240
     GluLysAlaAsnValGluSerAlaLeuArgLeuThrAlaLeuLeuGlnArgGlnAlaGln

241  aacgaccggtatggccttcgtcagtctgaaaccgtgggaagagcg  285
     AsnAspArgTyrGlyLeuArgGlnSerGluThrValGlyArgAla
```

```
  1  atggcttttggcgcagcactacactggatgtcccagccctacgaggctttaacttccgc
     MetAlaPheTrpArgSerThrThrLeuAspValProAlaLeuArgGlyPheAsnPheArg

 61  ggcgggatggttttaattcctgaactggcagccttaacgctggcactttcggtttataca
     GlyGlyMetValLeuIleProGluLeuAlaAlaLeuThrLeuAlaLeuSerValTyrThr

121  tctgcatttatcgccggagattatccgcgc  150
     SerAlaPheIleAlaGlyAspTyrProArg
```

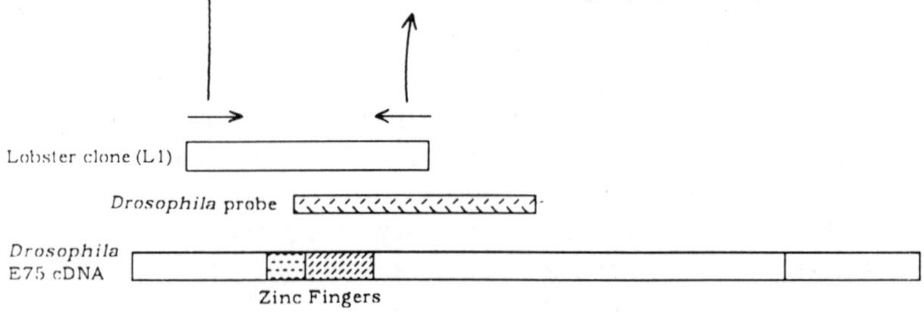

Figure 1. Partial sequence of lobster genomic DNA homologous to a Drosophila steroid receptor gene.

DISCUSSION

Sustained changes in the behavior, and therefore in the nervous systems, of vertebrate and invertebrate animals, result from their interactions with complex environments. External signals like changing seasons, the approach of potential mates or enemies, the availability of food or shelter, or internal signals like the cyclical release of hormonal substances, all are organizers of these sustained changes. Ultimately changes at the single neuron level underly the behavorial changes, and these must result from the constellation of neurotransmitters, neurohormones, hormones and patterns of activity seen by individual cells at any given instant in time. An understanding of how nervous systems are affected by these factors at the level of gene expression is a prerequisite to understanding the genetic basis of behavior. Using the American lobster, *Homarus americanus*, as a model system offers the advantage of an organism with a relatively simple nervous system containing individual cells that are large enough to be dissected and used for biochemical studies. In addition, the lobster is capable of sophisticated social behavior such as the establishment of dominance hierarchies (for review, see Kravitz, 1988).

Experiments have been initiated to study the receptor for the arthropod molting hormone, 20-hydroxyecdysone, which is known to regulate behaviors by acting on individual neurons in both larval and adult invertebrates. A first step in this study is the isolation of cDNA clones for the lobster 20-hydroxyecdysone receptor.

Other genes whose developmental control we are interested in include those that encode tryptophan hydroxylase, which is the rate limiting enzyme in serotonin synthesis, and the precursor for proctolin, which colocalizes with serotonin in some neurons, but at different times in development. Both proctolin and serotonin are likely to act as neurohormones that modulate specific aspects of lobster behavior. The lobster experimental system allows experimental manipulation of the interplay between such neurohormonal substances and behavior, and offers the ability to link changes in behavior and neurohormonal levels to alterations in the function of specific neurons. [Supported by the NIH.]

REFERENCES

Aviv, H. and P. Leder. 1972. Purification of biologically active globin messenger RNA by chromatography on oligothymidylic acid-cellulose. Proc. Nat. Acad. Sci. USA. **69**:1408-1412.

Beltz, B.S. and E.A. Kravitz. 1987. Physiological identification, morphological analysis, and development of identified serotonin-proctolin containing neurons in the lobster ventral nerve cord. J. Neurosci. **7**:533-546.

Chirgwin, J.J., A.E. Przbyla, R.J. MacDonald, and W.J. Rutter. 1979. Isolation of biologically active ribonucleic acid from sources enriched in ribonuclease. Biochemistry **18**:5294

Deng, G.R. and R. Wu. 1983. Terminal transferase: Use in the tailing of DNA and for in vitro mutagenesis. Meth. Enzymol. **100**:96-116.

Evans, R.M. and S.M. Hollenberg. 1988. Zinc fingers: Gilt by association. Cell **52**: 1-3.

Govind, C.K. 1984. Development of asymmetry in the neuromuscular system of lobster claws. Biol. Bull. **167**:94-119.

Grenett, H.E., F.D. Ledley, L.L. Reed, and S.L.C. Woo. 1987. Full-length cDNA for rabbit tryptophan hydroxylase: Functional domains and evolution of aromatic amino acid hydroxylases. Proc. Natl. Acad. Sci. USA. 84: 5530-5534.

Kravitz, E.A. 1988. Hormonal control of behavior: Amines and the biasing of behavioral output in lobsters. Science **241**:1775-1781.

Maynard, D.M. and H. Dingle. 1963. An effect of eyestalk ablution on antennular function in the spiny lobster, panulirus argus. Zeitschr. vergl. Physiol. **46:**515-540.

Neckameyer, W.S. and W.G. Quinn. 1989. Isolation and characterization of the gene for Drosophila tyrosine hydroxylase. Neuron **2:**1167-1175.

Sanger, F., S. Nicklen, and A.R. Coulson. 1977. DNA sequencing with chain-terminating inhibitors. Proc. Nat. Acad. Sci. USA **74**:5463-5467.

Weeks, J.C. and J.W. Truman. 1986. Steroid control of neuron and muscle development during the metamorphosis of an insect. J. Neurobiol. **17**:249-267.

Frontiers in Crustacean Neurobiology
Advances in Life Sciences

NEURONAL DEVELOPMENT IN THE CRUSTACEAN NERVOUS SYSTEM STUDIED BY NEURON-SPECIFIC ANTIBODY LABELLING

Thomas Meier and Heinrich Reichert

Department of Zoology, University of Geneva, 20 rue de l'Ecole-de-Médecine, 1211 Geneva 4, Switzerland

SUMMARY

A neuron-specific antibody is used to visualize developing neurons in the nervous system of the lobster, *Homarus gammarus*. The antibody stains the cell surface of embryonic neurons in the brain, in the segmental ganglia, in the peripheral nervous system and in the stomatogastric nervous system. This neuron-specific stain makes it possible to observe at the cellular level many aspects in neuronal development and reveals similarities in basic developmental mechanisms that operate in the nervous system of crustaceans and insects.

INTRODUCTION

In the past decade great deal of progress has been made in understanding the structural and functional organization of crustacean nervous systems. As many of the contributions to this volume attest, much of this progress has been due to the study of identifiable neurons, and a wealth of information is now available as to the morphology, connectivity, biochemistry and behavioral role of individual crustacean neurons. However, in contrast to the state of insect neurobiology, information on the cellular mechanisms of neuronal development in crustaceans is relatively scarce. Only very recently has research in crustaceans begun to focus on the questions of how neurons are generated, how they aquire their individual neuronal characteristics and how they establish synaptic connectivity (see articles by Helluy and Beltz, Kravitz et al., and Sandeman in this volume and Beltz and Kravitz, 1987). Thus, there is a large body of information on the neuronal organization of adult crustaceans that still awaits exploitation for the study of mechanisms of neuronal development.

Initial comparative studies on neuronal development in insects and crustaceans indicate that a number of cellular mechanisms may be common to both arthropod groups. With minor variations, the segmental nervous systems of insects and crustaceans seem to be built from the same common embryonic plan, implying a conservative evolution of the developmental program for both of these arthropod groups (Thomas et al., 1984).

Moreover some of the molecular control elements involved in neurogenesis in insects and crustaceans also appear to have been conserved (Patel et al., 1989). This suggests that many of the molecularly oriented methods that have been used to study insect neurogenesis may also be applicable to the study of neuronal development in crustaceans.

Here we show that a neuron-specific polyclonal antibody which has been used to investigate embryonic development of the nervous system in Drosophila and in the grasshopper (Jan and Jan, 1982; Snow et al., 1987), can also be used to characterize the developing nervous system of the lobster. This anti-horseradish peroxidase antibody (anti-HRP), which recognizes a neural-specific carbohydrate moiety shared by many surface glycoproteins in insects, also labels the surfaces of neurons in developing lobster embryos. By using this antibody to study neurogenesis in the lobster CNS we have been able to characterize features in the embryonic development of this animal´s brain, segmental ganglia and stomatogastric nervous system.

METHODS

Embryos of the lobster *Homarus gammarus* were obtained from females in berry that were kept in an aquarium in circulating filtered sea water. The age of the embryos was determined by measuring their eye index (Perkins, 1972) and then converting this parameter into the percent developmental scale introduced for *Homarus americanus* by Helluy and Beltz (this volume). We noted some differences in the details of embryonic development between *Homarus gammarus* and *Homarus americanus* in later embryonic stages. This is also reflected in the larger size of the larva of the two species (Charmantier, 1987). However, development is very similar up to about 50% of embryogenesis. Embryos were dissected from the egg in a solution of 4% formaldehyd in arteficial seawater and were kept in fixative for a total time of 1 hour. Thereafter they were transfered to phosphate buffered saline (PBS) and stored at 4°C. For immunocytochemistry, the fixed embryos were dehydrated in an alcohol/xylol series. Then they were embedded in paraffin and sectioned. After rehydration in PBS, the sections were incubated with 0.1% Triton and 1% normal goat serum in a solution of PBS. A 1:300 dilution of FITC-conjugated anti-HRP (Cappel) was applied in the same incubating solution to the sectioned material and the sections were incubated for several hours at room temperature. After rinsing in PBS, the stained sections were viewed in a Zeiss epifluorescence microscope and drawn or photographed.

RESULTS

All of the neurons in the developing central and peripheral nervous system of embryonic lobsters are stained with the anti-HRP antibody. In the developing brain, the large neuropilar areas stain most intensely, probably because the antibody recognizes cell surface molecules expressed on developing neurites and axons. This is especially pronounced in the neuropile of the developing optic ganglia, which in the embryo are still in close proximity to the rest of the brain (see color plate V). The cell surface of neuronal somata is also stained, but not the cell interior.

A similar staining pattern is observed in the segmental ganglia, where the intensely staining neuropilar areas form a ladder-like structure of connectives and commissures which are surrounded by the less brightly stained neuronal cell bodies. Initially all of the developing segmental ganglia are positioned close to each other (Fig. 1). Later in development they begin to separate and long connectives are formed between the individual ganglia. Exceptions are the five individual neuromeres of the subesophogeal ganglion which develop as individual entities but fuse later in embryonic development to form a single compact ganglion (Fig. 2). Similar fusion of individual neuromeres also occurs in the formation of the terminal ganglion. The peripheral nerves which exit the individual segmental ganglia are also stained by the antibody.

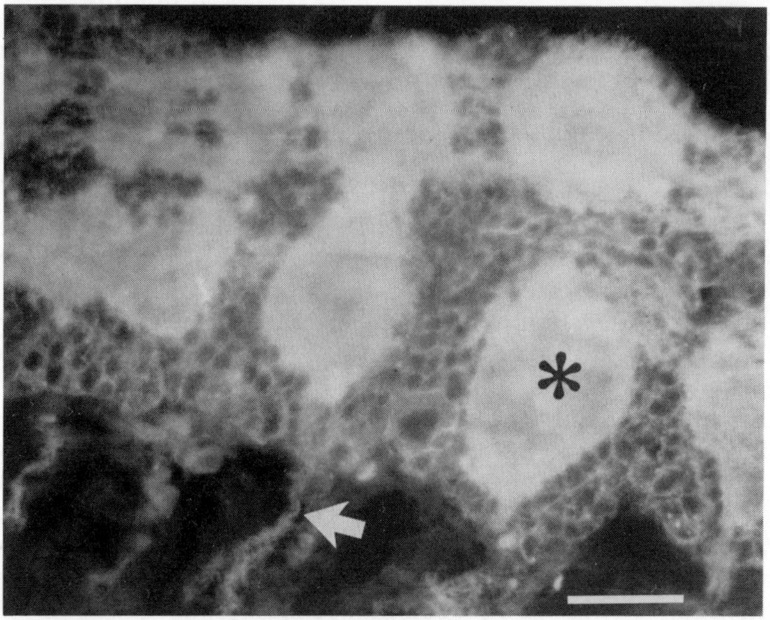

Fig. 1: Horizontal section through the thoracic ganglion neuromeres previous to ganglion fusion (Eye index of this embryo: 600μm). Neuropiles (asterisk) are brightly stained and segmental nerves leave the ganglion-neuromeres (arrow). The staining of the neuronal cell bodies is restricted to the cell membrane. Scale, 50μm.

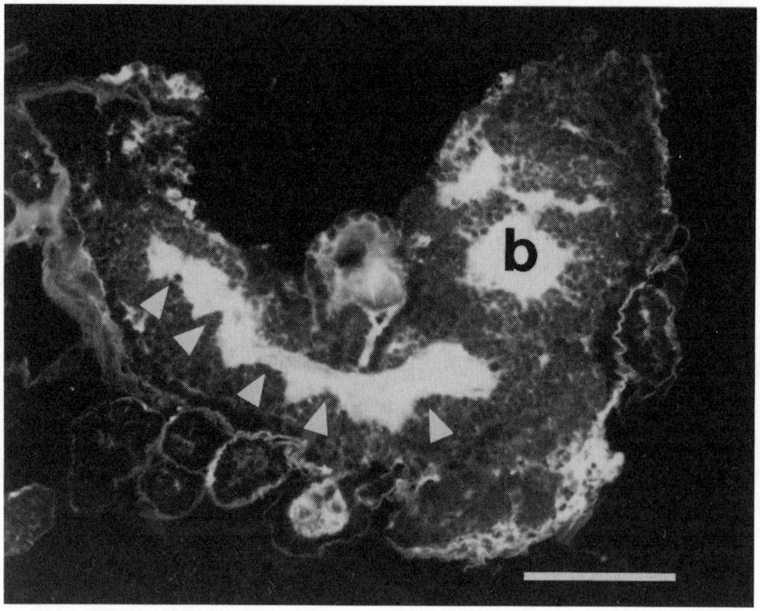

Fig. 2. Parasagittal section through a *Homarus* embryo of about 35% embryonic development. The neuromeres of the prospective suboesophageal ganglion are not yet fused at this stage. White arrowheads mark the borders of adjacent neuromeres which form the suboesophageal ganglion later in development. b, brain; Scale, 100μm.

Developing sensory cells in the appendages and in the body wall periphery as well as sensory cells inside the internal organs are revealed by the anti-HRP antibody. Figure 3 shows a cluster of putative chemosensory cells, found in the pyloric region of the stomach, that have not yet been described. In the developing appendages, the initial cells that are formed, project their axons towards the central ganglia and appear to make contact with regularly placed individual cell bodies which could have the same function as the guidepost or stepping stone cells in the developing insect limb. After formation of the initial axonal pathways from the periphery to the CNS by the pioneering cells, the axons of other developing sensory cells fasciculate with this pathway and thus participate in the formation of the peripheral nerves. This process of pioneering the peripheral nerve appears similar to that involved in peripheral nerve formation in insects (Bentley and Keshishian, 1982; Ho and Goodman, 1982).

Particular attention was focussed on the development of the stomatogastric nervous system. At approximately half way through embryonic development the stomatogastric ganglion is well formed, has a distinct central neuropilar region surrounded by a layer of cell bodies and in many respects resembles the adult ganglion (see color plate VI). Both the stomatogastric nerve and the nerves to the motor periphery are already established at this time and many of the neurons in the stomatogastric ganglion are relatively large (15-20 μm).

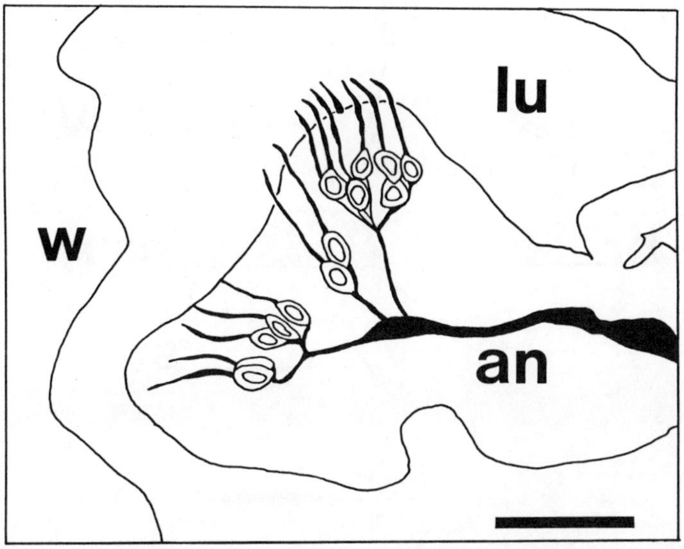

Fig. 3. Putative chemosensory cells in the developing stomach of the lobster. an, afferent nerve; lu, stomach lumen; w, stomach wall. Scale, 50μm.

The ganglion itself is in close apposition to the front of the developing stomach wall and is limited dorsally by a developing large blood vessel and anteriorly by the brain (Fig. 4). The distance from the stomatogastric ganglion to the developing oesophogeal and commissural ganglia, which are still close to the stomatodeal region, is relatively short at this developmental period. During later embryonic development the stomach enlarges greatly and the stomatogastric nerve elongates in this process.

DISCUSSION

The application of neuron-specific antibody staining techniques to the analysis of neuronal development in crustaceans should make it possible to follow at a cellular level those neuronal differentiation processes that generate functioning adult neurons and specify the interconnection of these neurons into neuronal networks. The anti-HRP antibody used here recognizes cell surface markers that label all of the neurons in the central and peripheral nervous system throughout most of embryonic development.

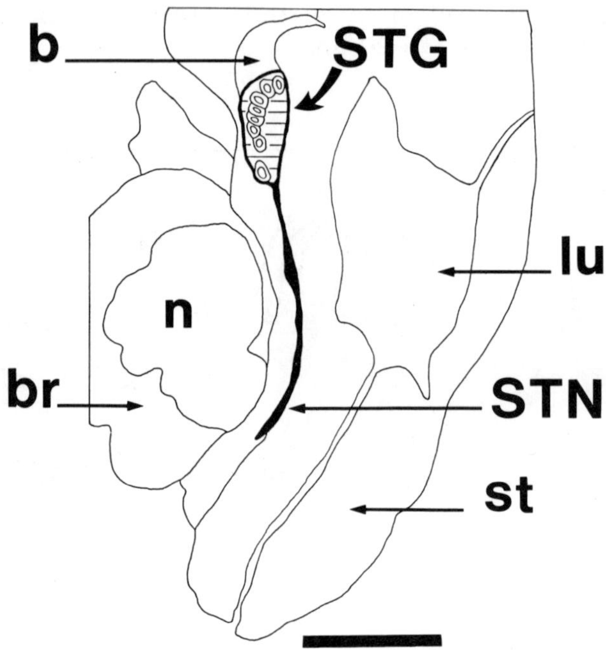

Fig. 4. Location of the developing stomatogastric ganglion. Sagittal section of an embryo halfway through embryonic development. STG, stomatogastric ganglion; STN, stomatogastric nerve; b, blood vessel; br, brain; lu, lumen of stomach; n, neuropil; st, stomatodeum. Scale bar, 100μm.

Thus, this technique is likely to be useful for studying questions of neurogenesis, pathfinding and synaptogenesis in many parts of the crustacean nervous system. Since the cellular organization of a number of neuronal systems in crustaceans have been characterized in great detail, a focussed developmental analysis of how these systems are generated during ontogeny is now within reach.

Currently, we are studying the development of small ganglia such as the stomatogastric ganglion, which are composed of limited numbers of identified neurons with known synaptic connectivity in the adult. Our goal is to describe the formation of entire ganglia as completely as possible in order to elucidate basic mechanisms of neuronal development. The crossreactivity of the anti-HRP antibody in crustaceans and in insects is especially encouraging in this respect, since it is a further indication that similar molecular signals operate during neuronal development in these two arthropod groups. It will be interesting to determine which molecules these are and how their expression is controlled during development.

The work reported here was carried out in close collaboration with M. Moulins and I. Cournil to whom we are extremely grateful. Supported by the Swiss NSF.

REFERENCES

Beltz, B.S. & Kravitz, E.A. (1987) Physiological identification, morphological analysis, and development of identified serotonin-proctolin containing neurons in the lobster ventral nerve cord. J. Neurosci. 7: **533**-546.

Bentley, D., Keshishian, H. (1982) Pathfinding by peripheral pioneer neurons in grasshoppers. Science **218**:1082-1088.

Charmantier, B. (1987) Le dévelopment larvaire et la metamorphose chez les homards (Crustacea, Decapoda). Oceanis **13**:137-165.

Ho, R.K., Goodman, C.S. (1982) Peripheral pathways are pioneered by an array of central and peripheral neurones in grasshopper embryos. Nature **297**:404- 406.

Patel, N.M., Martin-Blanco, E., Coleman, K.G., Poole, S.J., Ellis, M.C., Kornberg, T.B., Goodman, C.S. (1989) Expression of engrailed proteins in arthropods, annelids and chordates. Cell **58**:955-968.

Perkins, H.C. (1972) Developmental rates at various temperatures of embryos of the northern lobster (*Homarus americanus* Milne-Edwards). Bull. U.S. Fish. commission **15:**1-252.

Jan, L.Y., Jan, Y.N. (1982) Antibodies to horseradish peroxidase as specific neuronal markers in *Drosophila* and in grasshopper embryos. Proc. Natl. Acad. Sci. USA *79*:2700-2704

Snow, P.M., Patel, N.H., Harrelson, A.L., Goodman, C.S. (1987) Neural-specific carbohydrate moiety shared by many surface glycoproteins in Drosophila and grasshopper embryos. J. Neurosci. **7**:4137-4144.

Thomas, J.B., Bastiani, J.J., Bate, M., Goodman, C.S. (1984) From grasshopper to Drosophila: a common plan for neuronal development. Nature **310:**203-207.

Frontiers in Crustacean Neurobiology
Advances in Life Sciences

STAGES IN THE EMBRYONIC DEVELOPMENT OF THE AMERICAN LOBSTER WITH SPECIAL EMPHASIS ON ITS NERVOUS SYSTEM

Simone Helluy and Barbara Beltz

Department of Biology, Wellesley College, Wellesley, Massachusetts, 02181, U.S.A.

SUMMARY

The development of *Homarus* in the egg can be seen as a succession of different embryonic forms rather than as the continuous and gradual formation of a single body plan. Three periods of organogenesis are distinguishable, that of the nauplius, postnauplius and first larval stage (L1). Behavioral, morphological and anatomical landmarks are examined and their times of appearance are related to a biometric index based on the size of the lateral eye. This scale is transformed to a percent developmental scale. Serotonin immunoreactivity, studied as a marker of developing nervous structures, is first seen in the protocerebrum at approximately 11% development and by the time organogenesis of the L1 has begun (c. 50% dev.) all the prominent stained structures present at hatching in the optic lobes, brain and nerve cord have appeared, except for the accessory lobes of the deutocerebrum which develop during the organogenesis of the L1.

INTRODUCTION

As illustrated by this symposium, the nervous system of crustaceans has been extensively exploited over the past few decades for studies of the neural control of behavior. While many cellular and molecular phenomena involved in the function of the nervous system have been studied in detail, the developmental events that mold the crustacean nervous system into a finely tuned physiological instrument have not been carefully examined. In order to understand the processes that govern the formation of the crustacean nervous system, a more complete examination of developmental events is required. The ontogeny of *Homarus americanus* attracted much attention in the last century (see review in Herrick, 1895). More recently studies have focused on the development of a particular organ or on a particular period of embryonic life (see review in Aiken & Waddy, 1980). This study is an attempt to characterize the embryonic development of *Homarus* from the naupliar stage to hatching with behavioral, morphological and anatomical observations. As part of this effort, serotonin (5- hydroxytryptamine, 5-HT) was labeled immunocytochemically in the central nervous system and served as a marker of developing brain structures.

Homarus goes through several transformations in body form while in the egg. In the present study three periods of organogenesis are distinguished: that of the nauplius, postnauplius, and first larval stage. The different biological events taking place during embryonic development are related to a biometric index based on the size of the lateral eye (Perkins, 1972). This index is transformed to a percentage scale of embryogenesis. Quantitative staging and the variety of biological landmarks studied should insure greater precision in determining the developmental stage of *Homarus* embryos being utilized for anatomical and physiological studies.

MATERIALS AND METHODS

Eggs from a single brood were examined over a five month period, from the naupliar stage (Fig. 2A) to hatching. The female lobster, which carries her eggs externally on the ventral abdomen, was maintained in an aquarium filled with circulating, filtered artificial sea water at 18 °C (for details see Beltz & Kravitz, 1987). Because the exact extrusion date of the experimental eggs was not known, the early naupliar stage was given the approximate age of 8 days by comparison with data from Herrick (1895).

The eggs were examined 1-3 times each week until hatching. On observation days, the eye index [EI ; the sum in micrometers of the width and the length of the lateral eye divided by 2 (Perkins, 1972)] of each of 5 embryos was measured in the intact egg under a stereomicroscope equipped with a camera (Fig. 1). Each embryo was then separated from the yolk (Fig. 2A and B) and the length of the cephalothorax measured.

Additional observations on the progeny of other females confirmed that the experimental brood followed a normal developmental course. One hundred and seventy embryos of the experimental brood were examined with immunocytochemical methods at 33 different times during development. The nervous systems of early embryos (EI<270) were processed in situ whereas the optic lobes, brain and nerve cord were isolated from later embryos prior to processing. All the tissues examined were fixed in 4 % paraformaldehyde or 2 % paraformaldehyde/3 % picric acid in 0.1 M phosphate buffer and processed using a monoclonal serotonin antibody (1:1500 [Seralab]) and avidin-biotin-peroxidase labeling methods (Elite ABC [Vector Laboratories]; for protocol see Beltz & Kravitz, 1987).

Abbreviations, ab: abdomen, an1: antennula, an2: antenna, al: accessory lobe, br: brain, ch: corpus hemiellipsoid, ef: esophageal foramen, ep: eye pigment, gi: dorsal giant interneuron, he: heart, se: setae, md: mandible, me: median eye, mt: medulla terminalis, ol: olfactory lobe, op: optic lobes, pa: postmandibular appendages, pb: protocerebral bridge, pn: protocerebral network, ro: rostrum, se: setae, sp: spines, tt: tip of telson.

RESULTS

The nauplius (c. 0 - 8% development). The first organized structure to appear at the surface of the green yolk at about day 8 or 5% development (c. 5%) is a typical nauplius with three pairs of appendages: the antennulae, the

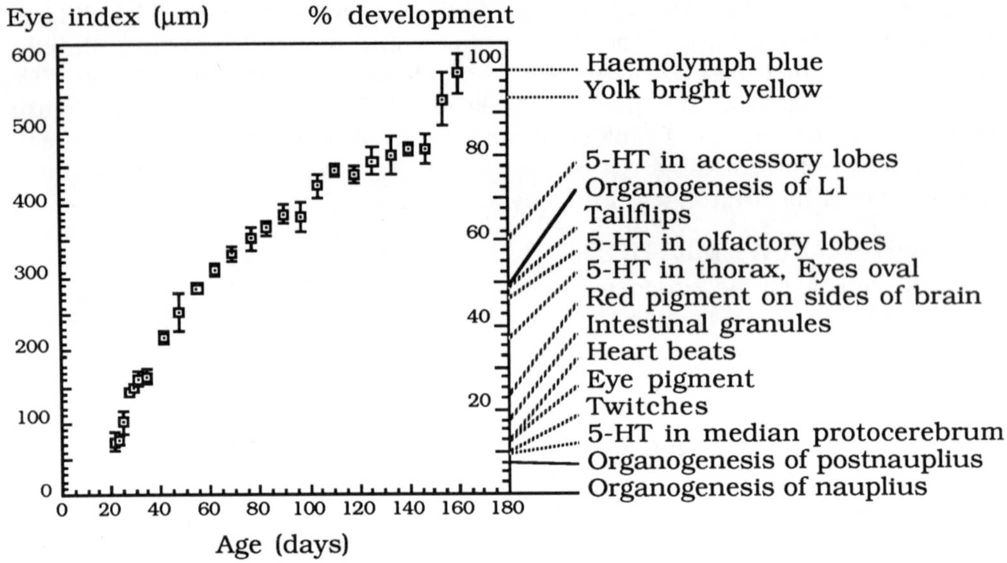

Fig. 1. Growth curve of eye index in *Homarus americanus* embryos and developmental landmarks.

antennae, and the mandibles. Four days later, the eye lobes are distinct, as well as the rudiments of the abdomen and the buds of several postmandibular appendages (Fig. 2A). The nauplius is a stage common to all crustaceans and in several taxa, the young hatch at that point (Gore, 1985).

Organogenesis of the postnauplius (c. 8 - 50% development). The postnauplius arises from the differentiation and growth of the postmandibular region. The dorsal side of the embryo is apposed to the yolk, with the abdomen folded on the ventral side of the thorax (Fig. 2A and B). The telson is bilobed and rounded. Six uniramous trunk limbs (the future third maxilliped and five walking legs) line each side of the thorax and point anteriorly. The following characteristics (listed chronologically) appear during this period (Fig. 1). At approximately day 17 (c. 11%) the first twitches of the antennae and the abdomen are evident upon removal of the external egg envelopes. Next the eye pigment appears as a small dark crescent lining the posterior part of the eye lobe; the eye index (EI) at that stage is 70 (c. 13%). The heart begins to beat at EI 75, and at that same time the pigmentation in the two-celled median eye (Fig. 3) becomes visible. Red pigment spots are seen on each side of the protocerebrum at

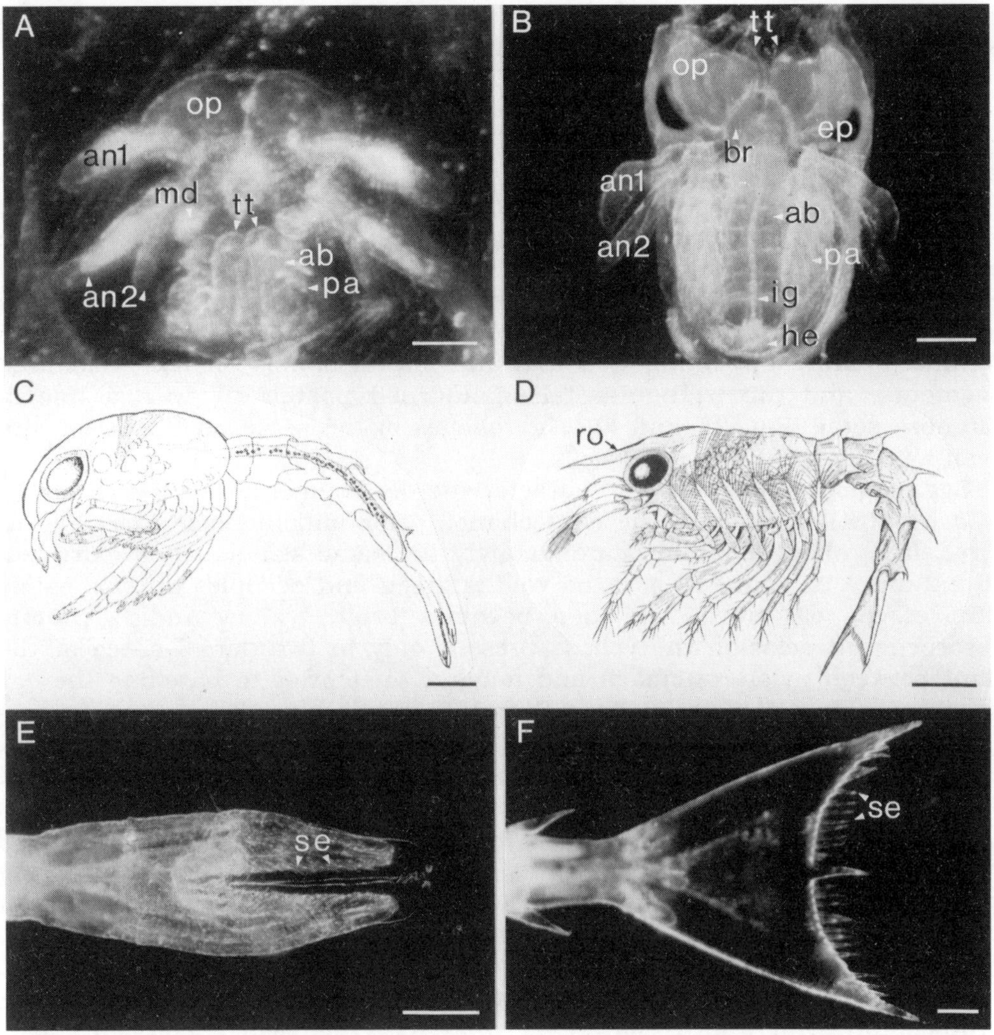

Fig. 2. The late naupliar stage of *Homarus americanus* (A) develops into a postnauplius (B) shown here with an eye index of about 160 µm; both embryos have been separated from the yolk on which their dorsal side was apposed. The prelarva (C), the form which hatches, possesses the external morphology of the postnauplius but harbors a fully formed first stage larva (D) (Drawings from Herrick, 1895). For example, under the rounded-shaped telson of the prelarva (E), the triangular telson of the first stage larva (F) is ready to unfold. Abbreviations in Materials and Methods. Scale bars, A: 100 µm, B: 200 µm, C: 0.5 mm, D: 1 mm, E: 0.3 mm, F: 0.3 mm.

EI 140, and from then until EI 280 (c. 50%), this pigmentation progressively invades the region of the mouth, the sides of the nerve cord, the appendages and the abdomen. At EI 160 (c. 30%) the telson grows beyond the optic lobes (Fig. 2B). At EI 210 (c. 40%) the crescent-shaped eye pigmentation becomes oval (Fig. 2C and D). The first tailflips occur at EI 280 upon removal of the external egg envelopes.

Organogenesis of the first larval stage (c. 50 - 100% development) and hatching. There are no obvious changes in the external morphology of the embryo from EI 280 until EI 580 (the eye index at hatching). However, the embryo grows dramatically and the structures typical of the L1 (Fig. 2D) form progressively beneath the cuticle of the postnauplius: the rostrum, biramous trunk appendages, dorsal and lateral spines on the abdominal segments, and the triangular telson adorned posteriorly with a line of plumose setae (Fig. 2E and F). The follicles of the setae on the telson are seen as early as EI 280 (c. 50%).

Egg pigmentation is also a characteristic developmental feature. From EI 470 (c. 80%) to EI 580, the eggs change color and increase markedly in size, from about 1.7 mm (approximately the same size as when extruded) to 2.2 mm. At about EI 470 the yolk is green and occupies approximately 25% of the egg mass. It then becomes bright yellow and is rapidly resorbed. At eclosion the yolk is present only in two dorsal caeca at the limit between pyloric stomach and midgut. Just prior to hatching the egg assumes a blue color due to haemolymph pigments.

At EI 580 the two outermost egg envelopes rupture. The form that emerges (Fig. 2C), referred to as a prelarva (see Charmantier and Aiken, 1987) or prezoe (Gore, 1985), has the rounded body shape of the postnauplius (Fig. 2B). However, within hours this prelarva molts into a fully formed first stage larva or zoe whose acuminate structures become slowly erect (Fig. 2D). The tegumentary red pigment disperses prior to hatching and remains dispersed well into the first larval stage.

Serotonergic labeling in the optic lobes, brain and nerve cord. The first trace of 5-HT immunoreactivity (IR) is observed medially in the protocerebrum at approximately 17 days (c. 11%), which coincides with the first muscular contractions. At this time, the primordia of the optic lobes are clearly delineated. The brain is elongated with the protocerebrum anterior to, and the deutocerebrum and tritocerebrum lateral to the esophageal foramen. 5-HT IR appears progressively laterally and anteriorly in fibers of the protocerebral network. By EI 100 (c. 18%) IR fibers are seen along the medulla terminalis, and later surround the corpus hemiellipsoid, both neuropiles of the lateral protocerebrum. By EI 160 (c. 30%) 5-HT IR is present in the protocerebrum, and in varicosities and fibers in the tritocerebrum and circumesophageal and subesophageal ganglia but not yet in the deutocerebrum. By EI 220 5-HT IR is detected in thoracic fibers, in identified paired cell bodies in the 5th thoracic and 1st

abdominal ganglia (see Beltz & Kravitz, 1983), and in peripheral tissues including those surrounding the heart. 5-HT IR is first detected in the

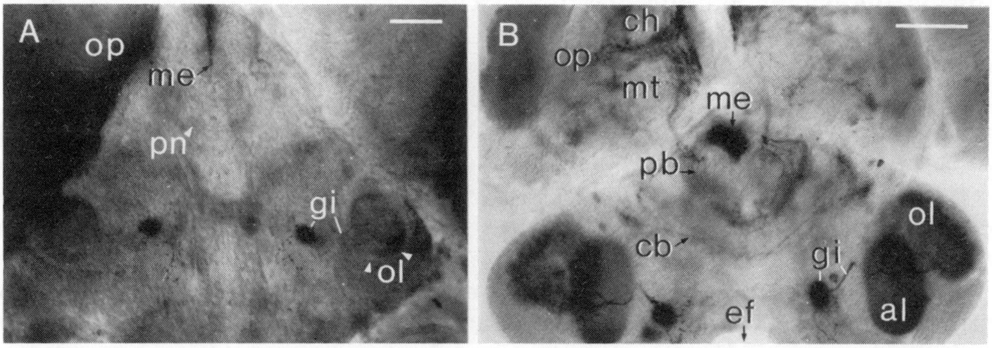

Fig. 3. Optic lobes and brain of *Homarus americanus* embryos showing serotonin immunoreactivity. A: EI 270, c. 50% development. B: EI 580, just prior to hatching. Abbreviations in Materials and Methods. Scale bars, A: 50 μm, B: 100 μm.

deutocerebrum at EI 230 (c. 40%): dorsal bilateral giant neurons (homologous to those in the crayfish based on their anatomy [Sandeman et al., 1988]) show staining in their cell bodies and axons projecting to the olfactory neuropiles which are labeled by EI 270 (c. 50%) (Fig. 3A). All the prominent stained cells of the adult, including an unpaired medial (SUM) cell in the 1st abdominal ganglion also label by this time. From then on, i.e. during the organogenesis of the L1, the major qualitative change in serotonergic staining pattern is in the appearance and progressive growth of the accessory lobe, which stains when the structure is first apparent at EI 350 (c. 60%) in the deutocerebrum. At eclosion, IR neurons in the thoracic and abdominal ganglia are very similar to that observed in the adult *Homarus* (see Beltz & Kravitz, 1987). In the brain and optic lobes, the protocerebral tract, protocerebral bridge, dorsal and ventral protocerebral networks, central body, olfactory and accessory lobes are brightly stained (Fig. 3B) in a pattern similar to that of the crayfish *Cherax destructor* (Sandeman et al., 1988).

DISCUSSION

Perkins (1972) reported that in *Homarus* the EI is 70 at the time eye pigment first appears, and 560 at eclosion. These figures agree with the present findings (EI = 70 and 580 respectively). The eye index has served as an accurate quantitative staging method for embryos in several neurobiological studies (Cole & Lang, 1980; Beltz & Kravitz, 1987). However, a percent staging scale is easier to comprehend (Bentley et al., 1979). The eye index (with an approximation for the period prior to the appearance of eye pigment) rather than time from extrusion to hatching was expressed in percent because developmental rates are different in the laboratory at constant temperature, and in the wild where development is arrested during the winter months (Perkins, 1972).

The early appearance (c. 11%) of 5-HT IR in the protocerebrum suggests that serotonin may serve a morphogenic function molding neuronal arborizations as suggested by Haydon et al. (1987). The development of the dorsal giant interneurons that project to the olfactory and accessory lobes, and the appearance of 5-HT IR in these cells, are of special interest in this regard. 5-HT IR is detected at about 40 % development in the cell bodies of the giant interneurons, at 50 % in the olfactory lobes, and at 60% in the accessory lobes. The accessory lobes are just beginning to emerge at 60% development and are then elaborated throughout the period of organogenesis of the L1. The fact that the accessory lobes are forming in the presence of 5-HT IR fibers from the dorsal giant interneurons may indeed suggest a developmental function for this amine in *Homarus*.

Supported by NSF grant BNS 8718938
and NIH grant NS 25915 to B. B.

REFERENCES

Aiken, D.E. & Waddy, S.L. (1980) Reproductive biology. In *The biology and management of lobsters.* Vol I, (ed. J.S. Cobb & B.F. Phillips) pp. 215-276. New York: Academic Press.

Beltz, B.S. & Kravitz, E.A. (1987) Physiological identification morphological analysis, and development of identified serotonin-proctolin containing neurons in the lobster ventral nerve cord. *J. Neurosci.* **7:** 533-546.

Bentley, D., Keshishian, H., Shankland, M. & Toroian-Raymond, A. (1979) Quantitative staging of embryonic development of the grasshopper, *Schistocerca nitens. J. Embryol. exp. Morph.* **54:** 47-74.

Charmantier, G. & Aiken, D.E. (1987) Osmotic regulation in late embryos and prelarvae of the American lobster *Homarus americanus* H. Milne Edwards, 1837 (Crustacea, Decapoda). *J. Exp. Mar. Biol. Ecol.* **109:** 101-108.

Cole, J.J. & Lang, F. (1980) Spontaneous and evoked postsynaptic potentials in an embryonic neuromuscular system of the lobster, *Homarus americanus. J. Neurobiol.* **11:** 459-470.

Haydon, P.G., McCobb, D.P., & Kater, S.B. (1987) The regulation of neurite outgrowth, growth cone motility, and electrical synaptogenesis by serotonin. *J. Neurobiol.* **18:** 197-215.

Gore, R.H. (1985) Molting and growth in decapod larvae. In Crustacean Issues. Vol 2 (ed F.R. Schram) pp. 1-65.

Herrick, F.H. (1895) The American lobster: A study of its habits and development. *Bull. U.S. Fish. commission* **15:** 1-252.

Perkins, H.C. (1972) Developmental rates at various temperatures of embryos of the northern lobster (*Homarus americanus* Milne-Edwards). *Fish. Bull.* **70:** 95-99.

Sandeman, D.C., Sandeman, R.E. & Aitken A.R. (1988) Atlas of serotonin-containing neurons in the optic lobes and brain of the crayfish, *Cherax destructor*. *J. Comp. Neurol.* **269:** 465-478.

Frontiers in Crustacean Neurobiology
Advances in Life Sciences

NEURAL PHYLOGENY - ITS USE IN STUDYING NEURAL CIRCUITS

Dorothy H. Paul

Department of Biology, University of Victoria,
Victoria, B.C. V8W 2Y2, Canada

SUMMARY

I reconstruct stages in the evolution of a trunk-driven (nonGiant interneuron-mediated tailflipping) into a limb-driven (with the uropods) mode of swimming in mole sandcrabs (Hippidae) by correlating taxonomic differences in neurons known to be involved in producing these behaviors with the accepted phylogenetic relationships among decapods. That prototypes of the 3 circuits for tailflipping may have evolved in the order MG, LG, nG is suggested by combined considerations of neurobiological data and the Bauplan and probable behavior of the first eumalacostracans. These neurophyletic hypotheses are useful in making predictions about the neuronal organization of decapod locomotion.

INTRODUCTION

Neural circuits are defined in terms of the behaviors they mediate (e.g., swimming, jumping) but the rationale of their organization is often obtuse. Embedded in their evolutionary histories must be explanations for their organization, since ancestral nervous systems provided the substrates from which extant neural circuits evolved (Dumont & Robertson, 1986; Paul, 1981; Wilson & Paul, 1987). Neurophylogenetic studies are used to discover how nervous systems are moulded as they evolve;i.e., what factors (adaptive and non-adaptive) constrain the organization of nervous tissue when natural selection alters body form and behavior? More immediately, they generate testable hypotheses about specific features of the nervous systems under study.

In favorable cases, the evolution of a specific neural circuit can be traced by correlating evolutionary changes in behavior with phyletic variations in components of the underlying circuitry. For example, the behaviors involving the malacostracan "tail" (3 types of tailfliping, backward walking, swimmeret beating) lend themselves to neurophyletic analysis because: a) they are amenable to study at various levels (behavior, sensory, neuromuscular, neuronal circuitry); b) the elongate abdomen and tailfan (the malacostracan "tail") are evolutionarily old and monophyletic structures; c) the direction of evolutionary change is clear, particularly in macruran and anomuran decapods (Fig.1); d) there is a wealth of knowledge about the crayfish abdominal nervous system (Wine, 1984; this vol.) that can be exploited to deduce evolutionary trends in the nervous systems of anomurans.

Two categories of tailflipping are widespread in Eumalacostraca: single escape tailflicks and rhythmic extensions and flexions of the "tail" for sustained backward swimming. A different mode of backward swimming occurs in mole sandcrabs (Anomura: Hippidae) who beat the uropods while keeping the telson flexed under the body. Comparative anatomical and physiological data suggest that neurologically this unique, limb-driven mode of swimming is a form of tailflipping in which the uropod movements are greatly exaggerated while the axial movements almost entirely suppressed or lost. Here, I reconstruct major stages in this transition (Table 1; Fig. 2); but first, I speculate about the origins of eumalacostracan tailflipping behaviors.

METHODS

Sandcrabs (*Emerita, Blepharipoda*) from Monterey Bay, CA and squat lobsters (*Munida*), prawns (*Pandalus*), mud shrimp (*Upogebia*) collected around southern Vancouver Island were held in recycling, 11o C sea water. Crayfish (*Procambarus, Pacifastacus*) were from commercial suppliers. Techniques used for studying neuromusculature and central anatomy of neurons are described in Paul et al. (1985) and Paul (1989a). Paraplast sections (7 um) were cut through nerve cords that had been block stained with osmium and ethyl-gallate (Skinner, 1985). Preparation of the stretch receptors for electron microscopy is described in Wilson & Paul (1990).

RESULTS & DISCUSSION

Tailflipping behaviors: single or separate origin(s)? One or more of the 3 types of tailflipping occur in Syncarida, Euphausiacea, and all decapod groups, except Brachyura and Paguroidea (Fig. 1). The sine qua non for these behaviors is the malacostracan tailfan, which probably originated to stabilize the body during forward walking over the Paleozoic ocean floor (Hessler, 1983). The skeletomuscular pattern in eumalacostracan abdomens is probably older, for it is similar in the phyllocarid Nebalia, except the muscles are not coiled (Hessler, 1964). The pattern in stomatopods is intermediate between phyllocarid and fully-developed eumalacostracan (Kunze, 1983). Giant neuron-mediated tailflips resemble the "caridoid escape response" thought to have evolved in conjunction with development of spiralled musculature, following the evolution of the tailfan (Hessler, 1983). In crayfish, the MGs' strong excitation of the largest leg promotor motoneurons suggests that limb-driven retreat (backward jumping) may have been the MGs' first function (Heitler, 1988) and presumably accounts for the leg promotion characteristic of MG-type flexions (Cooke, 1985). An extended "tail", although useful for stability during forward walking, would have been a liability during retreat and synchronizing its flexion with leg extension would have added power to escape jumps..

Giant interneurons that are structurally and functionally similar to, and surely homologs of, crayfish's LG and MG neurons (Fig. 2) mediate fast flexions in the evasive behavior of a syncarid (Silvey & Wilson, 1979). In this animal, as in crayfish, there are rostro-caudal asymmetries in the effectiveness of tactile stimulation in eliciting MG- or LG-type flexions, although they are less extreme than in crayfish. These data suggest that the MG and LG neurons were present in Ureumalacostraca and that giant neuron-triggered jumps assisted by forceful flexion of the body may be the oldest type of tailflip. The impetus to evolve nG tailflipping would have arisen only after evolution of escape tailflicks, which left the animals momentarily suspended off the bottom. Only then would there have been conditions favoring evolution of neural circuits to drive repetitive tailflipping in order to extended the distance travelled before settling back to the substrate. This evolutionary sequence (giant-mediated before nG-mediated tailflipping) is incompatible with the suggestion that "...the giant axon circuitry evolved from the more complex non-giant circuitry that still controls most tailflips..." (Wine, 1984, p.307). It is compatible with what is known about decapods and their ancestors.

Ureumalacostraca were benthic-epibenthic, ambulatory animals (Dahl, 1983). Separate origins of giant-mediated and nG-mediated tailflipping behaviors could also explain why their neuronal organization is so different (reviewed in Wine, 1984). Both phases (extension and flexion) of the motor output for nG tailflipping originate centrally, unlike MG- and LG-mediated tailflips, in which extension is reflexive. The circuitry for central generation of the motor rhythm for the uropods that underlies swimming in Hippidae (see below) is probably homologous to the nG neuronal circuitry (reviewed in Paul, 1990). Rhythmic extensions and flexions of the abdomen, but using the entirely separate, tonic neuromusculature, assist backward walking in crayfish and are (like nG tailflipping) generated centrally . This behavior has not yet been described outside these reptant decapods, so its antiquity is uncertain.

The transition from axial to limb-driven locomotion in Hippidae followed changes in neuromusculature of the telsons of tailflipping animals (Table 1). These changes provided a richer neuromusculature for independent control of the uropod movements relative to body axis (3 polyneuronally innervated T-U muscles replaced the mononeuronally innervated AT muscle: refs. in Paul, 1990). The adaptive value of the 2 new elements may be inferred from the chronology of their appearance (Table 1; Fig. 2): the stretch receptor (SR), which senses uropod elevation, followed by the return-stroke muscle (RS), which elevates (and in hippids, remotes) the uropod and thereby stretches the receptor In crayfish, the stiffness of the uropods during the powerful flexions of tailflipping is due largely to skeletal constraints.

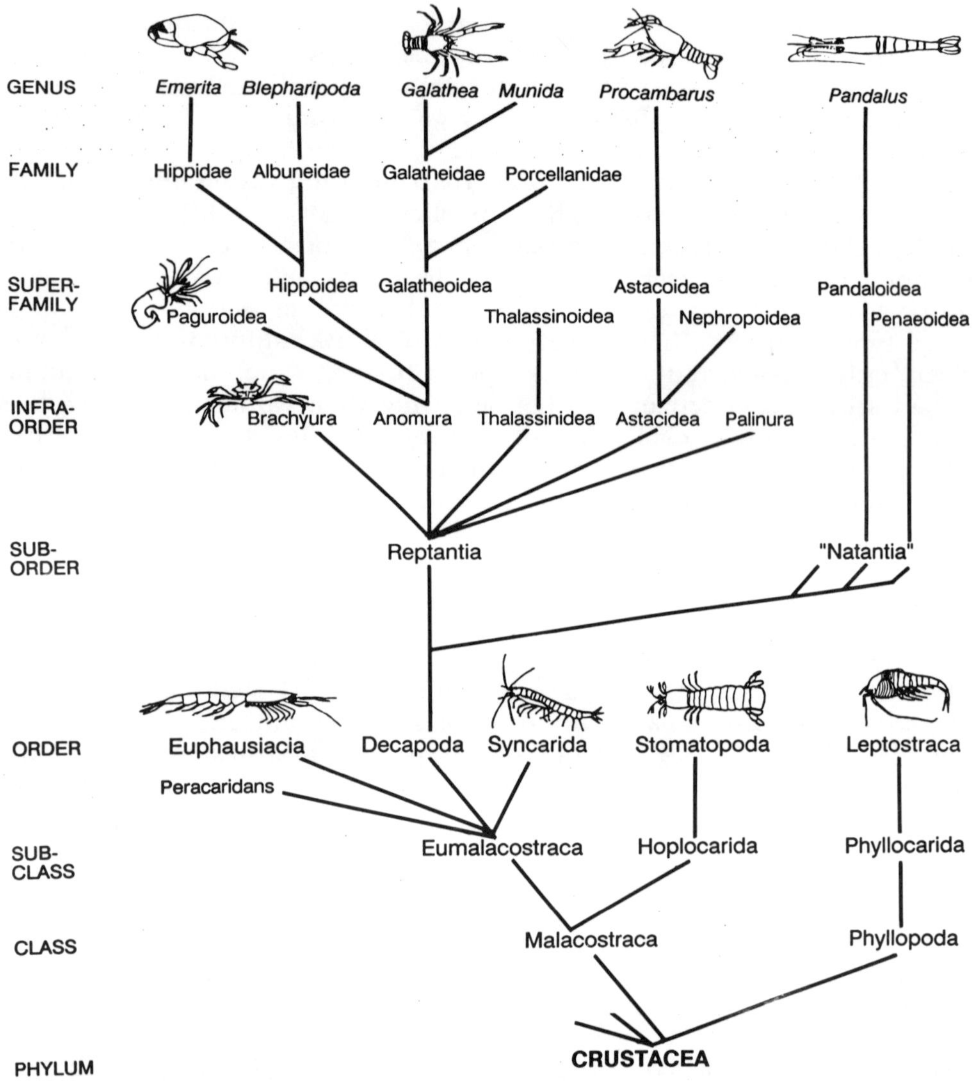

Fig. 1. Relationship and relatives of the most commonly studied crustaceans, the Decapods (modified from Schram, 1983, 1986). The "Natantia" (3 sub-orders) are generally recognized as having arisen from reptant forms. Phyllocarida (with 7 abdominal segments, the last without appendages) are excluded from Malacostraca (contrary to Bowman & Abele, 1982), making 6 abdominal segments and embryonic fusion of abdominal ganglia 6 and 7 diagnostic of this class.

BEHAVIOR	ANIMAL	TELSON FLEXORS		TELSON-UROPOD MUSCLES			STRETCH RECEPTOR
		PTF	AT	ATU	PTU	RS	
TAIL-FLIPPING	crayfish	++	++	+	+	o	o
	squat lobster	+	o	++	++	o	+
	spiny sandcrab	+	o	++	++	+	+
UROPOD BEATING	mole sandcrab	+ (VM)	o	++ (DM)	++++ (PS)	++++	+++

Table 1. Behaviors and elements in the telsons of crayfish (similar to stem decapods) and 3 anomurans (*Munida, Blepharipoda, Emerita*: Fig.1). Number of +s indicates differences in relative size of structures. O, absent. AT: anterior telson; ATU, PTU: anterior, posterior telson-uropod; PTF: posterior telson flexor; RS: return-stroke (of uropod). Alternate names of muscles in mole sandcrab Emerita: DM: dorsomedial; PS: power-stroke; VM: ventromedial (pronates uropod, a PS synergist). Modified from Paul et al., 1985.

The looser uropod articulation in anomurans would allow passive dorsal bending of the uropods (Paul et al., 1985), but this can be countered by resistance reflexes in uropod depressor muscles mediated by "new" stretc receptors. Sandcrabs alternate swimming off the bottom with burrowing into sand and during both behaviors their uropods must be subjected topassive depression. This is opposed by the new RS muscle which is active during tailflipping in *Blepharipoda* (Paul, 1981) and, in *Emerita*, during uropod beating for swimming or burrowing (the RS muscle is inhibited by the stretch receptor and no excitatory reflexes from uropod depression have been found; refs. in Paul, 1990).

Thus, when hippid sandcrabs moved into the intertidal zone, they were apparantly already endowed with all the basic sensory-motor elements for swimming with the uropods. The shift from trunk-driven to limb-driven locomotion entailed 1) changing the function of one muscle (PTF) from telson flexion to uropod pronation, accomplished by switching its insertion to the uropod coxa, and 2) reorienting 2 muscles from transverse to longitudinal, by elongating the telson, which converted them from elevator and depressor to remotor (RS) and promotor (PTU/PS) of the uropod (Table 1). A third set of changes involved the telson-uropod stretch receptor and is discussed below.

What inferences about the neural circuitry for swimming can be drawn from this reconstruction (Table 1)? That the changed insertion of the PTF muscle did not alter its basic function (power stroke in both behaviors).suggests that major phylogenetic changes in the circuitry for swimming need not have taken place. This inference is strengthened by 2 other observations.

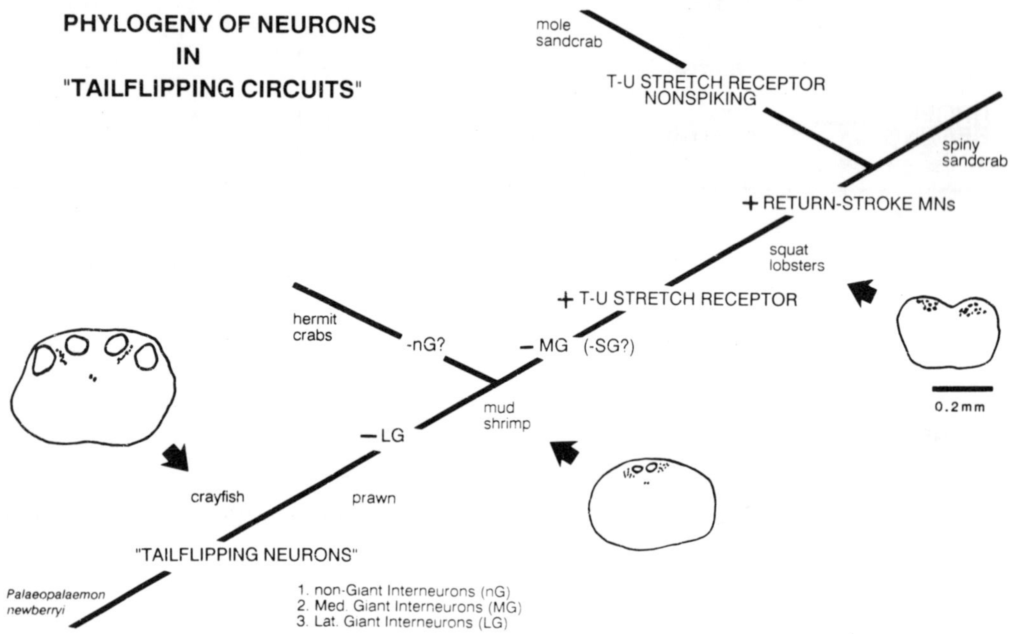

Fig. 2. Separate classes of neurons (nG, MG, LG) contribute to 3 kinds of tailflipping that use the phasic neuromusculature and were probably present in the stem Decapoda. All Anomura lack LGs, but hermit crabs (Paguridae) use MG & SG (segmental giant) neurons for escape withdrawal. Squat lobsters (Galatheoidea) and sandcrabs (Hippoidea) retain nG. Positions of flexor motor axons (solid) and the paired MG- and LG- axons, when present, (open), shown in cross-sections of abdominal connectives caudal to abdominal ganglion 3. The stereotyped position of flexor motor axons makes them useful landmarks for ascertaining whether there are small homologs of the giant interneurons´s axons in the connective in taxa ostensibly lacking MG or LG: apparantly not-LG homologs are absent in mud shrimp; the MGs and LGhomologs are absent in squat lobsters and sandcrabs (not shown). (-)=lost; (+)=gained. [For details about these neurons and differences in motoneurons, see: Paul (1990), Wine (1984), other papers in this vol.)]

First, the dendritic arbors of the homologous motoneurons innervating these (and other) muscles are highly conserved. Some motoneurons disappeared with the loss of the muscles they innervated or of the giant interneurons (Fig.2); others underwent adjustments in size in proportion to changes in the size of their muscles (Table 1).

However, the patterns of dendritic branching of all those examined closely so far remain unchanged, suggesting that substantial changes in their input have not occurred (refs. in Paul, 1990). Second, the temporal patterns of electomyograms recorded during tailflipping (in spiny sandcrabs, squat lobsters, and crayfish) and swimming with the uropods in the sandcrab *Emerita* are similar (Paul, 1981; Paul & Pye, 1988 & in prep.; Wilson & Paul, 1987). Together these data imply that similarly organized central networks underly swimming by tailflipping and by uropod beating. From information about one, one can make predictions about the other. The inclusion of the telson-uropod stretch receptor as a major component of sensory motor control of the tailfan, however , presumably involved some discrete synaptic changes in the terminal ganglion certain of which may have been in the neuronal circuitry for swimming (paul, 1989b, 1990).

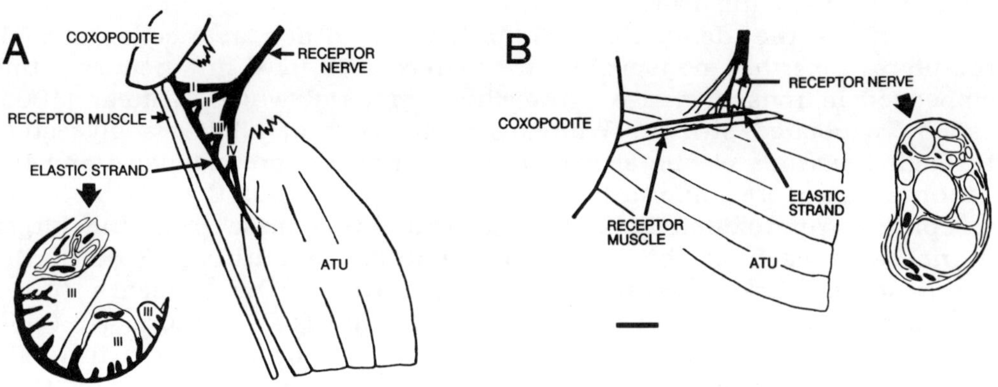

Fig. 3. Ventral views of telson-uropod SR and cross-sections of sensory neurons at levels indicated in *Emerita* (A: I, II, III, IV are peripheral dendrites of the 4 nonspiking sensory neurons) and *Munida* (B). In the cross-section of *Emeritas*` elastic strand (A), the dark fingers projecting inward into the branches of III are the vacuolated strings in which dendritic tips are embedded. Scale: Only the 2 largest neurons in *Munida's* receptor nerve terminate in structures of this kind and these are less elaborate than their counterparts in *Emerita's* elastic strand (Wilson & Paul, 1990). Scale: A: 200 μm, 10 μm; B: 360 μm, 30 μm.

The Telson-Uropod Stretch Receptor belongs to a class of serially homologous, axial-coxal receptors which are characterized by having sensory neurons with somata in the central nervous system and long dendrites which exit through segmental nerves to innervate their respective receptor strands. Their appearance and subsequent modifications in the galatheid - albuneid - hippid families highlights the importance of sensory input in motor control of freely moving limbs and probably engendered new and/or altered synaptic connections centrally (Paul, 1989b).

The 2 most prominent structural differences of *Emerita's* stretch receptor compared to those in tailflipping anomurans are the complete separation of the elastic from the muscular strand in the receptor complex (perhaps increasing sensitivity to changes in uropod position relative to the telson, because the elastic strand is freed from the muscle's viscoelastic inertia) and the large size of the sensory neurons innervating the elastic strand (Fig.3). *Emerita's* stretch receptor resembles more closely the axio-coxal receptors of other, highly mobile appendages used for locomotion [i.e., the crayfish swimmerets and walking legs of various Reptantia than it does the telson-uropod receptors of tailflipping anomurans (Maitland et al., 1982; Wilson & Paul, 1990).

Similar to the dendritic terminations in other axio-coxal stretch receptors, *Emerita*'s nonspiking stretch receptors have fine dendritic tips embedded in rods of dense extracellular material which Whitear (1965) called 'vacuolated strings' (Whitear, 1965). But, at all levels of section through *Emerita's* elastic strand, this material is more extensive and the dendritic tips more uniform in size and more numerous than in the other receptors. Approximately 21,000 dendritic tips arise from the larger branches of each of the 4 sensory neurons constituting 76% of the dendritic membrane within the elastic strand, this appears to be substantially more than in other axio-coxal axio-coxal receptors. We think that this morphology within the elastic strand is an adaptation to retain sensitivity during the much larger changes in length of the receptor than experienced by their homologs in tailflipping anomurans (Paul, 1990). If dendritic tips act as transducing units (their shape and dimensions change with stretch of the elastic strand), then the extaordinarily large number of tips may compensate for the small number of neurons by provididing a mechanism for range fractionation - small length changes would differentially compress only some tips, larger length changes would recruit more tips and add current to the smoothly graded receptor potential (Wilson & Paul. 1990). This analog signal is conducted decrementally to the CNS: see Bush (1981) and Paul (1989a, 1990) for discussions of nonspiking transmission in this type of sensory neuron.

Is the telson-uropod stretch receptor really phylogenetically new or, was there a prototype in stem decapods? A possible lobsters homolog of the anomuran telson-uropod rceptor lies ventrally, between abdominal segment 6 and the uropod (Laverack 1987). This raises the intriguing thought that prototype axio-coxal stretch receptors existed prior to evolution of the tailfan and that the terminal pair was retained when the 6th segment appendages transformed into the uropods to make the tailfan. This interpretation would be strengthened by the discovery of axio-coxal stretch receptors in Phyllopoda.

In conclusion, neural phylogeny is by nature eclectic and open to debate, but has several potential uses in analysing neural circuits. Our geneological perspective shapes our formulation of ideas about neuronal organization of the behaviors under study. Knowing the geneology of the behaviors in our experimental animals may help explain features which seem incongrous. Specific hypotheses about synaptic connections between identified neurons can be tested, after homologous neurons have been identified in different taxa. And, ultimately, it may be possible to understand how features of neurons and neuronal circuits are molded to mediate behavioral evolution

Research supported by NSERC of Canada

REFERENCES

Bowman, T.E. & Abele, L.G. (1982) Classification of the recent crustacea. In The Biology of Crusatacea, vol. 1 (ed. D.E. Bliss). N.Y.: Academic press.pp.1-27.

Bush, B.M.H. (1981) Non-impulsive stretch receptors in crustaceans. In Neurons without Impulses (eds. A. Roberts & B.M.H. Bush) Cambridge: Cambridge Univ. Press. pp.147-176.

Cooke, I.R.C. (1985) Further studies of crayfish escape behavior II. Giant axon-mediated neural activity in the appendages. J.exp.Biol.118:367-377.

Dahl, E. (1983) Malacostracan phylogeny and evolution. In Crustacean Phylogeny (ed. F.R. Schram). Rotterdam: A.A. Balkema. pp.189-212.

Dumont, J.P.C. & Robertson, R.M. (1986) Neuronal circuits: an evolutionary perspective. Science **233**:849-853.

Heitler, W.J. (1988) Thoracic output of crayfish giant command neurons. Neurosci.Abstr. **14**:999.

Hessler, R.R. (1964) The Cephalocarida: comparative skeletomusculature. Mem.Conn.Acad.Arts Sci. **16**:1-97.

Hessler, R.R. (1983) A defence of the caridoid facies: wherein the early evolution of the eumalacostraca is discussed. In Crustacean Phylogeny (ed. F.R. Schram). Rotterdam: A.A.Balkema. pp.145-164.

Kunze, J.c. (1983) Stomatopoda and the evolution of the Hoplocarida. In Crustacean Phylogeny (ed. F.R.Schram) pp.165-188.

Laverack, M.S. (1987) The nervous system of the crustacea, with special reference to the organization of the sensory system. In Nervous Systems in Invertebrates (ed. M.A. Ali) pp.323-352. N.Y.: Plenum Press

Maitland, D.P.M.S.,Laverack, M.S. & Heitler, W.J. (1982) A spiking stretch receptor with central cell bodies in the uropod coxopodite of the squat lobster Galathea strigosa (Crustacea, Anomura). J.exp.Biol.**101:**221-231.

Paul, D.H. (1981) Homologies between body movements and muscular contractions in the locomotion of two decapods of different families. J.exp.Biol.**94:** 159-168.

Paul, D.H. (1989a) Nonspiking stretch receptors of crayfish swimmeret receive efference copy of central motor pattern for the swimmeret. J.exp.Biol. **141**:257-264.

Paul, D.H. (1989b) Multiple functions of the telson-uropod stretch receptor in the sandcrab *Emerita*: neuroanatomical network. In Neural Mechanisms of Behavior, 2nd Internat. Congress Neuroethology, (eds. J.Erber, R.Menzel, H-J.Pflüger D.Todt), Stuttgart,: Georg Thieme Verlag. p.39.

Paul, D.H. (1990) A neurophylogenist's view of decapod crustacea. Bull.Mar.Sci. **45**(2) (in press).

Paul, D.H. & Pye, R.K. (1988) Crayfish swimming: different emg patterns in rostral and caudal abdominal segments. Neurosci. Abstr. **14:**999.

Paul, D,H., Then, M.A. & Magnuson, D.S. (1985) Evolution of the telson neuromusculature in decapod crustacea. Biol.Bull. **168**:106-124.

Schram, F.R., ed. (1983) Crustacean Phylogeny. Rotterdam: A.A. Balkema.

Schram, F.R. (1986) Crustacea. N.Y.: Oxford Univ. Press.

Silvey, G.E. & Wilson, I.S. (1979) Structure and function of the lateral giant neurone of the primitive crustacean *Anaspides tasmaniae*. J.exp.Biol. **78**:121-136.

Skinner, K. (1985) The structure of the fourth abdominal ganglion of the crayfish, *Procambarus clarkii*. I. Tracks in the ganglionic core. J.Comp.Neurol:

Whitear, M. (1965) The fine structure of crustacean proprioceptors. II. The thoracico-coxal organs in *Carcinus, Pagurus and Astacus*. Phil.Trans.Roy.Soc.Lond. B **248**:437-456.

Wilson, L.J. & Paul, D.H. (1987) Tailflipping of *Munida quadrispina* (Galatheidae): conservation of behavior and underlying musculature with lss of anterior contralateral flexor motoneurons and motor giant. J.comp.Physiol A **161**:881-890.

Wilson, L.J. & Paul, D.H. (1990) Functional morphology of the telson-uropod stretch receptor in the sandcrab *Emerita analoga*. J. comp.Neurol. (accepted).

Wine, J.J. (1984) The structural basis of an innate behavioral pattern. J.exp.Biol. **112:**283-319.

Frontiers in Crustacean Neurobiology
Advances in Life Sciences

A key of references to work on crustacean neurobiology not represented in this volume:

HERMANN SCHÖNE, MAX PLANCK INSTITUT FÜR VERHALTENSPHYSIOLOGIE, 813 SEEWIESEN, FRG

Schöne, H.(1954) Statocystenfunktion und statische Lageorientierung bei dekapoden Krebsen. Z.vergl. Physiol. **36**, 241-260.

Schöne, H.(1957) Kurssteuerung mittels der Statocysten (Messungen an Krebsen). Z. vergl. Physiol. **39**, 235-240

Schöne, H.(1965b) Release and Orientation of Behavior and the Role of Learning as demonstrated in Crustacea. Anim. Behav., Suppl.1, 135-144

Schöne, H.(1968) Agonistic and Sexual Display in Aquatic and Semiterrestrial Brachyuran Crabs. Amer.Zoologist **8**,(3) 641-654

Schöne, H., Neil, D.M., Stein, A., Carlstead, M.K.(1976) Reactions of the spiny lobster, Palinurus vulgaris, to substrate tilt. (I.). J.comp. Physiol. **107**, 113-128

Schöne, H., Neil, D.M., Scapini, F. (1978) The influence of substrate contact on gravity orientation. Substrate orientation in the Spiny lobster. J. comp. Physiol **126**, 293-295

Schöne, Hedwig, Schöne, H. (1980) Morphology and Function of the Antennular Joint and Its Strand Organ, Instrumental to Gravity Reactions in the Spiny lobster *Panulirus argus*. Zoomorphology **96**, 191-203

Schöne, H., Neil, D.M., Scapini, F., Dreismann, G.(1983) Interaction of substrate, Gravity and Visual Cues in the Control of compensatory eye Responses in the spiny lobster, *Palinurus vulgaris*. J.comp. Physiol. **150**, 23-30

Neil, D.M., Schöne, H., Scapini, F., Miyan, J.A. (1983) Optokinetic Response, Visual Adaptation and Multisensory Control of Eye Movements in the Spiny Lobster, *Palinurus vulgaris*. J. exp. Biol. **107**, 349-366

JELLE ATEMA, MARINE BIOLOGICAL LABORATORY (BUMP), WOODS HOLE, MA 02543, USA

Atema, J. (1985) Chemoreception in the sea: Adaptations of chemoreceptors and behavior to aquatic stimulus conditions. Soc. Exp. Biol. Symp. **39**, 387-423

Atema, J. (1988) Distribution of chemical stimuli. In: Sensory Biology of Aquatic Animals, Atema,J., Fay,R.R., Popper, A.N., Tavolga, W.N. (eds.), Springer Verlag, New York, pp. 29-56

Atema, J., Borrony, P., Johnson, B., Vogt, R., Handrich, L.(1989) Adaptation and mixture interaction in chemoreceptor cells: Mechanisms for diversity and contrast enhancement. In: Reception of complex smells and taste. Lang,D., Cain,W.,McBride R., Ache,B. (eds.) Academic Press, Sydney, pp. 83-100

Atema, J. (1986) Review of sexual selection and chemical communication in the lobster *Homarus americanus*. Canadian J. of Fisheries and Aquatic Sciences **34**, 2383-2390

Moore, P., Gerhardt, G., Atema, J. (1989) High resolution spatio-temporal analysis of chemical signals using microelectric, chemosensitive electrodes. Chemical Senses **14**,in press

Moore, P., Atema, J.(1988) A model of a temporal filter in chemoreception to extract directional information from a turbulent odour plume. Biol. Bulletin **174**, 355-363

JEFFREY J.WINE, DEPARTMENT OF PSYCHOLOGY, STANFORD UNIVERSITY STANFORD, CALIFORNIA 94305 USA.

His laboratory contributed valuable information on the cellular components and physiological properties of the mechanosensory pathway of crayfish monitoring water displacement. A few selected references are:

Sigvardt, K.A., Hagiwara, G., Wine, J.J.(1982) Mechanosensory integration in the crayfish abdominal nervous system: structural and physiological differences between interneurons with single and multiple spike initiating sites. J. comp. Physiol. **148**, 143-157

Reichert H., Plummer M.R., Wine, J.J.(1983) Identified nonspiking local interneurons mediate nonrecurrent, lateral inhibition of crayfish mechanosensory interneurons. J. comp. Physiol.**151**, 261-276

Krenz, W.D., Reichert, H. (1985) Lateralized inhibitory input to an identified local interneuron in the crayfish mechanosensory system. J.comp. Physiol. **157**, 499-507

Reichert, H., Plummer, M.R., Hagiwara, G., Roth R.L., Wine J.J. (1982) Local interneurons in the terminal abdominal ganglion of the crayfish. J.comp. Physiol. **149**, 145-162

Plummer, M.R., Tautz, J., Wine J.J. (1986) Frequency coding of water borne vibrations by abdominal mechanosensory interneurons in the crayfish, *Procambarus clarkii*. J.comp. Physiol. **158**, 751-764

Reichert, H.,Wine, J.J.(1983) Coordination of lateral giant and non-giant systems in crayfish escape behavior. J.comp. Physiol. **153,** 3-15

Afterward

Jeffrey J. Wine,
Psychology, Stanford University

Crayfish, which move fastest when going backward, always seemed an oppropriate subject for my own research, which all too often had that same property. Misdirections plague me still: Don Kennedy was assigned the Foreward and asked to look back, while I, in an Afterward, have the opportunity to make predictions and suggestions. Given the volatility of modern research, these should regale the participants of the next meeting. Here goes.

Although crustacean systems have not yet been subjected to a molecular biology blitzkrieg, their turn will come, and when it does, the many advantages of crustacean nervous systems, so amply illustrated in this volume, should provide outstanding opportunities to follow the pleiotropic effects of gene action on behavior. Steps in that direction are now being taken (see the 8th session) and I doubt that a single session will be sufficient to accommodate such research a decade hence.

At the opposite pole, I continue to hope, although with rare encouragement, that more neurobiologists will heed the words of Karl von Frisch (in translation): "If we use excessively elaborate apparatus, Nature herself may escape us" (1). For many reasons, some good and some not, behavioral studies will probably continue to claim only a small proportion of the resources of the neurobiological community. But it would be wise to ensure that this minor enterprise is carefully nurtured. Because modern neurobiologists typically underestimate the behavioral capacities of the animals they study, we need at least a few individualists to keep demonstrating that even invertebrates possess the rudiments of mind. Such studies put those behaviors that have been successfully analyzed into proper perspective, and challenge us to extend neurobiological analyses to more complex behavior, perhaps aided by the back propagation of insights gained from current computational studies of distributed parallel processing. Frank Krasne's work on the interaction between crayfish feeding and escape behavior (2) is one recent example of how higher order interactions can yield to neural analysis.

Perhaps the safest prediction is that the next decade will continue to be dominated by an elaborated but still recognizable application of the cellular-connectionistic approach, and justifiably so: it works, it is benefiting from powerful new methods, and the story it is telling is far from complete. Immunocytochemical mapping is just one new tool that holds spectacular promise for unraveling nervous systems. The initial results of it´s use in crustacea are so encouraging that they should fuel intense efforts toward further exploitation. Indeed, this symposium celebrates many successful research projects that have achieved the goal of "joining, in a rigorous way, observations at the cellular or even the molecular level with the behavior of the whole organism" (D. Kennedy, preface to this volume). Such successes are not confined to studies of crustacea, but their proportion, in relation to the resources devoted to neurobiological studies of crustacea, make the case that studies of crustacea are particularly cost-effective.

I end on a personal note. My premature disengagement from neurobiology, even though not yet complete, has already put enough distance between me and current research so that only the more prominent peaks and persistently repeated features are visible. From this distance, individual contributions, such as those so ably recounted by Ernst Florey in his introductory lecture, tend to blur, and one is left with a sense of the enterprise as a cooperative whole. From this remove, it appears that the achievements of the field, impressive as they are, could be amplified if a more narrowly defined goal could be agreed upon and pursued with a more coherent organization than now exists. Such a goal, perhaps the complete mapping of a central ganglion, or the completion of a behavioral circuit, while certainly not pursued to the exclusion of all other research, might yet focus energies and inspire cooperation in a way that would energize the whole field. As always, the success of such an enterprise lies in the details of organization, and only current practitioners can supply those. This symposium offers a marvelous opportunity to begin.

References

1. Karl von Frisch, The Dancing Bees, translated by Dora Ilse, New York: Harcourt Brace & World, 1953 (Orginally published as: Aus dem Leben der Bienen, Berlin-Göttingen-Heidelberg: Springer Verlag)
2. Krasne, F,B,& Lee, S.C. Response-didicated trigger neurons as control points for behavioral actions: selective inhibition of lateral giant command neurons during feeding in crayfish. J Neuroscience, 1988, **8**, 3703-3712

INDEX OF SUBJECTS

Symposium participants at Hamburg University in September 1989

INDEX OF AUTHORS